the HOME REFERENCE BOOK

the encyclopedia of homes

We extend our thanks to the following contributing authors:

Mr. Dan Friedman
American Home Inspection Service
Poughkeepsie, New York

Mr. Kevin O'Malley
Inspection Training Associates
Oceanside, California

Mr. Richard Malin
Richard D. Malin & Associates
Monroeville, Pennsylvania

James Dobney
James Dobney Inspections
Vancouver, British Columbia

the HOME REFERENCE BOOK®

27th edition

Carson, Dunlop & Associates Ltd.

120 Carlton Street
Suite 407
Toronto, Ontario
Canada
M5A 4K2

www.carsondunlop.com

Graphic Design: Neglia Design Inc.
Photo credit: ©iStockphoto.com/John Verner
Printed in Canada
ISBN: 9781895585742

Introduction

For many people a home is the largest investment they will ever make. At Carson Dunlop, we have learned a great deal about homes as we have studied them over the last 30 years. We have come to respect how important they are to the occupants, how complex they are, and how unique each one is. We have also learned that homes react to the people living in them. Different lifestyles and activities cause similar homes to behave very differently.

We have come to know that most people don't understand their homes and often cause damage, reduce the life expectancy of systems, suffer comfort issues, compromise safety and increase the cost of home ownership inadvertently. We believe a little knowledge can make a huge difference. And we have learned the importance of clearly communicating our knowledge to home owners.

A Word about Professional Home Inspectors

Home inspectors provide tremendous value, helping home buyers and owners determine the condition of properties. A professional home inspection is also an education in home ownership, providing extensive information on the care and preservation of a home. A home inspection is one of the best investments you can make, whether you are buying a home or already own one.

Most home inspectors follow a Standards of Practice set out by a professional association. The oldest and most respected is the American Society of Home Inspectors (ASHI). Their Standards of Practice can be found on their website – www.ashi.org.

This book is a tool used by many home inspectors to document their inspection findings. The report forms at the back of the book will be completed if you receive this book as part of a home inspection. The completed forms create a home inventory and condition report along with recommendations for improvements the inspector has noted. But the Home Reference Book is also a valuable resource for all homeowners – thorough, detailed and relevant, yet clearly written and simple to understand.

Back to the Home

A home is a complex set of inter-related systems and components with some parts that last indefinitely (e.g. foundations, wood framing and masonry) and others that need to be replaced from time to time (e.g. furnaces, roofs, water heaters). Home improvements are not always straightforward. Changes to one component can have unexpected results in another area of the home. Replacing a furnace, for example, can cause condensation problems on windows. Insulation improvements can cause mold and rot in the attic.

Houses are dynamic and have many moving parts. Regular maintenance extends the life of systems, improves comfort and safety, and minimizes operating costs. The Home Set-up and Maintenance program set out in the Book helps homeowners deal with these issues.

The Home Reference Book is not a how-to manual for the do-it-yourselfer, but a reference guide to help owners operate and maintain their home effectively.

The Book helps owners know when components are doing their job, and when they need attention. It is also very helpful in dealing with trades people, contractors and other specialists who propose repairs and home improvements. Is the work necessary? Are there alternatives? A leaking basement is a good example. While excavating, adding drainage tile, a drainage membrane, and dampproofing may be effective, this is a very expensive approach. In most cases small improvements to gutters, downspouts and surface drainage can solve the problem at a fraction of the cost. And by the way, a basement leak rarely has any significant adverse impact on the foundation or the stability of the home.

The Home Reference Book not only explains complicated systems in plain English with rich color illustrations, but it also provides typical life cycles for over 200 components and the ballpark costs to provide or replace these.

We have tried to write this book as though we were doing it for family and friends. Our goal is to give people the benefit of our life's work, quickly and painlessly.

How to use the Home Reference Book

We understand the book is not the great American novel and does not make riveting bedtime reading, unless sleep is your goal! Rather than consuming the book in a single sitting, we expect people to read it in pieces as they are faced with challenges or decisions to make about various components of their homes. It is after all, a 'Reference Book'.

We hope you find the book useful, and that it helps you enjoy your home a little more, while spending a little less.

TABLE OF CONTENTS

ROOFING, FLASHINGS AND CHIMNEYS

EXTERIOR

STRUCTURE

ELECTRICAL

HEATING

APPLIANCES

NOTE: APPLIANCES ARE NOT INSPECTED AS PART OF A STANDARD HOME INSPECTION. THIS SECTION IS INCLUDED AS A COURTESY.

LIFE CYCLES AND COSTS

SUPPLEMENTARY

HOME SET-UP AND MAINTENANCE

APPENDIX A – MORE ABOUT HOME INSPECTIONS

Roofing/Flashings/ Chimneys

INTRODUCTION

THE PRIMARY PURPOSE OF A ROOF IS TO PROTECT THE BUILDING FROM RAIN, SNOW, SUN AND WIND. ROOFS ALSO AFFECT THE APPEARANCE OF A BUILDING. ROOFS PROVIDE SOME MECHANICAL PROTECTION AGAINST FALLING OBJECTS, ALTHOUGH HAIL DAMAGE FOR EXAMPLE, IS COMMON. ROOF COVERINGS ARE NOT INTENDED TO KEEP OUT THE COLD. MOST ROOFS ARE VERY POOR INSULATORS.

1.0 Roofing

SLOPED AND FLAT

There are two main categories of roofing systems: sloped roofs and flat roofs. Roofing professionals call these steep roofs and low sloped roofs. Sloped roofing systems are not watertight; they shed water with overlapping shingles or tiles. Flat roofs, on the other hand, are watertight membranes. Flat roof is a bad name, since roofs should never be perfectly flat. They should slope to allow water to drain off them, because water standing on the roof will damage the membrane, and the weight of water can deflect the roof structure.

The difference between sloped roofs and flat roofs is the slope, or pitch, of the roof. The slope is described as a ratio of the vertical rise over a set horizontal run. The run is always defined as 12 feet. Therefore, a 6-in-12 roof would have a vertical rise of 6 feet over a horizontal distance of 12 feet. Roofs with a slope greater than 4-in-12 are considered **sloped**. Roofs with a slope between 4-in-12 and 2-in-12 are considered **low slope**, and roofs with a slope less than 2-in-12 are considered **flat**.

Just to make it confusing, professional roofers describe anything with a slope of more than 2-in-12 as steep roofing. Anything less is low sloped roofing.

1.1 Asphalt Shingles (Composition Shingles)

DESCRIPTION

Asphalt shingles (also called composition shingles) are the most common roofing material used today. The shingles consist of asphalt-impregnated felt paper or glass fiber mats, coated with a layer of asphalt and covered with granular material.

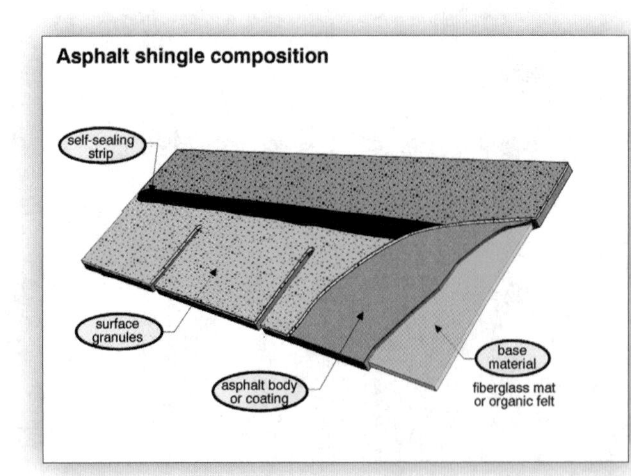

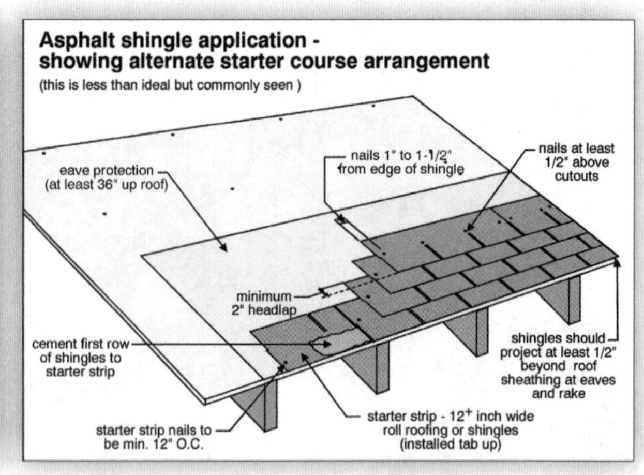

LIFE EXPECTANCY Asphalt shingles were historically classified by weight. Today, asphalt shingles are classified by the manufacturer's warranty. They are known as 15-year, 20-year, 25-year, 30-year or 35-year shingles. Modern shingles are available in various textures and patterns. While shingles with longer warranties will generally last longer than shingles with shorter warranties, the warranty period should not be considered a guarantee of service life.

WEAR FACTORS Regardless of the type of shingle used, there are two significant factors with regard to wear – exposure and slope. Sunlight is one of the biggest enemies of asphalt roofs and in many areas, the south and west exposures wear out the fastest. The steeper the slope, the longer the shingles will last.

As asphalt shingles wear, they lose their granular covering. The granular material protects the shingles from ultra-violet light. As granules wear off, the shingles dry out and become brittle. They crack, buckle, and curl. Shingles wear out first where the granular material is lost. This may be due to heavy foot traffic, abrasion from tree branches, erosion from downspouts discharging onto the roof surface, or manufacturing defects.

SELF-SEALING SHINGLES Most asphalt shingles have self-sealing strips, a strip of asphalt running across the middle of the shingle. The shingle above overlaps the lower shingle, with the bottom edge covering this strip. When the sun warms the roof surface, the two shingles stick together. This protects the shingles from being blown off in a heavy wind. Shingles installed in cold weather do not seal themselves until the weather warms up. They are vulnerable to wind damage during this period.

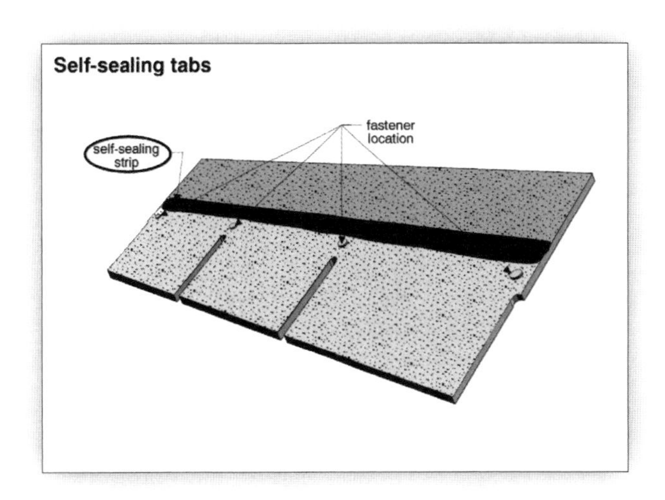

SHINGLES AND ROOF SLOPES Conventional asphalt shingles can be used on a slope as low as 4-in-12. Shingles can also be used down to a slope of 2-in-12 if the roof is first covered with non-perforated, asphalt-saturated felt papers or a waterproof membrane. The felt papers are overlapped by 50% and the section at the eaves (from the bottom edge up to 24 inches beyond the exterior wall) is cemented in place to provide extra protection. After construction, you can't tell whether this was done, especially since the shingles themselves may be cemented down.

In the past, special shingles were made for this application. These are no longer used.

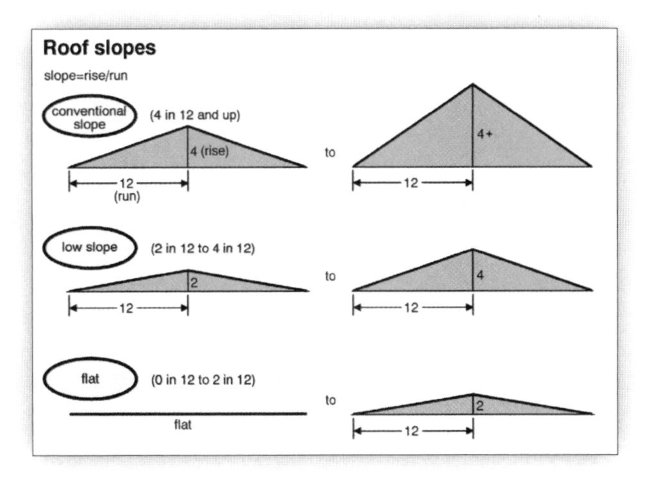

RE-ROOFING While it is better to remove old roofing before re-roofing, a second layer of shingles can be installed over one layer of shingles if the layer being covered is relatively smooth and flat. Longer nails must be used. If there are already two layers of shingles on the roof, all shingles should be removed before re-roofing.

Asphalt shingles are occasionally installed over a single layer of wood shingles or slate shingles; however, the new shingles will perform better and last longer if the old roofing materials are removed.

1.2 Wood Shingles and Shakes

DESCRIPTION Wood shingles are machine cut. They are typically smaller, thinner and more uniform than wood shakes. Traditionally, wood shakes were hand split or mechanically split, although machine-sawn shakes are also available. Wood shakes are thicker and split shakes have a much more uneven surface. Most wood shingles are cedar; however, redwood and pine are also used.

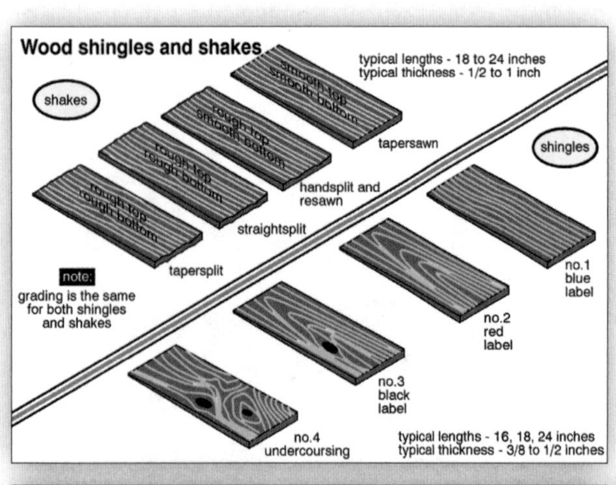

Wood shingles can be used on roofs with a slope as low as 3-in-12; however, 6-in-12 or more is recommended. Wood shingles vary in length between 16 inches and 24 inches. On a good quality installation, no more than one-third of each shingle is exposed to the weather.

Shakes may be up to 24 inches long, with no more than half of the shingle exposed. Shakes typically have heavy building paper interwoven with the shakes to prevent wind driven rain and snow getting into the roof between the shakes.

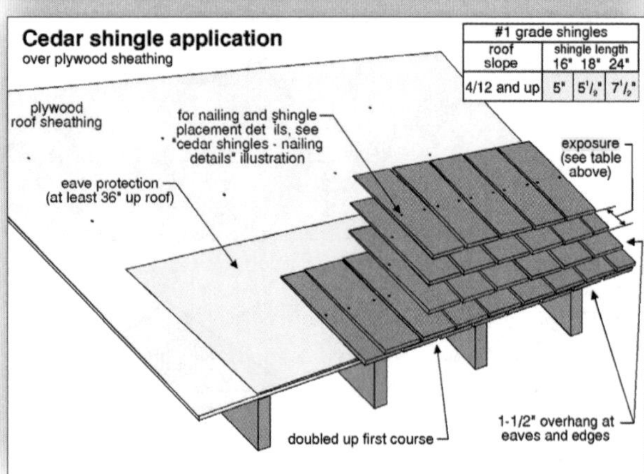

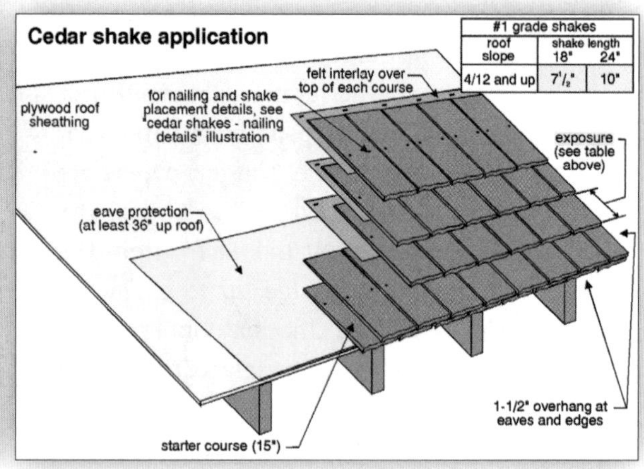

LIFE EXPECTANCY The life expectancy of good quality wood shingles is generally 30 to 40 years; however, low quality shingles deteriorate badly in 15 to 20 years. The rate of wear depends largely on exposure (the amount of shingle which is exposed to the weather), the slope (the steeper the better), the grade of shingle (there are four), and the amount of sun and shade they see. Sunlight dehydrates the shingles, resulting in splitting and cupping of the shingles. Some shingles 'burn through', with holes developing as a result of exposure to the sun.

Too much shade and moisture allows moss to grow. This can lead to rot. Wood shingles and shakes may suffer mechanical damage from tree branches, foot traffic, snow shovelling, etc. Another factor affecting the life of wood shingles is their ability to dry quickly. Wood roofing over spaced sheathing boards has lots of air movement on the back of the shingles or shakes, promoting uniform drying. This helps extend the life of the roof. Wood roofing applied over plywood sheathing does not dry as quickly or uniformly. Some experts say the use of plywood will halve the life of wood shingles.

ROOF TUNE-UP The shakes or shingles may deteriorate at different rates. The roof's life can be extended by several years by carrying out a roof tune-up. This typically involves spot replacement of damaged shakes or shingles (often located on the hip and ridge caps) as well as the addition of metal shims under any split shakes or shingles where the split is located directly over an adjacent keyway (the vertical joint between individual shakes or shingles). The tune-up should also include a roof cleaning if there is moss and/or algae growth.

It is important to keep wood roofing clear of organic debris, moss and algae buildup to extend its life. High pressure washing is not recommended as it may damage the roofing. Low pressure washing may successfully remove loose material without damaging the roof. The roofing can then be sprayed with a combination moss killer and non-toxic detergent to kill any moss, algae or fungus. A heavy rain will usually remove the dead moss.

The majority of wood roofing is western red cedar which contains natural oils that resist decay. There are various treatments available that claim to increase this natural decay resistance. These claims and their cost should be carefully evaluated.

RE-ROOFING Wood shingles or shakes can be installed over a single layer of asphalt shingles; however, it is better to remove existing shingles to allow the wood roof system to breathe. Wood roofing should never be installed over an old wood roof.

1.3 Slate Shingles

DESCRIPTION Slate is a natural sedimentary rock that is quarried; the quality can vary. High quality slate roofs can last 200 years. Low-quality roofs may fail in less than 20 years. Slate roofs are heavy, weighing three to five times as much as conventional asphalt shingles. A slope of six-in-twelve or more is recommended and, slates are usually installed with less than 50% of each slate exposed to the weather. The slate above covers more than half of the slate below.

WEAR FACTORS While some slates are of low quality and tend to flake and shale, the biggest problem with slate roofs is often the nails holding the slates in place. With time, the nails rust and allow the slates to slide out of position. Copper and stainless steel nails last longer than galvanized nails. Once one slate has come loose, water rusts the nails holding nearby slates in place. Good maintenance is important on an older slate roof. While it is not common practice, slate roofs should be inspected and repaired at least annually. Slates that have slipped are re-secured, and slates that have cracked or split as a result of mechanical damage are replaced. As a general rule, roof replacement makes sense when more than 10% is in need of repair.

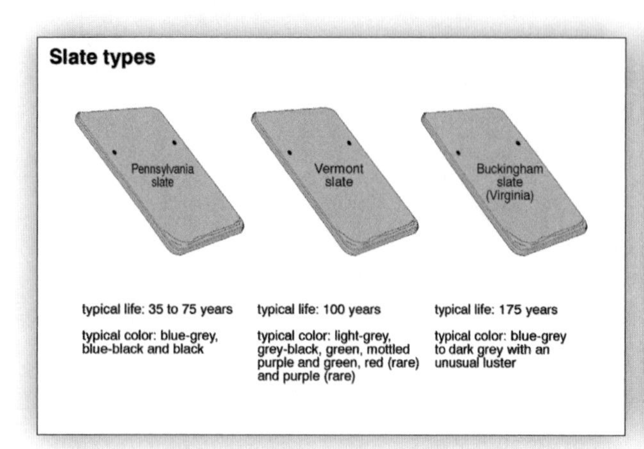

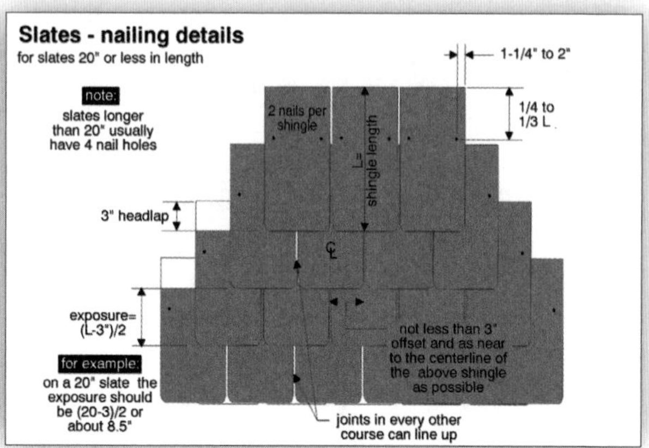

FLASHINGS The flashing materials do not last as long as the slates themselves. Metal flashings are used wherever the roof changes direction or meets an obstruction such as a chimney. When the flashings rust, a section of the roof may have to be removed to install a new flashing. This is an expensive proposition. Copper and lead flashings are expensive, but last longer than galvanized steel or aluminum flashings.

REPAIR WORK Another difficulty with slate roofs is finding qualified people to repair them. Since slate has not been used commonly for the past 50 years, their installation and repair is a vanishing art. Many slate roofs that can be saved are replaced with modern roofing materials, more familiar to the modern roofer.

RE-ROOFING Slate roofs should never be installed over another layer of roofing. New slate roofs on homes are rare because they are so expensive. Installing slate on a building not designed for slate often requires structural modifications to the roof to carry the weight of the slates.

1.4 Concrete and Clay Tiles

DESCRIPTION These are high quality roofing systems with life expectancies of 50 to 100 years. Like slate, these roofs are heavy, weighing four to five times as much as asphalt shingles. Modifications to the roof structure may be required if replacing asphalt shingles with concrete.

Concrete and clay tiles can be used on a slope as low as 4-in-12 but as with most roofing systems, steeper is better. Many current standards recommend 6-in-12 as a minimum. The amount of overlap (exposure of the tiles) varies depending on the roof system. Systems with a limited overlap are prone to leakage during wind-driven rains. Many loose-fitting concrete and clay tile roofs have a watertight membrane such as built-up roofing below, to act as a backup. The tiles provide protection against fire, ultraviolet light and mechanical damage.

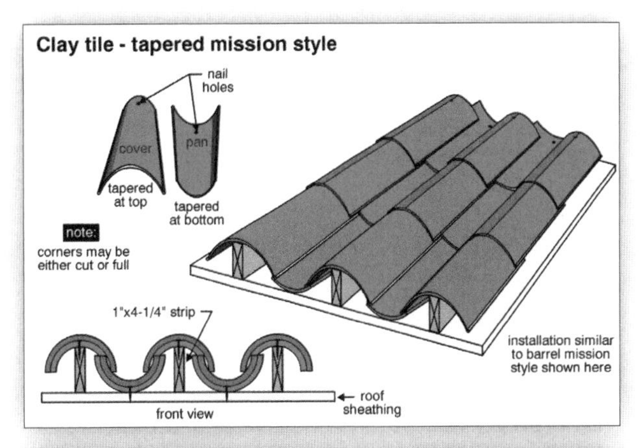

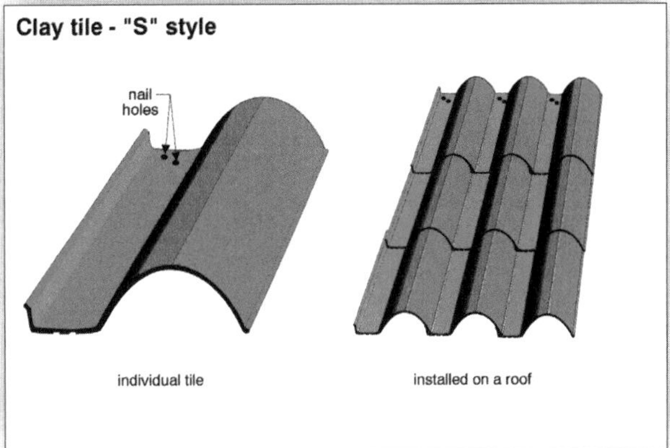

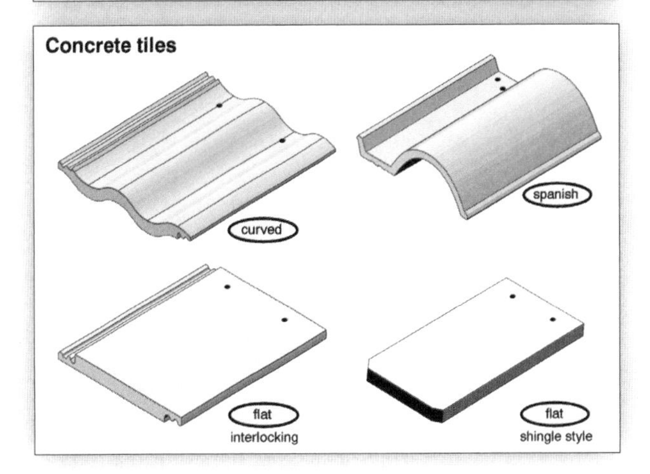

FASTENING Some systems are nailed in place while others use special clips or wire ties. In some regions, the tiles are mortared into place. In areas prone to high winds and hurricanes, these heavy tiles can be torn off roofs, becoming dangerous projectiles.

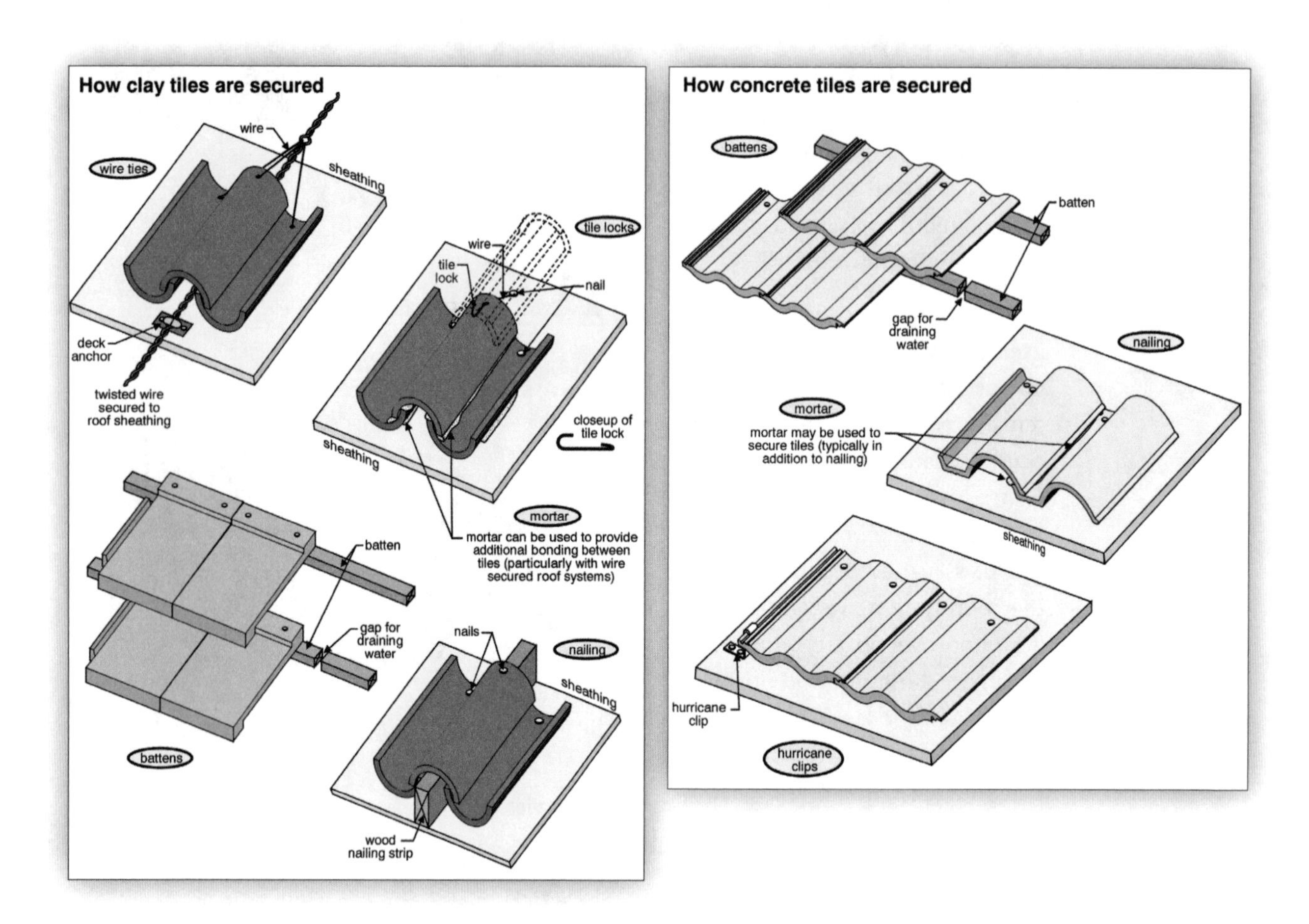

WEAR FACTORS Like any brittle roofing system, concrete and clay tiles are subject to mechanical damage, and like any long-lasting roof system, the fasteners may wear out before the tiles. Depending upon the design of the roof system, they can be very difficult to repair.

Concrete and clay tiles that are not flat are more difficult to flash.

RE-ROOFING Concrete or clay tiles cannot be installed over another roofing system, with the exception of a single layer of asphalt shingles or over a built-up roof. The roof structure may require modification to handle the additional load.

1.5 Fiber Cement Shingles

DESCRIPTION Fiber cement shingles consist of a mixture of Portland cement, water and fibers. Traditionally, asbestos fibers were used, but since the 1970s asbestos has been replaced by fiberglass or, more commonly, wood fibers. The type of fiber used in shingles is not determined during a home inspection.

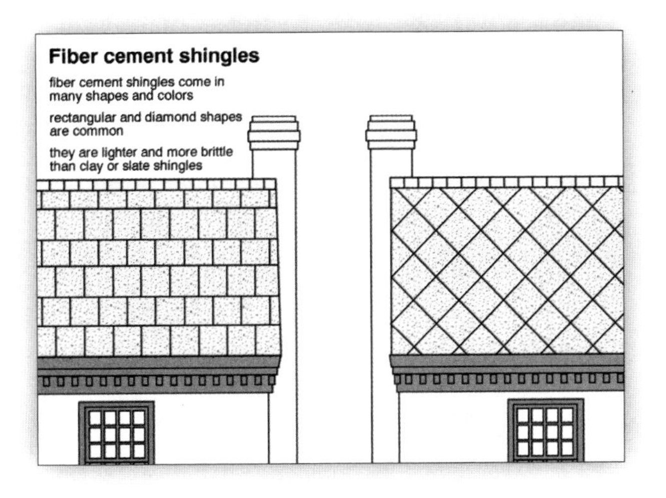

LIFE EXPECTANCY These shingles traditionally had a life expectancy of 30 to 50 years, although some newer shingles carry warranties as long as 60 years. Some fiber cement shingles are made to look like wood shingles.

Fiber cement shingles are brittle and are susceptible to mechanical damage. Older shingles often discolor and promote the growth of fungus or moss. They are difficult to repair and replacement shingles may be hard to obtain.

RE-ROOFING New fiber cement shingles are rarely installed. Ideally, existing asbestos cement shingles should be removed prior to re-roofing. Because of the asbestos content of old shingles, special provisions should be made for handling and disposing of the material.

1.6 Metal Roofing

DESCRIPTION There are many types of metal roofs. Copper, galvanized steel, pre-painted or coated steel, terne and tin are common. Some metal roofs have a granular surface embedded in the finish. Most metal roofs (particularly copper) are expensive systems, but they last longer than asphalt shingles. They can be installed as sheets or shingles. Sheets and shingles can be used on sloped roofs; however, flat roofs are only covered in sheets. Sheet metal roofs can have different types of seams including soldered and crimped.

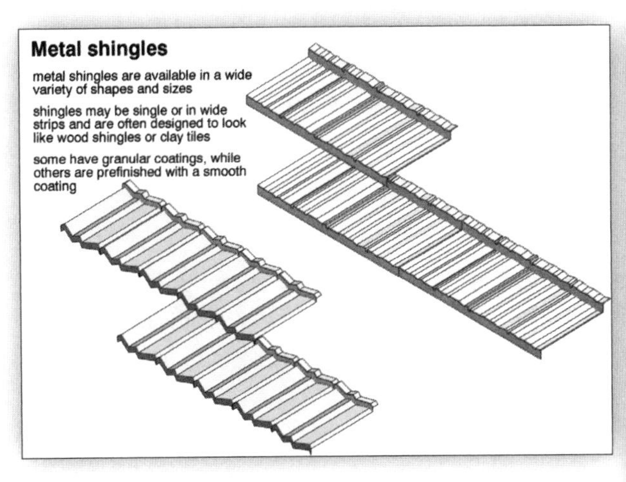

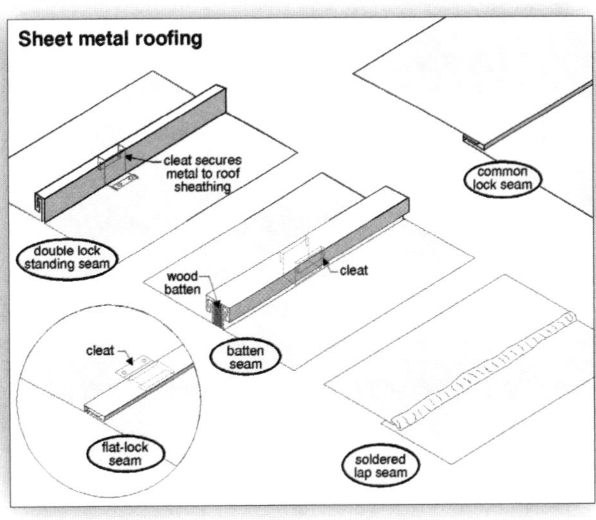

WEAR FACTORS Like any roofing system there are disadvantages; seams may split or be damaged. All metal roofs except copper and pre-painted or pre-coated roofs should be painted on a regular basis. Metal roofs should never be covered with tar because moisture trapped below the tar causes rusting. Tar covered metal roofs are usually near the end of their life. Metal roofs are difficult to repair and replacement is often the most practical alternative.

Leaks around the fasteners are common, and failed fasteners may make the roofing vulnerable to blowing off in high winds.

RE-ROOFING Moisture trapped in the old roofing system may cause premature deterioration of the new roof or of the sheathing below. Best practice is to remove old metal roofing before reroofing.

1.7 Corrugated Plastic Roofing

DESCRIPTION Corrugated plastic is a specialty type of roofing. It is a single ply, translucent roof surface that is generally used over patios and light structures. It should never be used over living areas as it is not considered to be truly watertight. Corrugated plastic roofs are weak and should never be walked on. They are generally considered to be low quality roofing systems that are easily damaged, discolor with sunlight and leak at the joints.

RE-ROOFING This roofing has to be removed before applying a new roof.

1.8 Built-up Roofing

DESCRIPTION Built-up roofs are commonly called tar-and-gravel roofs, even though most modern systems use asphalt instead of tar. They are a multi-ply roofing system, consisting of two, three, four or even five plies of roofing felts with a mopping (coating) of asphalt between layers. A flood coat of asphalt is then applied over the top and covered with gravel to reflect ultraviolet light and protect the roof from mechanical damage. These roofs are still common commercially, but are being replaced residentially with newer systems that are faster and easier to install.

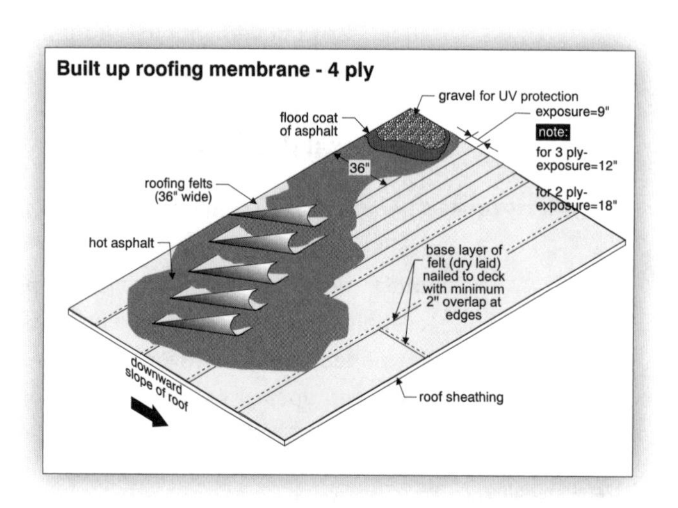

SLOPE Built-up roofs are designed for flat (low slope) applications and should not be used with a slope of greater than 3-in-12, unless special asphalt is used.

LIFE EXPECTANCY Two-ply built-up roofs have a life expectancy of five to ten years, while four-ply roofs normally last 15 to 20 years. Since the roof typically has a flood coat of tar and gravel, it is not possible to determine how many plies exist. It is also difficult to determine the condition of the membrane due to the gravel on top.

WEAR FACTORS Built-up roofs require skill to install properly. If moisture is trapped below or within the membrane, blisters and bubbles will form and reduce the life expectancy of the roof significantly. A lack of gravel causes rapid deterioration of the roof surface. A condition known as alligatoring occurs as the surface breaks down and cracks due to exposure to sunlight.

DRAINAGE Water ponding on a flat roof can shorten the life expectancy by as much as 50%. Rigid insulation or wood decking can be used when re-roofing to sculpt the roof surface to promote good drainage. As an alternative, additional drains can be installed. Good practice includes a secondary drain for flat roofs. Drains may be gutters or scuppers at the perimeter, or central drains running down through the building.

LEAKS Because of the construction of built-up roofs, leaks are difficult to isolate and repair. A water stain on a ceiling does not necessarily indicate a leak immediately above. Water can travel a significant distance through the plies of a roof before emerging on the interior.

Because of the complexity of built-up roofs, it is important that a reputable roofer, offering a meaningful guarantee, be used.

RE-ROOFING While it is common practice to install new built-up roofs over existing built-up roofing systems, moisture trapped in the old roofing system may cause premature deterioration of the new membrane. Best practice is to remove old roofing before applying a new membrane.

1.9 Roll Roofing

DESCRIPTION Roll roofing is sometimes known as selvage roofing. It typically comes in 18 or 36 inch wide rolls. It consists of the same material as asphalt shingles (asphalt impregnated felts covered with granules). The surface may be completely covered with granules or only 50% covered (designed for two-ply application). The material is most often installed as a single ply with very little overlap.

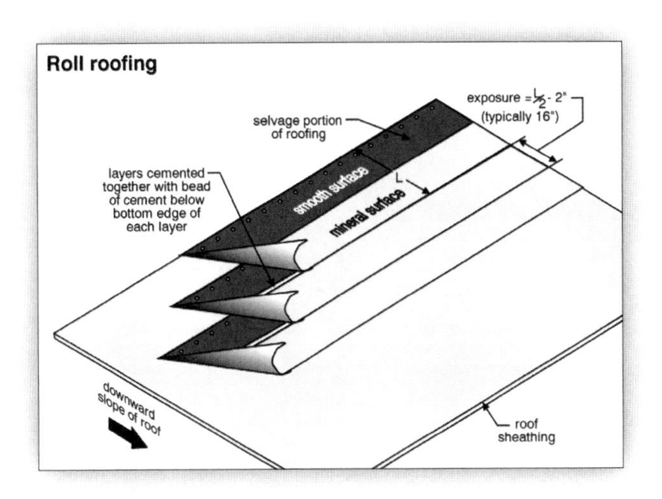

LIFE EXPECTANCY This low quality roof covering has a limited life expectancy of five to ten years. There is an exception to this rule. Sometimes, roll roofing is used to protect a built-up roof covering as an alternative to gravel. From a visual inspection it is impossible to tell. Modified bitumen roofing can be very similar to roll roofing in appearance. The home inspector may not be able to determine the roofing material.

WEAR FACTORS Because roll roofing material is installed in long strips, and because the material expands and contracts with changes in temperature, it may buckle or wrinkle. The granular covering breaks down quickly in the wrinkled areas, resulting in localized wear and short life.

The material is used on both sloped roof and flat roofs. It is sometimes installed with a full layer of roofing cement but is most often simply sealed at the seams or nailed at the edges. Where there is no protection for the nails, leaks often occur around nails.

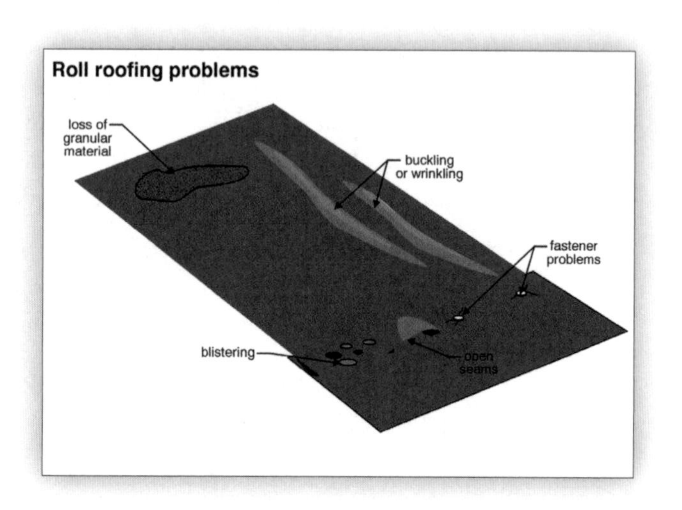

RE-ROOFING Moisture trapped in the old roofing system may cause premature deterioration of the new membrane. Best practice is to remove the old roofing material before applying a new membrane.

1.10 Modified Bitumen Roofing

DESCRIPTION Modified bitumen membranes are an alternative to built-up roofs. Polymer-modified asphalt is bonded to fiberglass or polyester reinforcing to form sheets of roofing membrane. Rolls of this rubberized asphalt membrane are typically torched onto the roof, bonded (mopped in) to the roof with hot asphalt, or adhered to the roof using a peel-and-stick backing. The surface of the membrane may be protected from ultraviolet rays by a coating of granules, foil, or paint. The sheets are approximately 40 inches wide and usually overlap each other by four inches. Modified bitumen roofs may be installed as either a single or double layer system.

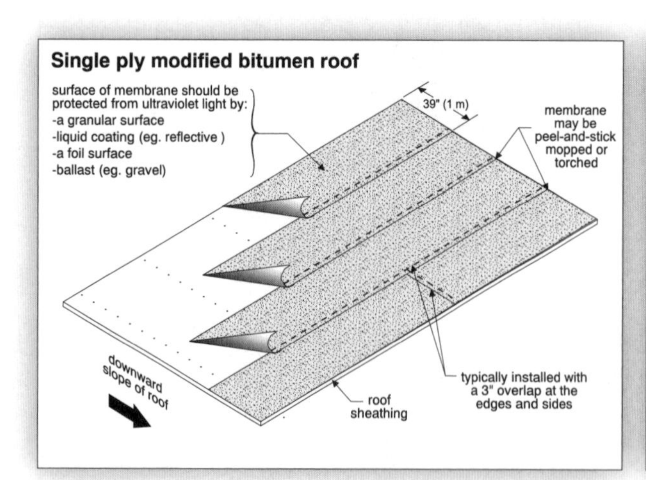

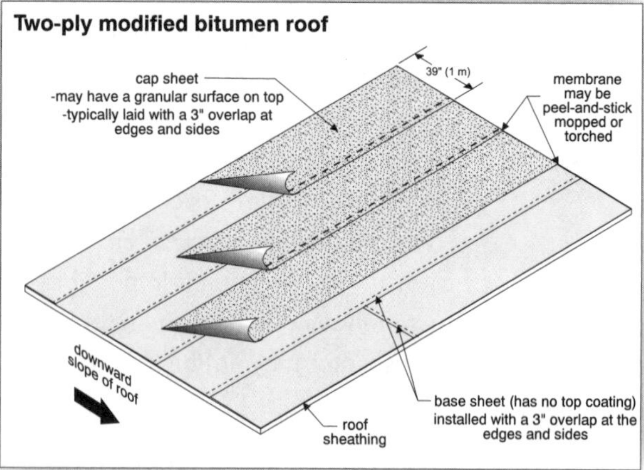

LIFE EXPECTANCY A lifespan of 15 to 20 years is typical.

WEAR FACTORS Roofs with ultraviolet protection last longer than those without. Two-ply installations are more durable than single-ply. Some types of membranes perform better in a cold or a warm climate. There is no way to determine the type during a home inspection.

Seam failure and installation problems are the most common issues. Regular foot traffic can shorten the life expectancy significantly.

RE-ROOFING Moisture trapped in the old roofing system may cause premature deterioration of the new membrane. Best practice is to remove old roofing before applying a new membrane.

1.11 Single-Ply Membranes (Plastic and Rubber)

DESCRIPTION Another alternative to built-up roofing is a single-ply membrane. There are a number of these products available, often used for high-end or commercial applications. These can be broken down into plastic-based materials and rubber-based materials.

Plastic, or thermoplastic, membranes include polyvinyl chloride (PVC) and thermoplastic polyolefin (TPO). Rubber or thermoset membranes include ethylene propylene diene monomer (EPDM) and butyl rubber (polyisobutylene – PIB).

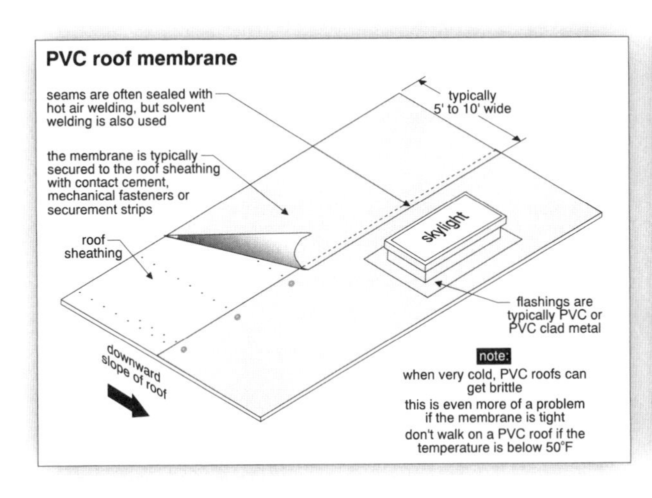

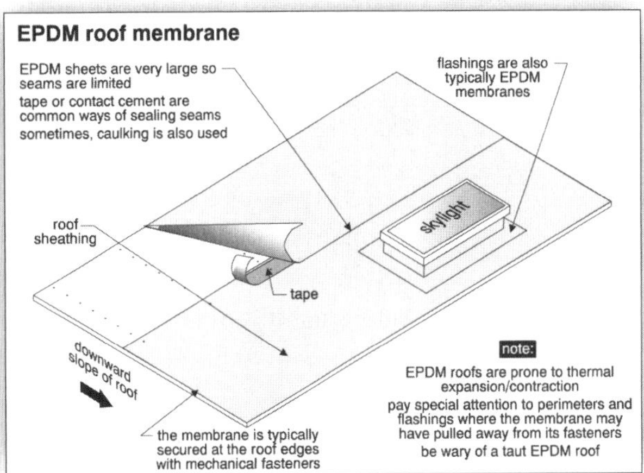

LIFE EXPECTANCY There are a wide variety of membranes with evolving chemical compounds and a number of installation methods. A lifespan of 15 to 20 years is common.

LEAKS Seam, flashing and installation problems are the most common issues. Since many of these membranes shrink, proper attachment is critical. Some systems can be damaged by contact with incompatible materials, including asphalt.

RE-ROOFING While some manufacturers of single ply membranes claim their product can be installed over existing materials, most recommend stripping the old roof off. Most plastic and synthetic rubber roof membranes are not compatible with asphalt. These should not be installed over built-up roofs.

1.12 Polyurethane Foam (PUF) Roofing

DESCRIPTION Sprayed-in-place PUF is a two-part foam mixture sprayed onto roof structures to form a single ply roofing membrane. The PUF is protected from mechanical damage, ultra violet light and moisture by an elastomeric rubber coating. PUF systems were first installed in the late 1960s. Numerous problems in the 1970s gave PUF roofing a bad reputation in some areas.

LIFE EXPECTANCY Life expectancies of up to 20 years are now projected for PUF systems, although many have had premature problems and failures.

WEAR FACTORS Common problems with PUF include deterioration of the PUF, cracking or splitting, delamination or blistering, ponding due to uneven application and coating problems.

RE-ROOFING Although PUF roofing is often installed over an old membrane, many do not recommend this approach. Moisture trapped in the old roofing system will cause premature deterioration of the new membrane.

1.13 Other Roof Coverings

There are many types of roof coverings on the market today. Examples include composite, hardboard and rubber shingles.

1.14 Common Problems with Roofing Systems

1.14.1 Problems that Affect All Roofs

LEAKS Roofing systems consist of several different types of materials and flashings. Leaks are most common at joints, seams and intersections with other materials. Water leakage may be caused by a number of factors operating together or independently. In some cases, the failure will be significant enough to warrant replacement of the roofing materials. In other cases, minor repairs or improvements are all that are necessary.

DAMAGE Worn, cracked, split, loose, or missing components of the roof can result in leakage. Roofing may be damaged by foot traffic, hail, raccoons or other animals. Missing shingles/tiles may be the result of fastener failure. Localized repairs are often an option, but as a general rule, when more than 10 to 15% of the roof requires repair, it is best to replace the roof covering.

OLD/WORN OUT As roofing materials grow old, they lose their ability to keep water out. Asphalt and wood roofing cracks, curls and shrinks. Wood roofing rots or burns through from the sun. Shingles or tiles may fall off as the materials or fasteners deteriorate. Built-up roofing dries out and cracks, sometimes referred to as alligatoring, because of the random crack pattern. Membrane roofs often fail at seams. Metal roofs rust. Slate may delaminate, and concrete may spall.

BLISTERS Blistering is a common problem with asphalt based roofs, sloped and flat. It is usually caused by moisture trapped in the roof membrane, and roofs often leak as blisters break.

LOSS OF GRANULAR MATERIAL Gravel or stone surfacing protects asphalt-based roofs from the sun. Loss of this material can lead to quick deterioration of the asphalt roofing material, and early failure. This may be caused by wind, downspout discharge, foot traffic or a material defect and is an issue on sloped roofs and flat roofs.

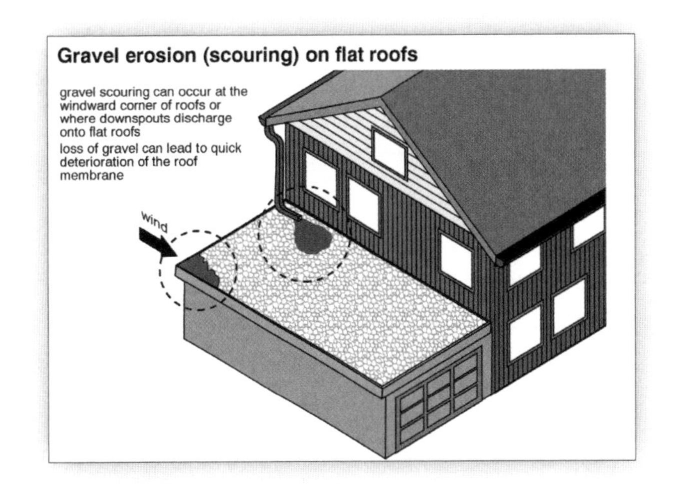

POOR INSTALLATION When roofing systems are not installed properly, the probability of failure increases. Installation defects include exposed fasteners, poor alignment of materials, incorrect materials, and too many layers of roofing.

TOO MANY LAYERS There are lots of good reasons to strip old roofing before adding new – The new roofing often lasts longer and there is an opportunity to identify and repair damage to the roof sheathing. Stripping old roofing adds to the cost of re-roofing and a second roof is often added over a first. This works better with some materials than others, but a third layer should never be added over second, no matter what roofing material is used.

Asphalt shingles over asphalt or over wood shingles are common double applications. Longer fasteners are needed, and the life expectancy of the new roof may be reduced.

MANUFACTURING DEFECTS Defective materials can fail early in their life. These defects include cracking, blistering or premature aging of the roof surface. Some defects, such as color variations, are simply cosmetic in nature.

VULNERABLE AREAS The typical vulnerable areas are where the roof changes direction or material (for example, where the roof meets a chimney or a wall). On a properly installed roof, these areas are flashed. Particularly vulnerable areas exist where two or more flashings intersect, for example where a chimney occurs in a valley.

Things that obstruct the flow of water off sloped roofs increase the risk of leaks. Skylights, chimneys and dormers are examples. Roof penetrations for plumbing stacks, electrical masts, etc. are also weak spots.

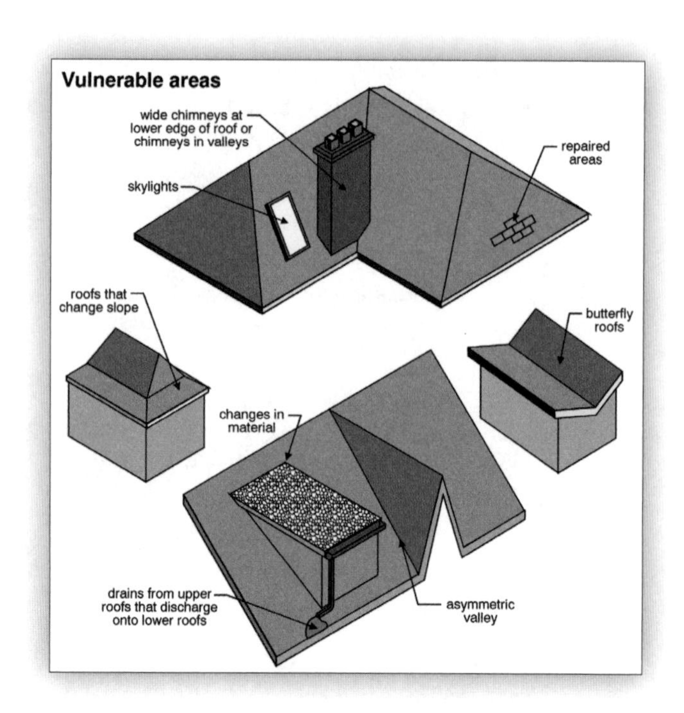

FLASHINGS Flashings are perhaps the most vulnerable areas of the roof, as they represent an interruption in the surface of the roof. These are addressed in more detail in Section 2 of this chapter.

PATCHED/ PREVIOUS REPAIRS Areas that have been repaired are vulnerable. Previous repairs indicate prior problems.

UNSUITABLE MATERIALS Roofing materials that are suitable for one application are sometimes used for another. Metal shingles designed for a slope of at least 3-in-12, are sometimes used on a flat roof. Built-up roofing is sometimes used incorrectly on a slope of 4-in-12. It fails by sliding down the roof surface over time.

TREE BRANCHES CONTACTING ROOF Trees should be kept trimmed away from roof and wall surfaces. The abrasive action of branches rubbing against the roof can damage the roof system. Tree limbs touching buildings also provide easy access to the home for pests.

SEVERE WEATHER Weather can cause a new, perfectly-installed roof to leak under the right conditions, including a wind-driven rain from an unusual direction, or a heavy snow followed by warmer temperatures and rain. Strong winds can damage roofs, blowing shingles or tiles off sloped roofs and eroding gravel from built-up roofs. Hail can damage most roof surfaces.

1.14.2 Problems Unique to Sloped Roofs

ICE DAMMING IN COLD CLIMATES Ice damming occurs when snow and ice collect, often at the eaves. Melting snow on the upper portion of the roof, warmed by the attic, cannot drain properly as it is trapped behind the still-frozen dam at the cold eaves. If the dam is large enough, water will back up under the shingles and leak into the eaves, exterior walls or building interior.

Some roofs are more prone to ice damming problems than others. Ice dams are most common on low slope roofs or roofs that change from a high slope to a low slope. The largest dams tend to form over unheated areas, such as eaves, porches, and attached garages. Ice dams are also common above party walls in attached houses.

Ice damming problems do not necessarily occur every winter. They normally occur after periods of heavy snowfall when daytime temperatures are at or slightly above freezing while nighttime temperatures are below freezing.

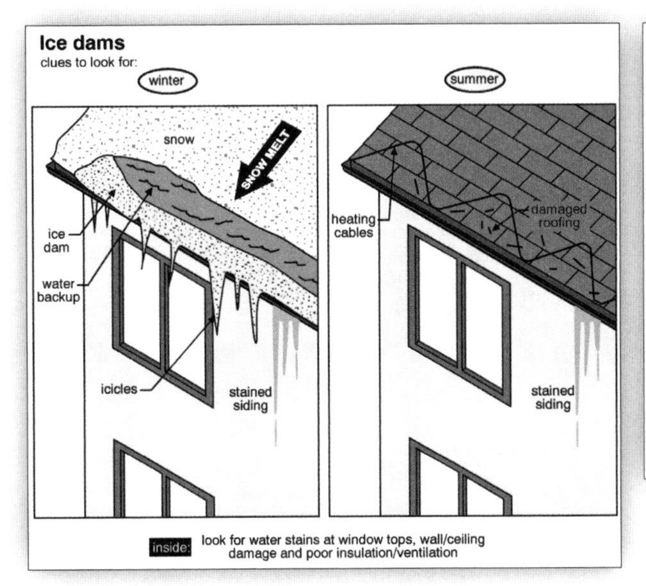

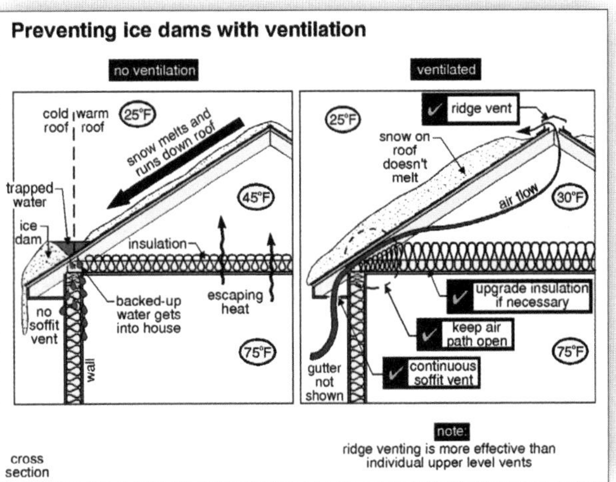

SOLUTIONS Effective solutions to ice damming problems are increased attic insulation and ventilation. These two measures reduce the attic temperature so snow over the heated portions of the house does not melt so quickly.

Heat may also leak into the attic through openings in the attic floor. Pot lights, exhaust fans, plumbing stacks, chimneys and attic access hatches can allow heated air into the attic unless they are well sealed. This is a key element in controlling ice dams.

Heating ducts in the attic should also be well sealed and insulated to avoid warming the attic and melting the snow above.

EAVE PROTECTION When re-roofing, eave protection should be provided along the lower part of the roof, from the edge up to roughly two feet beyond the exterior wall. Eave protection is often a waterproof rubberized asphalt membrane. In extreme climates, metal roofing is sometimes used on the lower part of the roof. The metal is watertight and allows snow and ice to slide off the roof. A metal or vinyl drip edge flashing will help protect the lower edge of the roof sheathing and direct water into the gutter.

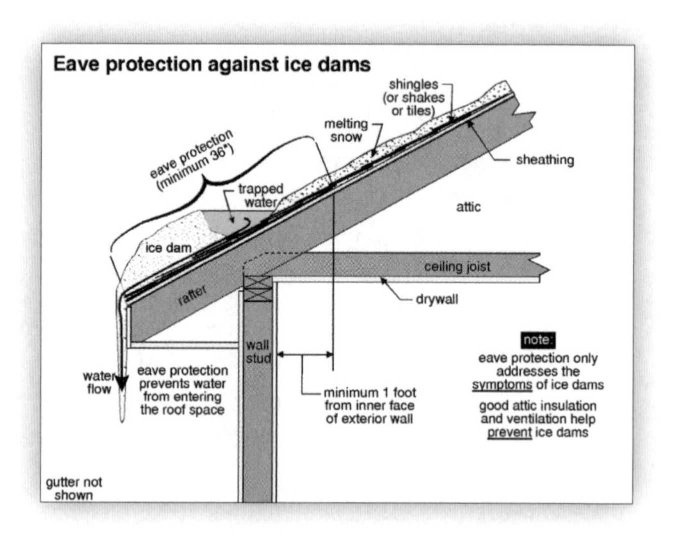

AVALANCHE GUARDS Small metal devices that protrude above roof surfaces (usually on the lower section of roof) are designed to hold snow on the roof and prevent avalanches. These are common on slate roofs and larger homes and commercial buildings. Some say these may worsen ice-damming conditions.

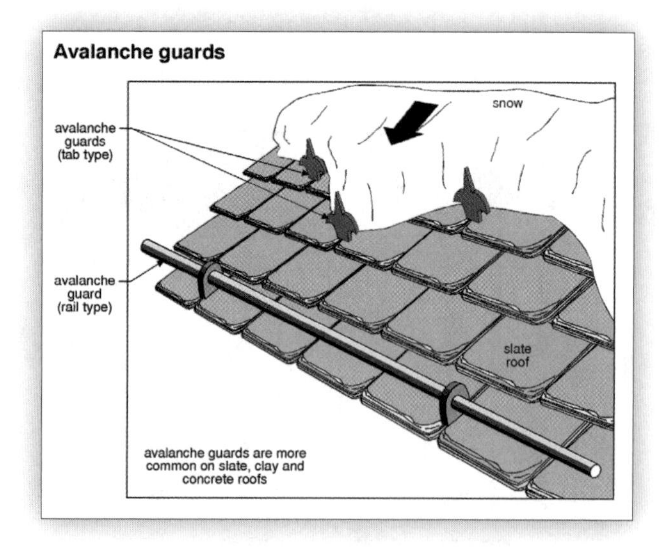

HEATING CABLES Electric heating cables along roof edges may be used to prevent ice dams. They have to be turned on before snow and ice accumulate to be effective. In some cases, they can aggravate rather than improve a situation if they are turned on after the ice dam has formed. Heating cables are not tested during an inspection.

NO KICKOUT FLASHING This flashing should be provided at the bottom of the roof that is against the side wall. Where the flashing is omitted, water may get in behind the siding and cause damage to the wall around and below the bottom of the roof.

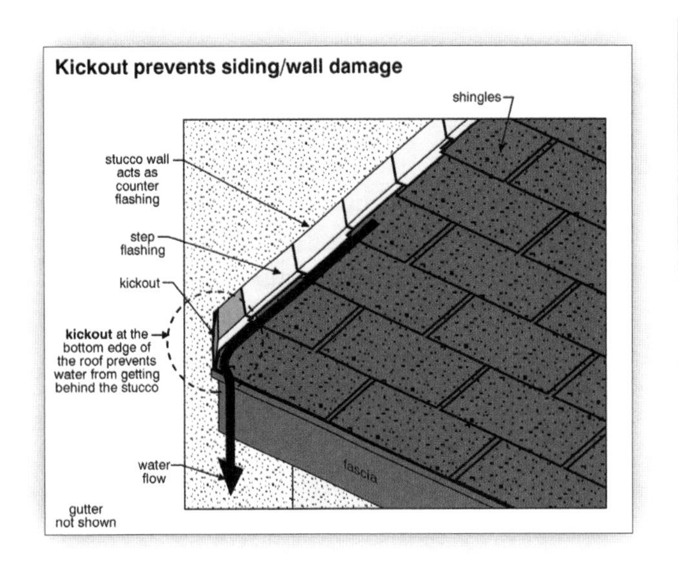

1.14.3 Problems Unique to Flat Roofs

PONDING ON FLAT ROOFS Ponding water on flat roofs reduces the life expectancy by as much as 50%. Flat roofs should not really be flat; they should have enough slope to drain water, usually described as 1 in 50 or 2%. We think that is cutting it pretty fine, and recommend more slope where possible.

While ponding is most often caused by inadequate roof slope, it may also be the result of missing or clogged roof drains. When leaks do occur, they do more damage if there is a large volume of water ponded on the roof.

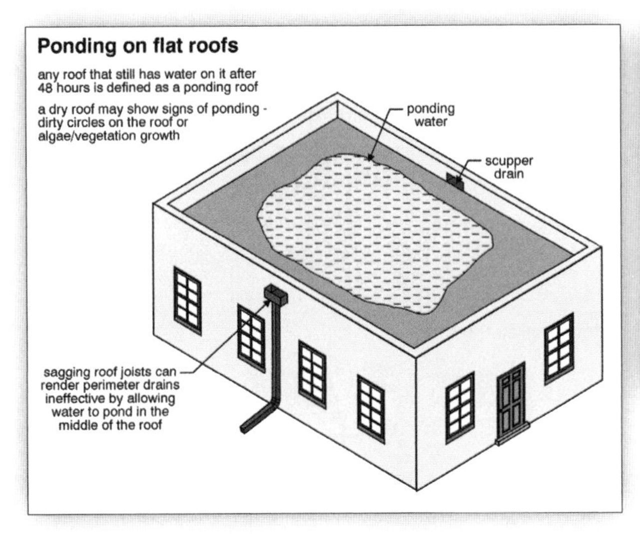

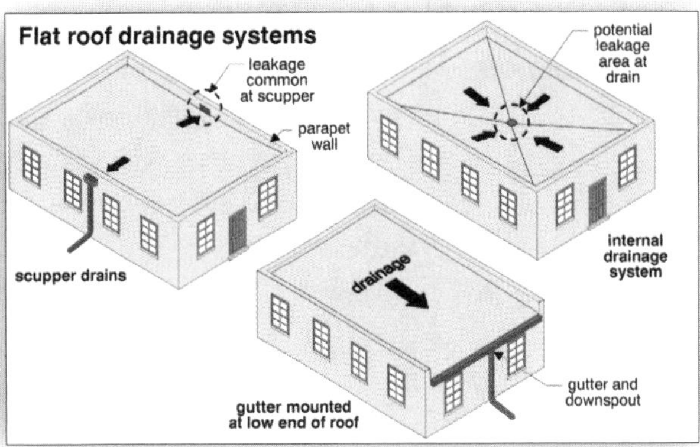

BUCKLING, WRINKLING, OPEN SEAMS Buckling, wrinkling and open seams in membranes may be caused by poor installation, membrane slippage, thermal expansion or contraction, and moisture trapped in the roof. These conditions can lead to leaks as the membrane opens up or develops holes.

Wrinkles or ridges that create openings at seams are sometimes called fishmouths.

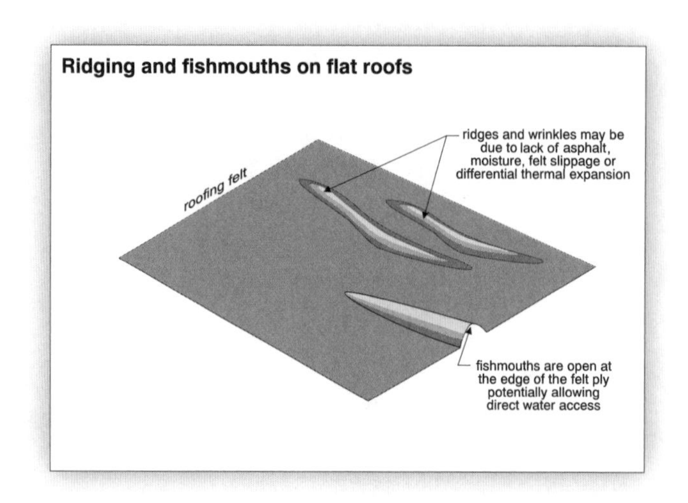

2.0 Flashings

DESCRIPTION Flashings are designed to keep water out. They are used where dissimilar materials meet, where a material changes direction, at roof penetrations and at joints in materials. Flashings are often galvanized steel; however, they can also be tin, terne (steel containing copper, coated with a lead-tin alloy), aluminum, lead or copper. In valleys, roll roofing material may be used as a flashing. Roll roofing is similar to asphalt shingles, except that it comes in rolls, roughly 18 or 36 inches wide.

LOCATION When a roofline changes direction, a ridge, a valley, or a hip is created. Ridges are horizontal and are found at the peak. Hips and valleys are high spots and low spots respectively.

2.1 Valley Flashings

DESCRIPTION All valleys should have flashings. Metal valley flashings are better but more expensive than roll roofing. Where the flashing is visible, it is known as an open valley. Metal valley flashings are typically 24 inches wide; however, much of the material is hidden by the shingles. When roll roofing is used, two layers are installed; one being 18 inches wide, and the top one 36 inches wide.

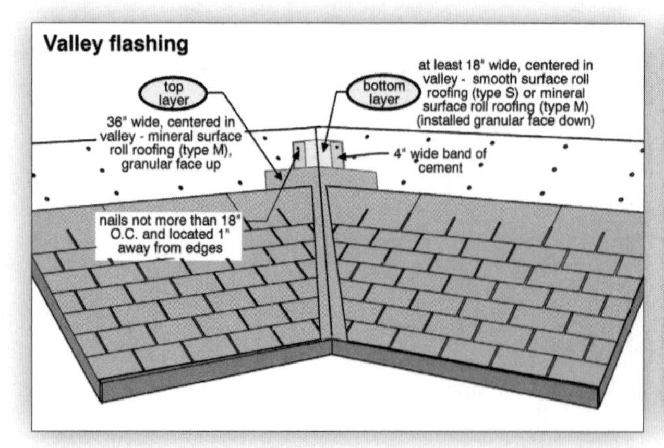

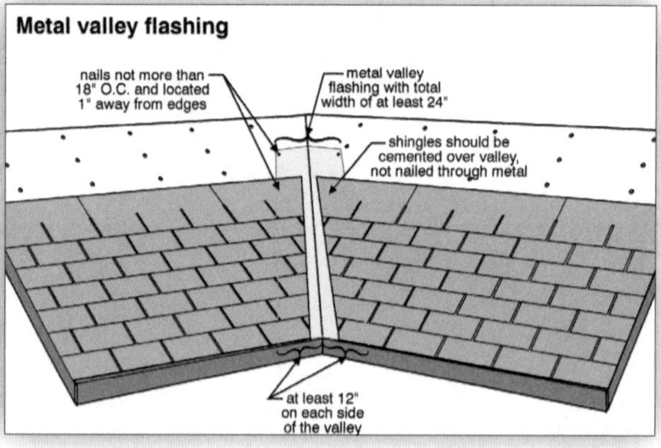

Sometimes a valley flashing is installed and then covered with shingles. This is called a closed valley. These may be closed cut or fully woven.

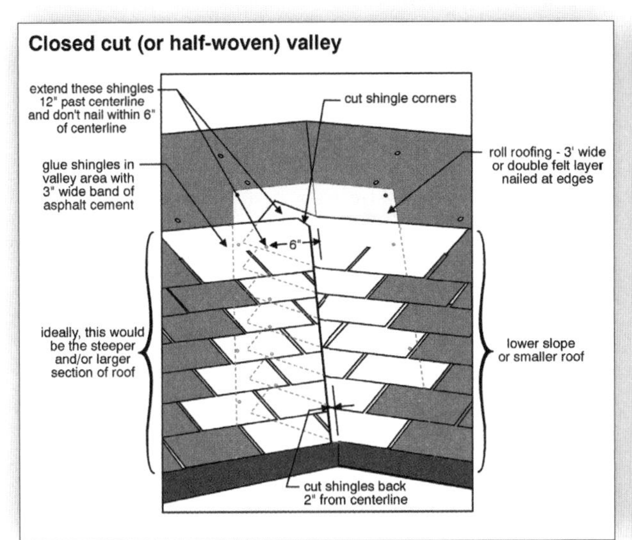

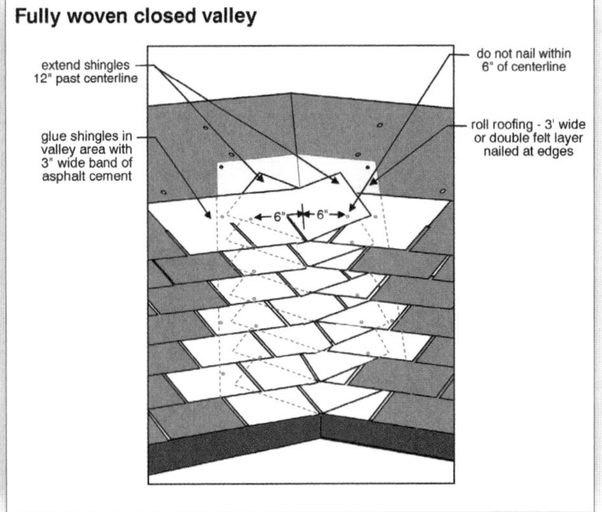

2.2 Hip and Ridge Flashings

DESCRIPTION Flexible shingles (such as asphalt) are simply cut and bent over hips and ridges to make them watertight. Metal flashings are often used with brittle roofing materials (wood shingles, slate, and asbestos cement) at the ridges and hips. Flashings may also be made from the roofing material. On some roofs, the flashing is covered by a layer of shingles.

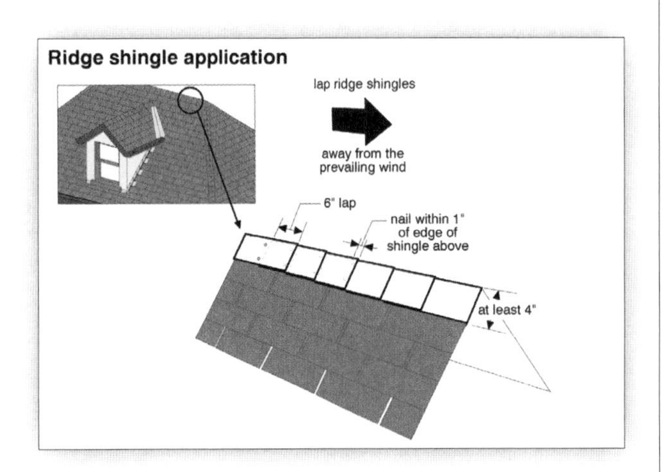

2.3 Sloped Roof to Flat Roof Flashings

DESCRIPTION When the flat roof is below the sloped one, the flat roofing material is typically applied first and extended up the slope. The sloped roofing covers the flat membrane. There may be metal flashing used at the change in direction. When the flat roof is above the sloped roof, a metal flashing protects the top of the sloped roofing material. The metal flashing extends onto the flat roof and is covered by the flat roof membrane.

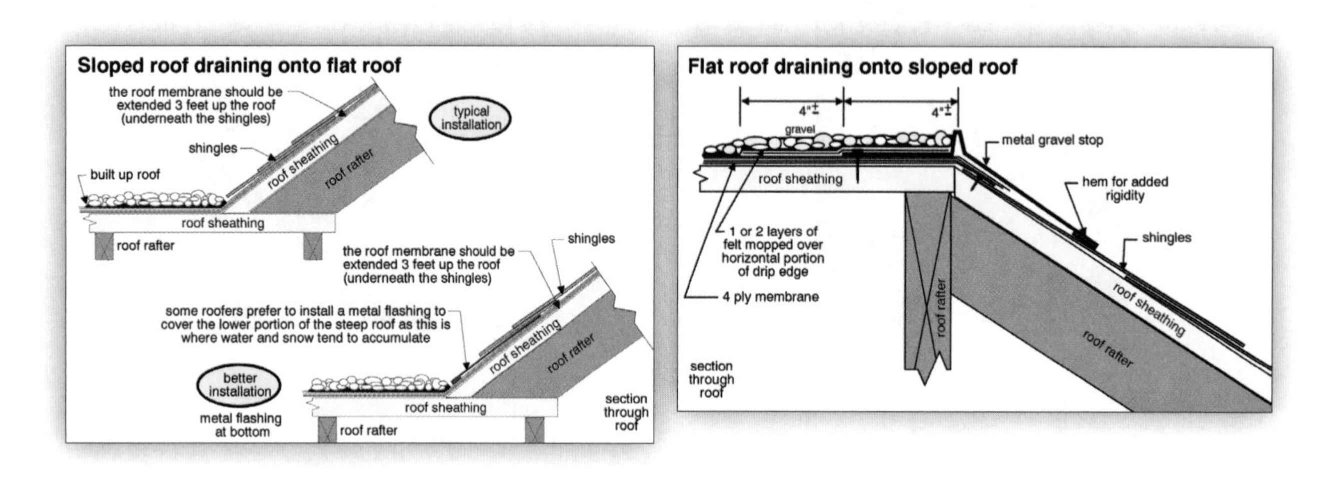

2.4 Roof to Wall Flashings

DESCRIPTION Special flashing is used when a roof intersects a wall. The flashing depends on the configuration and the roofing material. If the top of the roof meets a wall, a counter flashing can be installed over the roofing material. This metal skirt covers the top of the roofing material and extends up the wall behind the siding. On masonry walls, the metal flashing is let (embedded) into a mortar joint or sealed to the masonry surface with caulking (the less desirable approach).

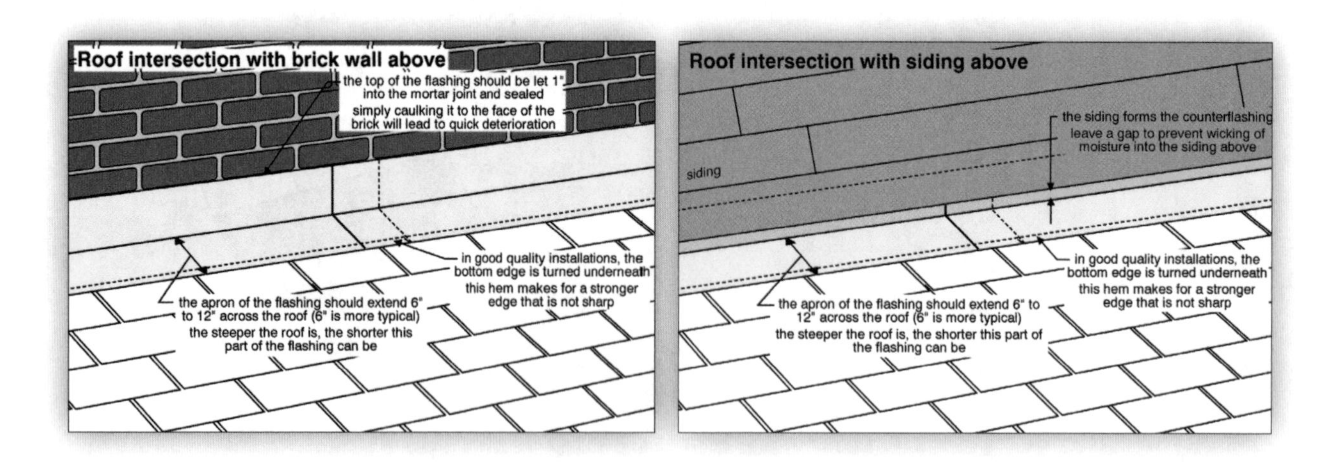

When the side of a roof ends at a wall, two sets of flashings are used. L-shaped step flashings are installed between each layer of shingles. The vertical part extends up the wall and is covered by siding or a metal counter flashing. Counter flashings are used on masonry walls, and the top may be let into mortar joints or sealed to the face of the masonry with caulking (a less permanent approach).

We looked at kickout flashings on Page 19.

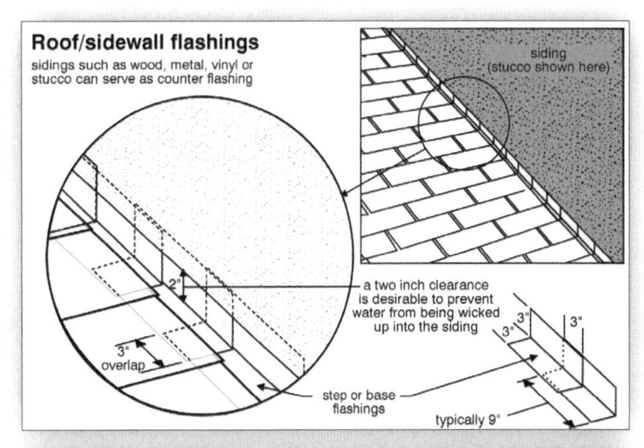

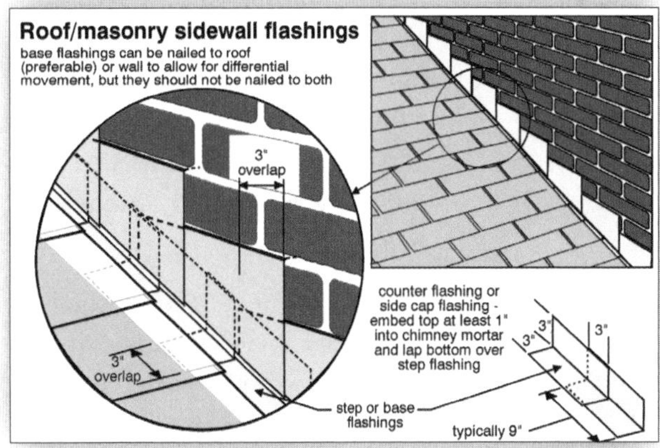

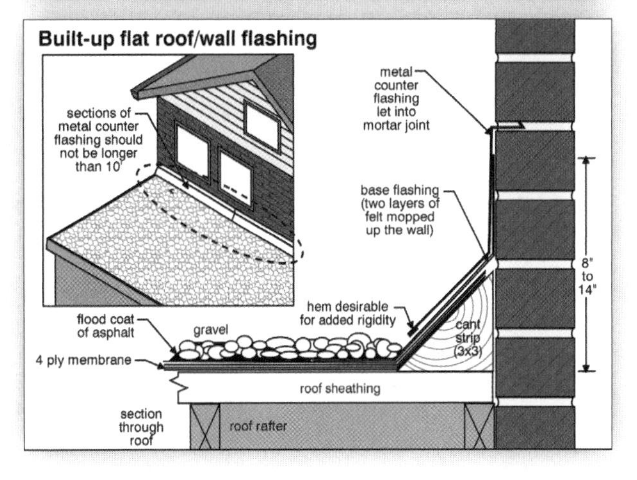

2.5 Chimney Flashings

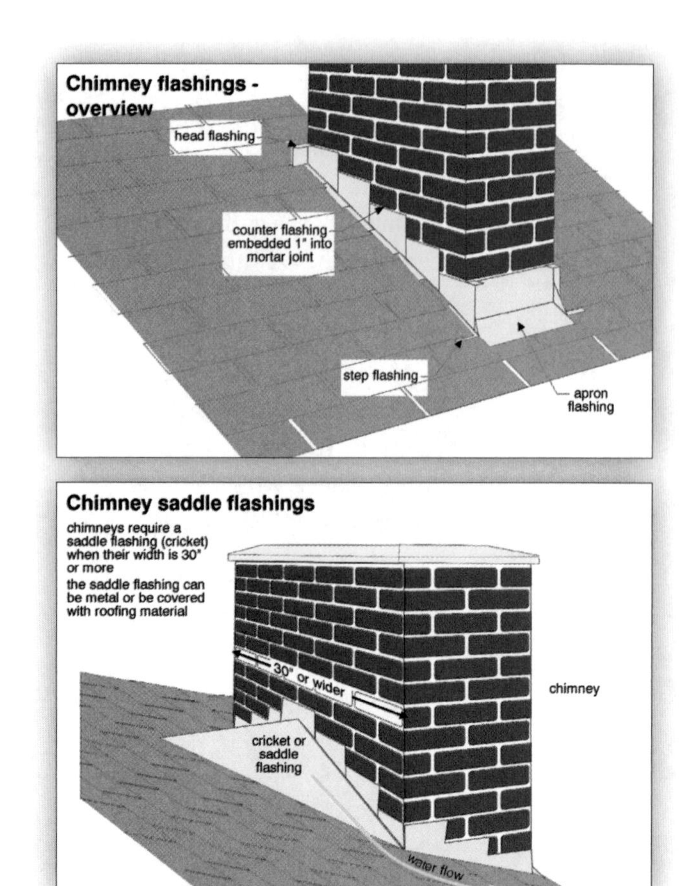

DESCRIPTION The flashings used on the sides and downhill portion of the chimney are similar to the wall flashings described above. The weakest part of a chimney flashing is the high side, facing up the roof. Water running down the roof must be diverted around the chimney. The flashings on the high side typically extend up at least six inches or one-sixth of the width of the chimney, whichever is greater. The flashing should continue up under the roofing to an equal height.

When a chimney is more than 30 inches wide, a saddle (or cricket) should be used to divert water around the chimney. This is a small peaked roof that directs water around the chimney.

LOCATION The location of a chimney affects how prone it is to flashing leaks. A chimney near the peak of a roof is better than a chimney at the bottom of a roof, which is better than chimney in a valley.

2.6 Parapet Wall Flashings

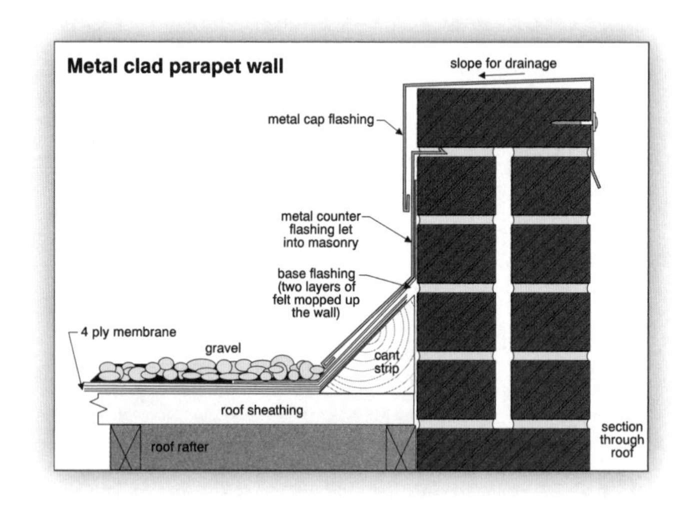

DESCRIPTION The exterior house wall may protrude above the roofline, forming a parapet wall. Where the roof meets the wall, typical wall/roof flashings are used. A cap flashing should also be provided over the top of the wall to prevent water penetration into the wall system.

2.7 Plumbing Stack/Electrical Mast/Exhaust Flue Flashings

DESCRIPTION A metal or rubber flashing is provided where anything penetrates the roof.

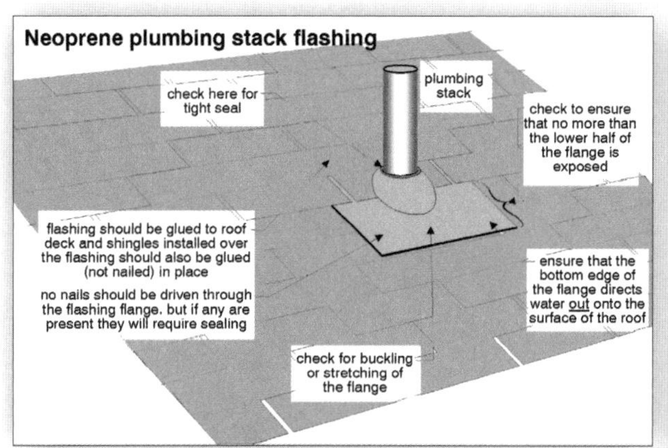

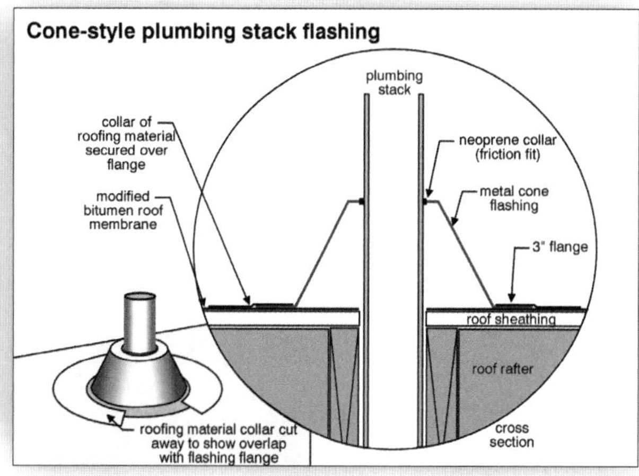

PITCH PANS (PITCH POCKETS) On flat asphalt roofs, pitch pans are sometimes used. A sheet metal pan around the stack or mast is filled with pitch or tar to a depth of one or two inches. Some experts consider this a poor flashing.

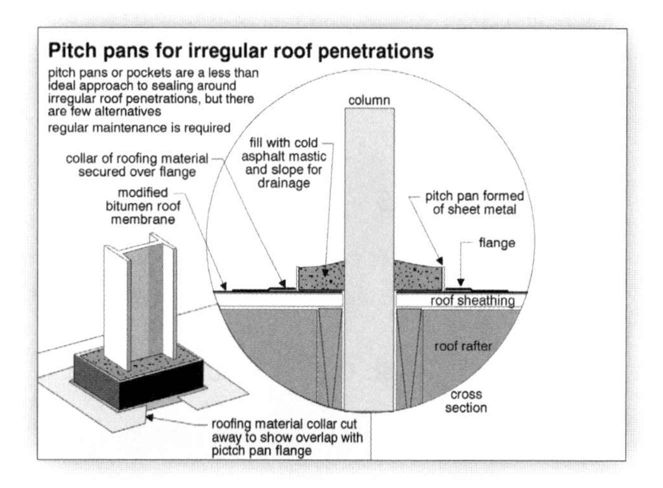

2.8 Skylight Flashings

DESCRIPTION Skylights should be flashed much like chimneys. A skylight should be installed on a curb or box that protrudes above the roof surface (unless the skylight comes with a pre-manufactured flashing assembly). This allows for the installation of proper flashings and limits snow accumulation on the skylight in cold climates.

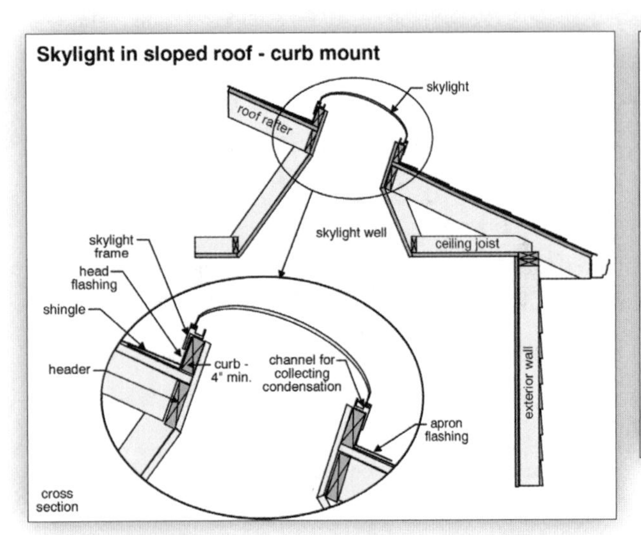

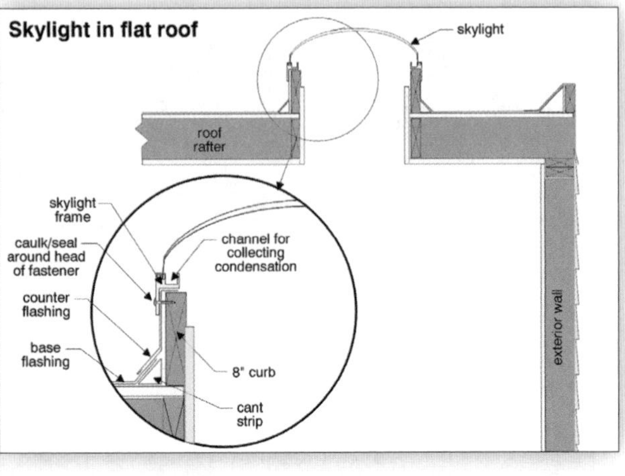

2.9 Drip Edge Flashings

DESCRIPTION This metal flashing is provided along the lower edge of some sloped roofs. It is intended to protect the roof sheathing and fascia from water damage.

2.10 Gravel Stop Flashings

DESCRIPTION On most built-up flat roofs, a gravel stop flashing made of metal is used at the perimeters. This metal flashing typically has a low profile and performs several functions, including securing and protecting the roof membrane at the edge of the roof, preventing the gravel from sliding off the roof, and forming a drip edge to keep water run-off from damaging the wood fascia.

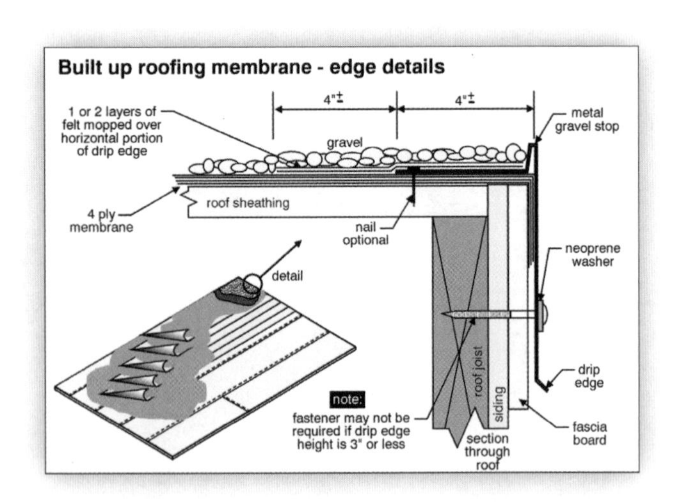

2.11 Roof Vent Flashings

DESCRIPTION Flashings are built into most roof vents. The flashing slides under the shingle material on the sides and uphill portion of the vent. On the downhill side, the flashing is exposed, overlapping the roofing material. The amount of overlap of shingles and flashing, as well as the quality of the installation determines the effectiveness.

Common Problems with Roof Flashings

Roofs leak when flashings don't do their job properly. Flashing problems are one of the most common sources of roof leaks. When re-roofing, we recommend flashings be replaced even if they are not worn out. It is expensive to replace flashings part way through the life of a roof.

MISSING, POORLY INSTALLED The most common problems with flashings are that that they are missing or not properly installed. Poor installation includes loose or missing components, poor fastening, inadequate height or length and poor sealing at the top. The illustrations below show a good way and an inferior way to attach a flashing to a brick wall.

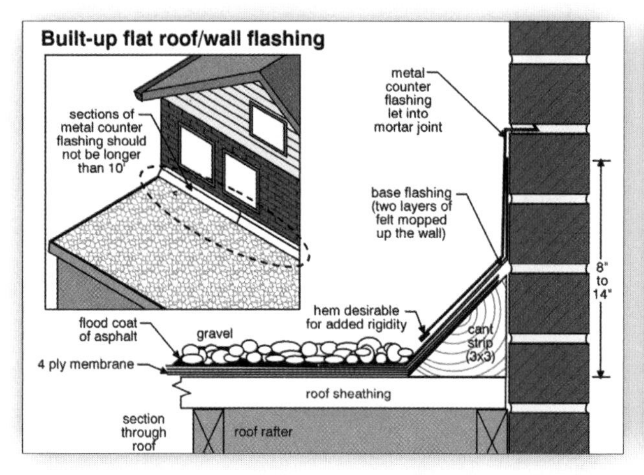

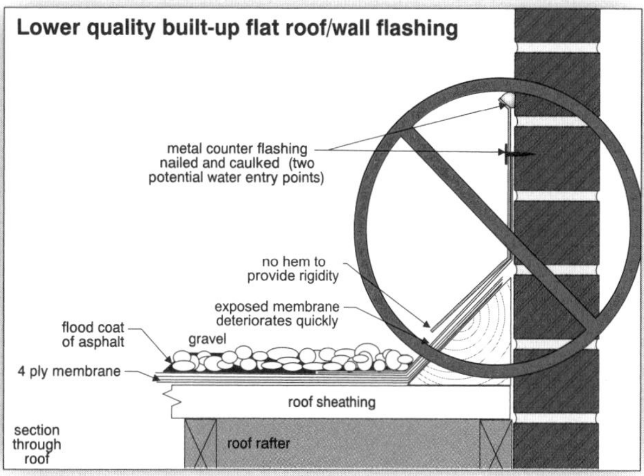

DAMAGED/ DETERIORATED/ PATCHED Flashings deteriorate over time – rusted metal and torn membrane flashings are common. Patches indicate previous issues and may suggest future problems.

VALLEY FLASHING ISSUES Valley flashings are often damaged by foot traffic or obstructed with leaves, twigs and pine needles, for example. Valleys may suffer ice dam problems in cold climates. Valleys that are too long at the bottom may allow water to overshoot the gutter. This allows water to collect against the foundation wall, and may lead to wet basements or crawlspaces.

ROOF-TO-SIDEWALL FLASHINGS – INADEQUATE CLEARANCE Where wood siding is used as a counter flashing, it should stop roughly two inches above the roof surface so that the wood is not constantly wet. Wood close to the roof surface is prone to rot.

SADDLE MISSING Saddles (or crickets) should be provided for chimneys wider than 30 inches to divert water around the chimney. A missing saddle may result in roof leaks at the chimney.

PITCH PANS (PITCH POCKETS) ON FLAT ROOFS Pitch pans should be kept full of pitch or asphalt to avoid collecting water, which causes leakage. These high maintenance flashings are often neglected.

PARAPET FLASHINGS – PONDING Parapet flashings should drain water quickly. When water accumulates on the top surface, premature rusting and leakage may occur.

SKYLIGHT FLASHINGS Leaks are common where there are no curbs or very short curbs. Other common problems include incomplete or improper flashing details around the skylight.

GRAVEL STOP FLASHINGS Gravel stop flashings are sometimes loose, rusted or missing altogether. It is common to find the roof membrane pulling away from the gravel stop. This can lead to leaks at the roof edge.

3.0 Chimneys

MATERIAL Chimneys are typically masonry or metal. Masonry chimneys can be brick, block or stone and are sometimes stuccoed or parged. In some areas, asbestos cement chimneys are common.

FLUES Chimneys often have more than one flue. Each flue is a separate channel for the smoke. Each appliance has a separate flue, with a few exceptions. Two gas furnaces on the same floor within a house can share a common flue, as can a gas furnace and a gas hot water heater on the same level.

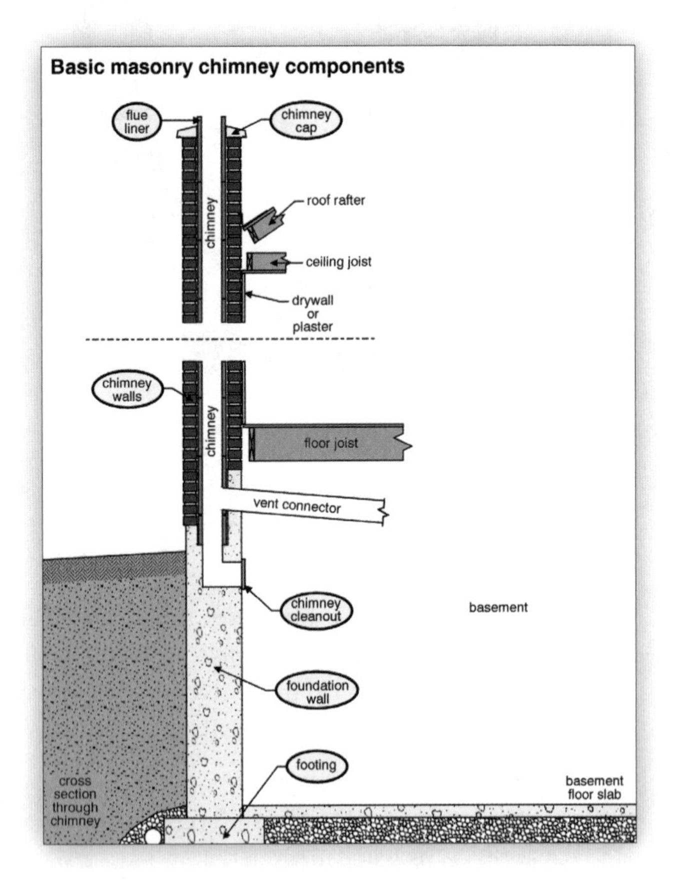

FLUE LINERS Some flues have masonry exposed on the inside. Unlined chimney flues are common in houses built before 1940. These unlined masonry flues often work well for fireplaces and oil-fired furnaces. Gas-fired furnaces usually require a liner because the cooler exhaust condenses, producing slightly acidic water that can damage unlined flues.

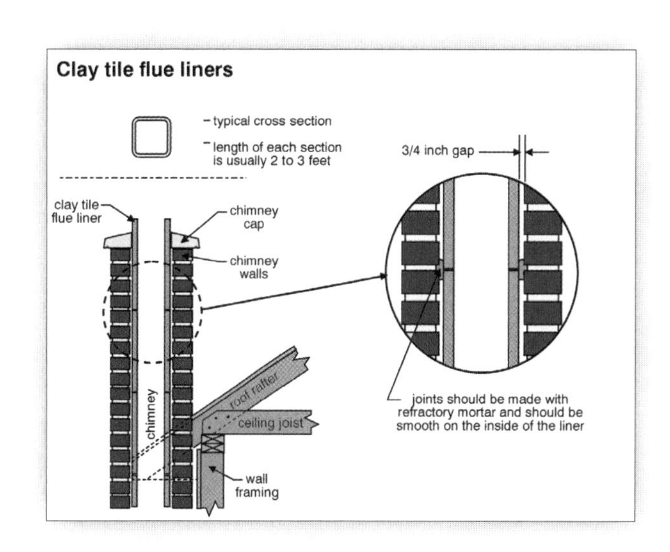

Flues are typically lined with clay tile, metal, or asbestos cement pipe. For more information on chimney liners, refer to the Heating chapter.

VERMIN SCREENS Raccoons, birds and squirrels may nest in chimneys. Vermin screens on the top of the chimney flues can be used to prevent this.

CHIMNEY CAP – MASONRY The purpose of a chimney cap is to protect the top surface of a masonry chimney from water. The chimney cap should not be confused with the rain caps that cover chimney flues to prevent water from entering the flues. Chimney caps are usually concrete; however, some are stone or metal. A cap normally overhangs the chimney sides at least one inch to protect the chimney from water dripping off the cap.

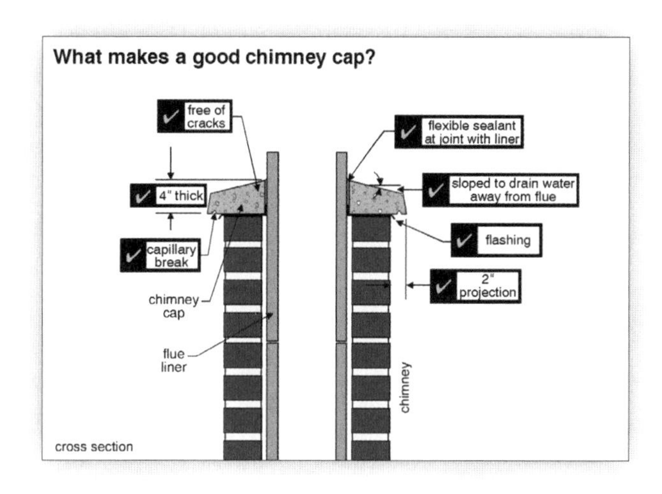

CHIMNEY CAP – METAL Caps on metal chimneys are designed to keep rain out and help promote good draw by preventing downdrafts. Caps for wood burning appliances often include a screen to prevent sparks and embers escaping from the chimney top.

HEIGHT Chimneys should be a minimum of three feet above the point of penetration through the roof and two feet higher than anything within ten feet of them to help ensure good draft. Minor liberties can be taken with this rule when considering single flue metal chimneys for furnaces. A common solution for fireplaces that draw poorly is to extend the chimney or divert down drafts.

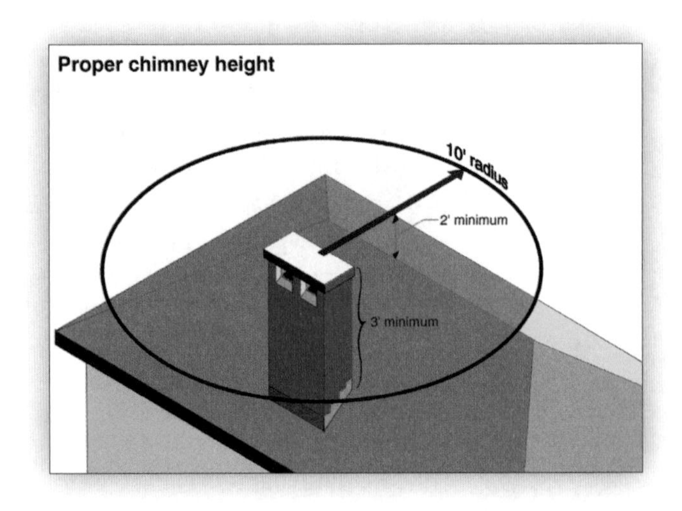

MUTUAL CHIMNEYS Many attached and row houses share chimneys. One chimney may have one or more flues for each house. Prior to working on a mutual chimney, co-ordination with the neighbor makes sense. Shared flues present a safety concern. This is discussed in the Interior chapter.

REMOVED Many idle chimneys are removed down to below roof level during re-roofing. This eliminates the need for flashing, a common source of problems.

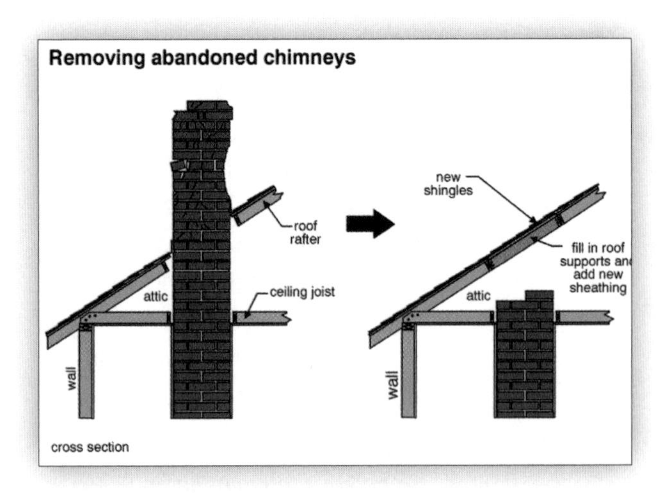

Common Problems with Chimneys

WATER DAMAGE Chimneys often deteriorate as a result of water. Metal chimneys rust, and masonry chimneys suffer damage to mortar, brick, stucco, etc. The source of the water can sometimes be wind-driven rain or condensation within the chimney.

One of the by-products of burning fossil fuels is water vapor. As exhaust gases travel up the chimney, they cool, sometimes reaching the dew point, forming condensation. The water is absorbed into masonry chimneys and sits on the interior of metal chimneys. The somewhat acidic water droplets cause corrosion in metal flues and deterioration within masonry flues.

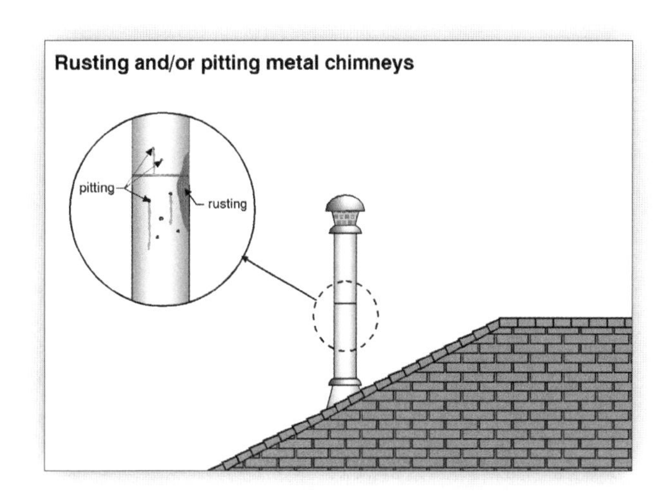

FREEZE/THAW Damage may occur in masonry chimneys because of cyclical heating in cold climates. The moisture absorbed into the masonry freezes and expands as the temperature drops. This causes mortar to deteriorate, bricks to spall and stucco to loosen. Small amounts of loose mortar can be replaced, but extensive damage to the mortar or the masonry usually requires re-building of the affected portion of the chimney.

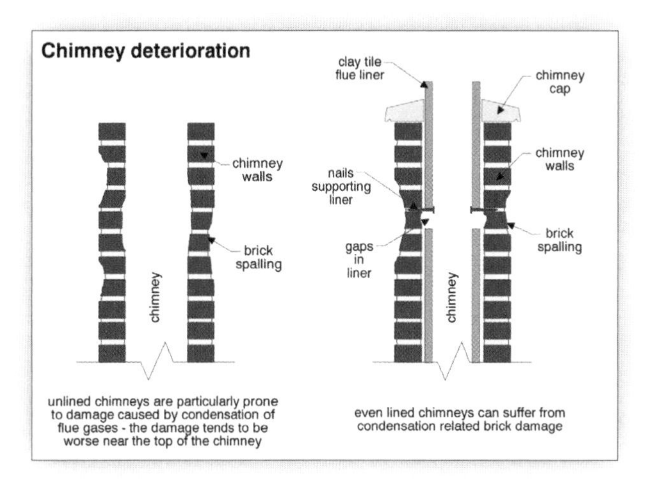

GAP IN LINER Some masonry chimneys lined with clay tile have a gap in the liner. The top flue tile should protrude two to four inches beyond the top of the chimney. If the top section of clay tile was too short to protrude (two-foot lengths are common), some masons simply raised the top tile, leaving a gap between the top two tiles. A ring of deterioration may show up on the exterior of the chimney, corresponding to the gap in the clay tile liner.

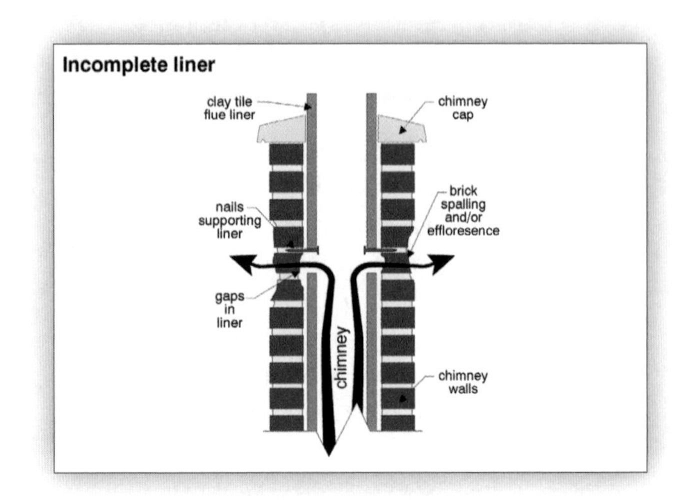

MISSING CHIMNEY CAP – MASONRY In many cases, a proper cap is not provided. Bricklayers often put a thin coat of mortar over the top surface of the chimney around the flue. This cement wash has no overhang to keep water away from the chimney. Over time, this cracks and eventually becomes loose. The rate of deterioration to the top of a chimney that does not have a cap depends largely upon the type of masonry used to build the chimney and the quality of the mortar.

CRACKED CHIMNEY CAP – MASONRY A cracked cap allows water to penetrate the chimney causing premature deterioration and in cold climates, freeze/thaw damage.

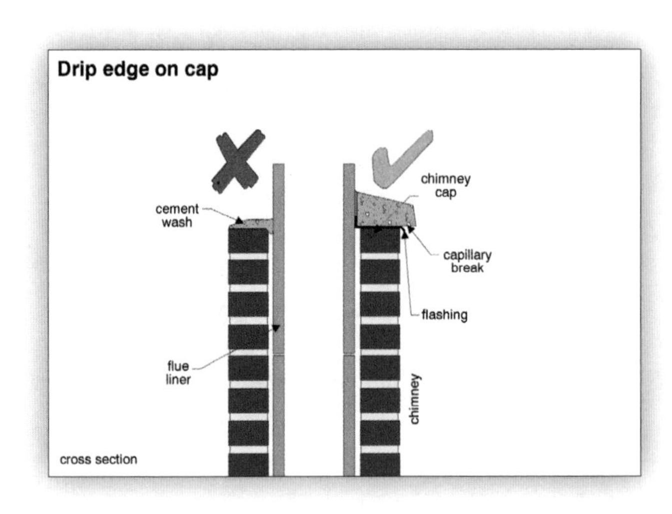

DEBRIS Debris can accumulate in the bottom of the chimney and may block off the appliance vent if not cleared. Many chimneys have a clean-out door to allow removal of accumulated debris.

MISSING CHIMNEY CAP – METAL A missing cap on a metal chimney can lead to water damage to the chimney interior. It may also lead to downdraft problems.

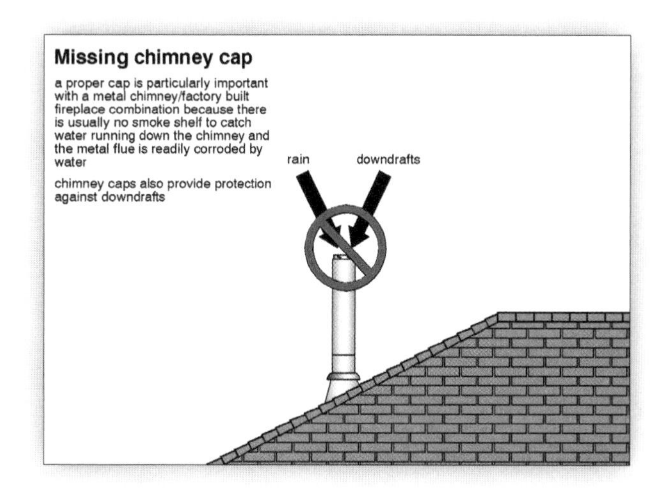

DRAFT PROBLEMS Short chimneys are prone to downdraft problems, depending on the chimney location, roof shape and prevailing winds.

BRACING Tall chimneys, masonry or metal, should be braced to stabilize them. The requirements for bracing are not only based on the height of the chimney but also on the width and depth of the chimney.

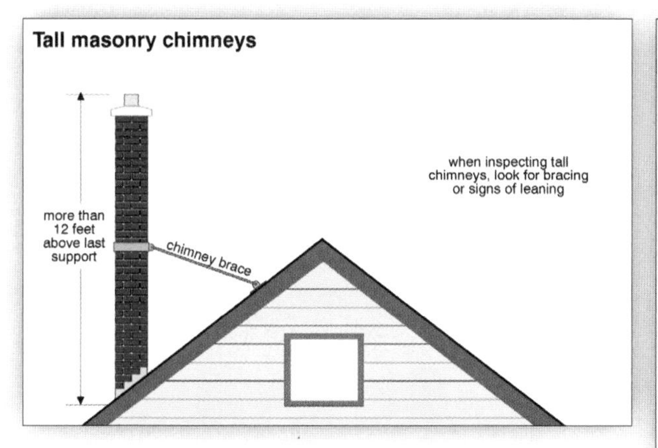

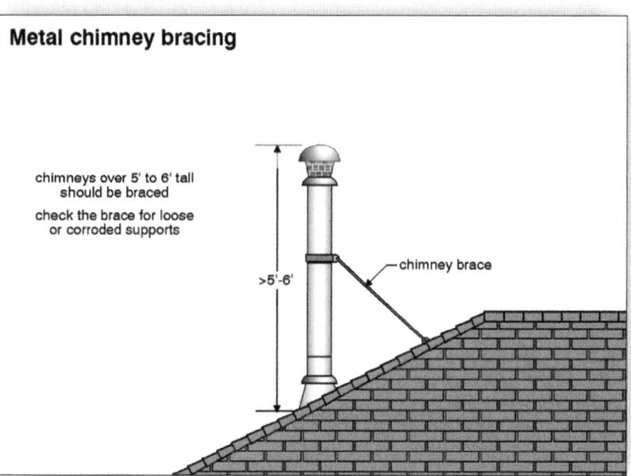

Exterior

INTRODUCTION

THE EXTERIOR COMPONENTS OF A BUILDING WORK TOGETHER TO PROVIDE A WEATHERTIGHT SKIN, IF ALL THE PARTS ARE DOING THEIR JOB. PROTECTION AGAINST INTRUDERS, BOTH ANIMAL AND HUMAN, IS ALSO OFFERED BY THE BUILDING SKIN. GOOD EXTERIORS ARE ATTRACTIVE, DURABLE AND REQUIRE LITTLE MAINTENANCE. EXTERIOR COMPONENTS ARE OFTEN THE MOST NEGLECTED PARTS OF A HOME.

1.0 Gutters and Downspouts

DESCRIPTION Gutters and downspouts have two major functions. Firstly, they protect the walls of a building from water that would ordinarily run off the roof. This water can damage the wall surfaces and cause localized erosion at ground level.

The second and most important function of gutters and downspouts in homes with basements or crawlspaces, however, is helping to ensure a dry basement. (We'll say basements to mean both basements and crawlspaces in this section.) Regardless of the foundation type, there is always the risk of water penetration. The less water there is in the soil near the foundation wall, the lower the risk of water penetration into the basement. Gutters should collect all water run off, and downspouts should discharge the water into proper drains or onto the ground well away from the foundation walls.

SIZE On most houses, the gutters are attached to the fascia board at the edge of the eaves. In some houses, gutters are integral to the design of the eaves. The two most common sizes of gutters are four-inch and five-inch widths. Four-inch gutters are good for relatively small roof areas; however, five-inch gutters are preferred because of their additional capacity. Five-inch gutters are also less likely to allow water to overshoot the gutters when the water is draining off a steeply pitched roof.

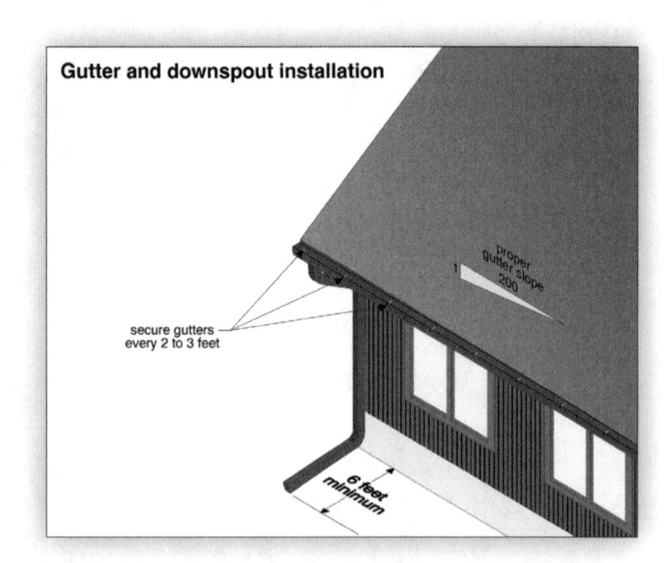

MATERIALS Gutters can be made of several materials; however, the most common are aluminum, galvanized steel, plastic and copper. Integral gutters are usually framed in wood, and lined with metals such as lead or copper. There are advantages and disadvantages to the various materials used.

ALUMINUM Aluminum gutters do not rust but they dent easily, particularly with tall, heavy ladders. Joints in aluminum gutters are usually riveted together and caulked. The caulking must be renewed every few years. Aluminum gutters usually have very few joints, since the gutters are typically fabricated on the job site from long rolls of aluminum stock. Aluminum gutter is also pre-finished and does not require regular painting. Life expectancy is estimated to be 20 to 25 years.

GALVANIZED STEEL Some galvanized steel gutters are also pre-finished but most are not. Galvanized steel requires periodic painting. Joints in galvanized gutters are usually soldered together. This type of gutter has a 20 to 25 year life expectancy.

PLASTIC Plastic gutters are generally designed for the do-it-yourselfer. Plastic comes in a limited color selection and some types tend to discolor with time. Plastic gutters are usually relatively small and some of the earlier systems are prone to cracking during cold weather. The life expectancy is dependent upon the quality of the kit and the installation.

COPPER Copper gutters are considered to be the best; however, they are very expensive and not common. Copper can last 50 to 100 years.

Common Problems with Gutters and Downspouts

LEAKAGE – HOLES/SEAMS/ END CAPS The most common problem with gutters is leakage. Leakage will occur with galvanized gutters as they rust through. Holes can develop in copper gutters as well. All gutters are prone to leakage at the joints and seams. Missing end caps and poor connections to downspouts are other common sources of leakage. Leakage can cause considerable damage to fascias, soffits and walls below. Leaks can also result in basement water problems.

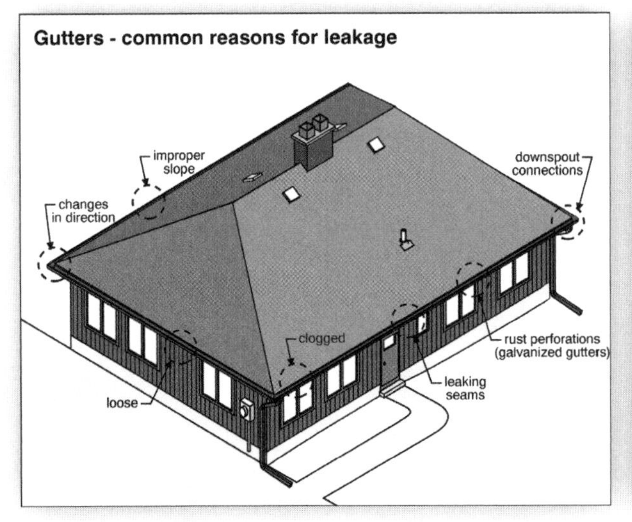

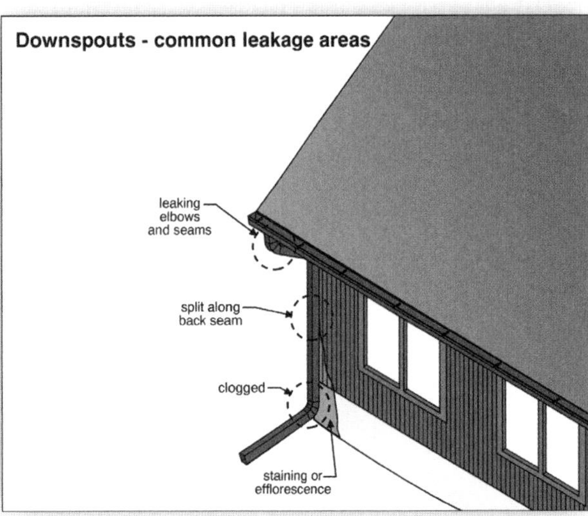

LOOSE Gutters and downspouts may become loose and require re-securing. This is normally due to improper fastening during original installation or damage caused by snow and ice during winter months. Downspouts can become disconnected from gutters.

DAMAGED/OLD Gutters and downspouts suffer from mechanical damage due to ladders, tree limbs, and the like. Downspouts tend to split open at the seams (from freezing in cold climates). The seam is usually against the wall and the split may go unnoticed. Downspouts along driveways or sidewalks are sometimes crimped. Aluminum gutters and downspouts are more easily damaged than galvanized steel. Galvanized steel downspouts often rust near grade level or where blockages have occurred. Galvanized gutters and downspouts eventually rust through.

PAINT Galvanized steel gutters and downspouts should be painted regularly to prolong their life. Although not often done, some say painting the inside is as important as painting the outside. Special paints are sometimes used inside gutters since they are often wet for considerable periods of time.

POOR SLOPE Gutters should slope properly towards downspouts to drain water.

CLOGGED Gutters and downspouts often clog with debris. Screens or deflectors are sometimes installed to prevent leaves and twigs from getting into the troughs. These rarely work well. They become loose and often fall out. They also make cleaning more difficult. Special screens are available for the top of downspouts to prevent the entry of debris. These work better, but must be cleaned regularly.

NUMBER OF DOWNSPOUTS On many houses, the number of downspouts is inadequate. As a general rule, a downspout should be provided for every 35 to 40 feet of gutters.

DOWNSPOUT DISCHARGE Downspouts collect water from the gutters and discharge it into drains or onto the ground. Underground drains (usually made of clay tile, cast iron or plastic) become clogged or break below grade. If an underground downspout malfunctions, water problems will likely develop in that part of the basement. There are two options. Exterior digging and repairs can be undertaken; however, it is faster and cheaper to simply disconnect the downspout and redirect it to discharge away from the house. It's also easier to monitor the performance, and problems are corrected easily.

Downspouts should discharge above grade onto the ground at least six feet from the home. The slope of the ground in this area should be away from the house, to direct water away from the basement.

On older homes, (pre-1950) downspout drains are often connected to floor drains in the basement. If there is a significant amount of debris in the discharge from the downspouts, it can plug the basement floor drains and cause backup. A more complete discussion of wet basement problems is included in Section 10 of the Interior chapter.

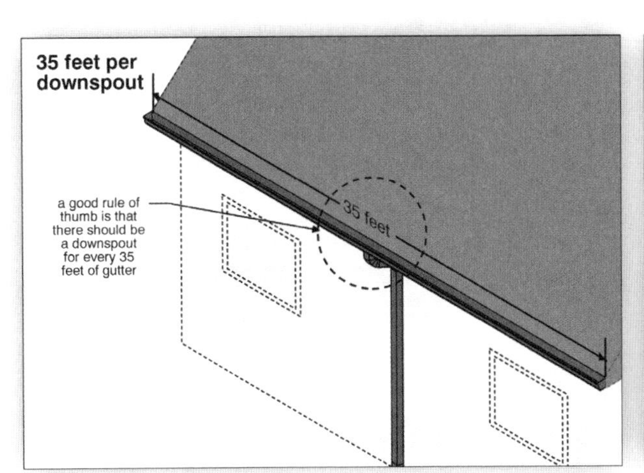

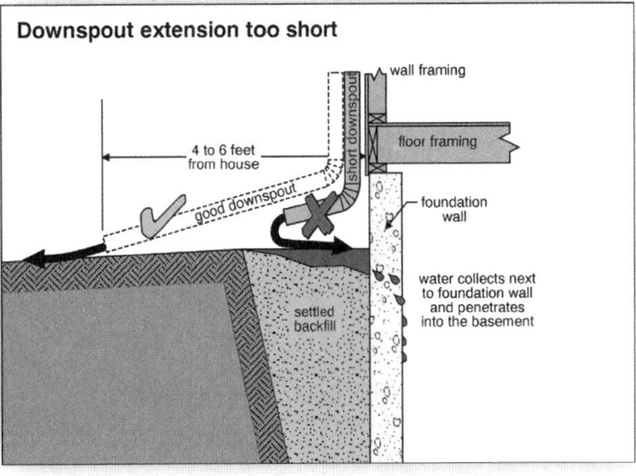

DISCHARGE ONTO ROOF Where gutters or downspouts discharge onto roof below, the lower roof in the path of the water will deteriorate quickly. The lower roof can be protected by extending the downspout along the lower roof to discharge directly into the lower roof gutter.

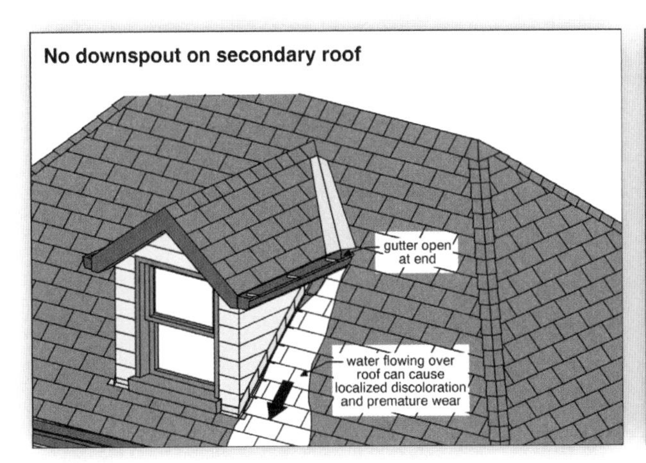

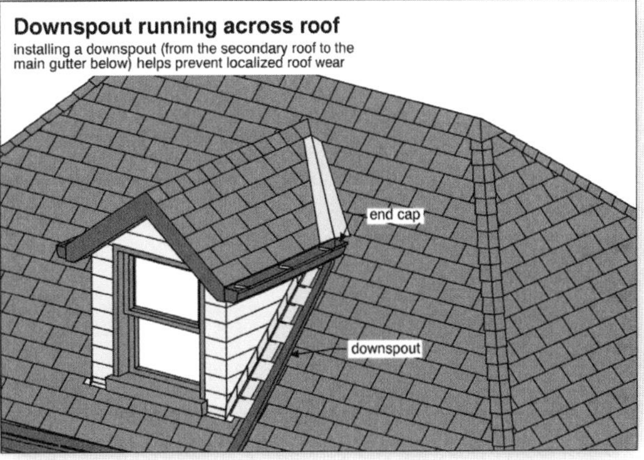

INTEGRAL OR BUILT-IN GUTTERS Malfunctioning integral gutters can be very serious. The leaking water usually ends up in the structure, causing rot and other damage. Repairs often include adding a single-ply roofing membrane as a gutter liner.

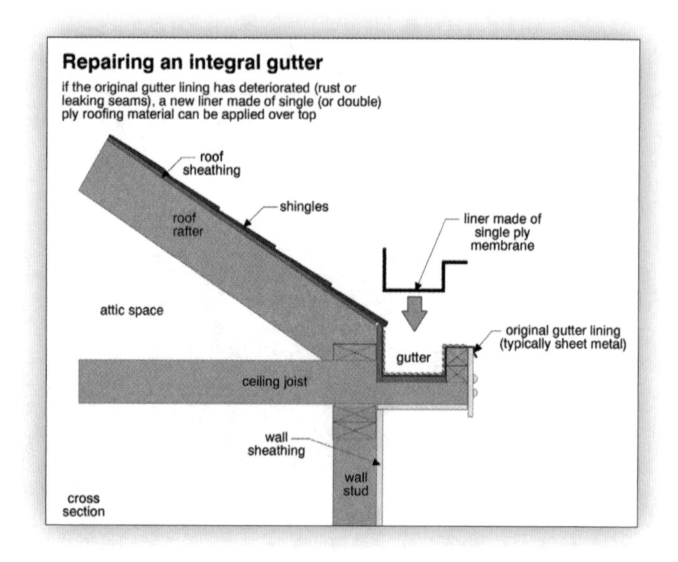

2.0 Lot Grading

DESCRIPTION Proper lot grading is an important consideration when dealing with wet basements. No foundation wall system is completely waterproof. Water accumulating in the soil outside the building will usually leak through eventually. The secret is to keep the soil outside the building dry. If the ground around the building slopes so that surface water runs away from the building, soil close to the foundation is dry and the basement is far less likely to leak.

Common Problems with Lot Grading

WET BASEMENTS The theory is simple. If there is no water in the soil on the outside of the foundation wall, no water will get into the interior. Most wet basement problems can be eliminated or dramatically reduced with good grading and proper performance of gutters and downspouts. The ground around the home should slope down six inches for the first ten feet away from the home. This can often be done by adding topsoil (not sand or gravel).

Where the general topography directs water towards the house, further measures are sometimes required. A swale (a shallow ditch with gently sloped sides) may have to be constructed to divert water run off around the house to areas that are lower-lying.

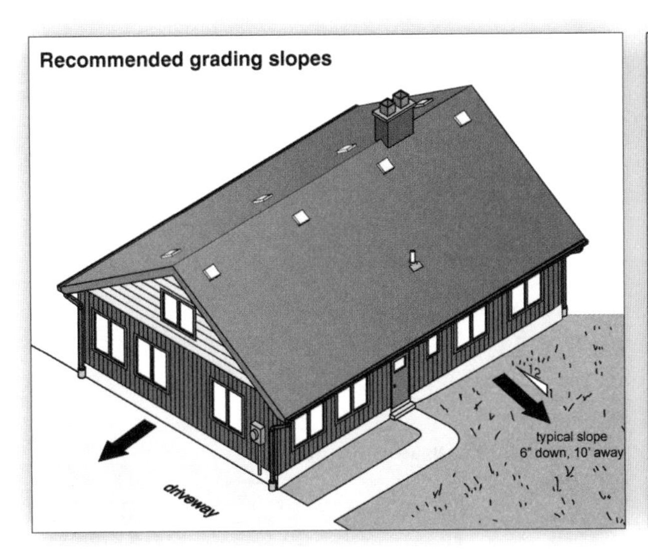

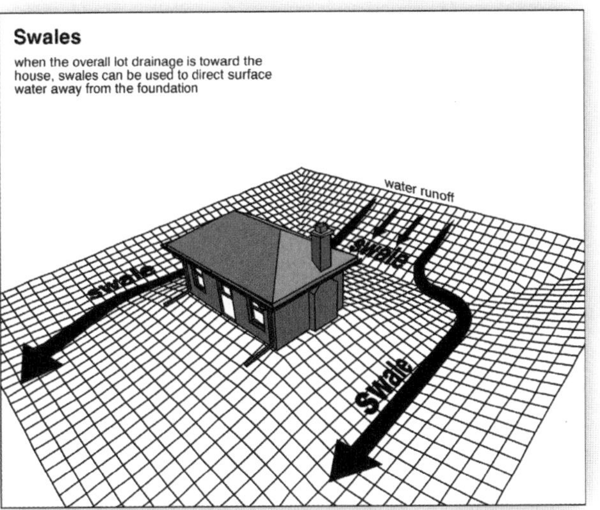

If the general topography of the neighborhood is such that the house lies in the lowest area, grading improvements may improve the situation; however, further measures may be necessary. See Section 10 of the Interior chapter for more information on wet basement problems.

RAVINE LOTS Ravine lots have potential erosion problems, which can have catastrophic effects. Erosion can compromise the structural integrity of the house if the tableland keeps disappearing.

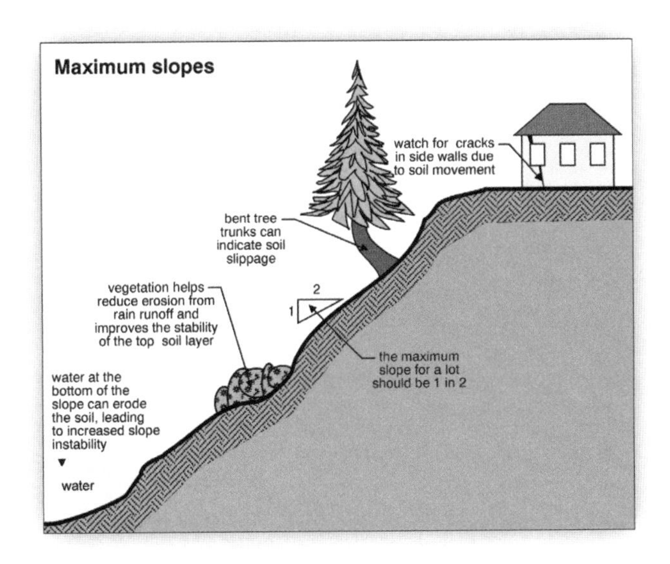

From a one-time visit, it is not possible to determine the rate of erosion (if any); however, mature trees and heavy vegetation on the slope suggest little movement and their roots help prevent erosion.

To prevent continuing problems, a soils engineer and/or landscape architect should be engaged to design retaining walls or other systems to hold back the earth, where erosion is noted.

2.1 Window Wells

DESCRIPTION Window wells are created with small retaining walls that keep the earth away from windows that are at or below grade. Window wells may be concrete or a corrugated steel shell. Chemically treated wood is sometimes used; however, it should be avoided in termite prone areas.

Window wells should be large enough to allow light in and should allow for easy cleaning of the window and well. Re-grading work to drain surface water away from the home may create the need for window wells, as the grade level is often raised around the foundation.

DRAINAGE AND COVERS Ideally, the bottom of the window well should contain several inches of gravel to allow water to drain from the well. A drainage pipe, filled with gravel (to prevent it from collapsing, but still allowing water to pass) should extend down to the drainage tile around the perimeter of the footing (if one exists). As an alternative, a clear plastic dome cover is installed over the window well to keep water and debris out.

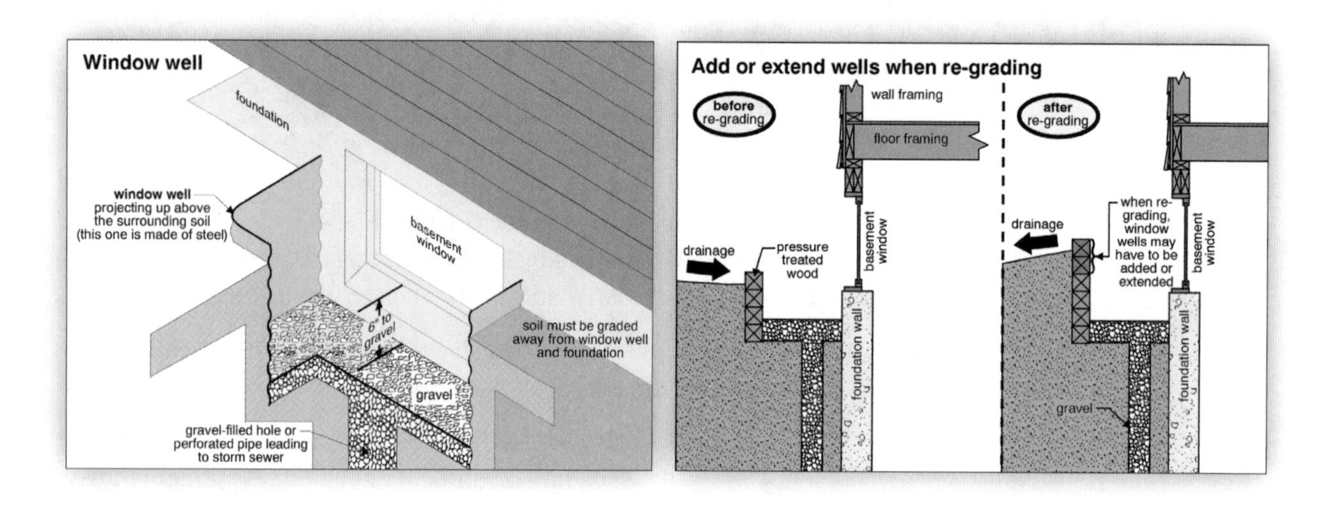

Common Problems with Window Wells

Wells may be missing or too shallow to protect the window. They may be clogged with debris (a maintenance issue) or they may not drain properly, even when clean. Wood rots, metal rusts and concrete spalls. Nothing is forever.

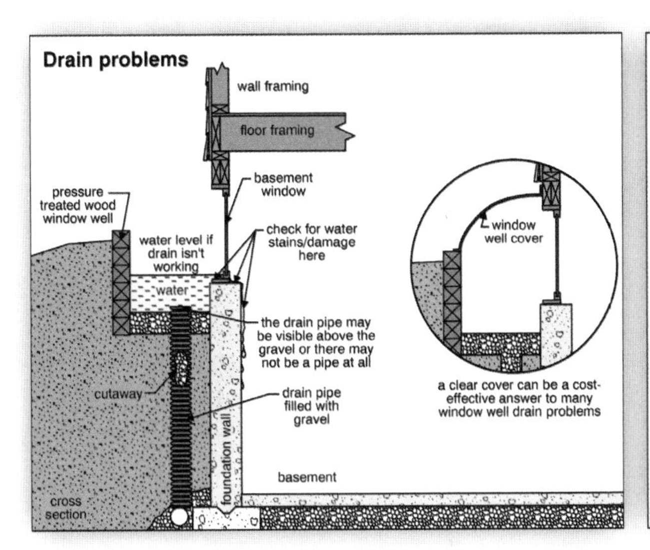

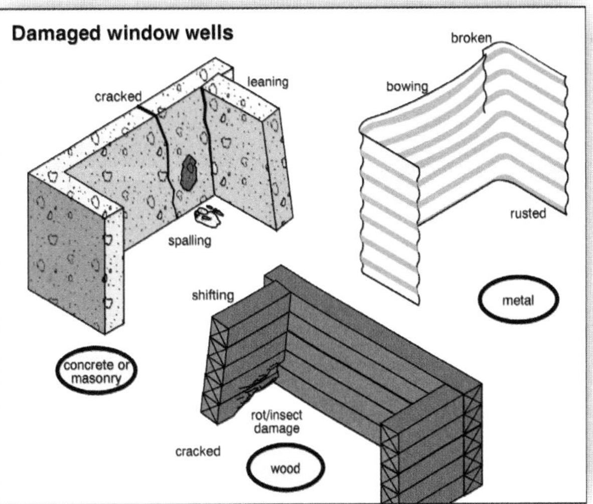

3.0 Wall Surfaces

DESCRIPTION Wall finishes protect the building skeleton and interior from weather and mechanical damage. In some cases, the wall surfaces enhance the structural rigidity of the building (e.g. houses constructed of solid masonry, or log houses). We will start by looking at some issues common to many types of siding and then look at individual materials.

3.1 Common Problems with All Wall Systems

FOUNDATIONS: MORTAR, CRACKS, SPALLING Foundation walls may be poured concrete, concrete block, cinder block, stone, brick, clay tile or wood. Mortar repair (re-pointing) is often necessary on the above grade portion of masonry foundations. Cracks in poured foundations should be patched. Spalling concrete or masonry can be replaced or parged.

FOUNDATIONS: PARGING Sometimes, the exposed foundation wall is parged (covered with a thin layer of concrete). This is necessary on porous foundations such as brick or concrete block. It is not uncommon for the parging to separate from the foundation wall and break off. Localized patching of deteriorated parging is easily undertaken. If, however, large-scale deterioration or separation has occurred, removal and re-parging will be required. Expanded metal lath (of the non-rusting variety) should be secured to the foundation wall to provide a good base for the parging in areas where adhesion is questionable.

Lime based parging is better than Portland cement based because it is more permeable. Impermeable parging breaks off in large sections, due to moisture trapped behind it. The impermeable parging also causes dampness to rise up the wall to a level above the parging where evaporation can take place. Evaporation results in efflorescence (defined on Page 12) forming on the wall surface and within the wall itself. This causes spalling brickwork and mortar deterioration. Lime-based parging prevents this phenomenon from happening as moisture can pass through it. The parging itself is subject to efflorescence and spalling, but this is treated as sacrificial material.

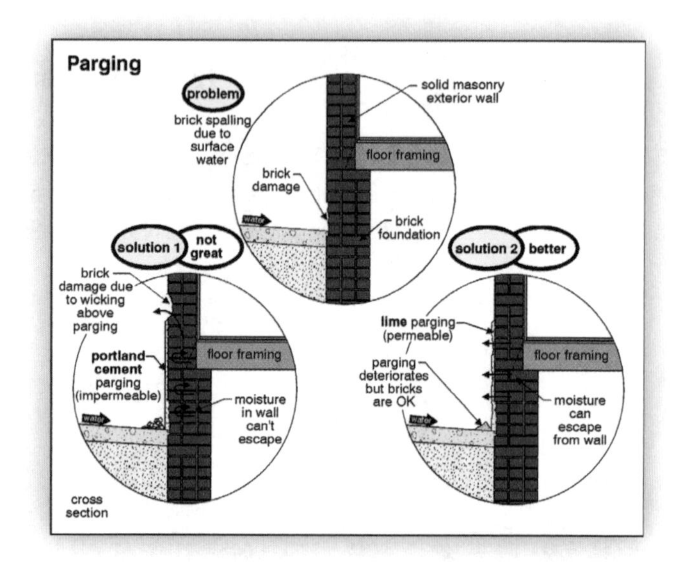

SIDING TOO CLOSE TO GRADE

Siding materials are not meant to be in contact with the ground and will deteriorate if they are at or below grade. On virtually every house, at least the top four to six inches of the foundation wall should be visible outside. We prefer to see six inches for masonry and eight inches for wood siding. There are two reasons – the first is that siding may deteriorate from chronic dampness. The second is the risk of rot and/or insect infestation to the structure. Even brick homes have wood structural members inside.

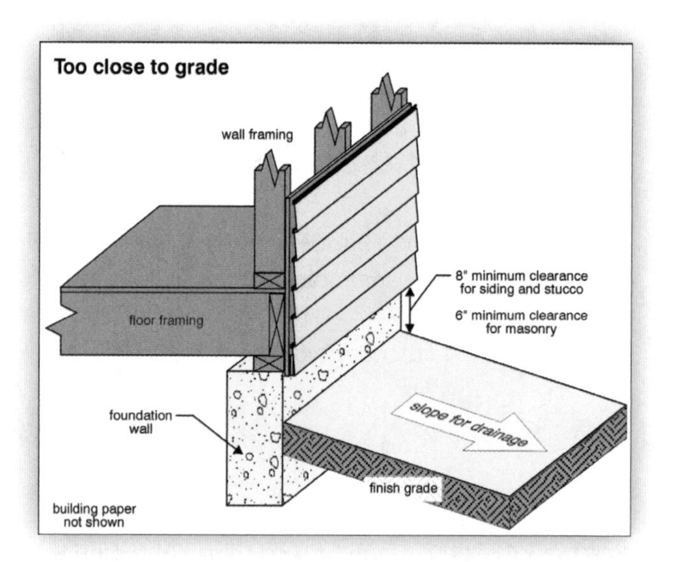

PLANTERS OR GARDENS AGAINST WALLS Even if the grading around the house is fine, there may be problems from raised planters or gardens with soil against the house wall. These can cause considerable damage to the house. Planters and raised gardens should be kept away from the wall.

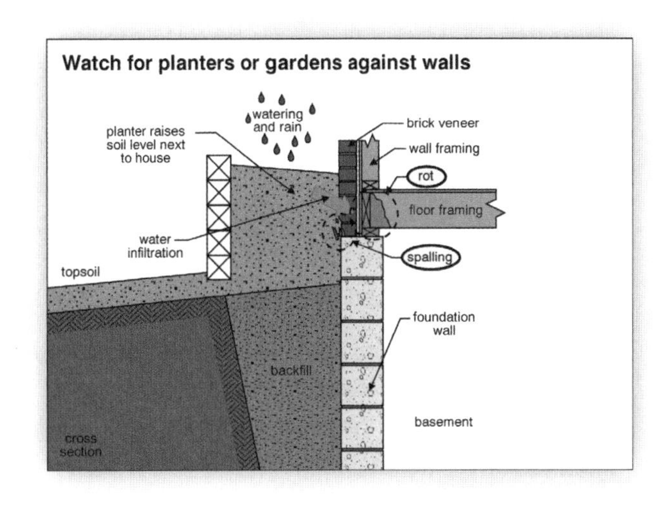

SIDING TOO CLOSE TO ROOF BELOW Most siding materials deteriorate if they are chronically wet. These materials should stop roughly two inches above roof surfaces below. Where they do not, the siding may fail prematurely.

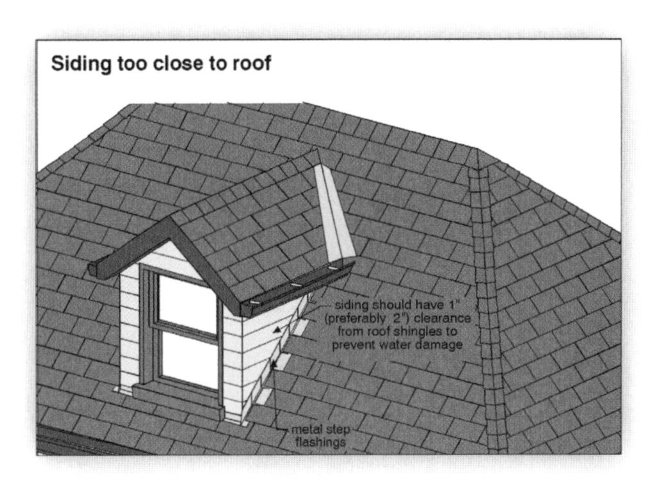

NO KICKOUT FLASHINGS Damage to walls at roof junctions can occur if appropriate flashings are not provided at the bottom of the roof. These are typically called kickout flashings. They direct the water away from the siding so that it does not get in behind.

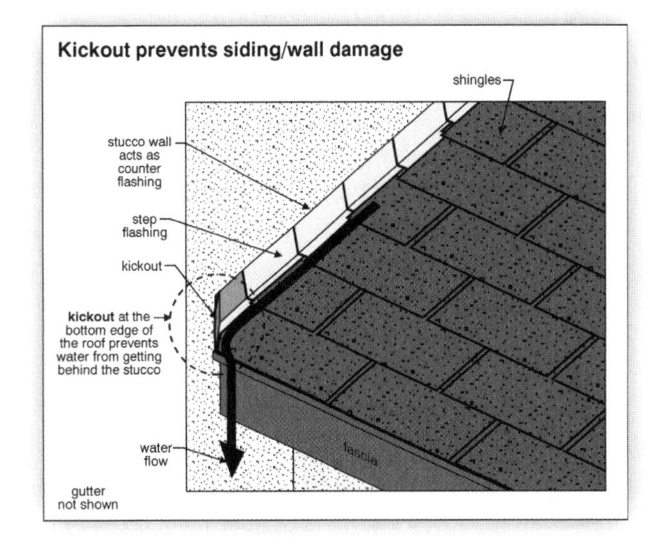

VINES Vines and other vegetation are often found growing on wall surfaces. The disadvantages include increased levels of moisture held against the wall surfaces, and increased insect and vermin problems in the house. Depending on the type of plant, damage can be done, especially to wood surfaces. Extensive damage to masonry walls is rare.

Vines should be kept away from wood trim around windows, doors and eaves for example, and should not obstruct water flow through gutters and downspouts.

3.2 Brick

DESCRIPTION Brick may be made of clay or concrete. The characteristics of brick vary dramatically. Some brick surfaces are relatively soft, and erode with time. Other bricks are extremely hard. Some can be easily damaged by mechanical action; others may crack due to water penetration and freeze-thaw action. Some bricks are extremely porous; others less so. Some bricks have a hard glazed outer surface; others are uniform throughout. Most bricks are not designed to be in contact with the soil, and should be kept at least four inches above grade.

MORTAR Mortar is a mixture of a binder (Portland cement, lime, masonry cement), an aggregate (sand), and water. There are many types of mortars with different strengths, colors, and durability. Additives such as calcium chloride can enhance cold weather workability at the expense of strength and durability.

Mortar has several functions. It bonds individual masonry units together and prevents moisture penetration between units. It allows a tight joint between different masonry units despite size variations from one unit to the next. It provides a base for ties and reinforcing used to secure a masonry wall to a back-up wall, or to enhance the strength of the entire wall. Mortar can form part of the architectural appeal of a masonry wall. Mortar deterioration is more common than brick deterioration. Ideally, the strength of mortar should be similar to, but not greater than, the strength of the brick.

Common Problems with Brick

SPALLING Damage to brick surfaces, whether due to mechanical damage, freeze-thaw action or something else is known as spalling.

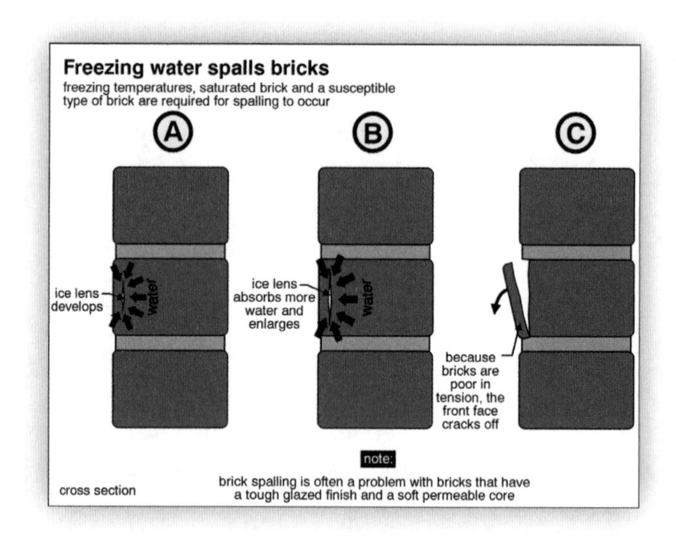

SANDBLASTED Brick is usually damaged by sandblasting. Brick with a soft core and a harder crust is common on older houses (the same houses that tend to require brick cleaning). Sandblasting removes the outer crust and makes the brick more prone to deterioration. Once a house has been sandblasted, it may deteriorate relatively quickly. The rate of deterioration can't be determined during a single home inspection. This often requires monitoring to determine if any remedial action is necessary. Sandblasting and high pressure liquid cleaning often damage mortar, and re-pointing is usually necessary.

EFFLORESCENCE The white, salty deposit that appears on masonry walls is known as efflorescence. It is a result of water carrying dissolved salts to the surface of the unit and evaporating, leaving the crystalline salts on the surface. Efflorescence may be caused by low quality mortars or masonry units, or by excessive water penetration into or through the wall. In most cases it is not serious, and will disappear within a few months of new construction or chemical cleaning. Occasionally, efflorescence precedes mortar or masonry deterioration.

MORTAR PROBLEMS Mortar often deteriorates more quickly than the brick. Mortar may crack or crumble. Mortar repairs are typically called repointing.

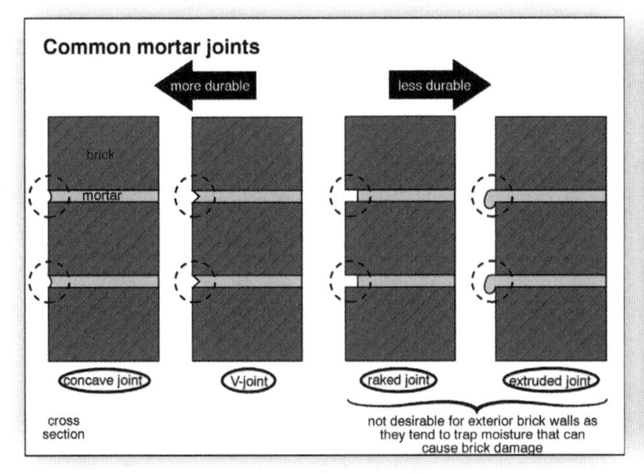

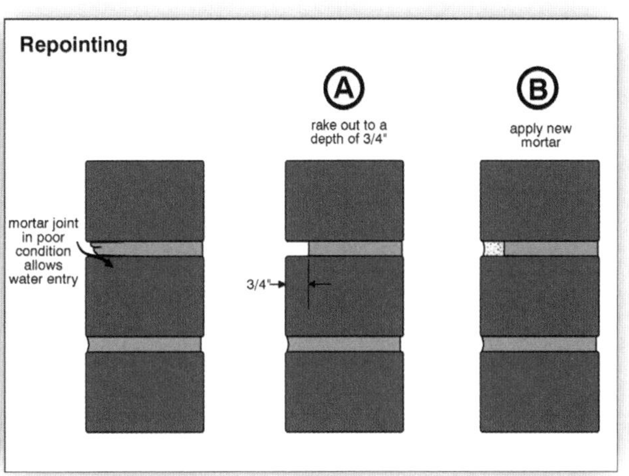

WEEP HOLES IN BRICK WALLS BELOW GRADE Some brick walls have weep holes at the bottom to allow water to drain out. If these drain holes are not several inches above grade, water may drain into rather than out of the wall system and damage the wood framing behind the brick.

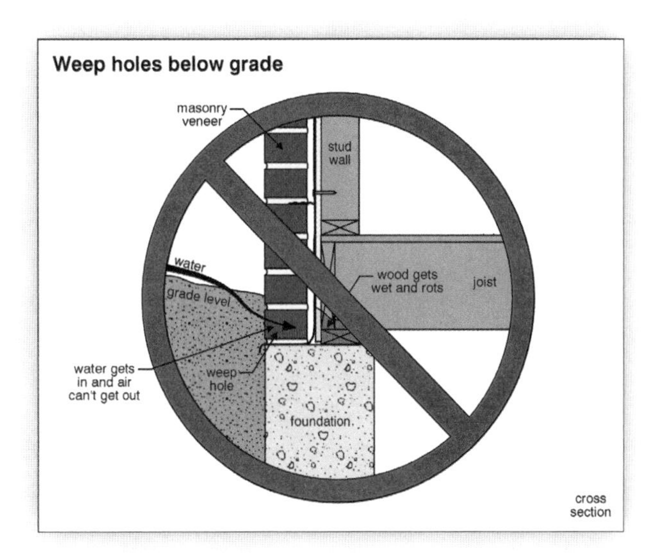

3.3 Stone

DESCRIPTION Many different stone surfaces are used in home construction. Stone can be anything from granite to limestone.

Common Problems with Stone

Stone and brick walls suffer similar problems. Stone can crack or erode depending on its quality. Mortar can deteriorate, and mortar repairs are more often needed than stone repairs. Natural stone can stain or rust, depending on the minerals in the stone. This is a cosmetic issue.

3.4 Artificial Stone

DESCRIPTION There are two common varieties of artificial stone, typically made of concrete. One is a brick substitute used on all or a portion of the exterior. It is typically three to four inches thick, and installed like any other masonry, laid in a bed of mortar. The other is a thin veneer-type covering that is less than one inch thick. The thin veneer is usually installed by providing wire mesh over the existing wall surfaces and setting the slices in a bed of mortar. The performance of this material is largely dependent upon the quality of the installation.

Common Problems with Artificial Stone

The most common problems are detachment from the building itself. Loose or damaged pieces should be re-secured to prevent moisture getting into the wall system.

3.5 Concrete Block

DESCRIPTION The use of concrete blocks as exterior wall coverings for residential construction is relatively rare, although concrete blocks can make a good exterior wall surface.

Common Problems with Concrete Block

Deterioration largely depends upon the configuration of the block (surface texture and shape) and the quality of the concrete. Concrete blocks are relatively porous and some can allow a significant amount of water penetration through the block. Painting the block can reduce water penetration significantly. As with all unit masonry construction, spalling and mortar deterioration are common problems.

3.6 Conventional Stucco

DESCRIPTION Stucco is the exterior equivalent of plaster, made of cement, lime, aggregate and water. Stucco can be thought of as a thin coat of concrete, with the cement and lime acting as binders, the aggregate providing the bulk and the strength, and the water initiating the chemical reaction. Much like plaster, stucco requires periodic maintenance as cracks develop. The amount of maintenance required depends largely upon the mix of the stucco, the lath used (if any), and the surface to which the stucco is applied. Stucco is typically applied in a two-or three-step process.

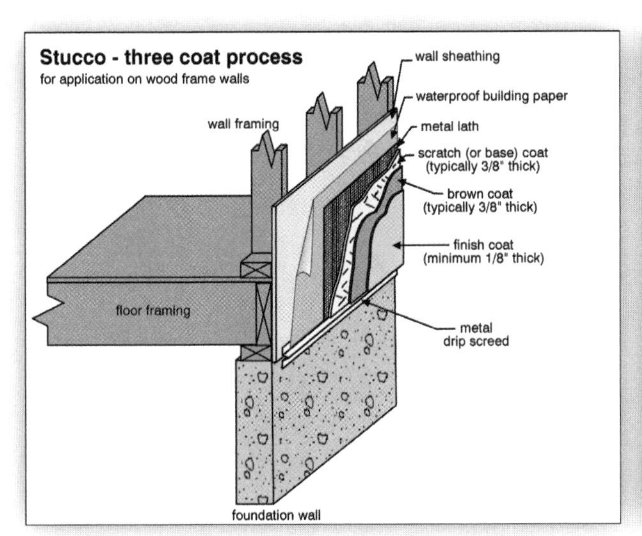

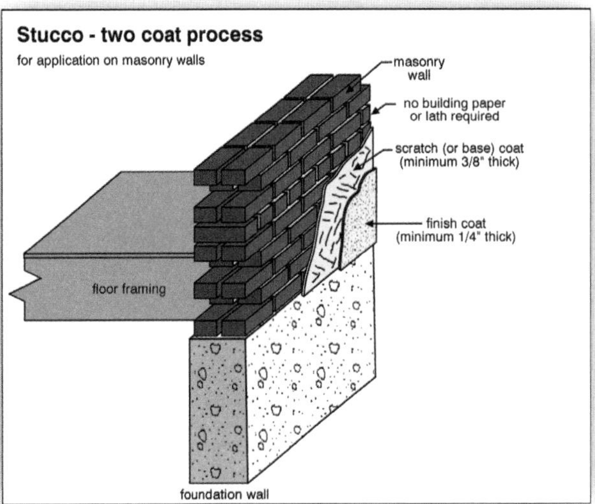

Common Problems with Stucco

CRACKS/BULGES/ LOOSE Stucco over masonry walls tends to stand up better than stucco over wood-frame construction. The rigidity of a masonry structure allows for virtually no flexing of the stucco, and consequently, less cracking and surface separation is likely to occur. Wood-frame walls expand and contract with changes in temperature and humidity, at a different rate than stucco. This leads to cracking that allows moisture deterioration, and separation of the stucco from the lath. Cracks and bulges often appear near floor levels because wood framing members shrink most in this area. Sections of stucco may come loose and fall off the building.

Cracking can allow water penetration, which may cause damage to the wall structure behind that goes unnoticed for some time. Repairs that match in color and texture are difficult to make. Stucco can be painted.

3.7 Synthetic Stucco (EIFS)

DESCRIPTION Exterior Insulated Finish Systems (EIFS) look similar to stucco but are different. Rigid wall sheathing, such as plywood, is covered with foam insulation board. A thin base coat reinforced with fiberglass mesh is then applied and covered with a thin acrylic finish coat. It is a two-step process, and the finished coating is more flexible than conventional stucco.

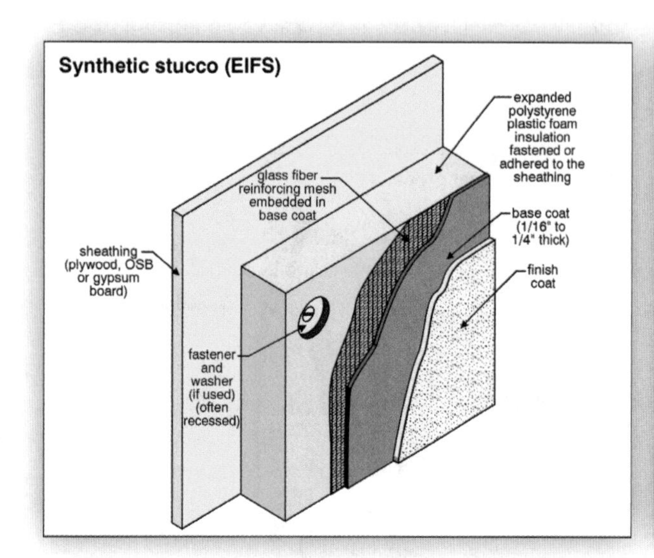

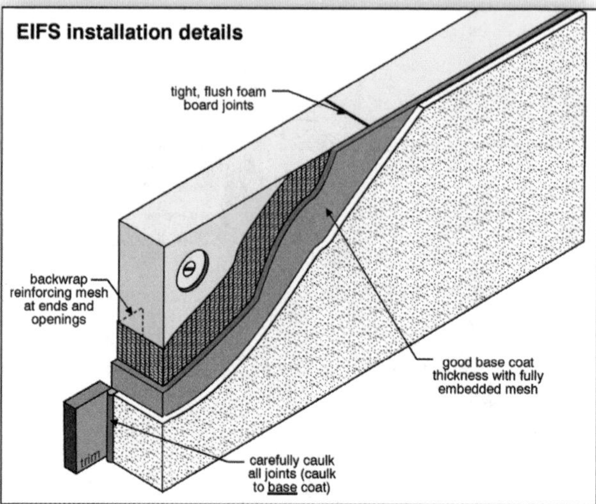

Common Problems with Synthetic Stucco

Problems arise when water gets trapped behind the finish and insulation. The water ultimately leads to rot of the sheathing and other structural components.

CONCEALED WALL DAMAGE Water may enter the wall system through wall penetrations around doors and windows unless all details are perfectly weather tight. As there are seldom ideal flashings at these locations, it is important that the seams be well caulked. Caulking is an ongoing maintenance issue.

There has been extensive damage to some homes, and entire wall systems have been replaced. There have been class-action lawsuits around synthetic stucco. Improved installation methods include the use of building paper between the insulation and sheathing and a drainage path for any water that does get into the wall.

Unfortunately, neither trapped water nor rot in the wall cavity are visible during a home inspection.

3.8 Wood Siding

DESCRIPTION There are many types of wood siding, including panels, boards, shingles, and shakes. Good siding installations prevent or minimize rot and water penetration. Rot occurs wherever wood surfaces are subject to excessive moisture. Painting or staining on a regular basis protects the wood. Even rot-resistant woods such as cedar and redwood are helped by staining. Stain reduces warping, splitting, rot and discoloration.

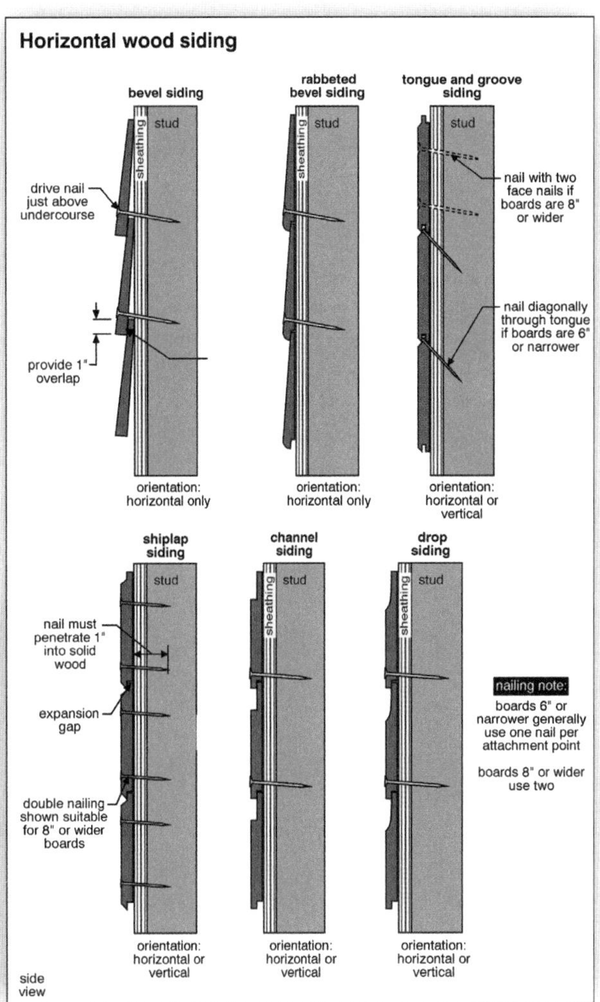

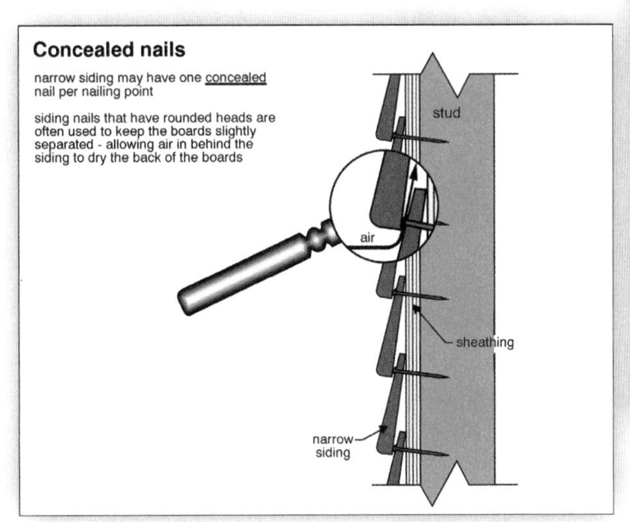

Water penetration and rot problems are most common at joints, penetrations and changes in direction or material. Joints should prevent water penetration. The horizontal joints on clapboard siding, for example, overlap one another; however, most vertical joints do not. Therefore, vertical joints should be protected with flashings or caulking. Caulking is a maintenance issue.

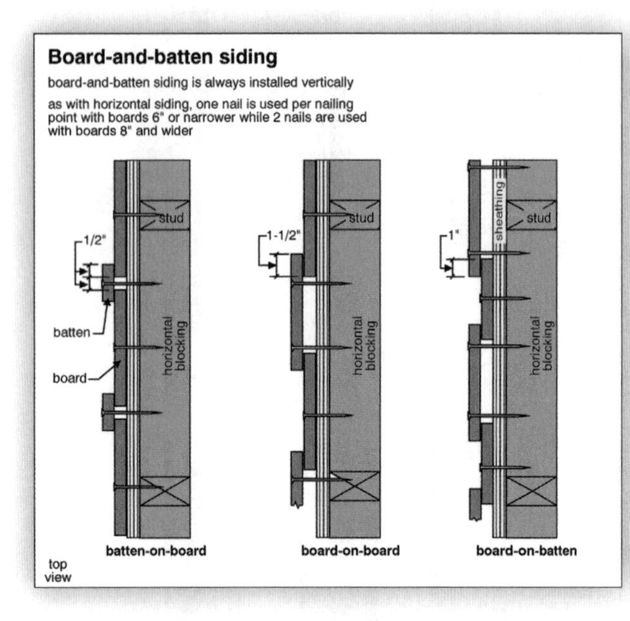

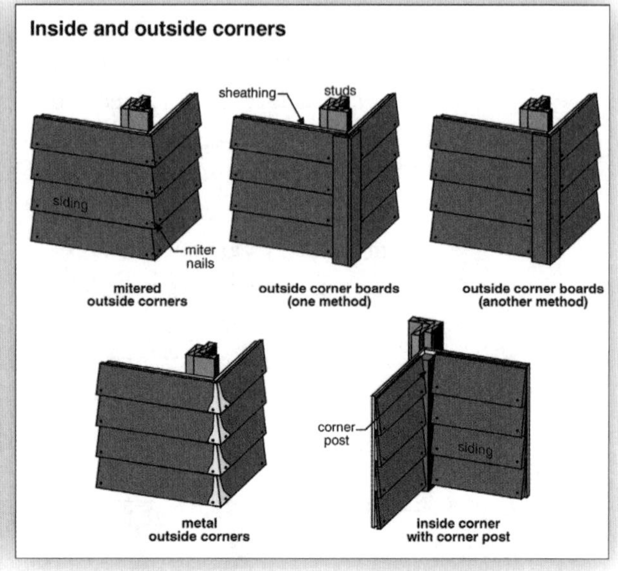

VENTILATION Wood siding holds paint better and lasts longer if the back of the siding has some air circulation. Old siding nails had round heads so that the overlying piece of siding above would not sit tightly against the lower piece. This allowed air circulation and broke the capillary joint between the two pieces of wood. This is a practice that has unfortunately disappeared. Where peeling paint is a problem, shims can be driven between the boards to promote drying. While it seems strange to say that wood walls should breathe, that is what we want.

JOINTS With panel-type wood siding, most problems occur at horizontal joints, as there is usually no overlap or batten strip. In well-executed installations, a flashing is installed at horizontal joints to prevent water penetration.

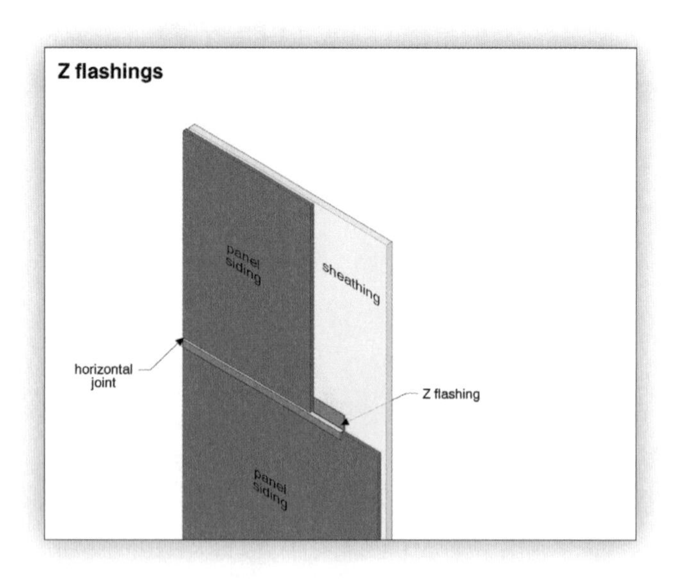

Many wood siding systems require pieces of wood trim to be installed over the joints. The top surfaces of these pieces of trim are prone to rot. The rotted wood eventually allows water penetration at the joints. Horizontal surfaces should be kept well stained or painted, should be slightly sloped so water will drain off, and should be caulked where they meet vertical surfaces.

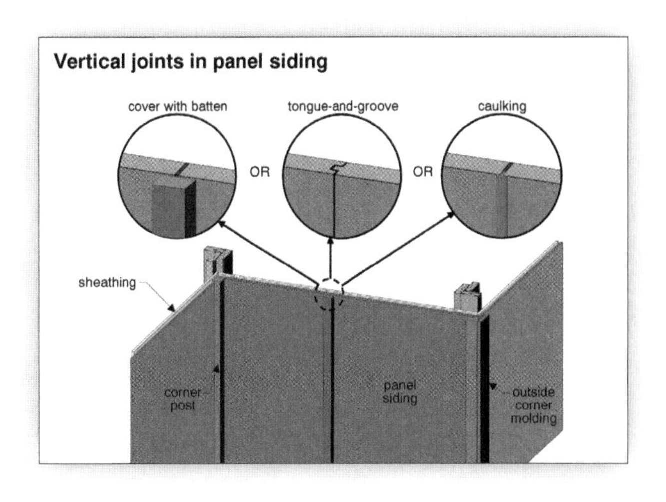

Common Problems with Wood Siding

ROT Prolonged exposure of wood siding to moisture will eventually result in deterioration and rot. Continual maintenance on exterior wood surfaces is very important.

SPLITTING Wood siding may split if improperly nailed. Too many nails may prevent natural expansion and contraction. Nailing too close to the edges will result in splitting.

WOOD/SOIL CONTACT Wood/soil contact should be avoided, as it promotes rot and provides an ideal environment for wood-boring insects. Wood siding should be at least six inches above the soil.

PAINT/ STAIN With the exception of cedar, redwood, and pressure treated lumber, all wood used outside should be protected with paint or stain. Painting or staining is usually done every three to five years. Chronic paint blistering and peeling may indicate moisture problems in the wall behind.

CRACKING With age, wood shingles will lose their resins, and begin to warp and crack. There are several different qualities of wood shingles. Better shingles last longer. When more than 15% of the shingles require repair or replacement, total replacement may be advisable.

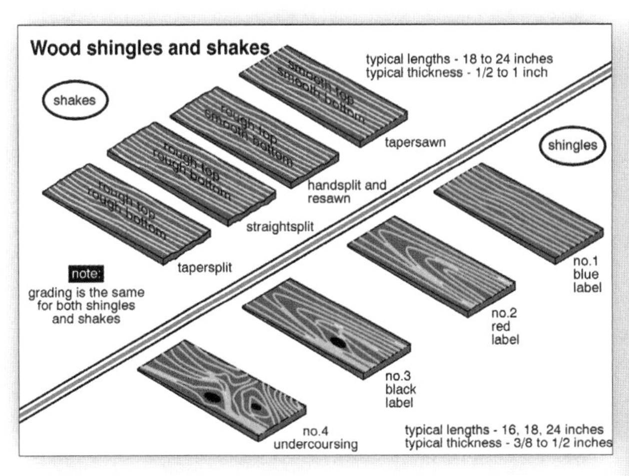

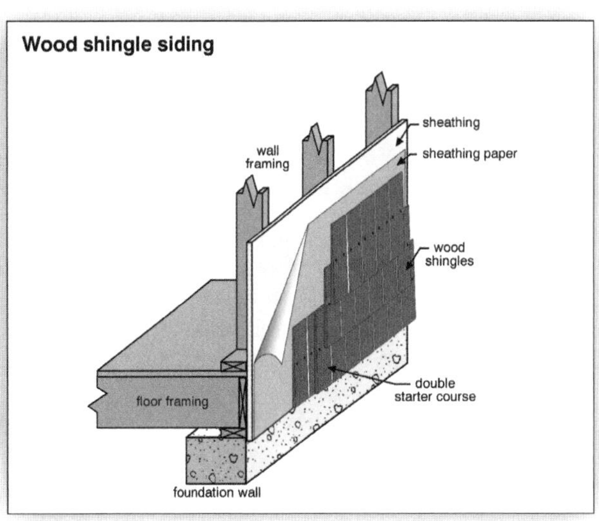

3.9 Hardboard, OSB and Plywood Siding

DESCRIPTION There are a variety of hardboard, oriented strandboard (OSB) and plywood sidings on the market. Some simulate wood siding, while others simulate stucco. Depending upon the type of material, the joints may be covered with trim, as discussed earlier.

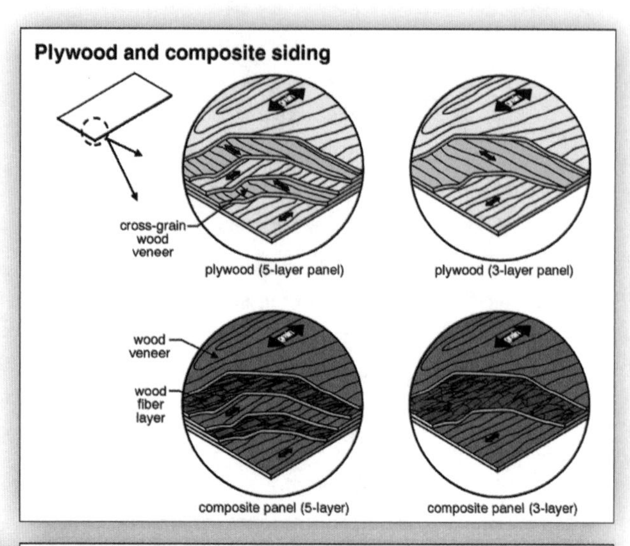

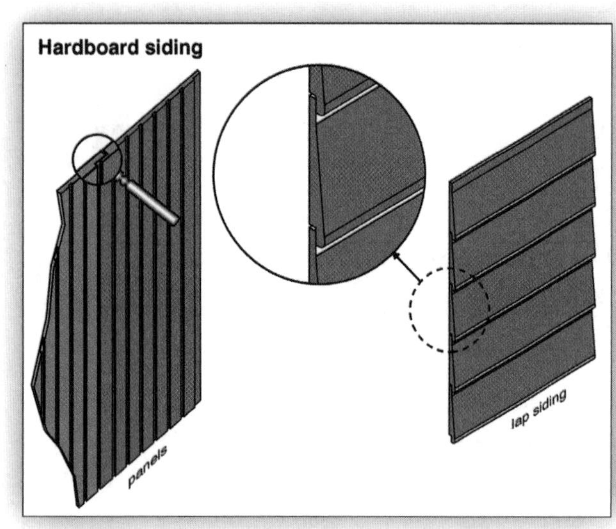

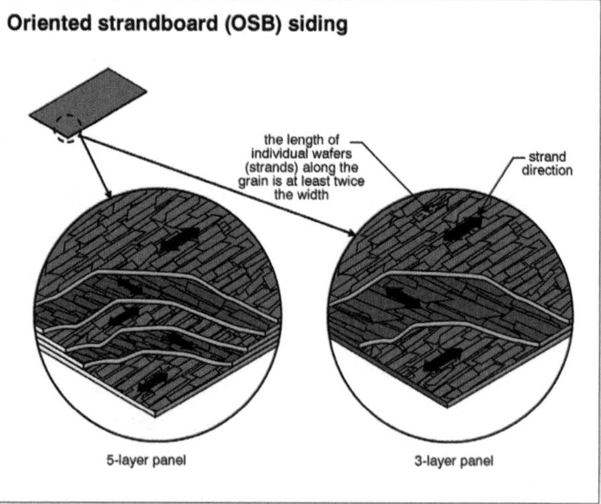

Common Problems with Hardboard, OSB and Plywood

WATER PENETRATION Water penetration behind the trim deteriorates the trim itself, and allows water to collect at the edges. This can lead to swelling, delamination and failure of the siding. Proper sealing and caulking of the horizontal surfaces of trim are required. Horizontal edges of panels not covered with trim should be installed with flashing, unless the joint in the material is specifically designed to prevent water penetration.

ROT Rot may result from water penetration behind the trim or on the surface of the siding.

BUCKLING Buckling of hardboard siding is a problem caused by expansion of the hardboard when wet. This material expands more than wood when wet and, if it is tightly nailed at each stud, it may buckle in or out. Securing the boards with clips or using smaller pieces help prevent buckling.

PAINT Prefinished systems do not require regular painting. Unfinished wood siding requires painting or staining to protect it from the elements.

3.10 Metal Siding

DESCRIPTION A variety of metal sidings are available. They can be boards or panels, with a variety of surface treatments, often intended to mimic wood. Some are installed vertically, while others are installed horizontally. The most common material is aluminum although steel is also used.

Metal sidings usually have a baked-on enamel finish and, generally speaking, the painted surfaces stand up well. However, some lower quality or older sidings tend to fade and chalk.

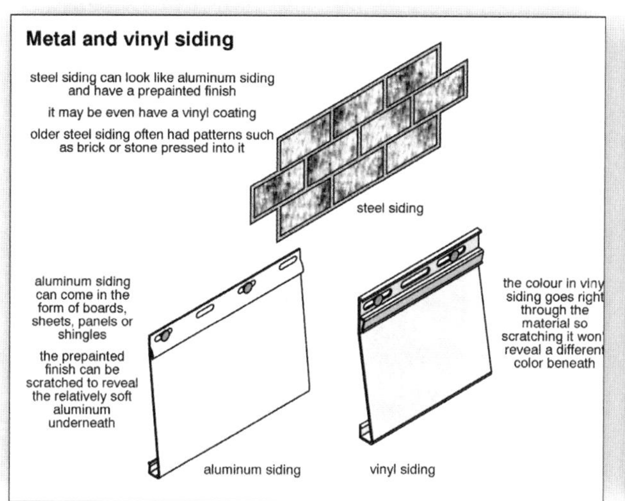

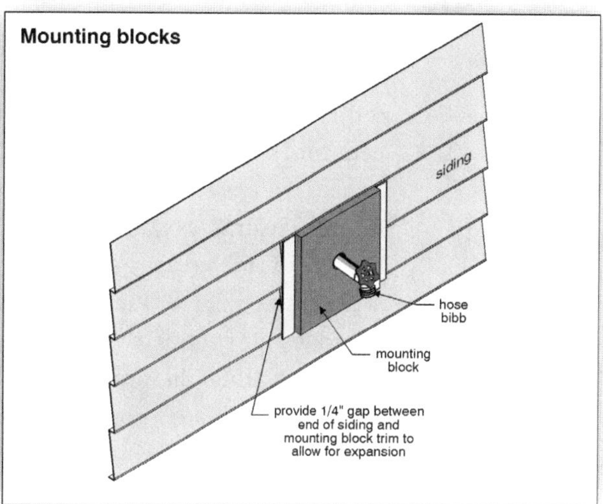

VENTILATION AND INSULATION Metal sidings should be ventilated to allow air and moisture pressures to equalize on either side of the metal. Some early sidings did not breathe well and led to moisture problems in walls. Insulated metal siding is available, although the amount of insulation is typically small.

Common Problems with Metal Siding

INSTALLATION ISSUES Most problems associated with metal sidings are installation defects, rather than material defects. A lack of adequate fastening, and a lack of moldings and trim pieces where the siding butts other materials or changes direction are the most common problems.

DENTING/ BUCKLING Metal sidings are prone to denting (particularly aluminum). Damaged sections can be replaced on an individual basis. Metal sidings expand and contract with changes in temperature. It is not uncommon to hear expansion noises when sunlight warms a wall of the house. Slots in the siding accommodate the nails. As the siding expands and contracts relative to the substrate, the siding can slide. If the nails are secured too tightly, the siding may buckle.

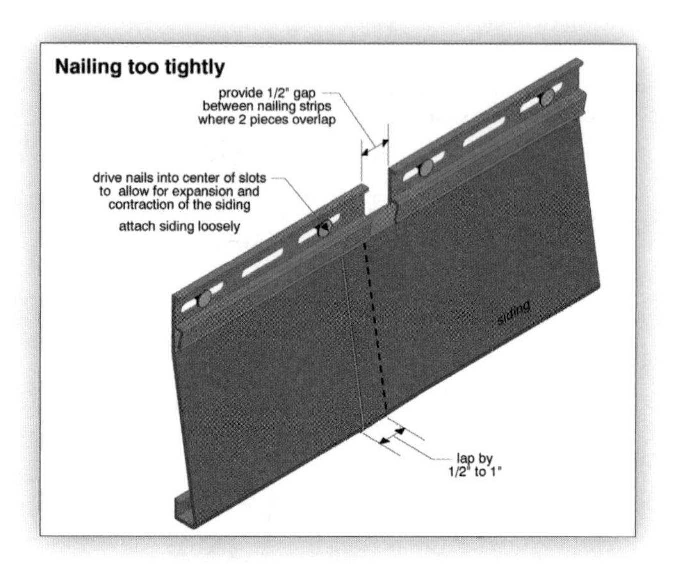

3.11 Vinyl Siding

DESCRIPTION Vinyl siding is extruded polyvinylchloride (PVC). The colors go through the material, so scratching the surface will not reveal a different color below. Also, the color cannot peel or chip off the surface. The material comes in boards or panels, often intended to look like wood. Some of the newer products can be painted successfully, although this turns a maintenance-free siding into a maintenance-dependent siding.

Common Problems with Vinyl Siding

Vinyl sidings are similar to metal sidings in that the majority of the problems are associated with installation, rather than the material itself. A lack of proper securing, and improper detail work at edges and corners are the most common deficiencies. Some vinyl sidings discolor with age. Most come in a limited color selection. Vinyl siding can become brittle during cold weather, and can be punctured or cracked. Individual pieces, however, can be replaced.

TEARING/ BURNED/ BUCKLING Vinyl siding can tear as a result of mechanical impact. Barbecues too close to vinyl siding may melt or burn the siding. Buckling vinyl siding may be the result of shrinking wood framing behind, or securing the siding too tightly to the substrate. The siding expands and contracts with changes in temperature, and must be able to expand and contract on the wall.

3.12 Asphalt Shingle Siding

DESCRIPTION Asphalt roofing shingles are sometimes used as siding. See the Roofing chapter for a description of asphalt shingles. Where roofing shingles are typically secured with four nails or staples per shingle, six fasteners per wall shingle is typical.

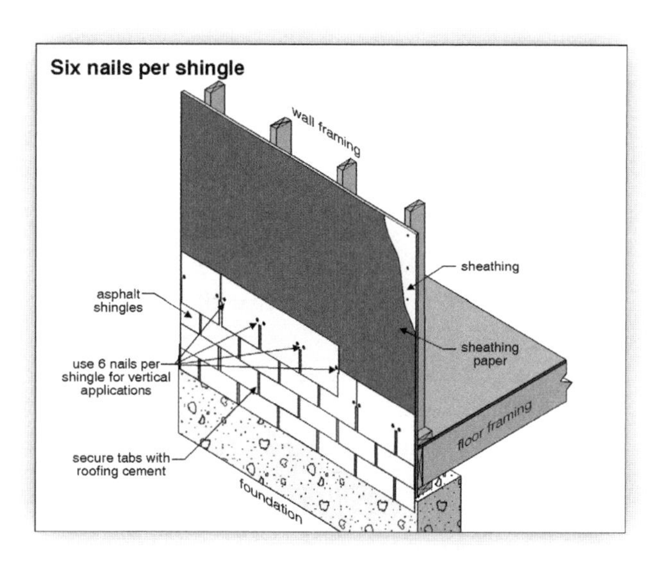

Common Problems with Asphalt Shingles

LIFTING SHINGLES The biggest problem associated with using shingles on walls is that the shingles do not tend to lie flat. Modern shingles are of the self-sealing variety. A tar strip on the upper portion of one shingle is supposed to adhere to the lower portion of the shingle above, and should prevent the shingle from lifting or curling. Unfortunately, this process relies on gravity (the weight of the shingles) and sunlight (to heat up the shingles and soften the adhesive). This process works well on roofing systems; however, it does not work well when shingles are installed vertically. Therefore, shingles tend to lift, curl, and be prone to wind damage. (Shingles that have just begun to lift can be sealed in place.) They are easily patched, but matching colors is sometimes difficult.

3.13 Fiber Cement Siding

DESCRIPTION Fiber cement siding comes in shingle, plank and panel form. This is a strong, rigid siding that typically performs well. Older versions used asbestos as the fiber and were called asbestos cement siding.

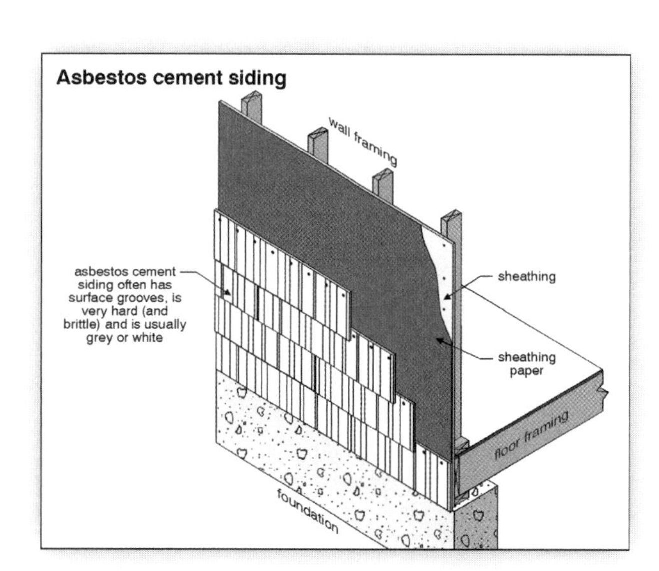

Common Problems with Fiber Cement Siding

CRACKED/ BROKEN Older fiber cement shingles have a long life expectancy; however, they are brittle and subject to mechanical damage. Replacement pieces that match may be difficult to find. The life expectancy of newer fiber cement products is expected to be similar.

IMPROPER NAILING Modern fiber cement siding is often applied with pneumatic nailers. Nails are sometimes driven too far into the siding and the siding may not be well secured to the building.

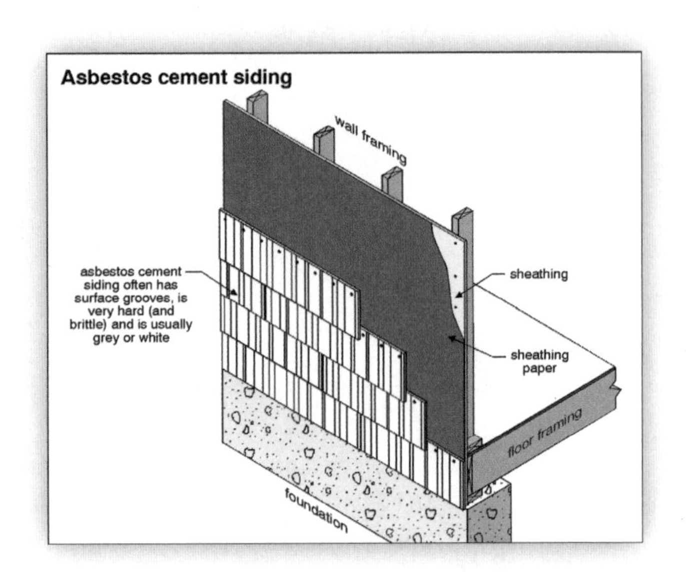

3.14 Clay Tiles and Slate Shingles

DESCRIPTION Clay tiles and slate shingles were often used on Victorian-era and circa-1900 houses for siding on small areas, such as dormers and gables.

Common Problems with Clay and Slate

CRACKED/ BROKEN These shingles will easily last 100 years; however, they are brittle and subject to mechanical damage.

FAILED FASTENERS Clay tile and slate can often last a long time, but the nails that hold them in place rust, allowing the tiles/slates to slip out of position. Patching can be undertaken; however, it is often difficult to match the color and texture. The general rule is that if more than ten to fifteen percent of the tiles/slates are damaged, an alternative siding material should be considered.

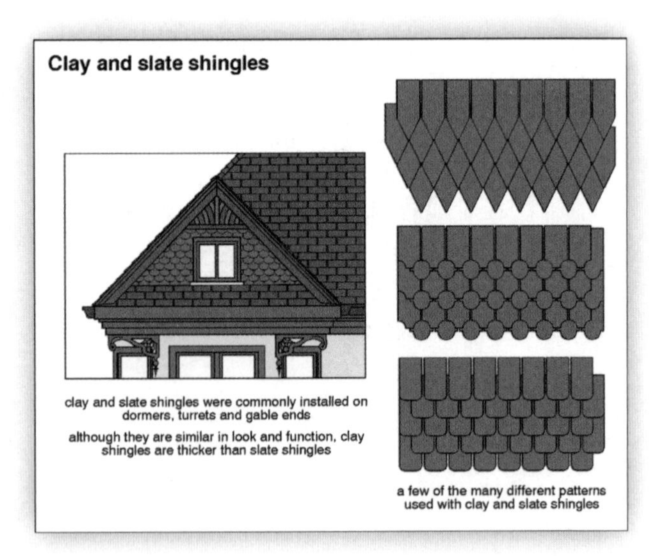

3.15 Insulbrick Siding

DESCRIPTION Despite its name, Insulbrick has very little insulating value. Various types of Insulbrick were commonly used from the 1930s to the 1950s. Insulbrick can be considered the forerunner to aluminum siding.

Insulbrick consists of a fiberboard sheathing coated with tar and sprinkled with granular material. The surface is embossed to look like brick, or sometimes stone.

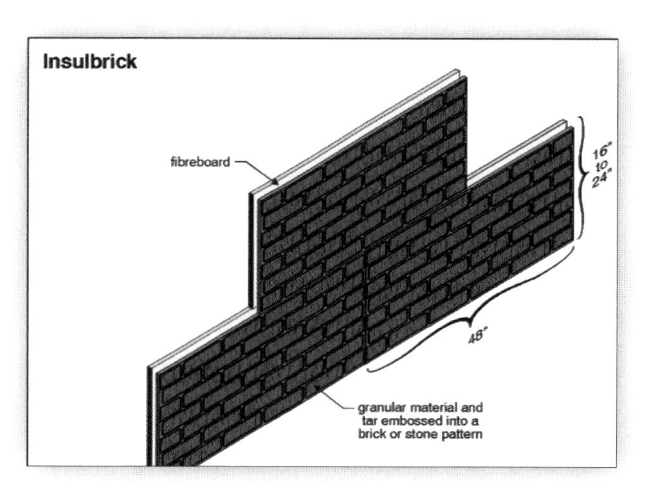

Common Problems with Insulbrick

WORN/ DAMAGED Insulbrick siding will eventually wear out; however, the majority of the problems are physical damage, and leaking joints. Caulking and re-securing are necessary from time to time. Obtaining replacement pieces is difficult, as the material is no longer made.

INSURANCE ISSUES Insulbrick is frowned on by some insurance companies and lending institutions. This is thought to be due to its combustibility, and the fact that to some people, it suggests low-quality construction. Its bad reputation is unwarranted; however, the material can easily be covered with an alternative siding.

4.0 Doors, Windows and Trim

DESCRIPTION The purpose of doors and windows is apparent. We will focus on door and window trim here. Doors and windows are discussed in the Interior chapter. The trim on the exterior of a house helps protect the structural components from weather, prevent the entry of vermin, cover joints at changes in material or direction, and improve the appearance of the house. Trim is most often wood, vinyl or aluminum, although other materials, including stone, are also used.

Trim is usually found around doors and windows, and at the eaves. The two most common components of the eaves are soffits and fascia. The soffit is installed horizontally, and covers the underside of the eaves. The fascia is a vertical component at the edge of the eaves. Gutters are often fastened to the fascia.

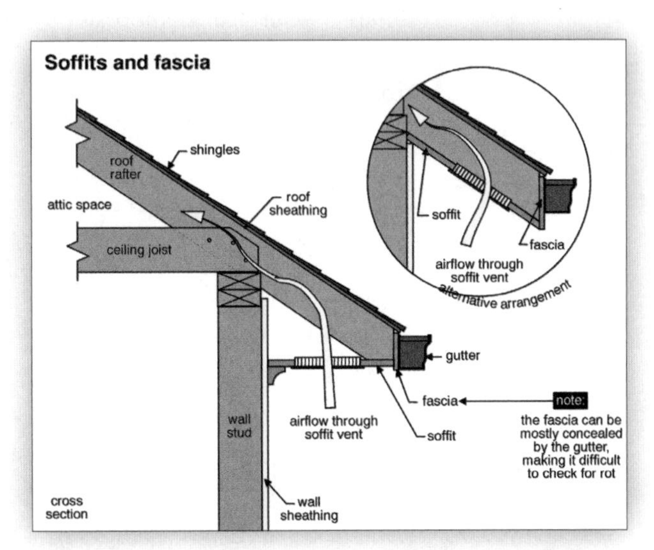

Common Problems with Trim

ALUMINUM – LOOSE/MISSING/ DAMAGED Well-installed aluminum trim is relatively maintenance free. Poorly secured, missing or damaged trim can be an issue.

WOOD – PAINT/ ROT/LOOSE/ MISSING/ DAMAGED Wood trim components require regular painting, and maintenance, and are subject to all of the issues that affect outdoor wood. Trim components are often rotted, missing, loose or damaged by vermin. Squirrels, birds and raccoons damage soffits and fascia to gain access to the attic space.

PAINTING AND CAULKING Exterior trim components including those around windows and doors, as well as soffits and fascia, are prone to weathering and to opening up at seams and joints. Improvements to paint and caulking should be considered regular maintenance items with some work typically required annually.

4.1 Door and Window Flashings

DESCRIPTION Some exterior doors and windows project out horizontally from the wall surface. Water can collect on the top, rotting the trim and leaking behind it. Metal flashings are often provided in these areas. The exposed edge of the metal flashing is bent out to prevent water from dripping on the surfaces below. The flashing tucks up behind the siding above or is let into a mortar joint in brick construction. (Most windows in masonry houses do not require flashings because the window frames are recessed.)

Flashing is not required where the opening is protected by a roof overhang. As a general rule, if the distance from the window or door to the overhang is less than one-quarter of the overhang width, no flashing is needed.

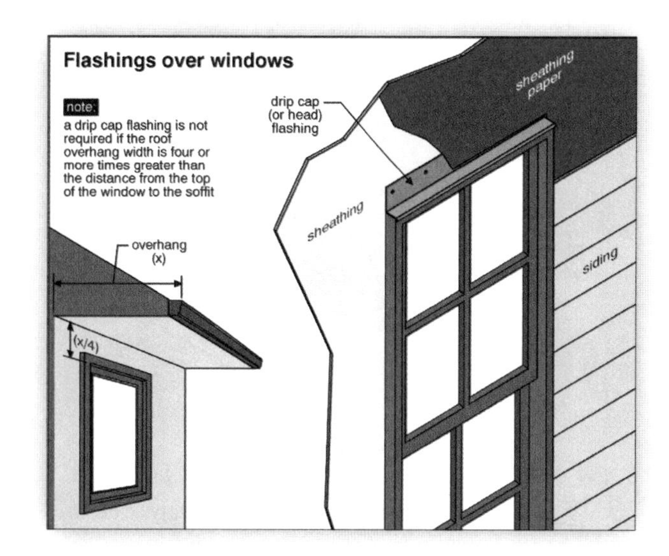

SILL SLOPE Door and window sills should be sloped so that water drains away from, rather than toward the door or window. The sill should project far enough out so that water can drip off without wetting the area below. Good design incorporates a capillary break (groove or projection on the underside of the sill), which prevents the water from being drawn back into the siding by capillary action.

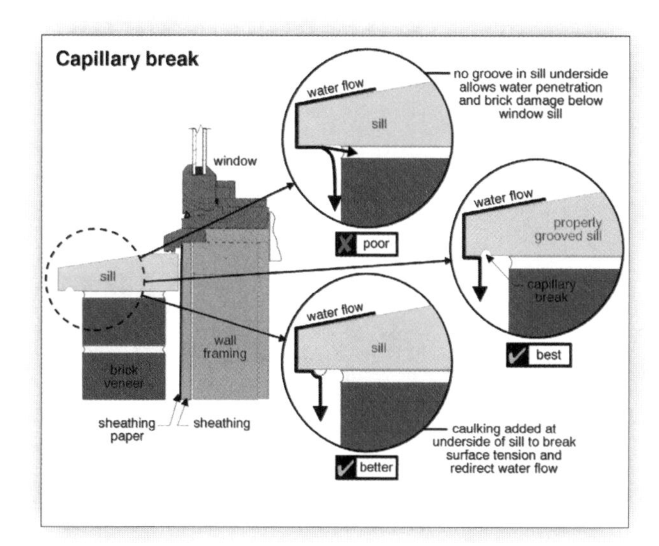

PAINT/ROT/ LOOSE/MISSING/ DAMAGED/ WATER ENTRY Wood components rot if water does not drain freely away or if maintenance is poor. Flashing, window sill and door threshold details are common problem areas. If doors and windows are not fit and maintained properly, water can get into the wall system and damage the structure.

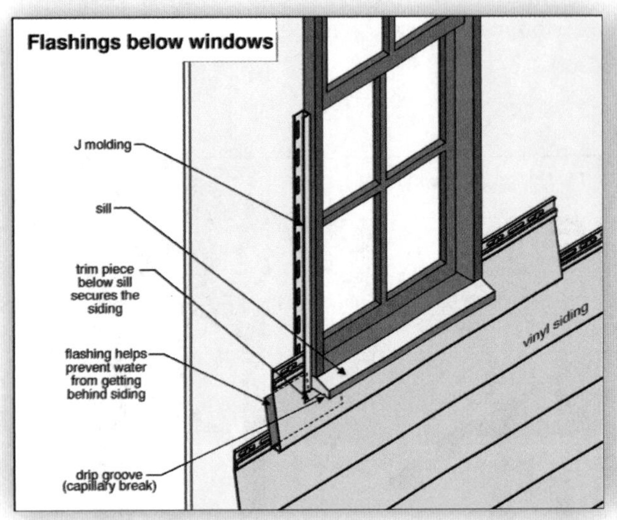

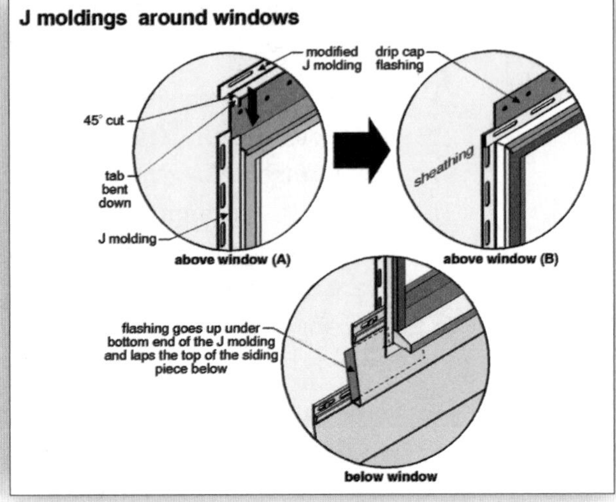

LOW THRESHOLD Door thresholds should be at least six inches above exterior grade, steps, decks or landings in climates where snow may accumulate.

5.0 Exterior Structures

DESCRIPTION These include porches, decks, patios, balconies and entrances. They are attached to the home but not an integral part of the house itself. They may include steps, railings, columns, beams, joists and floors.

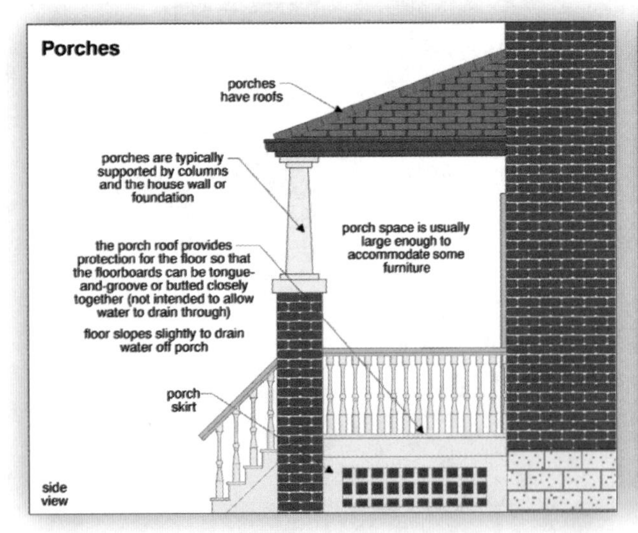

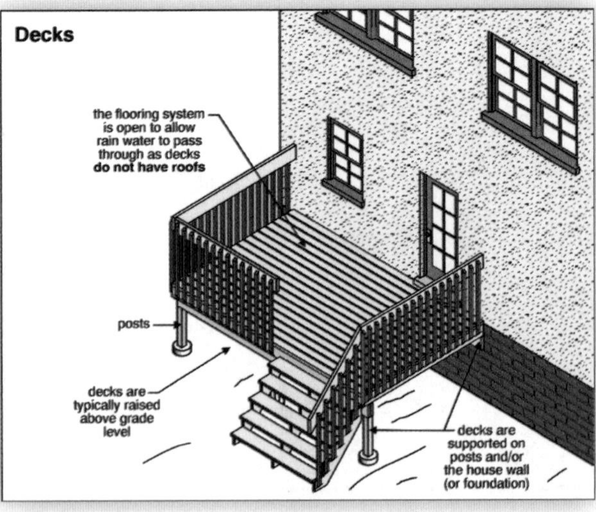

5.1 Steps

DESCRIPTION Steps are commonly made of wood, concrete or masonry. Wood steps should be sturdy enough not to flex with typical traffic. One to 1-1/2 inch thick treads are normally fine, depending on the spacing of the stringers that support the treads.

Concrete steps may have a footing to avoid settling and frost heaving. They may also be attached to the building, or may be floating prefabricated concrete units.

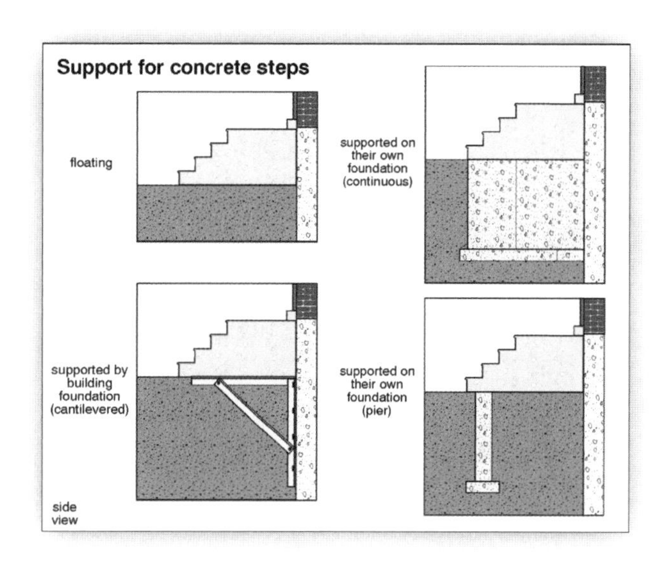

RISE AND RUN Regardless of the material used, all steps should be easy to negotiate. Steps should have at least 10-inch deep treads and be no more than roughly 8 inches high. Steps should be sloped slightly to drain water.

LANDINGS When stepping through a door, it is easier to have a landing to step on than stairs. Landings are typically at least three feet by three feet. Landings should be six inches below door thresholds so water does not leak in through the door.

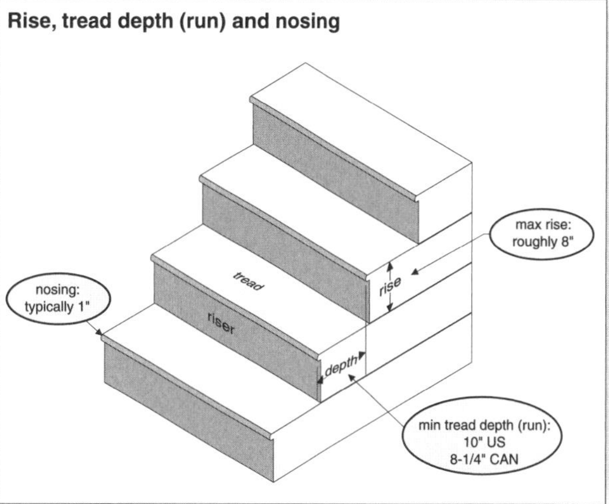

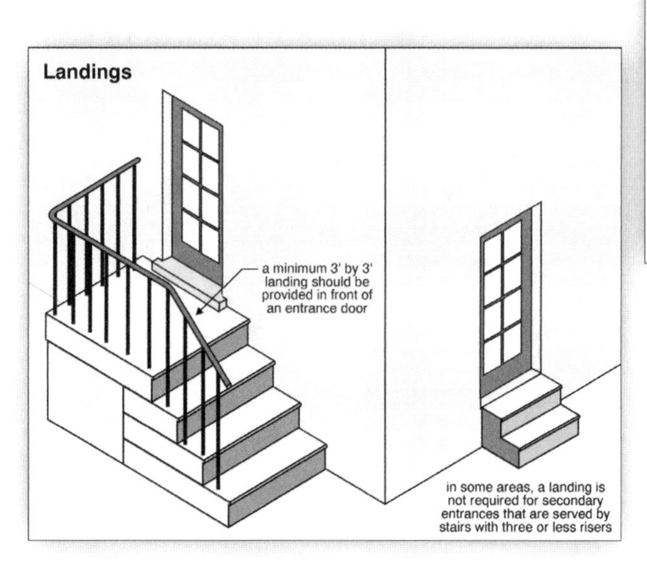

Common Problems with Steps

ROT/INSECT DAMAGE The most common problems associated with wood steps are rot and attack by insects. Direct wood/soil contact should be avoided to minimize damage by rot or insects. Carpeting on wood steps retains moisture and promotes rot. Plywood is not a good material for steps, since the layers of glue tend to trap moisture, creating rot and delamination of the plywood.

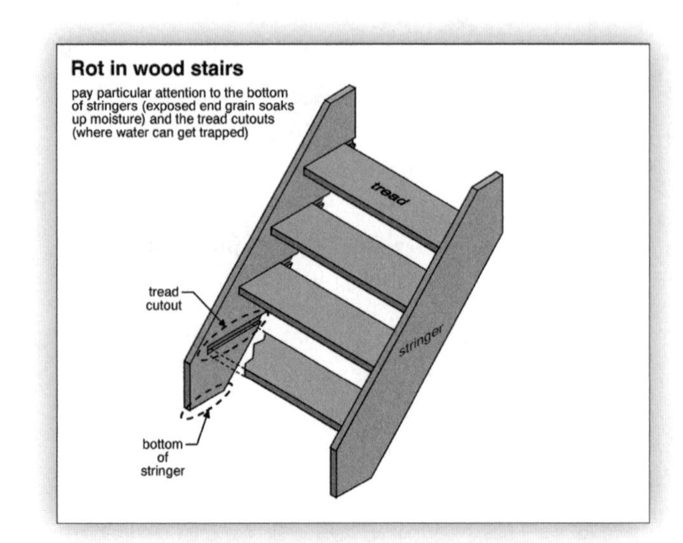

SPRINGY Poorly designed steps move considerably when they are walked on. Strengthening is sometimes required.

SPALLED OR DAMAGE Concrete steps tend to crack or spall. Avoid using salt on these surfaces. Some steps are constructed of brick. Certain types of brick should not be in contact with the soil as they absorb a considerable amount of moisture and suffer deterioration from freeze/thaw action.

SETTLED OR HEAVED This is a common problem with concrete steps.

RISE/RUN/ UNIFORMITY/ LANDINGS Steps should be uniform so that they can be traveled easily. The rise should not be more than 8 inches, and the run should be at least 10 inches. Landings should be provided where needed at the top of steps, so people do not get knocked over by opening doors.

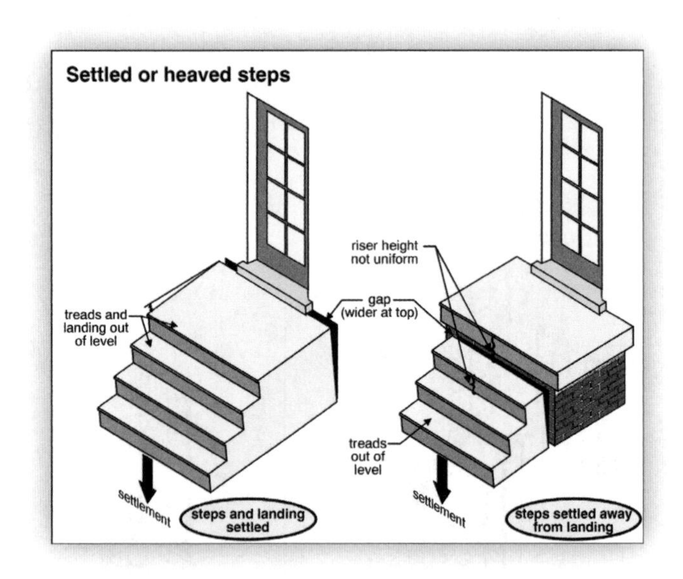

5.2 Railings

DESCRIPTION Railings should be provided wherever there is a danger of falling, or when the deck is more than 24 to 30 inches off the ground. Railings should be sturdy enough to resist a person's weight and openings in the railing should be small (four inches or less) so children cannot crawl through. Railings should be high enough to provide adequate protection; 36 inches is common. On wide stairways, railings should be provided on both sides. Railings should not prevent drainage of water off porches, decks and balconies. They should not have horizontal members that children may climb.

Railings should be easy to grab to help prevent a fall.

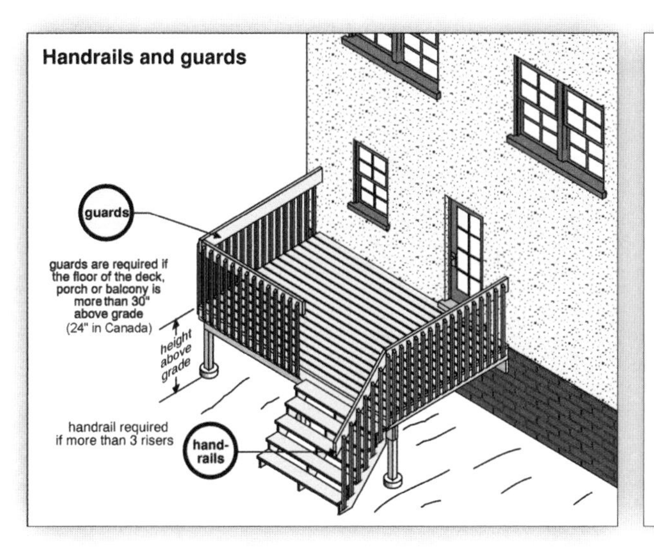

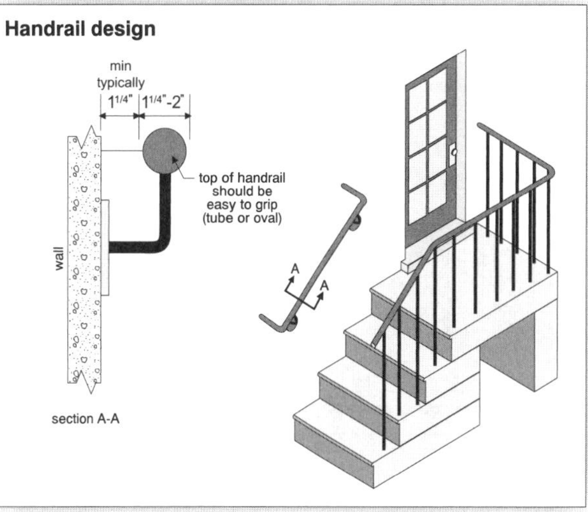

Common Problems with Railings

MISSING/ LOOSE/ ROT/ RUST The most common problem is missing railings. Railings are also often loose, rotted or rusted. Many railings are not strong enough or not well enough secured to prevent someone falling through the railing. This is difficult to determine without damaging the railing.

POOR DESIGN Railings may be too low, have openings that people may fall through, or have horizontal members that make it easy for children to climb the railings. These are safety issues.

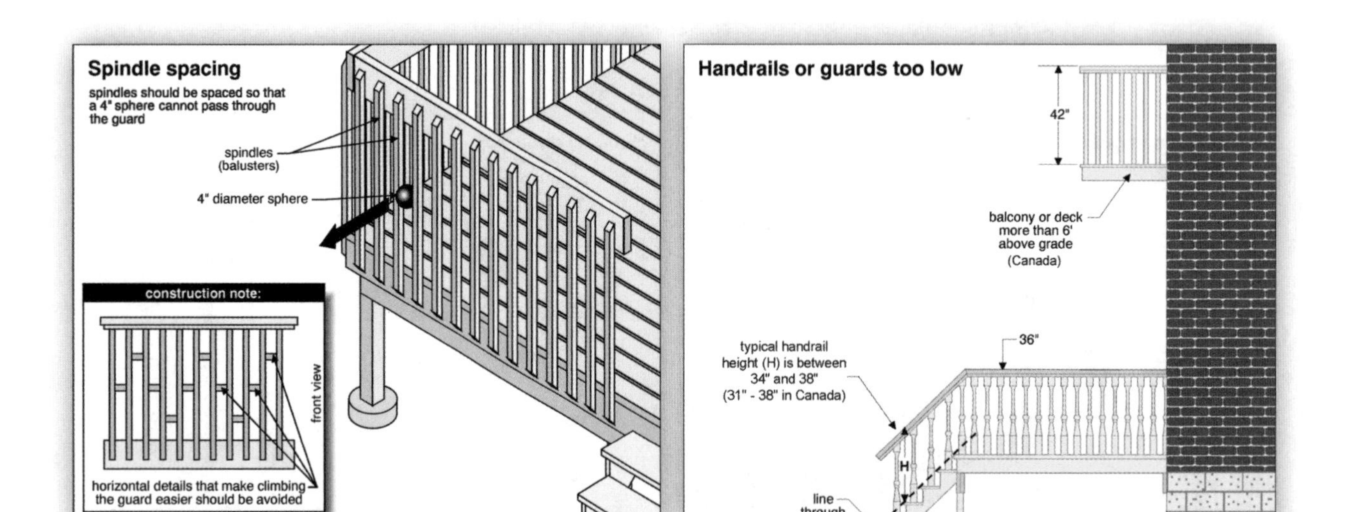

5.3 Columns

DESCRIPTION Porch columns support a roof and/or a floor system. They can be wood, metal, poured concrete, masonry or a combination of these. They must be strong enough to handle the imposed load and must have proper foundations and footings to prevent settling or frost heaving. Wood soil contact should be avoided.

Common Problems with Columns

DETERIORATION/ DAMAGE The most common problems with porch columns are the result of simple deterioration. Brick columns absorb moisture, damaging the brick and mortar by frost action. Wood columns rot and are subject to insect attack. Direct wood/soil contact should be avoided.

Columns can be mechanically damaged by impact, although this is not common.

OUT OF PLUMB Columns may be installed out of plumb or they may shift. Where they are unstable, replacement is necessary.

5.4 Beams and Joists

DESCRIPTION Beams and joists should be strong enough to transfer the roof or floor loads (people, furniture, and snow) to a wall or column. They are typically wood, but can be steel.

Beams and joists should be adequately supported, well connected and arranged to minimize rot and wood/soil contact.

Common Problems with Beams and Joists

SAGGING The most common problem with porch beams is that they are undersized (overspanned), resulting in sagging. Overspanned joists result in a springy floor system. Additional supports can often be added to stiffen structural members, or they can be enlarged or replaced.

END BEARING Porch beams are often poorly supported when columns have been removed or have shifted. Joist and beam ends should rest on 1-1/2 inches of wood support, or on three inches of concrete or masonry support, respectively.

DECKS HAVE TO BE WELL SECURED TO BUILDINGS Joists should be well secured to the building. A board that is lag-bolted to the structure may support the joists from below. Joist hangers may also be used. Many serious injuries have resulted from improper deck support. This detail should also be protected with flashing so the water does not get into the wall system. After construction it is difficult to determine whether support is adequate. Alternatively, the deck may be completely detached from the building.

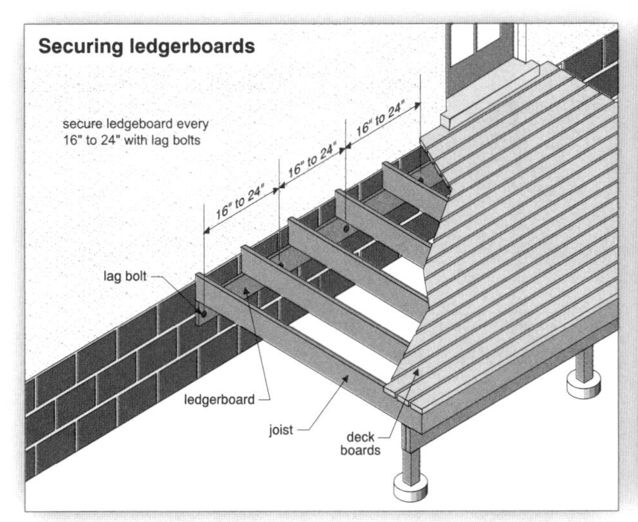

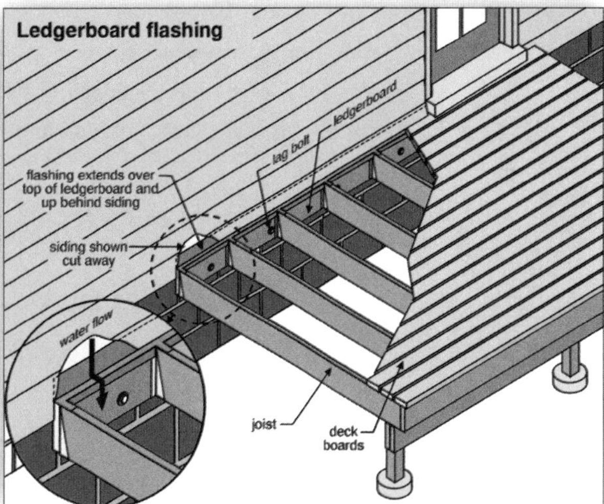

ROT Trapped moisture in a porch or deck structure rots wood beams or joists, weakening the structure and providing an ideal environment for insects. Many porch beams are concealed in a roof structure and are not visible, but years of roof leaks cause beams and joists to rot and the roof system to sag.

CANTILEVERED DECKS AND BALCONIES – ROT These have special problems, usually related to the support joists that extend through the building wall. These structures may be weak due to poor initial construction, or the joists may rot where they go through the building wall. The building wall may also rot as a result of water penetration around cantilevered joists.

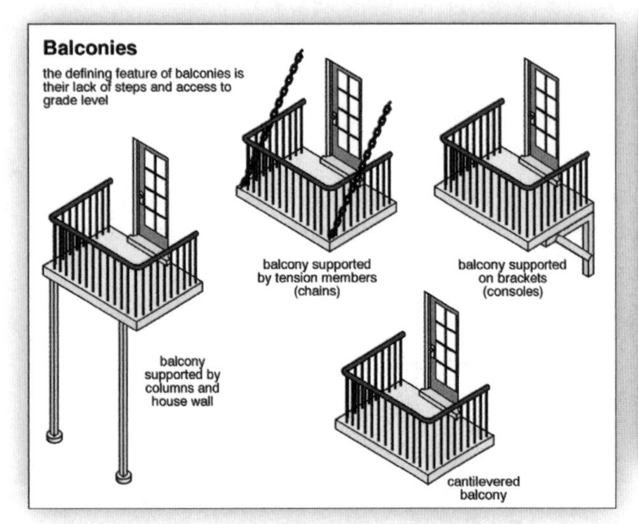

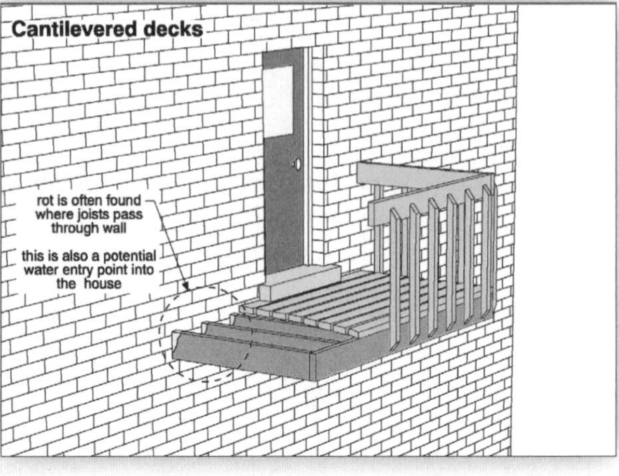

5.5 Floors

DESCRIPTION Porch floors slope to drain water off, unless they have spaced flooring like decks. Carpeting is not used as it holds moisture, promoting rot. Plywood or waferboard should not be used for the same reasons.

Some porch floors are covered with metal, vinyl or canvas. In many cases, these materials have deteriorated and replacement is required. Some porches are covered with roll roofing or roofing felts. These materials are not suitable for regular foot traffic.

Common Problems with Floors

Rot and sagging are the most common problems.

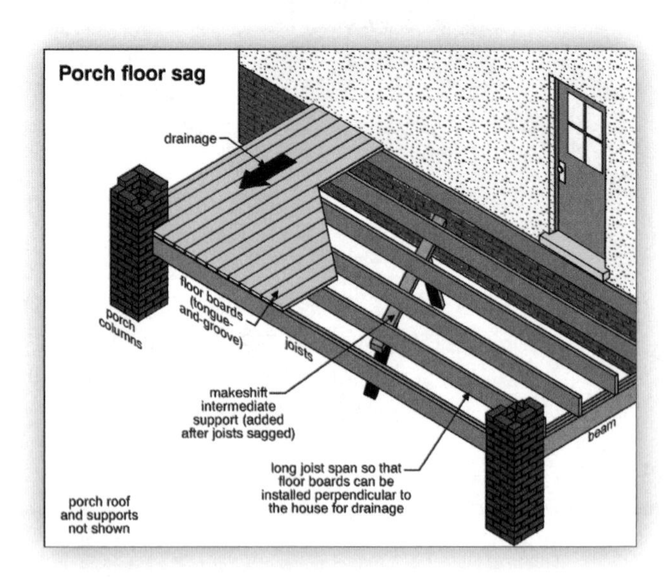

6.0 Garages and Carports

DESCRIPTION Garages may or may not be attached to the house. Garages have many of the same features as houses and can be thought of as secondary buildings. Most floors are concrete slab-on-grade, walls are often the same type as the house walls, and the roof may be integrated with the house roof. Garages may be tucked into the home with living space above.

Vehicle doors may be wood, hardboard, aluminum or steel. There are a variety of ways in which garage doors can open; however, overhead sectional doors are common. There may be a 'man-door' in the garage.

CARPORTS Carports are simple roof structures supported on columns. They may be attached to the home on one, two or three sides.

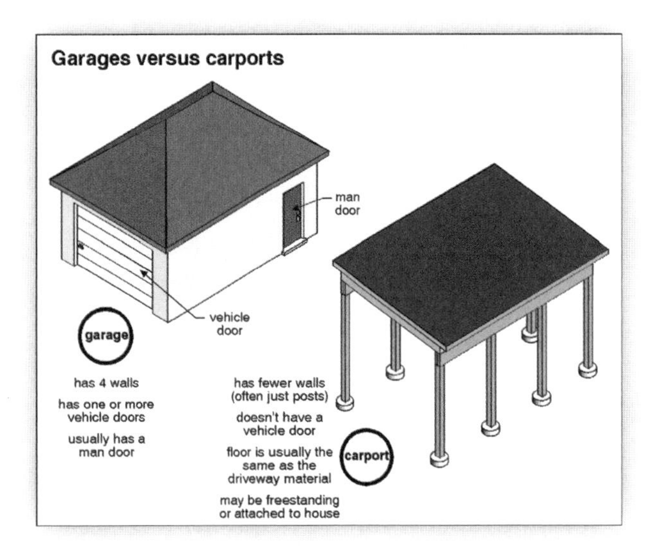

Common Problems with Garages and Carports

LOW QUALITY DETACHED GARAGES Garages are often lower quality than the house, and in poorer condition. They are just for cars, after all. The necessity for repairs is subjective, and different homeowners have different standards for what is acceptable.

Problems with the garage framing, roofing and siding for example, are addressed the same way as house problems. Detached wood-frame garages often have no foundations and footings. Wood frame walls may sit directly on or very close to the soil. The garage itself may heave with frost action in cold climates, but more importantly, the bottom of wood walls rot and the garage begins to lean. Misalignment of the overhead door comes first, then structural failure.

Corrective action includes straightening the structure and replacing at least the bottoms of wood walls. Depending on the overall condition of the garage, it may be more cost effective to rebuild it.

FIRE PROOFING The doors, walls and ceilings of attached garages that connect to the home may be required to have a fire separation from the house.

COMBUSTIBLE INSULATION Insulation is often added in garages. Combustible plastic insulation is very common. It should be removed or covered with a non-combustible surface such as drywall since it is a fire hazard.

CRACKED FLOOR Minor cracks in garage floor slabs are common. Serious cracks and/or settling may indicate structural problems, but more commonly indicate an improper base below the concrete. Concrete floors should be at least three and a half inches thick.

POOR DRAINAGE Garage floors should be sloped to drain water out of the garage. If this is not possible, a drain should be provided. Often, drains in garages are neglected and are plugged, broken, or undersized. Settlement of garage floor slabs may affect the drainage so that water will not flow out. Drains in garages are not permitted in many areas for fear people will drain oil and other fluids into the sewer system.

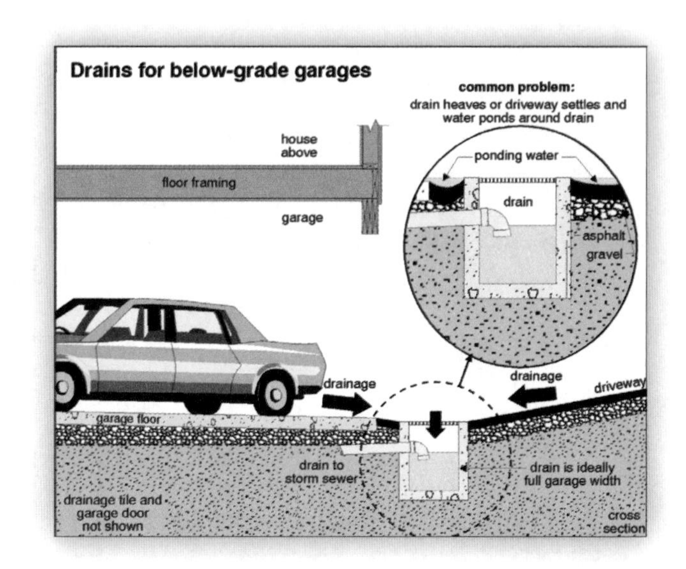

VEHICLE DOOR PROBLEMS The most common problems with garage doors are hardware issues. Hinges, tracks, springs and counterweight systems often require adjustment. Garages that have settled, resulting in a door frame that is out of square, contribute to the problem.

The bottom edges of wood garage doors tend to rot and the bottom edges of steel doors rust. The decision to repair or replace is somewhat subjective. Metal doors may be dented. In most cases this is a cosmetic issue. Damage from vehicle impact may render the door inoperative.

DOOR MISALIGNMENT Garage door openers sometimes fail due to misalignment of the garage door or track. Some jurisdictions require that the opener be plugged into an electrical outlet not more than six feet from the opener.

AUTOMATIC REVERSE All garage door opening devices should automatically reverse the door if it strikes something while closing or if something blocks a photo-electric eye near the floor. This feature reduces the risk of injury. Garage door openers should have a sensitivity adjustment. It is often set incorrectly.

SPRING RESTRAINT Where overhead door springs do not have a rod going through them, they are often strapped to prevent the spring from becoming a projectile if it fails.

MAN-DOOR ISSUES Any door between the house and the garage should have an automatic door closer, should be tight-fitting and be fire-rated. It may also be a solid exterior-type door at least 1-3/8 inches thick.

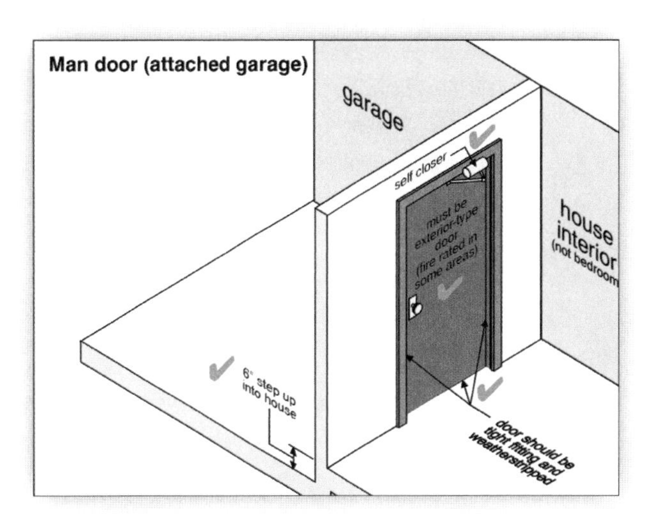

7.0 Walkways, Driveways and Landscaping

These components are addressed in a home inspection to the extent of their impact on the building.

WALKWAYS, DRIVEWAYS & PATIOS Walkways and driveways may be gravel, asphalt, concrete, stone, or pavers (individual paving stones or bricks). Regardless of the material, they should be slightly sloped to drain water away from the house. They should be relatively smooth, easy to walk on and free of trip hazards.

Common Problems with Walkways, Driveways and Landscaping

POOR SLOPE Improper slopes often cause wet basement problems, and in some cases, erosion and/or frost damage to building foundations. Where walks or driveways pull away from the building, water can accumulate along the foundation wall, again resulting in wet basement problems. In some cases a drain is required to carry surface water away. The drain should be arranged to prevent clogging with debris or frost damage to the drain assembly. The pipes leading from these drains cannot be examined during a home inspection.

TRIP HAZARD Heaved or uneven sections of walkways or patios may create trip hazards.

TREES/SHRUBS/ PLANTERS – TOO CLOSE TO BUILDING Shrubs, trees, and planters may add to the appearance and value of a property, but can adversely affect the building. Shrubs and trees too close to a building can hold water against walls, prevent wood components from drying out and provide pests with good access into the house.

Tree branches can cause mechanical damage to roof and wall surfaces, leaves can clog gutters and downspouts, and roots can clog drainage pipes and in severe cases, dislodge foundations. Raised flower gardens or planters can cause wet basement problems, especially as a result of heavy watering of flowers during the summer months.

RAISED GRADE LEVEL ISSUES Where the original grade level has been raised by adding topsoil, there are three concerns. The building wall may be subject to damage if wood components are in contact with the soil. Water may leak into the building if the soil is above the top of the foundation wall. The increased load exerted on the foundation wall can push the foundation wall inward, particularly in areas where frozen soil conditions may exist.

8.0 Retaining Walls

DESCRIPTION Analyzing retaining walls is a tricky business. With most retaining walls, the important components are not visible. Also, determining the rate of movement of a retaining wall is impossible from a one-time visit. Monitoring is normally required. In some cases, the angle of the wall gives a clue to the performance. Most walls are built with a slight lean to the higher side. If the wall is leaning away from the high side, it has probably moved. Once retaining walls begin to move, they rarely stop, although the movement may be slow and seasonal.

MATERIALS Retaining walls can be constructed of concrete, masonry, stone, wood or steel. There are several different designs.

CANTILEVERED WALLS Poured concrete retaining walls are typically a cantilever design. Looking at a cross section through the wall, the wall would look like an inverted "T". The bottom portion of the inverted "T" is buried beneath the soil. The portion of the "T" under the high side of the wall uses the weight of the soil to resist movement of the wall. The portion of the "T" protruding under the soil on the low side of the wall keeps it from tilting forward. Steel reinforcing bars keep the "T" from breaking at the joint. Cantilevered retaining walls extend below the frost line in cold climates to prevent heaving.

PILE WALLS Pile walls have vertical members driven into the soil. They resist rotational movement caused by the soil on the high side of the wall. Piles can be wood or steel.

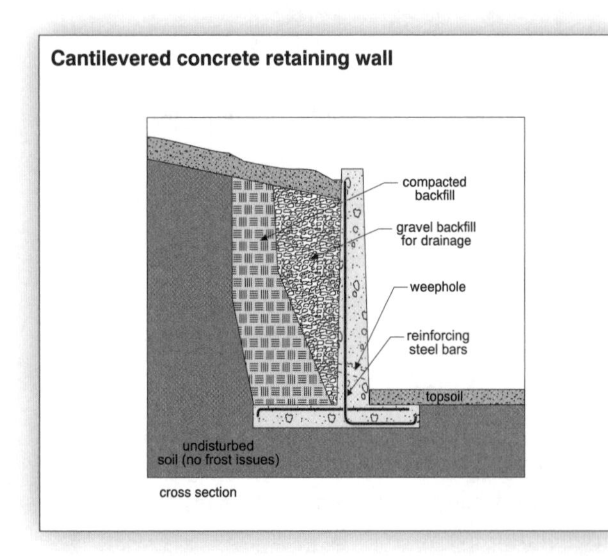

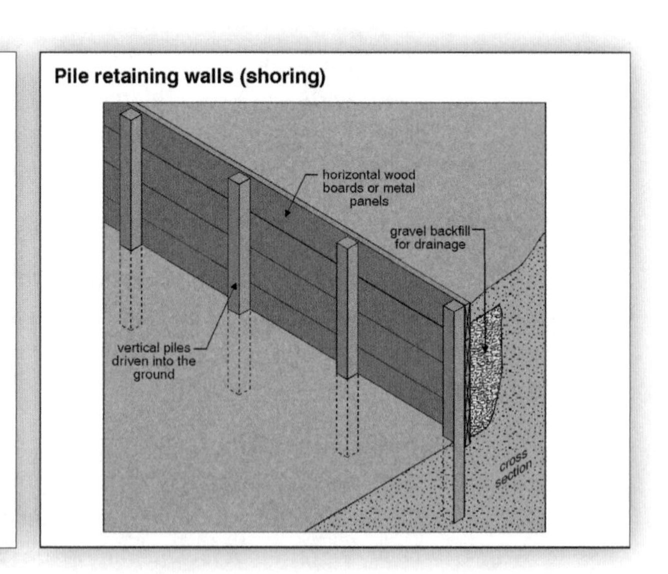

WOOD WALLS Wood retaining walls are common. Horizontal members are tied back into the soil with anchors (tie-backs) – wood members heading back into the soil. Tie-backs are staggered through the wall system to provide resistance to movement. In some cases, "dead men" are attached to the ends of the anchors to help secure the anchors. These horizontal members run parallel to the retaining wall itself. These walls do not extend below the frost line.

PREFAB WALLS Precast concrete wall systems with interlocking sections also use tie-backs and dead men.

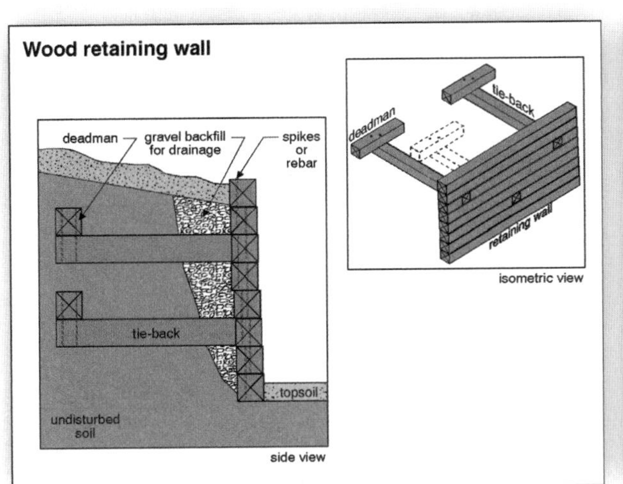

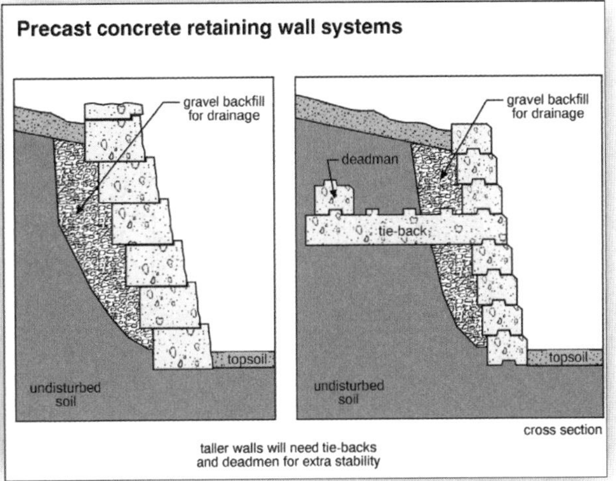

GABIONS Gabions are also used as retaining wall systems. A gabion is a rectangular wire mesh basket filled with rock. They are commonly seen along river banks to prevent erosion.

Common Problems with Retaining Walls

MOVEMENT / CRACKED/ROT The single biggest enemy of retaining walls is water. Saturated soil puts pressure on retaining walls. If saturated soil freezes, expansion forces can be significant. Walls may move as a single unit, leaning away from the hill or may crack and break apart. Water also promotes rot of wooden retaining wall systems.

POOR DRAINAGE Well-built retaining walls have a layer of gravel behind the wall and weep/drainage holes at the bottom. We don't want water trapped behind the wall. Open wall systems with wood timbers for example, have enough natural openings that drainage holes are not needed.

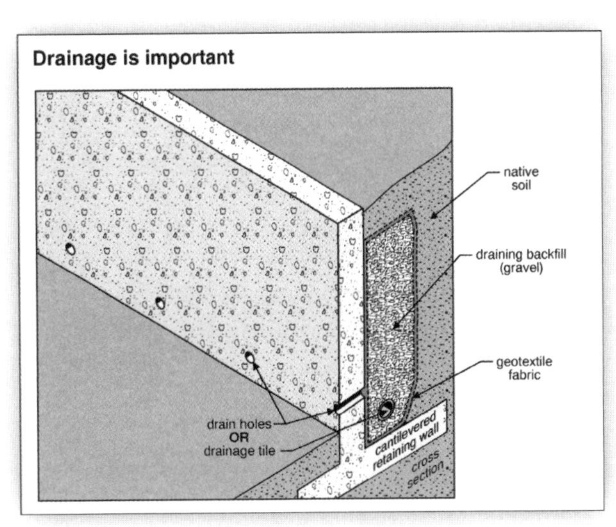

Minor repairs to retaining walls can be done by the homeowner. Patching cracked concrete retaining walls allows for monitoring of future movement. Major retaining wall repairs or modifications should be left to an expert. Retaining walls are often poorly built and can be very expensive to repair or replace.

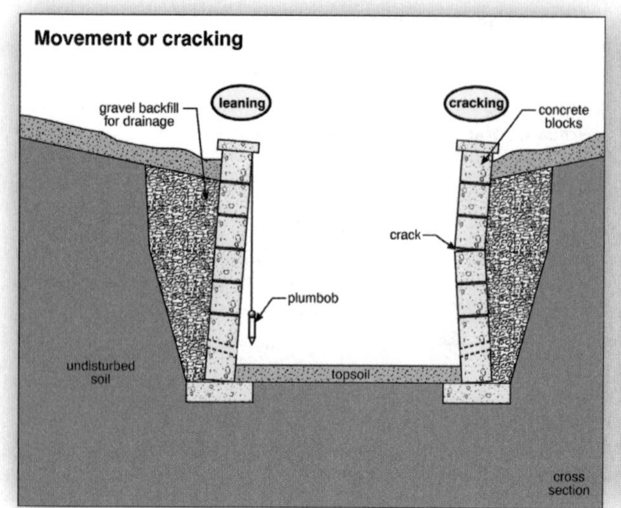

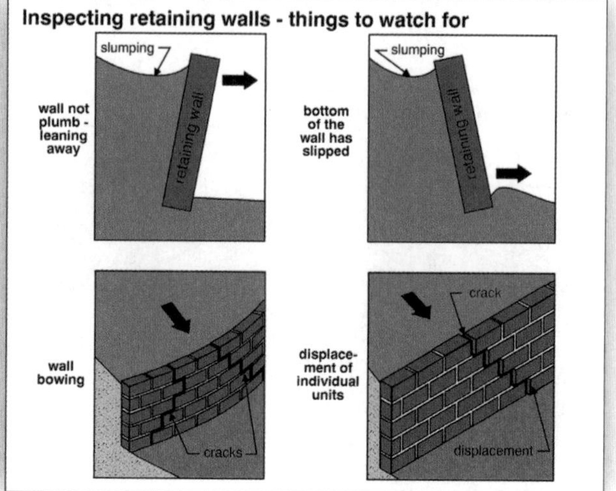

Structure

INTRODUCTION

THE STRUCTURE OF A HOME IS THE SKELETON, WHICH INCLUDES THE FOUNDATIONS AND FOOTINGS AS WELL AS THE FLOORS, WALLS, AND ROOF. STRUCTURES ARE JUDGED BY HOW WELL THEY ARE ABLE TO STAND STILL. SUCCESSFUL STRUCTURES DO NOT MOVE; UNSUCCESSFUL ONES DO, SOMETIMES DRAMATICALLY.

IN THIS SECTION WE WILL DESCRIBE THE PURPOSE OF THE STRUCTURE, AND THEN LOOK AT ALL THE STRUCTURAL ELEMENTS. WHERE THERE ARE SEVERAL TYPES, WE WILL BRIEFLY OUTLINE EACH. WE WILL DESCRIBE WHAT THE COMPONENTS DO, WHAT CAN GO WRONG, AND WHAT THAT MEANS TO THE HOME.

1.0 Why Buildings Move

GRAVITY What causes structures to move? – In a word, gravity. Gravity is constantly working to get things closer to the ground. Strong structures resist gravity.

STRUCTURE FAILURES There are two common ways a structure may give in to gravity.

a) If it is sitting on something that is not strong enough, the ground below it will fail. Better to build on bedrock than quicksand.

b) If the structure itself is weak, it will not support the loads imposed on it. The total load is made up of the following –
Dead load – the weight of the structure itself, **Live load** – furniture, people, wind, snow and earthquakes.

Overview of house structure

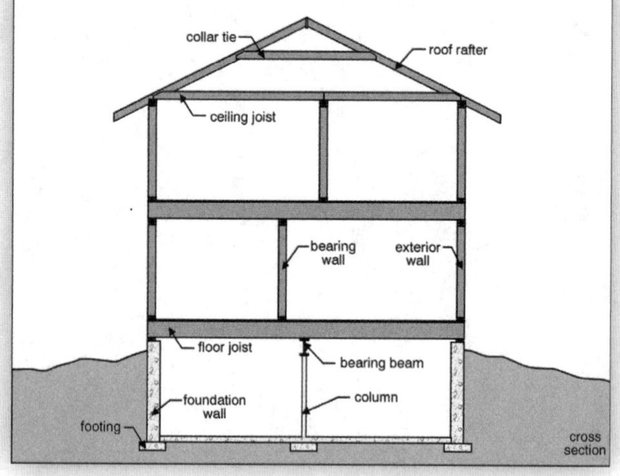

WIND Wind acts intermittently on structures. Wind forces can push, pull or lift buildings. Buildings must be strong enough to resist the lateral and uplift forces of wind as well as the downward force of gravity. Hurricanes and tornadoes are extreme wind conditions. These often result in mechanical damage caused by projectiles.

EARTHQUAKES AND EROSION Earthquakes also create forces, which can cause structural failures. Like wind, these forces are intermittent and variable and can push, pull or lift buildings. Erosion is a slower form of earth movement, but it can have a devastating effect on structures as well.

COMPONENT FAILURES House components may fail because they were poorly built with improper materials, or the materials were poorly assembled. Rot, insects, fire and mechanical damage can cause well-built structures to fail. Rust can attack metal components.

COMPRESSION AND TENSION What forces affect individual structural components? The two basic forces are compression and tension. A material is under compression when it is being pushed from both ends. A material is under tension if it is pulled on. Components in compression tend to get shorter or are squashed. Components under tension tend to get longer or are pulled apart. Many building components feel a combination of compression and tension.

Some building materials are good in compression, others work well in tension and some perform well in both. A pile of bricks is very good in compression; you can stand on it. However, it is very poor in tension. A child can pull the pile apart. A chain, on the other hand, is very good in tension. You can pull quite hard on both ends and nothing will give, but the moment you try to push on it, the chain collapses. It is not very good in compression.

SHEARING AND BENDING Different materials fail in different ways. Shearing and bending are common modes of failure. Shear occurs when adjacent faces of a material move in opposite directions. When a beam splits, or a brick cracks, it is because of shear.

Bending is movement without shearing. A plank spanned between two chairs will bend if someone stands on it, particularly if they stand near the middle. The upper half of the plank is pushed together under compression; the bottom half gets slightly longer because it is in tension.

Building components that fail by bending are said to sag or buckle. Some materials can bend a significant amount without losing their strength. Brittle materials, however, do not bend much before they break. Ductile materials do. Ceramic tile is brittle, rope is ductile. Some ductile materials are elastic. This means they will go back to their original shape after being bent. A rubber ball is elastic; a nail is not.

DEFLECTION Deflection is a mild form of bending. If structures deflect just a little, people do not mind. Building codes stipulate how much deflection is acceptable. A typical floor joist, for example, is allowed to deflect 1/360th of its span.

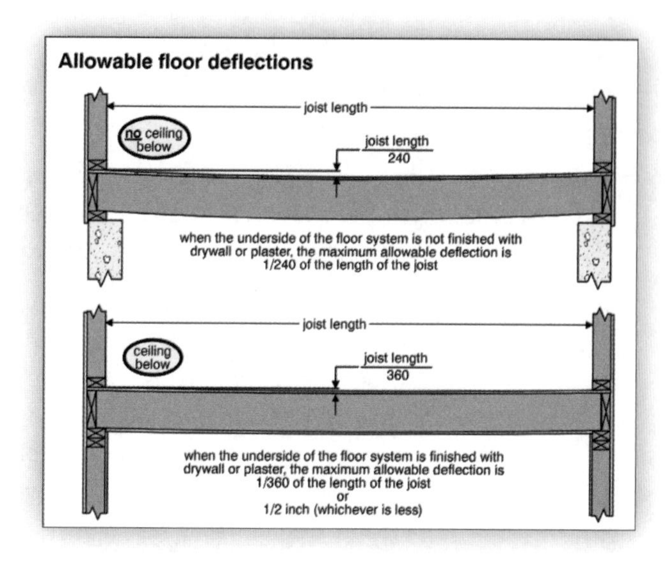

MATERIAL SELECTION What makes a good building material? It should be good at resisting the forces of tension and compression. It should be cheap, easy to work with, light, long lasting, water, rot and fire resistant, and stable under different temperature and humidity levels. No one material does it all. That is why houses are made of many materials. Wood is one of the better materials for small buildings. It is relatively good in both tension and compression. Steel is also good in both tension and compression.

Building materials are chosen based on cost-effectiveness. The goal is to assemble a structure that will perform well for as small a cost as possible. This can lead to some very small margins of safety and, of course, some failures. As new materials are developed, they are tried; in some cases, with great success; in other cases, with very poor results.

The structure is by far the most important part of the house. The safety and usability of the entire home depends on its structural integrity. Since many structural components are buried below grade or behind finishes, much of the structural inspection is done by looking for evidence of movement. Where no movement has occurred, imperfections may go undetected. New interior or exterior finishes and patching work may conceal imperfections over the short term. In these cases, problems will not be identified.

REPAIRS Structural repairs can be very costly, and in some cases the problem is so severe that the building is torn down. In many cases, a structural engineer should be consulted before making repairs. An incomplete understanding of a problem may lead to incorrect solutions and a life-threatening situation.

CHAPTER ORGANIZATION In this chapter we'll look at foundation configurations briefly, then discuss the various structure components one at a time, starting with the footings and finishing with the roof.

2.0 Configuration

Homes may have a basement, a crawlspace, both, or neither. Many houses have partial basements and/or partial crawlspaces. The configuration is determined by climate, cost, regional building practices and restrictions imposed by the building site. In areas prone to hurricanes and flooding, buildings may be built on posts or stilts to keep the home well above grade.

2.1 Basement

DESCRIPTION Where frost footings are required, a trench is needed around the house perimeter for the footing and foundation system. Since this excavation is necessary, it is not much more expensive to dig a big hole and create a basement. In warm climates where frost footings are not required, basements are rare.

The below-grade space is inexpensive to build once the hole is dug, and can be used for anything from rough storage to living space. Basements commonly contain the mechanical and electrical systems and may include a work room and laundry (although the laundry is upstairs in many modern homes). Game rooms and family rooms are often located in basements, and complete apartments can also be built below grade.

Disadvantages of basements include the susceptibility to water leakage and lack of natural light. Windows in basements are usually small and high on the wall, since most of the wall is underground. Basement ceilings are often low, and even if there is no water leakage, they can be cool and damp.

2.2 Crawlspace

DESCRIPTION Where a trench is dug for the foundations, and the earth under the house floor is not removed, a crawlspace is created. It may have an earth floor, although a concrete slab is more desirable for storage and moisture control. Many modern codes call for crawlspaces to be 36 inches high where access must be gained, although many old crawlspaces are less. Some are entirely inaccessible. Restricted access makes inspection, maintenance and repair more difficult and expensive.

VENTING Crawlspaces are often ignored for long periods. Where moisture levels are high, structural damage, due to rot and insect activity, can go unnoticed. Some building standards call for one square foot of venting for every 500 square feet of crawlspace area. This is rarely provided. Where the crawlspace is dry, this may not be a problem.

2.3 Slab-on-Grade

DESCRIPTION In this type of construction, a poured concrete floor rests directly on the ground. The concrete slab is at least three inches thick and may or may not be reinforced with steel bars. Immediately below the slab, a moisture barrier is typically laid over about six inches of gravel. In modern construction, insulation is often provided below the slab. Slabs are typically supported by footings and foundations.

There are several types of slab-on-grade construction, including monolithic slab, supported slab, and floating slab. A monolithic slab is a concrete floor and foundation all poured as one. This can be thought of as a floor slab that is thicker around the edges.

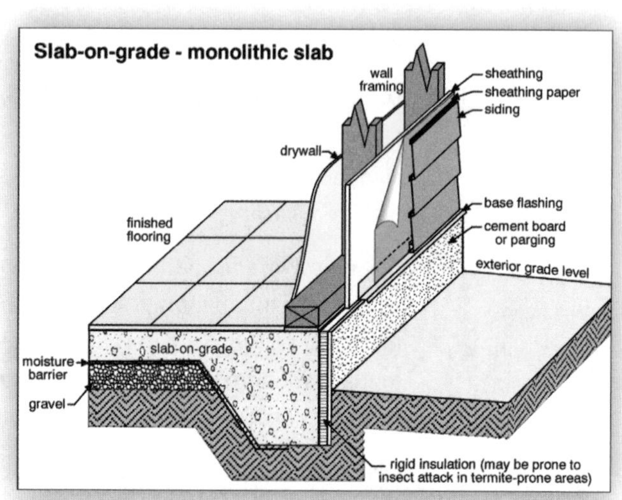

A supported slab is not poured together with the foundation, but it does rest on the foundation. The footings and foundation wall are installed first, with a ledge at the top of the foundation to support the slab. Basement floor slabs are often supported slabs.

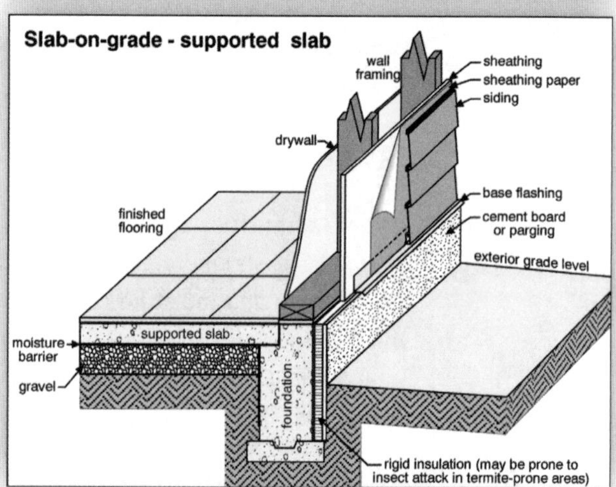

The floating slab is entirely independent of the foundation. The foundation is poured or built first. The slab is not supported by or connected to the foundation. This type of slab is common in garages.

From an inspection and maintenance standpoint, slab-on-grade is more restrictive than homes with basements or crawlspaces because none of the foundation is accessible.

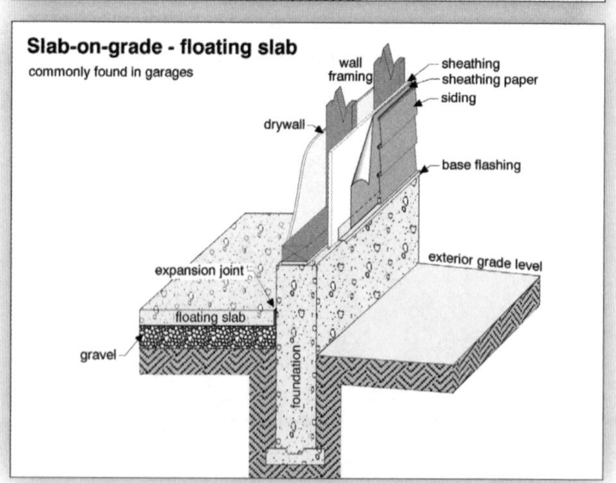

SYSTEMS CONCEALED Basement or crawlspace floors are often left as exposed concrete. Problems with water or insect infestation, for example, can be picked up early. With slab-on-grade, the concrete slab is normally covered by subflooring and finish flooring. Problems can go undetected for some time.

Where the slab is poor quality concrete, too thin, or missing the reinforcing bar, the floor is prone to cracking and shifting. Subsurface erosion can also result in slab failure, as can areas excavated for plumbing or heating pipes. This leads to broken, uneven floor surfaces with more points of entry for water and insects. Substantial shifting can damage the plumbing, heating and electric services buried in or below the slab. Expansive soils can heave the slab, resulting in similar problems.

3.0 Footings

DESCRIPTION The function of footings is to transmit the weight of the house to the soil, without allowing the house to sink. Footings are located below the foundation walls, or at the perimeter of slabs, and below columns or piers. The horizontal surface of the footing is larger than the foundation, so the load of the house can be spread out over a wide area. Footings are typically 16 to 24 inches wide and six inches to 16 inches thick. In cold climates, footings carry the house loads below the frost line. The heavier the building and the weaker the soil, the larger the footing should be.

Footings may be concrete, brick or stone. In modern construction, most footings are poured concrete, often reinforced with steel bars.

FOOTING TYPES Strip footings (also called spread footings) run continuously below foundation walls, typically around the building perimeter. Pad footings (also called spot footings) are smaller and typically support columns or piers.

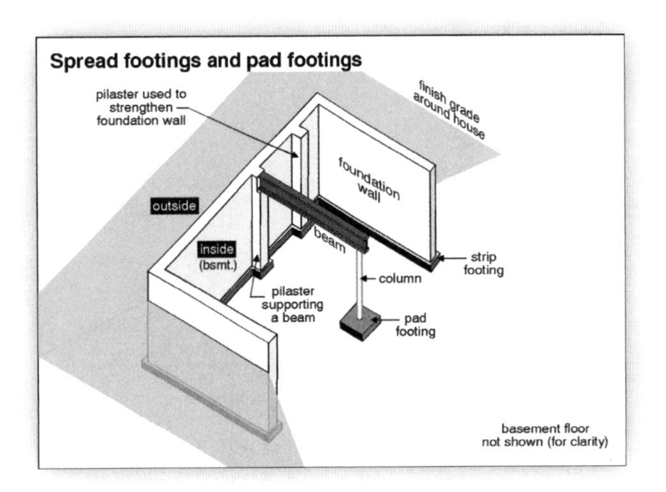

PIER AND GRADE BEAM Pier and grade beam construction is common in areas with expansive soils. Concrete piers are poured down to a depth where the soils are stable. Grade beams, which often form foundation walls, span between the piers. These grade beams are often reinforced concrete.

Common Problems with Footings

When the footings fail, the entire house moves. This is often a very serious problem. It is almost always expensive, and sometimes impossible, to correct. Since the footings are located below the soil, they cannot be seen. It is often difficult to know why they have failed.

Settlement is the most common form of failure, although heaving is common in cold climates due to frost expanding the soil below footings.

Sometimes footings fail in one area, and in most cases the failure is not uniform, (i.e. the building does not sink straight down but leans to one side or another). Often, one part of the house will pull away from the rest. This leads to cracking of interior and exterior wall surfaces.

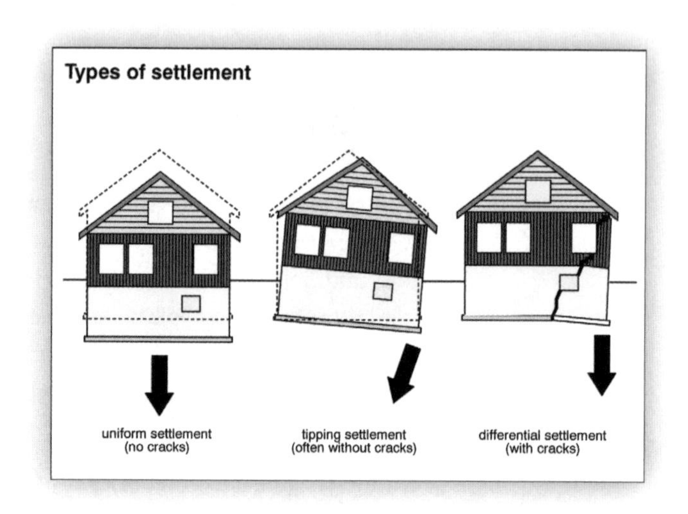

SETTLEMENT – WEAK SOILS Soils prone to compaction or movement do not support footings well. This includes recently disturbed soil. For example, if an excavation for a foundation is dug too deep, then backfilled to the correct depth, the disturbed soil under the footing is likely to compact over the first few years, resulting in building settlement.

SETTLEMENT – ABSENCE OF FOOTINGS This is not common on professionally-built houses, but may occur in casual construction as well as on porches and poorly built additions. Some homes were built on mud sills – wood beams laid on the ground with walls built on top of the beams. These mud sills are replaced with a foundation and footing system as the sills rot, heave or settle.

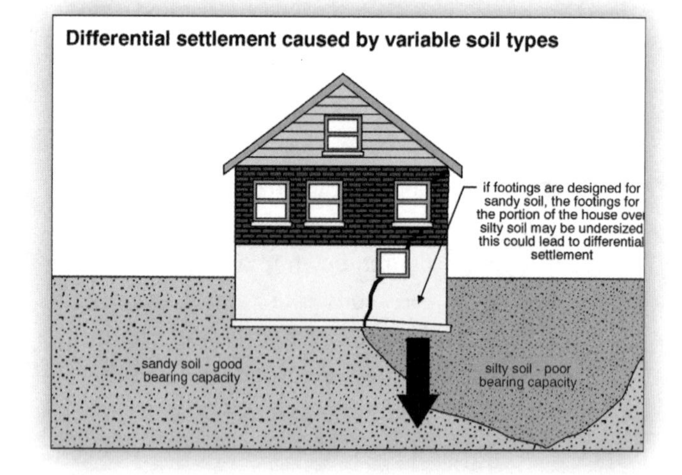

SETTLEMENT – UNDERGROUND STREAMS These may erode or weaken soil below the footings, causing severe building settlement. It is, of course, very difficult to locate and trace underground streams. They often flow only at certain times of the year.

SETTLEMENT – UNDERSIZED FOOTINGS Settlement may be the result of poor design, or an additional load that has been added. For example, when a second floor is added to a bungalow, the weight may cause the footings to sink. The additional weight of a masonry chimney can also cause localized footing failure.

SETTLEMENT – FOOTING DETERIORATION The footing must be strong enough not to break apart under a load, and must be able to stand up to continuous exposure to damp soil.

SETTLEMENT – UNDERMINED OR CUT FOOTINGS If the basement floor is lowered, there is the risk that the footings will be broken off on the inside or will lose their support. Even if excavation is not done below the footings but down to the bottom of them, the lateral support for the footing may be lost, and the footing and foundation wall may move inward.

SETTLEMENT/ WALL FAILURE – LOWERED BASEMENT FLOORS When a basement floor is lowered, the footings should be underpinned (lowered and, in some cases, enlarged). Alternatively, only the central section of the basement should be lowered, to avoid disturbing any of the soil near the footings. Depending upon how much the basement floor is lowered, the required clearance from the footings varies. A soils engineer is often consulted and a concrete curb (also called a bench footing or Dutch wall) may be needed around the inside edge of the footings to ensure they are not compromised. Building settlement and failure of foundation walls are both risks when lowering basement floors.

One of the dangers in lowering basement floors is the increased risk of basement leakage. Notice in the following illustrations how the drainage tile outside is no longer in the correct location once the floor is lowered. It is too high to be effective.

When excavation is done on the exterior, (e.g. for an addition or swimming pool) the footings can be damaged or undermined in a similar fashion.

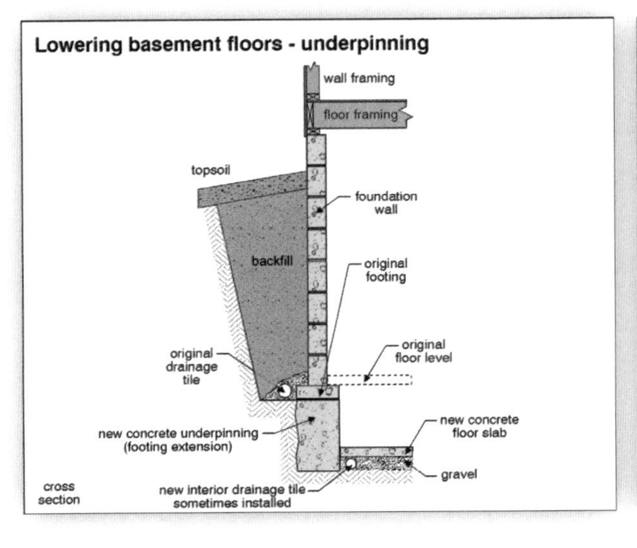

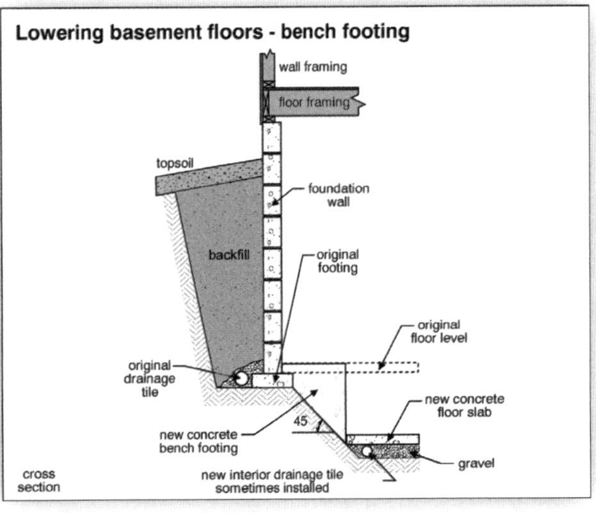

SETTLEMENT – LOT SLOPE Houses built on or close to slopes may be subject to failures as a result of soil moving down the slope. This may be a slow steady process or a sudden event triggered by heavy rains for example. This can be extremely costly to correct.

SETTLEMENT – CUT AND FILL LOTS Houses built on sloping lots may be more prone to footing and foundation failures. The chances of building on disturbed soil are increased on lots such as these. Efforts made to level and terrace the lot may result in soil being cut out of the hill to form a level terrace under the back half of the house. This soil is then used as fill in the adjacent area where the front half of the house is to stand. The downhill half of the house may be built on fill that may not be well compacted or may not be able to stay in place and support the house.

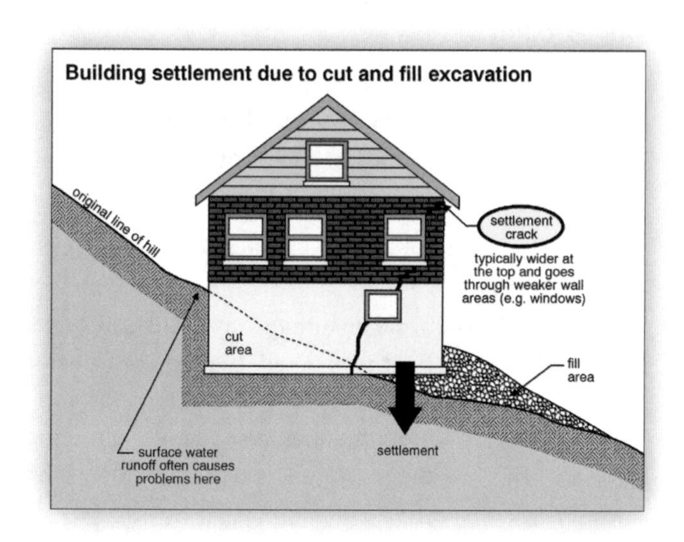

On sloping lots, large lateral earth thrust and hydrostatic pressure can be built up by the soil on the high side of the home. Water running down the slope is blocked by the building and accumulates here.

On the downhill side, the footings may not be deep enough in cold climates. Frost heave can result where the footings are less than four feet below grade. The side of the house with the lower grade often has a walk-out basement, and chances of a footing being too shallow are greatest here.

SETTLEMENT/ HEAVING – EXPANSIVE SOILS Some clay soils that expand and contract significantly with different moisture contents may also result in failure. These expansive soils can heave floors and foundations when they get wet. When they dry, they shrink and allow the building to drop. This is a significant cause of house structure problems in some areas.

Tree roots can affect the moisture content of soils noticeably. Most soils have strengths that change with different moisture contents. Some clay soil strengths change dramatically. These are poor building soils. Silts are also poor building soils, in many cases much weaker than clay.

EXPANSIVE SOILS AND SLAB-ON-GRADE HOMES Where expansive soils are common, heaving soil below the slab can push the slab upwards at the center or at the perimeter, breaking the concrete and damaging utility lines. Where these soils are common, the slabs are sometimes post-tensioned. This means there are steel reinforcing cables laid within the slab and project beyond the slab edge. The cables are tightened after the concrete is poured to strengthen the slab, helping it resist the forces of the expansive soils. The slabs are sometimes thickened in places, often with beams running in both directions on the underside of the slab. These are called ribbed foundations.

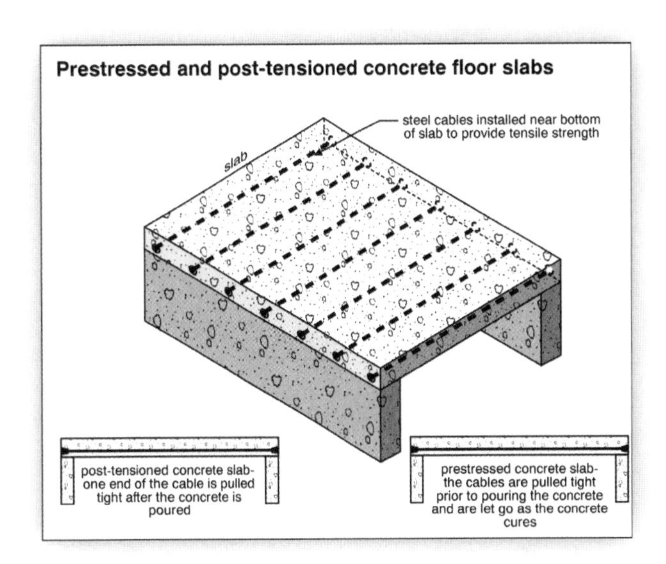

The expansive soils below the slab are often saturated during construction before pouring the slab so the soils will be a maximum height when the slab is poured.

FROST HEAVE – FOOTINGS TOO SHALLOW If the footings and foundations are not deep enough, the ground below them may freeze. Frozen ground expands and may pick up all or part of the building. This can do serious damage.

FROST HEAVE – OUTSIDE BASEMENT STAIRWELL Exterior basement stairwells may compromise the footings in cold climates. In order to be effective, the footings in cold climates must be below the frost level. When an exterior basement stairwell is added, the stairwell opening effectively lowers the exterior grade level, and also lowers the depth to which frost can penetrate. After the stairwell is in place, the frost can go several feet below the bottom of the stairwell opening. This can lead to frost heaving of the footings and the foundations.

A properly added exterior stairwell will include deepened foundations, or a completely insulated approach, to prevent frost penetration below the building footings.

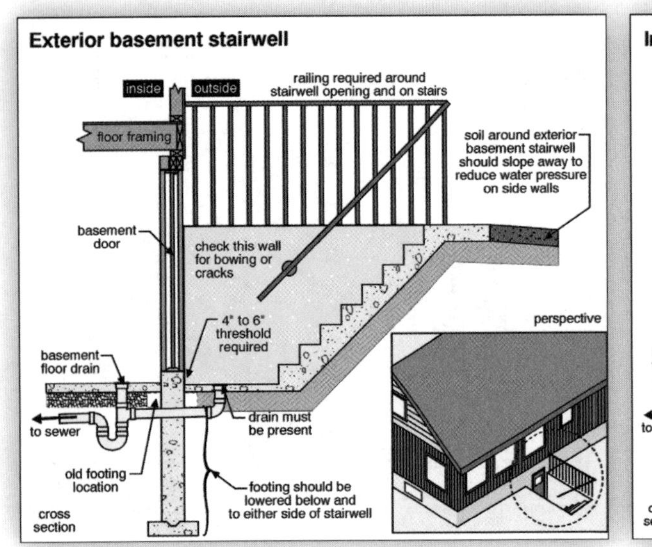

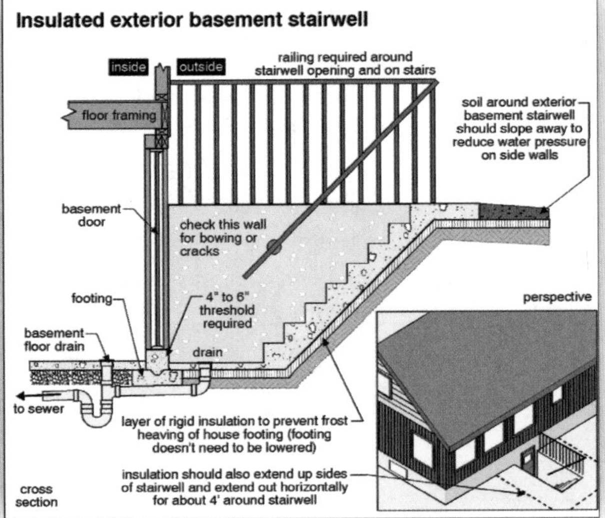

IDENTIFYING THE PROBLEM During an inspection, the results of footing failure can usually be seen. It is, however, difficult to know whether the building is still moving, and if so, at what rate. It is often necessary to monitor the building over a period of months or even years, to know whether the problem will warrant repair. Many footing failures are not severe enough to warrant repairs.

REPAIRS – UNDERPINNING The usual corrective action is to underpin the footings. This means digging under the existing footing, and adding a new footing wider and/or deeper than the original. This may have to be done in small sections on strip footings since one cannot excavate under the entire house at one time. Usually two to four foot sections are done at a time. This is very expensive work.

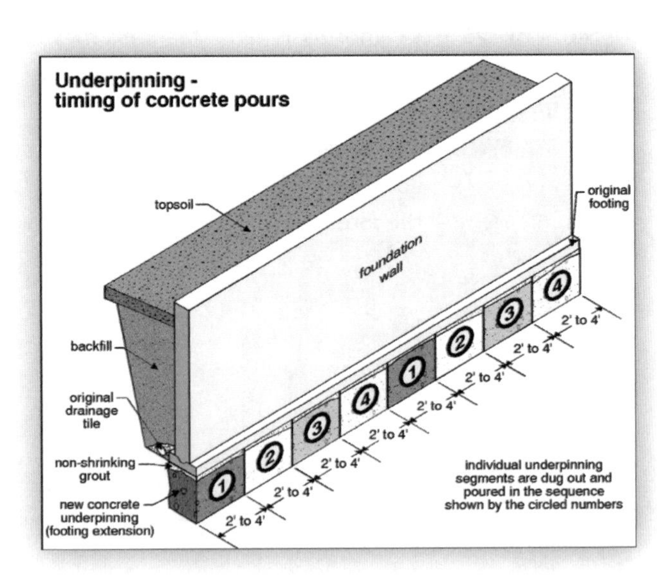

REPAIRS – PILES AND HELICAL ANCHORS In some cases, where the soils are moving or are likely to move, underpinning is not appropriate. Piles driven deep into the ground are an alternative, but may not be cost-effective for an existing building. Helical anchors are sometimes screwed into the soil to support failed footings.

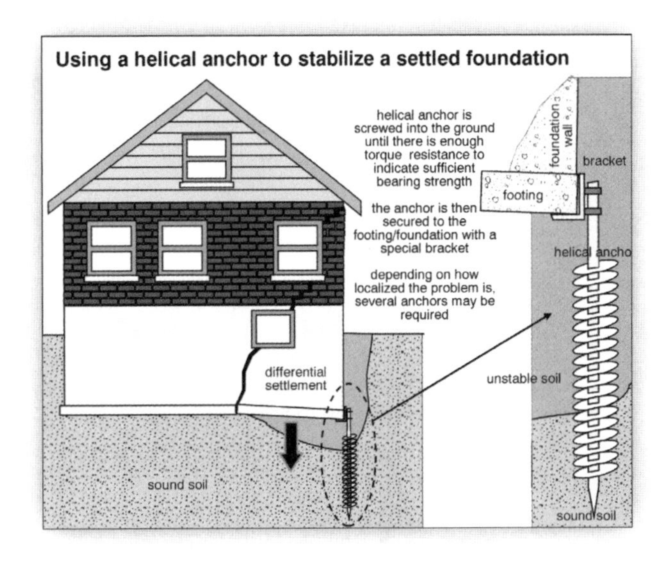

4.0 Foundations

4.1 General

DESCRIPTION Foundations transmit the weight of the house from the above-grade walls and floors down to the footings. Where there is a basement or crawlspace, foundations also resist the lateral pressure of the soil. The foundation acts as a retaining wall in this sense. In cold climates, foundations carry the weight of the house below the frost line to prevent frost heaving.

Typical foundation materials are stone, brick, poured concrete, concrete block, cinder block, insulated concrete forms, clay tile, and wood. Most of these materials behave similarly. Wood foundations are the exception.

COMMON FOUNDATION TYPES Foundations may be continuous walls (stem walls), often made of concrete, masonry block or insulated concrete forms (ICF). Foundations may also be piers supported by pad footings. Where flooding is a risk, homes may be built on piers that are well above grade. Piers may be below grade, and may be connected by grade beams.

Where soil conditions are poor, the building may rest on piles that are driven or turned down into the ground to some depth to provide adequate bearing strength to support the home.

Two common foundation arrangements are illustrated below.

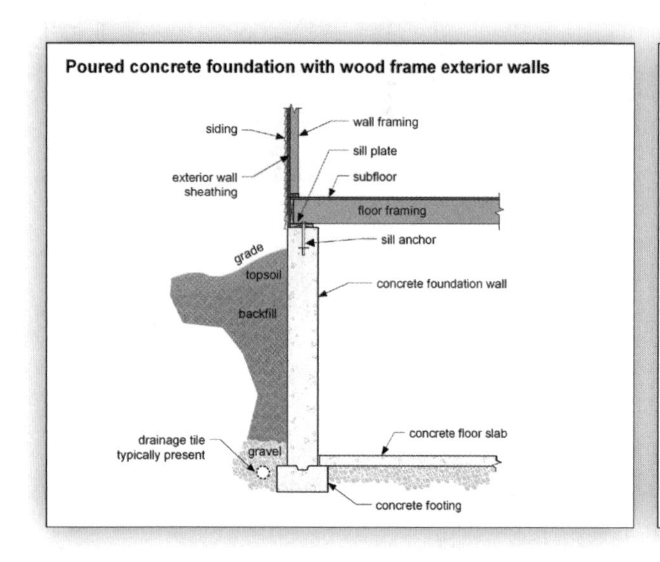

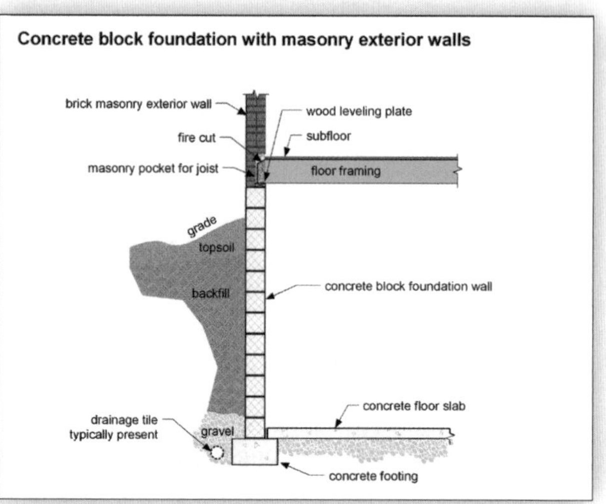

Common Problems with Foundations

CRACKS/ BOWING/ SPALLING Foundation walls may crack, bow, spall or shift. Cracks may be due to shrinkage, settlement or lateral forces. Some cracks are serious while others are insignificant. Bowing is usually the result of lateral forces. Spalling indicates poor quality materials or chronic water problems. Some of the causes of foundation defects are outlined below.

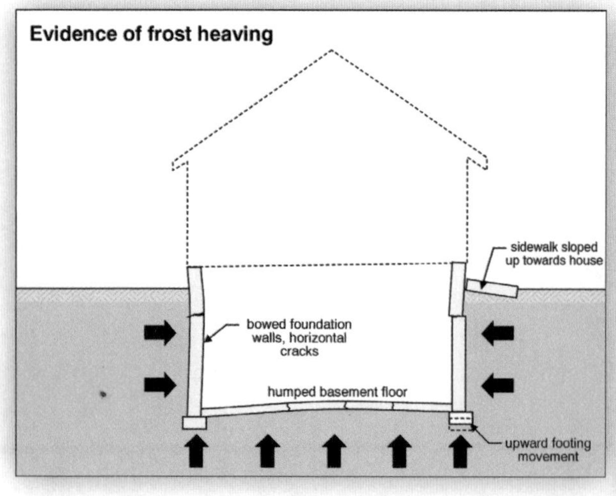

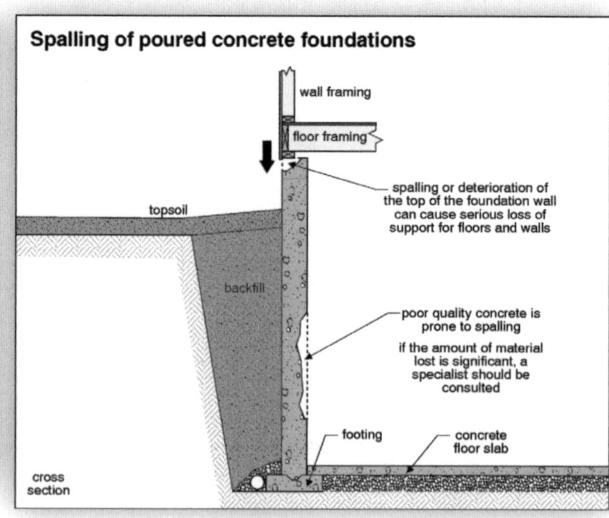

INADEQUATE LATERAL SUPPORT Basement and crawlspace foundations are really retaining walls, holding back the soil outside. If the foundations do not provide enough lateral support, they will deflect inwards. This may be the result of mechanical forces exerted during back-filling; back-filling with frozen soil (cold climates only); unusual frost development in the soil immediately outside the building (cold climates only); foundation walls that are too thin, too tall or do not have adequate reinforcement; or the house floor system does not provide adequate bracing for the top of the foundation wall. This last problem is common on the high side wall on a sloping lot. Both masonry walls and poured concrete walls can fail if not properly built.

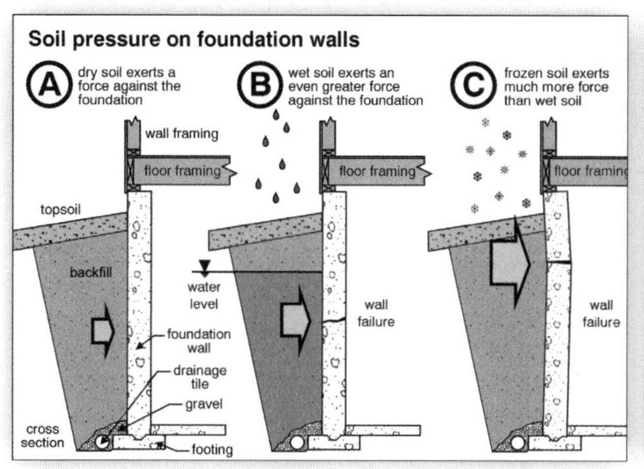

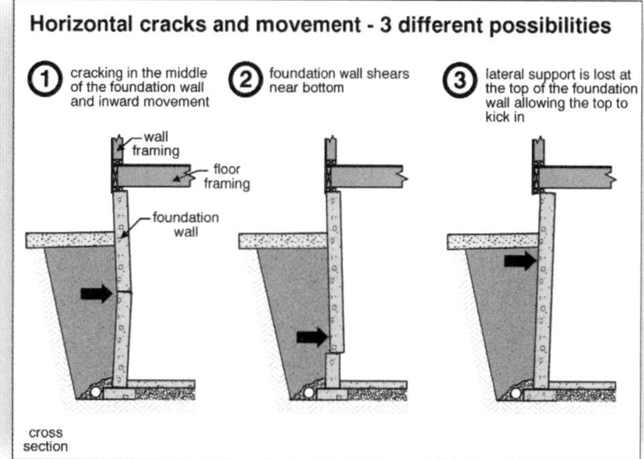

INWARD BOWING Foundation walls that move inward can be repaired by tying them back from the outside, using ties and anchors. Alternatively, buttresses can be provided on the interior. These often are concrete or concrete block structures built against the basement walls. Steel beams are sometimes used. There are also modern structural fabrics that can be applied to strengthen walls. Another choice is to build a new foundation wall inside the old. In some cases the foundation is replaced.

BOWING/ CRACKS – MECHANICAL DAMAGE Mechanical damage caused when backfilling during construction for example, can generally be repaired on a localized basis, although re-excavation is often necessary. Using heavy equipment next to the home (to re-pave a shared driveway, for instance) can also exert high horizontal loads and result in bowing and cracking in the foundations of one or both houses.

BOWING/ CRACKS – HEIGHT OF BACKFILL The height of soil outside a foundation may exert enough force to cause the foundation to fail. Conventional foundations can typically tolerate 3 feet to 7 1/2 feet of soil height on the outside. The strength of the foundation is determined by its material – concrete or concrete block for example, the strength of the concrete, the thickness of the wall, whether the wall is laterally supported at the top, and whether the wall is reinforced.

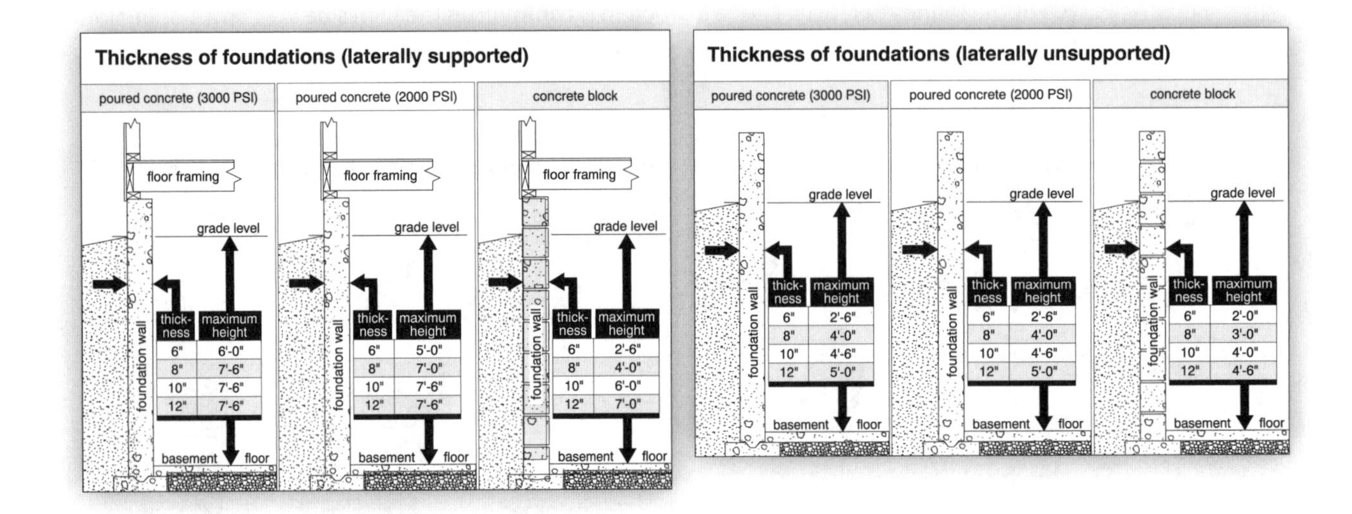

BOWING/ CRACKS – TREE ROOTS The force exerted by large tree roots on the foundation wall can lead to deflection of the foundations. Some soil types shrink considerably as they dry out. If a large tree draws water from such soils below a footing, the footing may drop as the soil compacts. In this case, the tree damages the house without actually touching it.

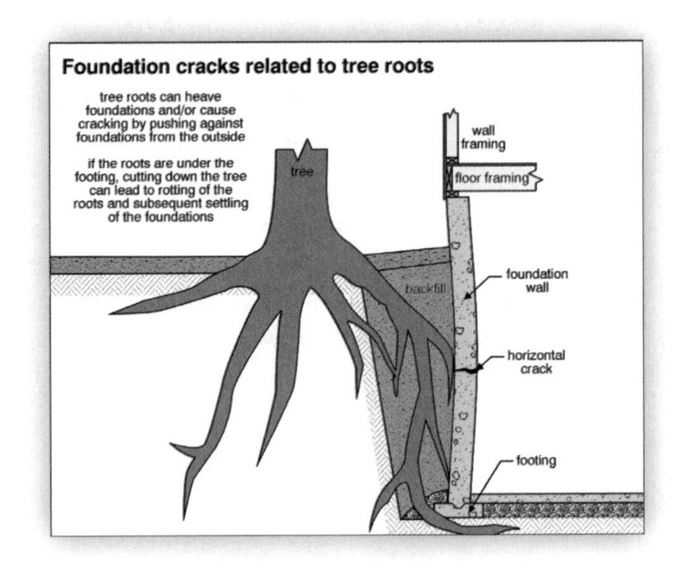

In the short term, tree root damage can be arrested by cutting down the tree and leaving the roots in place. Over the long term, the roots may be expected to rot, leading to soil settlement, resultant water leakage and, in some cases, building settlement. The roots may have to be removed.

SPALLING/ DETERIORATION – WATER PENETRATION Water penetration can deteriorate the mortar in masonry foundations, reducing its strength and ultimately allowing shifting to occur. This is usually a slow, long-term process.

SPALLING/ DETERIORATION – SURFACE WATER Water related problems and wall deterioration due to moisture penetration can be minimized or eliminated with control of surface water on the exterior. Good exterior grading with ground sloping down away from the building is important. Proper performance of gutters and downspouts is equally important. All roof run-off must be directed into a drainage system or onto the ground at least six feet away from the building.

SPALLING/ DETERIORATION – GROUND WATER Where ground water is the problem (an underground stream or high water table), grading and downspout approaches may not prove adequate. Drainage tiles and/or a sump and pump, are often necessary. Consultants specializing in situations such as these should be engaged. See Section 10 in the Interior chapter.

SPALLING/ DETERIORATION – POOR QUALITY CONCRETE Low quality concrete subjected to damp soils may deteriorate, losing its strength. This is common in poured concrete foundations, built in the early 1900s. The interior or exterior face of the concrete may crumble (spall). Reducing moisture penetration will retard this action, but if the damage has progressed to a point where the structural integrity is compromised, sections of the foundations may have to be completely replaced. This is an expensive undertaking.

SPALLING/ DETERIORATION – POOR QUALITY MASONRY Some bricks are designed for use below grade, but many are not. The use of inappropriate brick will result in a shortened foundation life. Ultimately, the bricks have to be replaced.

FOUNDATIONS TOO SHORT If the foundation walls do not extend well above grade level, the walls sitting on top of them may be exposed to damp soil and rot or deteriorate. Foundations should extend at least four to six inches above grade level.

Common Problems in Cold Climates

FROST HEAVE – TOO SHALLOW In cold climates, if the foundations are too shallow, frost may heave even the best-built footings and foundations. On sloped lots, the possibility of shallow foundations is greatest on the low side. Properties with basement walk-outs are often vulnerable to freezing damage.

FROST HEAVE – UNHEATED HOUSES Conventional cold climate construction assumes the house will be heated. An unheated house may have frost penetrating through the basement floor below the footings, leading to heaving. There is a risk involved in leaving a house unheated.

ADFREEZING Adfreezing is a phenomenon whereby damp soil on the outside of the building actually freezes to the building and as the soil heaves, it will lift the top part of the foundation wall. Horizontal cracks in foundation walls just below grade are typical.

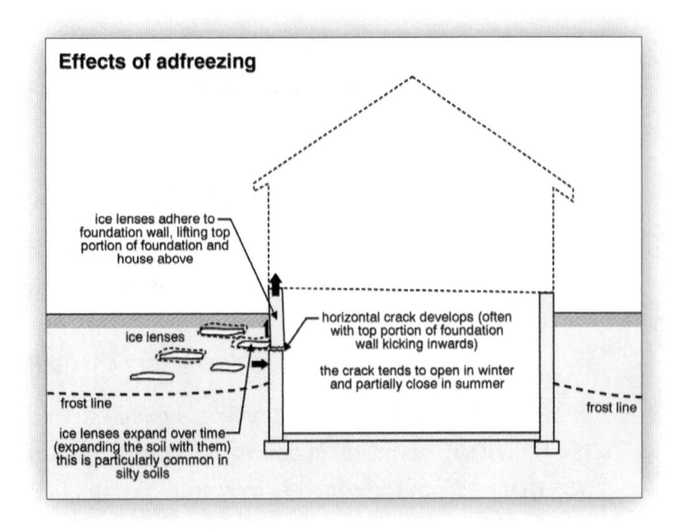

4.2 Wood Foundations

DESCRIPTION Preserved wood foundations were introduced in the early 1960s. Several thousand units have been installed. Life expectancies of the below-ground wood are estimated in the 50 to 100 year range, considerably less than many traditional building foundation materials. Some manufacturers offer 60 year limited warranties.

The wood is chemically treated to retard rot. Chemical treatment for wood used in foundations is more intensive than that typically used in wood for decks, fencing, etc. The wood foundations may rest on concrete or wood footings. With wood foundations, special care must be taken to ensure that the foundation is able to perform its retaining wall function (adequately resisting lateral forces).

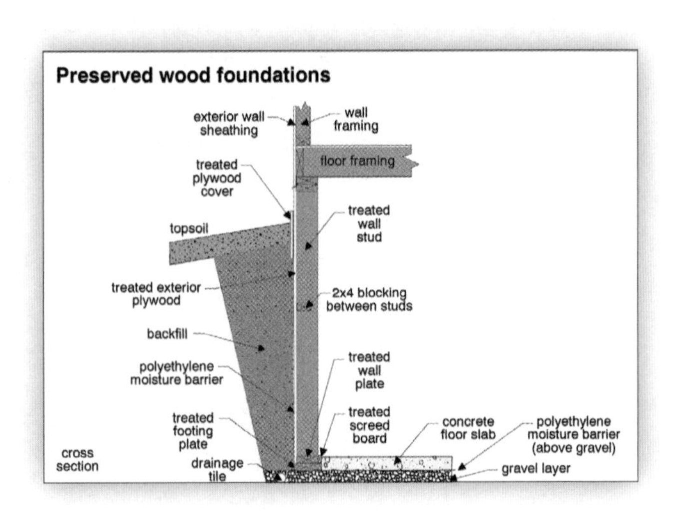

Common Problems with Wood Foundations

ROT/INSECT DAMAGE Rot and insect damage are the major enemies of wood foundations. Wood foundations should not be used in areas prone to wood-destroying insects such as termites.

4.3 Pile Foundations

DESCRIPTION Piles are steel, wood or concrete columns driven into the soil. They are used in weak soils and may extend down through the poor soil, to reach a soil with good bearing strength. Piles may depend on friction between the sides of the pile and the soil for their support. They may also be point bearing at the bottom. The building itself rests on beams or walls that straddle the piles. Piles are expensive and once the building is up, there is often no way to know if piles have been used and where. Again, the presence or absence of building settlement is the only way to determine how successful the approach has been.

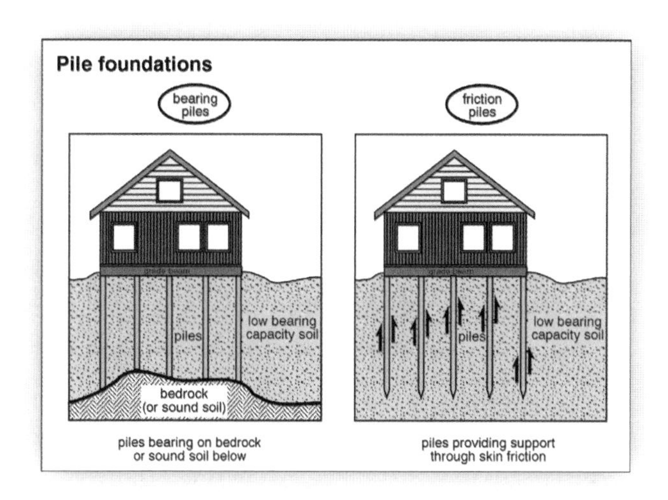

PILES AND GRADE BEAMS In some areas, garages are typically constructed on piles. The piles support poured concrete grade beams for example, which in turn, support the floor and wall systems. The garage floor is then poured on the undisturbed soil.

4.4 Pier Foundations

DESCRIPTION Where continuous foundations are not provided, individual columns or "piers" may be used to support a building. The piers should rest on a footing below the frost line in cold climates and typically the pier supports a beam. The beam, in turn, supports the floor, wall and roof loads.

Piers are commonly found in houses where there is no basement or a partial basement. A crawlspace often has a pier system supporting the structure above. Porches are also commonly supported by piers.

Piers may be stone, brick, concrete block, cinder block, or wood. Most of these materials behave in a similar fashion. Wood, of course, is the most vulnerable to rot and insect damage. As a rule, wood/soil contact is best avoided.

Concrete piers are often used with grade beams where expansive soils are an issue.

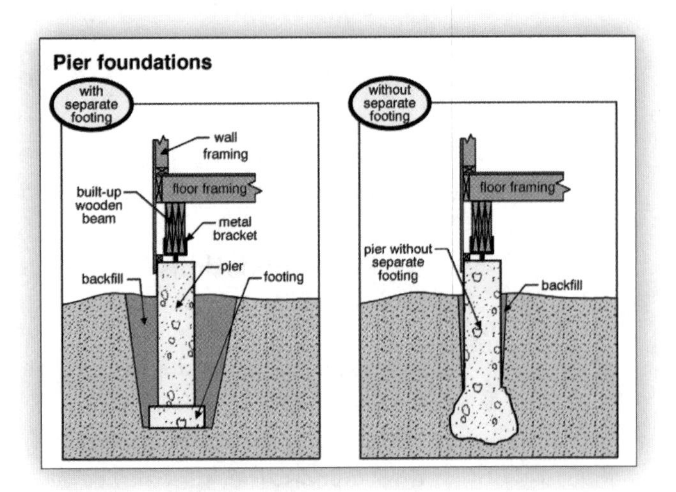

Common Problems with Piers

SETTLEMENT – INADEQUATE FOOTINGS Pier problems are often the result of inadequate footings. This will result in settlement of the pier and, of course, the building above. If the pier base is not below the frost line in northern climates, frost heaving can be a problem. In both these cases, the piers usually have to be rebuilt. Similar problems can result in areas with expansive soils.

OVERSPANNED If the piers have too great a span between them, the beams may sag or the concentrated loads may cause the piers to sink. Adding piers is the typical solution here.

TOO SLENDER OR OUT OF PLUMB If the piers are too slender or are out of plumb, they may not be capable of carrying their intended loads. Diagonal wood braces are used in some areas to help hold piers in place. Piers that are deteriorated as a result of moisture or mechanical damage should be repaired or replaced as necessary.

Wood piers can rot, be attacked by wood-boring insects, fire or be damaged mechanically.

SKIRTING Preserved wood performs better than most species of untreated wood. Where piers are used in lieu of a continuous foundation, the space between the piers usually has to be filled in to prevent soil from falling into the basement or crawlspace. In above-grade situations, skirting keeps out animals and, to some extent, rain, snow and cold. Skirting may be wood, masonry or poured concrete, for example. Where the skirting is not structural, repairs to deteriorated skirting are often deferred. Wood skirting often deteriorates where it contacts the soil.

5.0 Floors

Floors provide the bearing surface for people and furniture. They also tie the building together, adding rigidity and providing a surface for floor coverings above and ceiling finishes below. We will look at floor components one at a time.

5.1 Sills

DESCRIPTION Wood sills provide a level, continuous pad between the foundation top and the bottom of the framing system. The sills secure the floor system to the foundation.

ANCHORED TO FOUNDATION Typically, the floor joists rest directly on and are secured to the sill. Sills should be anchored to the foundation. This is often accomplished using bolts anchored into the top of the foundation wall, passing through the sill and secured with a washer and nut.

In new construction, the sill is typically a wood framing member (2x4 or 2x6) laid flat. In older construction it may be a substantial wood beam (e.g. 8x8). Wood sills can support wood framing members but should not support brick or stone.

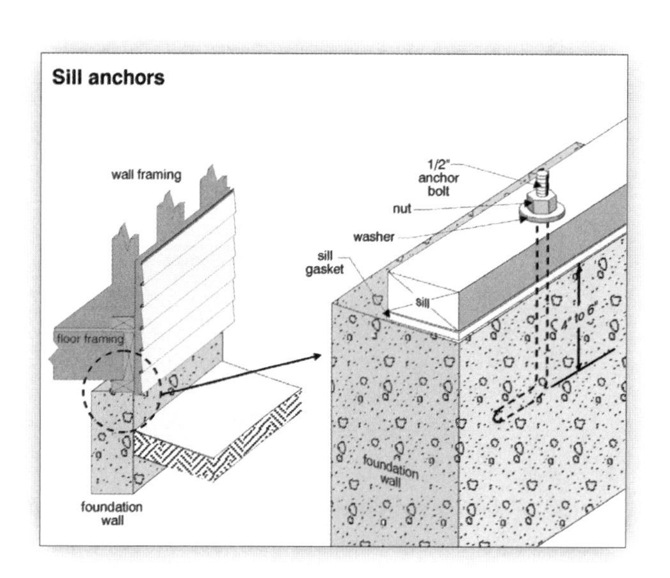

Common Problems with Sills

CRUSHED – CONCENTRATED LOADS Sills may be crushed as a result of concentrated loads. Steel posts built into walls will sometimes cause this.

CRUSHED – INADEQUATE END BEARING If the beams or joists are too short, and only the very end rests on the sill (less than one inch, for example), the concentrated loads may crush the sill.

MOVEMENT – INADEQUATE ANCHORING Where the sills are not secured to the foundations, there is danger of the building shifting during high winds, when significant upwards and lateral forces can be generated.

ROT/INSECT DAMAGE Wood sills close to grade level are subject to rot and insect attack because they are wet much of the time. Soil is typically damp. Sills may rot and crush under the weight of the framing system. This will weaken the structure, allowing it to settle slightly and break the connection between the floor and foundation.

5.2 Beams

DESCRIPTION Beams carry floor and wall loads horizontally to the foundations, walls, columns or posts. Beams may be wood (solid, built-up or engineered), plywood or steel.

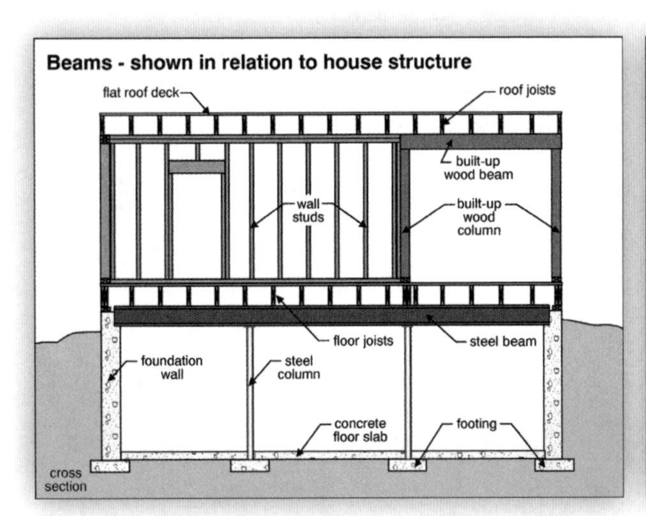

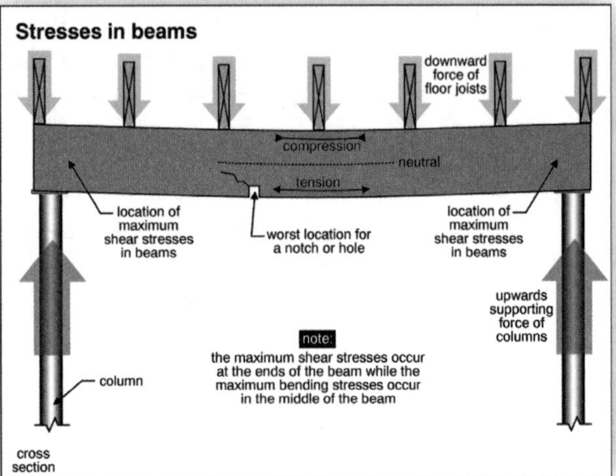

Common Problems with Beams

SAG – OVERSPANNED Undersized or overspanned beams may sag or crack. This may lead to failure of the entire framing system. Fortunately, this rarely happens, and almost never suddenly. Overspanned wood beams can usually be identified readily, and posts can be added or the beam can be strengthened.

CRUSH/FALL – END BEARING Where the end bearing is inadequate, the beam can crush itself or its support. There is also potential for the beam to slip off its support. Typically, three inches is considered a minimum end bearing for beams when supported by masonry or concrete.

ROT/INSECT DAMAGE Wood building components are vulnerable to rot, damage, insect attack and fire. Rot and insect damage are common where there is wood/soil contact. Beams below grade should have 1/2 inch clearance along the sides and at the end to allow for air circulation.

DAMAGE/ NOTCHED/ DRILLED Mechanical damage can be done accidentally or intentionally. Wood beams that are notched, cut or drilled are weakened. The location and size of the damage determines whether corrective action is necessary.

TWISTING/ ROTATION Rotation of wood beams due to warping or poor support is relatively uncommon but can lead to damage and ultimate failure.

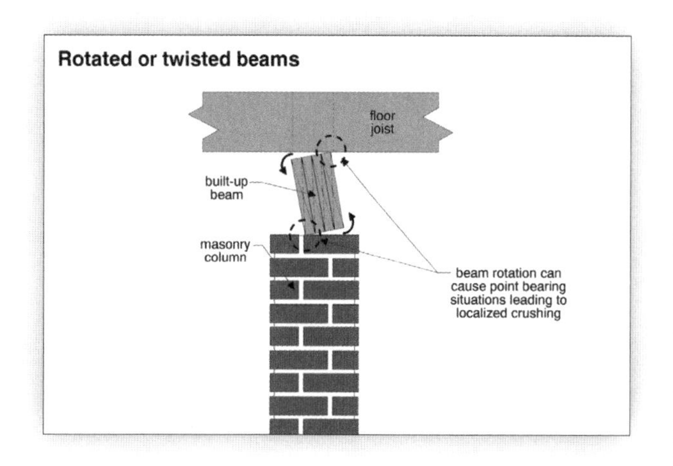

NAILING AND BUTT JOINTS Built-up wood beams may not be adequately nailed. Normally, nails should be provided in double rows every 18 inches along the beam. Where butt joints occur in wood beams, they should be located over the supports or as follows: the butt joints should be within six inches of the quarter point of the span. For example, if the span is 12 feet, the joint should be within six inches of the three-foot mark or the nine-foot mark of the span; (i.e. the joints should be 2-1/2 to 3-1/2 feet from the end supports).

RUST Steel beams are susceptible to rust, particularly if the basement is damp. Steel should be painted to prevent rust. Lateral support for steel beams is typically provided by wood strapping secured to the joists.

LATERAL SUPPORT Lateral support for steel beams is typically provided by wood strapping secured to the joists. There are several ways to provide lateral support for wood beams. See the illustration below.

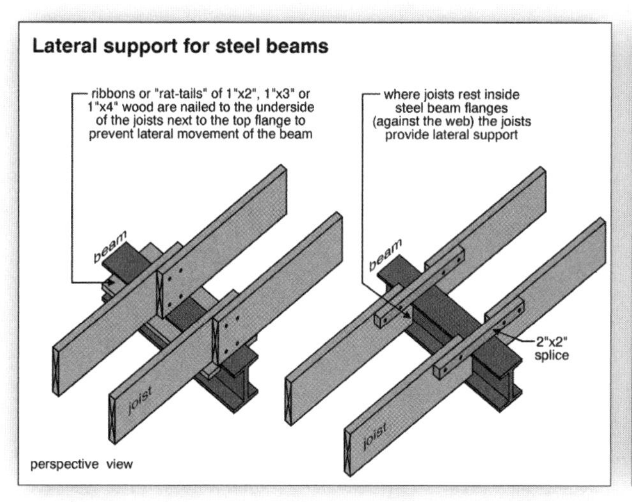

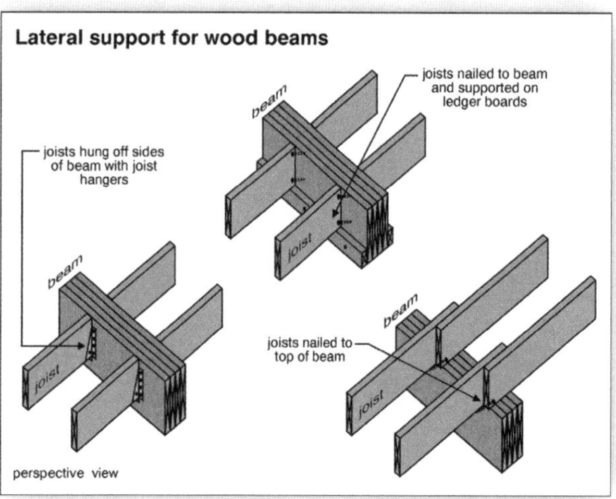

SECURING TO POSTS Steel beams may be poorly secured to posts. Wind uplift may cause the beam to lift off the post, or impact may shift it so that support is no longer offered. The beam and post should be bolted, welded or clipped together. In hurricane or earthquake areas, additional fastening may be necessary. Special straps are used to accomplish this.

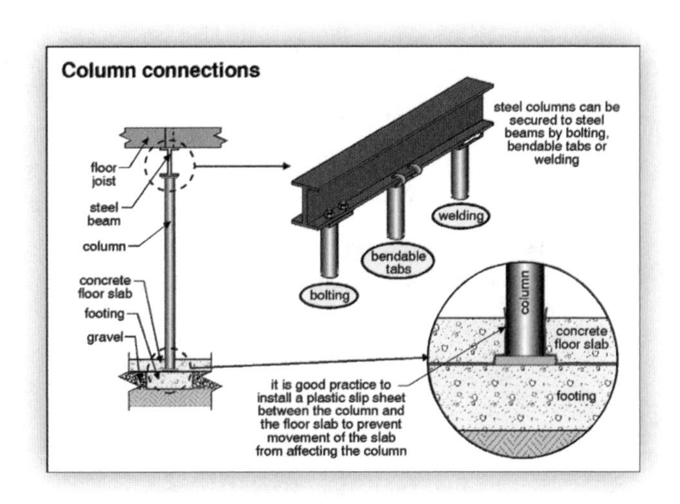

STRENGTH A visual inspection of a steel beam cannot determine its strength because it depends on more than size. The shape of the beam, the length and thickness of both the flanges and web, and the weight per linear foot, all influence beam strength. The carbon content of steel also affects its performance.

STEEL VERSUS WOOD Steel beams can be much stronger than wood beams and are more resistant to rot, insect and mechanical damage, but are more expensive, heavier, and more difficult to work with. Engineered wood beams can be stronger than solid wood, yet are light, easy to work with and less expensive than steel. Wood beams can be cut on site more easily than steel. Steel beams should rest on steel posts or masonry. Wood beams can rest on wood members.

FIRE Fire is a concern with both wood and steel beams. Interestingly, a steel beam will lose its strength much earlier in a fire than a wood beam, although a wood beam burns and a steel beam does not. Steel loses its strength after being exposed to temperatures of 1000° F. for about four minutes. Steel beams sag like spaghetti during a fire, allowing buildings to collapse quickly. Wood burns but loses its strength much more slowly.

5.3 Posts and Columns

DESCRIPTION Posts or columns (two names for the same thing) carry the load of the beam vertically down to the footings. They may be brick, concrete block, poured concrete, wood, or steel.

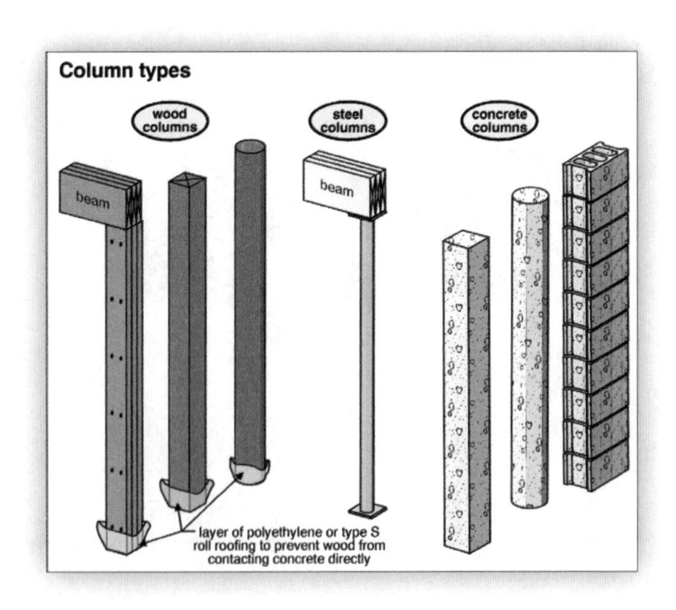

Common Problems with Posts and Columns

SPALLING/ MORTAR DETERIORATION Masonry posts may be deteriorated as a result of moisture or poor mortar. Rising damp is a common problem with brick columns. This is characterized by deteriorated mortar and efflorescence (white salty deposits) on the bottom of the post. In some cases, the brick itself deteriorates (spalls).

OUT OF PLUMB Posts that are out of plumb lose a good deal of their strength. Generally speaking, if the column is out of plumb by roughly one-third of its thickness, there may be concern about its integrity.

RUST Rust on steel posts can be a concern. This is often a serious problem at the bottom of the post in a chronically flooding basement. Rust will quickly reduce the load carrying capacity of a steel post.

ROT/INSECT DAMAGE Wood posts are vulnerable to rot and insect attack. This is especially true where the post penetrates the basement floor slab. Corrective action often includes simply cutting off the bottom of the post and placing it on a concrete pad.

FOOTING – MISSING OR TOO SMALL A sinking post is usually the result of a missing or inadequately sized footing. Obviously, suitable footings should be provided. Every post or column should have a footing. These can't typically be seen once the home is built.

UNDERSIZED OR DAMAGED Column collapse is somewhat unusual but is normally the result of an undersized column or one that has suffered mechanical damage.

NOT WELL SECURED TO BEAM A post that is not well secured to the beam above can allow the house to shift during wind uplift forces. The beam should also be supported laterally to prevent it from moving sideways. See Section 5.2.

5.4 Floor Joists and Trusses

The function of these framing members is to carry and transfer loads from the floors to the foundations, beams or bearing walls.

DESCRIPTION

5.4.1 Conventional Wood Joists: Joists are traditional dimensional lumber, typically 2x8, 2x10, or 2x12. These horizontal members can be 12 to 24 inches apart, although 16 inches is the most common. They are laid on edge so that the subflooring is nailed to the two-inch side. Floor joists should extend at least 1-1/2 inches onto the foundation or beam at either end.

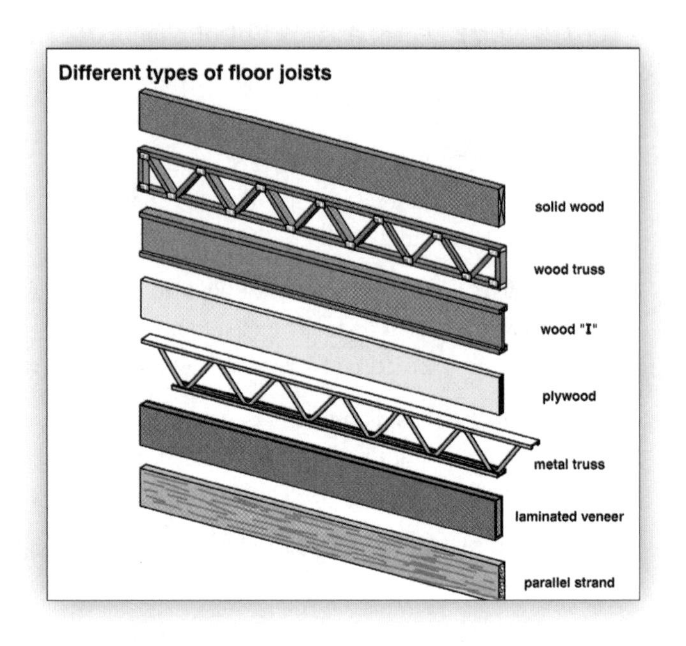

JOIST STRENGTH

The strength of a joist comes largely from its depth. Doubling a joist by putting another of the same size beside it will double its resistance to bending. Doubling the depth of a joist increases its resistance to bending by eight times! For example, the equivalent strength (considering deflection only) of two 2x10s compared to four 2x8s can be compared by multiplying the base times the height cubed. It is interesting that two 2x10s are more resistant to bending than four 2x8s.

The deflection of a floor and joist system in modern construction may be quite surprising. Many codes allow a floor to deflect 1/360th of its length under normal loading if there is a finished ceiling below. For example, the following situation is acceptable by many codes: 2x10 floor joists spaced 16 inches on center span about 15 feet. When the room is occupied with furniture and people, the center part of the floor can be 1/2 inch lower than the floor edges. This is completely safe, and the floor is not at risk of failing. However, this may not be satisfactory to some homeowners. Codes are a minimum standard. Brittle floor finishing materials like ceramic tile may not tolerate a flex like this. More rigid floors are often used where the flooring material is brittle.

SPRINGY OR BOUNCY FLOORS

Floors are often bouncy or springy when people walk across a room, but this is not necessarily indicative of problems. Light framing causes this condition, and while the floor can be stiffened, this is rarely done.

Common Problems with Conventional Wood Joists

OVER SPANNED Floor joists that are over spanned (undersized) are prone to sagging. The acceptable span of a joist is determined by the load it will carry, the species and grade of lumber used, the depth of the joist, and the spacing between joists. Over spanning can be readily corrected by adding joists, or adding a beam below the joists in most cases. The implication of over spanning is typically a noticeable sag, and in some cases, a bouncy floor system.

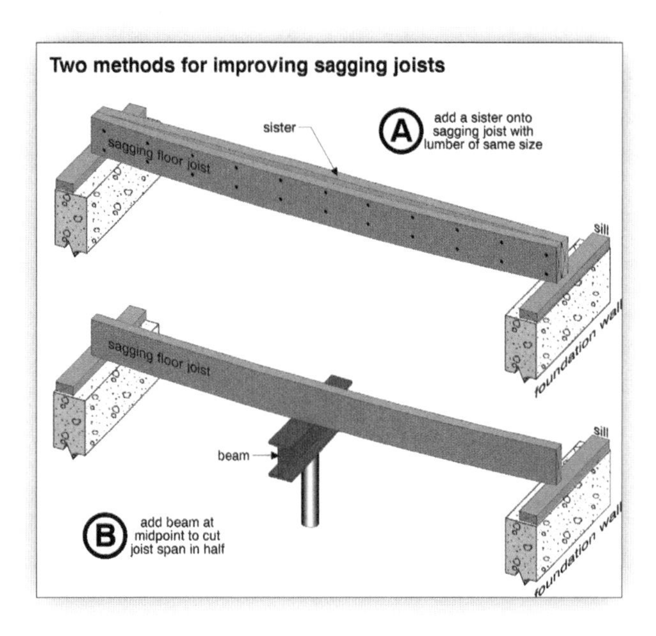

DAMAGE/ NOTCHED/ DRILLED Mechanical damage to joists is common. Joists are commonly notched, drilled and cut through to accommodate heating, plumbing and electrical systems. In some cases, joists are cut around stairwells to improve headroom. Some damage is typical, and there are several guidelines on acceptable limits. Joists are sometimes notched at the end to rest on a beam or foundation wall. This can weaken the joist considerably. The joist usually cracks horizontally from the top of the notch towards the mid-point of the span.

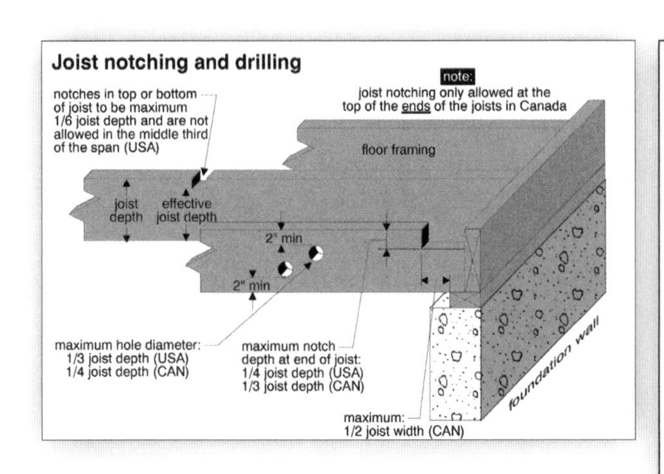

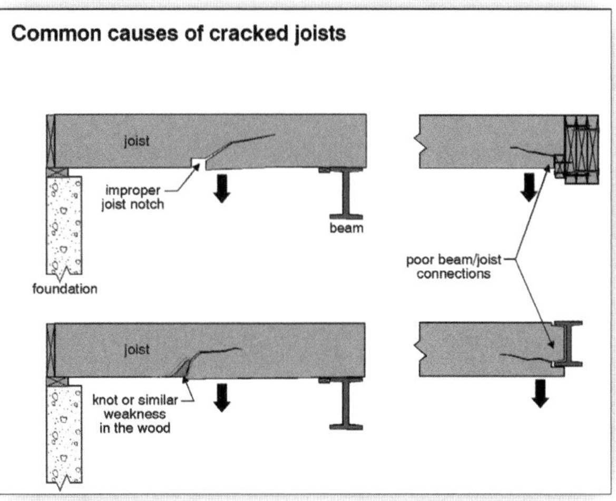

INADEQUATE END BEARING Joists may be prone to crushing at the ends and/or slipping off the beam or foundation where there is less than 1-1/2 inch of end bearing.

JOIST HANGER PROBLEM Metal brackets called "joist hangers" are used where joists cannot rest on a support. Here, the joists are cradled in and nailed to the hangers, which are secured to the side of a beam or header. Joist hangers may be undersized or inadequately nailed.

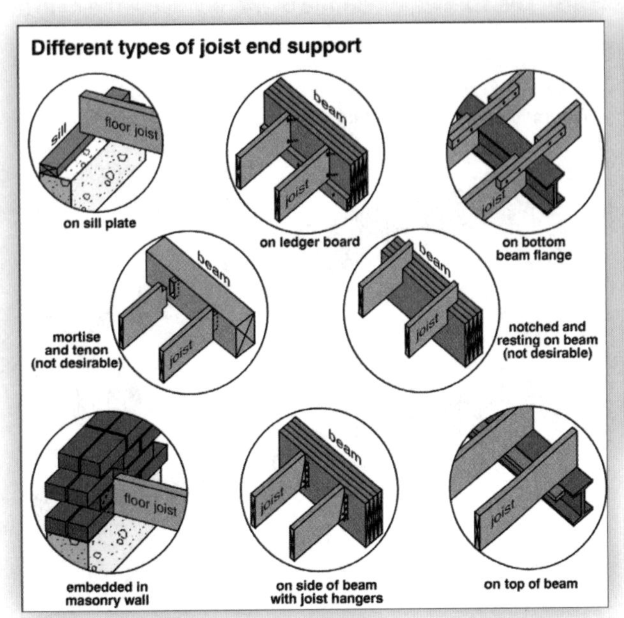

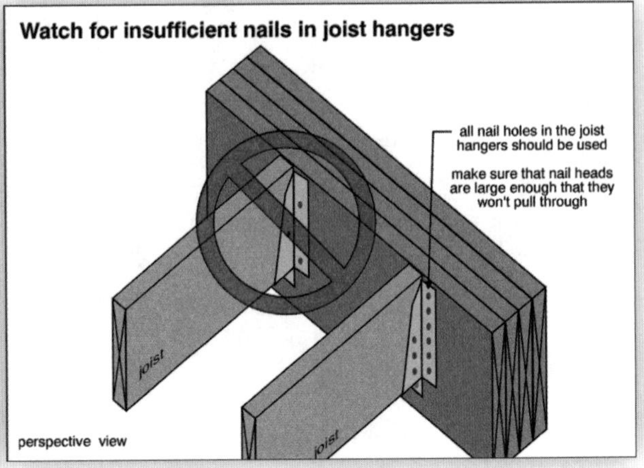

ROT/ INSECT DAMAGE Rot and insects can attack any wood components. Joist ends close to outside walls are vulnerable, especially if the outside soil level is as high as the joists.

SAG – CONCENTRATED LOADS Most floors are designed to carry live loads of 30 to 40 pounds per square foot (psf). Larger loads can lead to sagging and ultimately, failure. Special consideration may be needed for pianos, waterbeds, aquariums, and floor-to-ceiling book storage, for example.

SAG – JOISTS BELOW WALLS Joists that see concentrated loads are more prone to sagging. A joist below a non-bearing wall should be strengthened, often by doubling it. Joists should not be used below load-bearing walls. Beams or bearing walls should be used here.

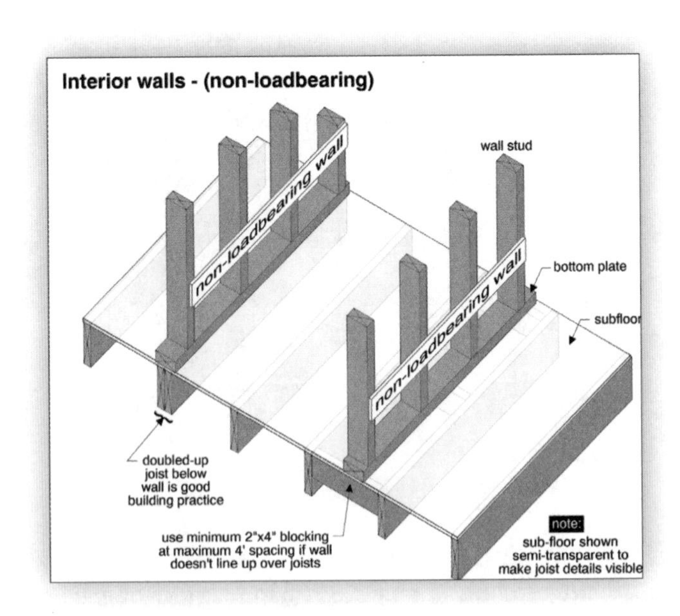

SAG/HUMP – OFFSET BEARING WALLS One of the problems often unfairly blamed on joists is caused by an offset bearing wall. Many houses have a beam or a bearing wall in the basement or crawlspace supporting the first floor. There is often a bearing wall above, supporting the second floor or roof structure. Ideally, the first floor wall is directly over the beam or wall below. If the wall is offset enough (sometimes 12 inches is enough), the joists will sag under the first floor wall above. This will lead to a low spot in the floor where the wall sits and a hump in the floor above the beam or bearing wall below. This sort of movement is rarely dangerous but it does make some people uncomfortable.

DESCRIPTION **5.4.2 Engineered Wood Joists:** Engineered joists may have conventional lumber top and bottom plates, or the top and bottom plates (flanges) may be LVLs (Laminated Veneer Lumber), PSLs (Parallel Strand Lumber), or LSLs (Laminated Strand Lumber). Webs may be plywood, oriented strandboard (OSB) or metal.

LVLs, PSLs, and LSLs can also be used as joists, beams, sills, headers (lintels), columns, studs, rafters, etc. Glulams (glue laminated lumber), made up of conventional lumber pieces glued together, can also be used for many wood structural members.

These systems have much longer spans than conventional lumber, and are less prone to shrinkage and warping problems than conventional lumber. The rules for engineered wood are different than for conventional joists, and some of the rules are specific to individual manufacturers. As always, a home inspection is a visual evaluation of field performance rather than a design analysis.

Problems Specific to Engineered Wood Joists

DAMAGE Mechanical damage is common. Joists are notched, drilled and even cut through to accommodate heating, plumbing and electrical systems. In some cases, joists are cut around stairwells to improve headroom. Holes may be too big or in the wrong place (many systems have knockouts that indicate where the holes must be). Split, notched or cut flanges may be a problem. The top and bottom flanges of wood I-joists (as engineered wood joists are often called) and trusses are critical. Any weakening will seriously affect the strength of the system.

INADEQUATE END BEARING Inadequate end bearing is a problem. More end bearing than conventional joists is often required. 1-3/4 inches is a common minimum.

JOIST HANGER PROBLEMS Metal hangers called "joist hangers" are used where joists cannot rest on a support. Here, the joists sit in the hangers, which are secured to the side of a beam or header. Joist hangers may be too short, too wide, the wrong type, and may not have enough nails or may have the wrong kind of nails.

RIM JOIST ISSUES Proper rim joist material may not be used. Engineered wood may require 3/4-inch plywood or special rim joist materials. Rims should not be conventional lumber. Inadequate load transfer through rim joists is a common problem.

SQUASH BLOCKS MISSING/ INCOMPLETE Blocking (squash blocks or web stiffeners) may be missing or incomplete where joists rest on beams or where loads from bearing walls above are transmitted down through engineered wood joists to beams or sills.

BRIDGING MISSING/ INEFFECTIVE Inadequate bridging or load sharing can be a problem. Different systems have different requirements for bridging.

DESCRIPTION **5.4.3 Floor Trusses:** The top and bottom horizontal members are called "chords". The shorter interior pieces are referred to as "webs". They are made from wood, steel and/or plywood. Trusses can span greater distances than conventional wood joists. Beams and posts or bearing walls can be omitted or removed with the use of floor trusses. These systems also allow heating, plumbing and electrical systems to run through the trusses, leaving more headroom below. Trusses do not normally require bridging or bracing.

Trusses are deeper than joists and can restrict headroom in some cases. As a general guide, the truss depth is 1/12 to 1/20 of its span. Most trusses are 10 to 18 inches deep.

Common Problems with Floor Trusses

UPSIDE DOWN Many trusses have a top and a bottom, and must be installed in the correct orientation. A truss installed upside down is considerably weakened.

CUT Trusses cannot be cut around openings, the way joists can. Conventional joists can be field cut to appropriate lengths. A truss cannot be cut. All odd-length trusses must be engineered. Site conditions that are not foreseen or last minute plan changes, can lead to wasted money and delays, when working with floor trusses.

SPAN Trusses may be overspanned just like joists. These engineered systems can only be evaluated in the field by their performance. Home inspectors do not review the design of engineered systems like trusses.

DAMAGE/ROT/ INSECTS Wood floor trusses are vulnerable to mechanical abuse, rot and insects.

DESCRIPTION **5.4.4 Headers and Trimmers:** Headers and trimmers strengthen an opening in the floor joist pattern for a stairwell or chimney. Also, basement windows often prevent floor joists from resting on the foundation walls and these openings in the framing pattern must be strengthened.

Normally, joists that cannot rest on a wall or beam are secured to a header. A header is typically made of the same size lumber as the joists (e.g. 2x8s). The header, which runs perpendicular to the joists, carries the load from the short joists (tail joists) over to trimmer joists. Trimmer joists are the joists on either side of the opening that run full length.

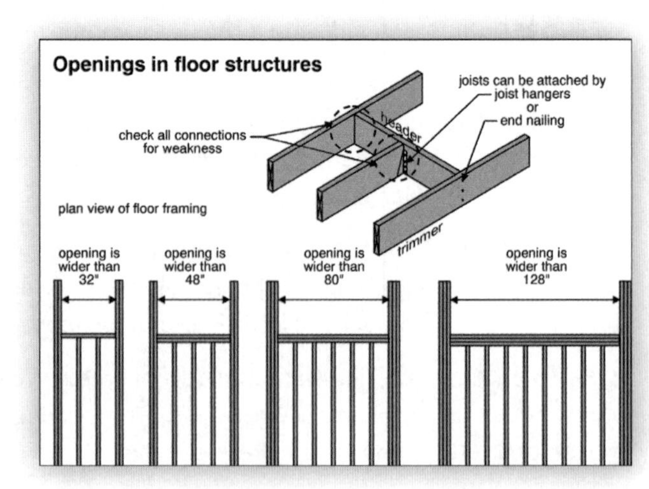

POSTS Posts can be provided at the corners of the opening to carry load from the header directly down to the floor. In this case, the trimmers could remain single. The header can also be supported with a bearing wall running under the header.

Common Problems with Headers and Trimmers

UNDERSIZED/ NOTCHED Undersized trimmers and headers are common. It is also common to have the trimmer notched at the bottom of the stairwell to improve head room. This, of course, weakens the arrangement.

POOR CONNECTION The short (tail) joists may be poorly secured to the header. Joist hangers (metal brackets) can be used to re-secure these tail joists. Headers may also be inadequately secured to the trimmers. Again, joist hangers can be used.

ROT/INSECT DAMAGE Rot and insects can weaken the stairwell opening framing.

DESCRIPTION **5.4.5 Bridging and Blocking (and Strapping):** Bridging/blocking prevent the joists from twisting. Diagonal bridging is usually 2x2 wood blocks or metal strapping. Solid blocking is the same size as the joists. To be effective, the bridging or blocking should be in a straight line and should extend the full length of the floor.

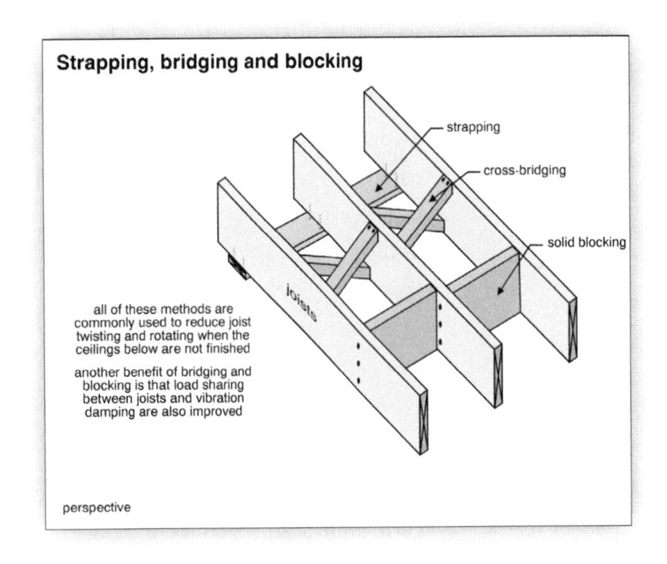

Solid blocking is required at the ends of joists. Tall joists require bridging or blocking at least every eight feet. More blocking may be needed where earthquakes are a risk.

DESCRIPTION **5.4.6 Cantilevers:** Floor joists may be cantilevered (extended) slightly beyond their supports. A common example is a balcony. This is often done on an upper floor, where support posts would be expensive and unsightly. The principle is that since wood is relatively stiff, if part of a joist is well secured at one end and part way along its length, the other end can be unsupported. Roughly 1/6 of the joist span between supports can be usually be cantilevered safely beyond a support.

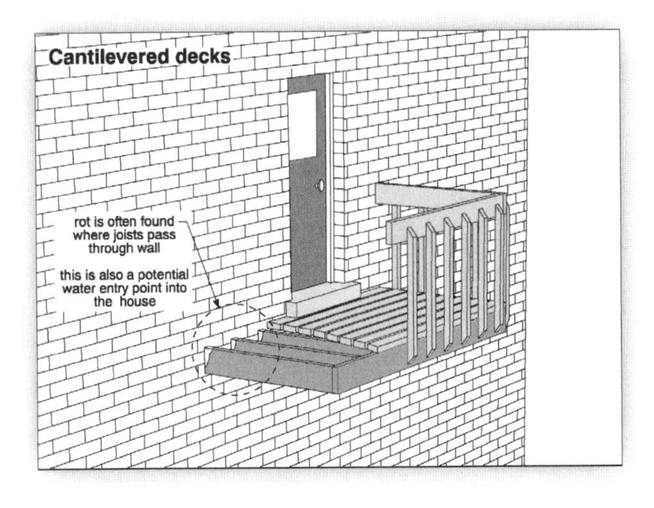

Common Problems with Cantilevers

OVERSPANNED Where the joists are cantilevered too far, the deck or balcony will be weak. This is usually detectable by the springiness of the structure when walking on it. In severe cases, failure is possible. Posts or braces can be added below the deck.

WATER PROBLEMS Since the joists penetrate the building wall, there is the possibility of leakage into the walls or directly into the home at the connection points. The joints between the joists and the wall must be kept well sealed. This is a common spot for rot to develop, attacking both the cantilevered joists and the wall structure.

ROT/INSECT DAMAGE Cantilevered wood structures are susceptible to rot and insect damage.

DESCRIPTION **5.4.7 Steel Floor Framing:** Structural framing elements are generally either C-shaped or U-shaped steel components. C-shaped elements are designed as load-bearing elements, such as joists, while the U-shaped pieces are tracks, or channels, designed to hold the load-bearing components in place.

Steel framing members are normally screwed together, although they may also be welded. Members may be screwed directly to each other, or clips (clip angles) may be used to join members together, with the clip being screwed to both elements. Screws are also used to join wood framing, sheathing, and drywall finished to steel framing. Securing joists to steel beams requires the use of clips and powder-actuated fastener guns.

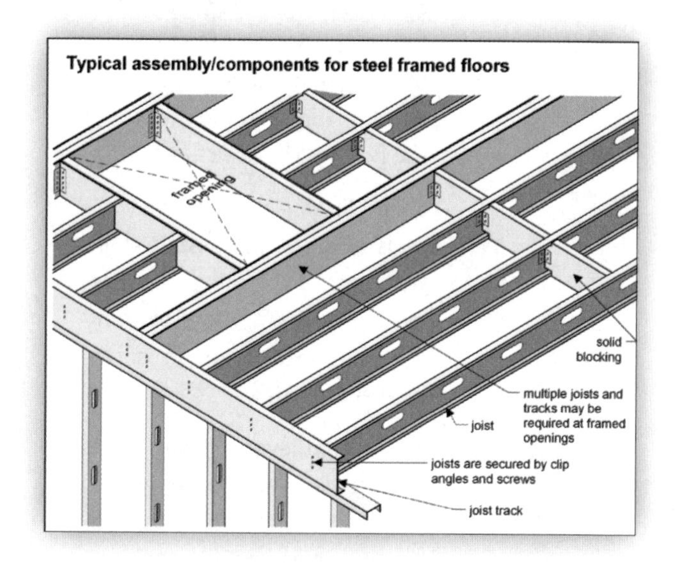

BEARING STIFFENERS Bearing stiffeners (web stiffeners) are required where a concentrated load, such as a door jamb, rests on a floor joist. These usually take the form of a section of stud or track mounted vertically on either side of the joist below the point load. Web stiffeners are also required where the joist rests on a load bearing beam or wall.

HOLES/NOTCHES Steel floor joists usually come with pre-punched holes for plumbing and electrical wiring, and should be installed so that these holes are aligned for easy installation of the mechanical and electrical systems. There are industry-specified requirements for other holes. Joists should not be notched.

BRIDGING/ BLOCKING Floor joists will twist and bounce under load if the tops and bottoms are not properly braced. The top is typically braced by the flooring. The bottoms can be braced with a drywall ceiling for example. Where there is no ceiling, the joist bottoms should be braced every 12 feet. This can be X-bracing, flat straps along the undersides and/or solid blocking.

FRAMING AROUND STAIRS AND CHIMNEYS When the joist pattern is interrupted by openings for stairwells and chimneys for example, reinforcing with headers and trimmers is required, in much the same way it is done with wood framing.

Common Problems with Steel Floor Framing

RUST/ CORROSION Steel framing members in contact with moisture for a prolonged period of time will corrode. This may be an issue in below-grade areas or below roof or plumbing leaks.

OVERSPANNED The span of a steel floor joist depends on its height, width and the gauge of steel used. While there are general guidelines, individual manufacturers have specific requirements.

POOR CONNECTIONS Weak screw connections can be an issue with steel framing.

CONTACT WITH OTHER MATERIALS – DETERIORATION Steel reacts with copper plumbing for example, and should not be in contact with dissimilar metals. Unless special consideration is given, steel framing should not be embedded in concrete.

5.5 Sub-flooring (Also called Floor Sheathing)

DESCRIPTION Sub-flooring transmits the live loads of the people and furnishings to the floor joists. Sub-flooring may be covered with a finish flooring material or may serve as a finish flooring itself.

One-inch thick wood boards were used as sub-flooring until roughly the 1960s. More recently, plywood and waferboard have been used. Thin concrete subfloors are less common.

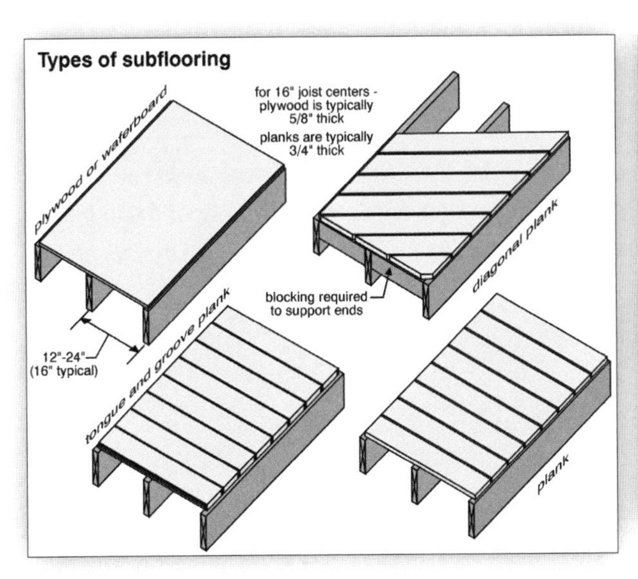

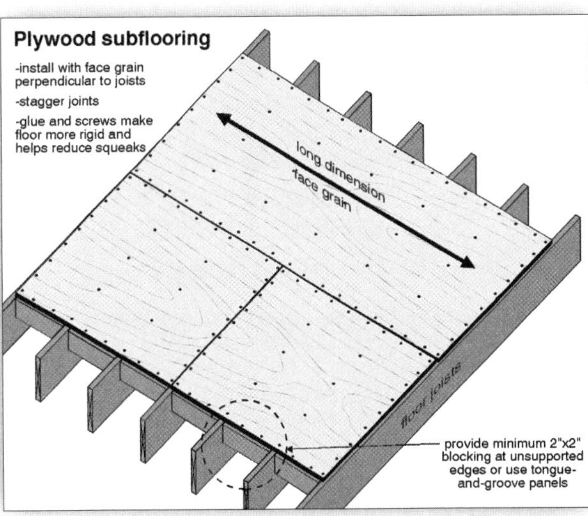

Common Problems with Sub-flooring

SPRINGY FLOORS Subflooring that is too thin will be springy and may fail under concentrated loads (e.g. a piano). This should be overlaid to provide a stiffer subfloor.

SQUEAKY FLOORS Subflooring not adequately secured to the floor joists may be squeaky. The weight of someone walking on a floor will temporarily push the subfloor down onto the joist. When the foot is removed, the subfloor will lift off slightly again. The noise is the nails squeaking as they slide in and out, or pieces of wood rubbing against each other. Solutions to this nuisance include re-nailing, screwing and gluing the subfloor to the joists.

WATER DAMAGE Waferboard subflooring can be damaged by relatively small amounts of water. The board tends to swell, resulting in floor unevenness. The swelling also pulls the nails out of the joists or through the waferboard. Ultimately, the board can lose its strength.

EDGE SUPPORT Diagonal plank subflooring must be supported where it meets the wall. The ends of some of the planks may be several inches from a floor joist and if adequate blocking is not provided, the floor will be weak in this area. Where plywood or waferboard subflooring sheets meet, the joint should be supported by joists, blocking or tongue-and-groove connections between the sheets.

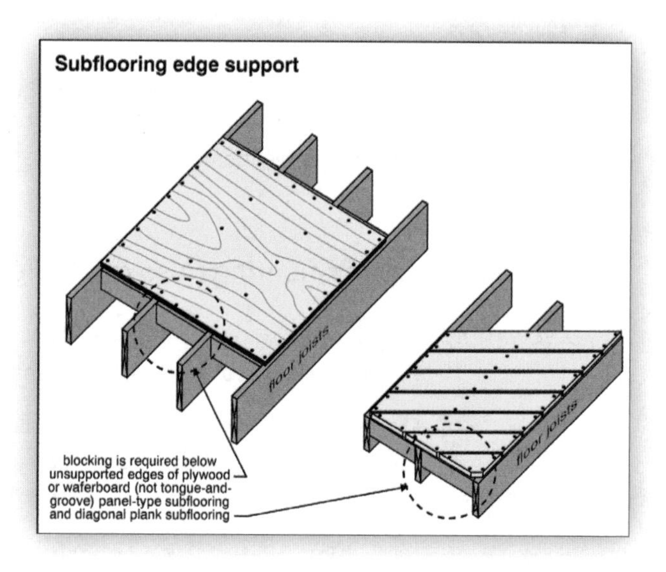

DAMAGE Any subflooring can be mechanically damaged and, unless repairs are made, this can lead to an unsafe situation. A common problem is a hole cut for a heating register that was never installed. If carpet is laid, this may not be noticed until a furniture leg is put on the weak spot. Repairs are, of course, simple and inexpensive.

UNEVEN Uneven subflooring can be a nuisance. Uneven joist installation is a common cause, as is debris on the top of the joists when the subfloor is laid. Swollen waferboard or delaminated plywood can also result in unevenness. Careless joining of tongue-and-groove sheets can lead to surface irregularity.

ROT/INSECT DAMAGE Subflooring is susceptible to rot and insect damage.

5.6 Concrete Floors

DESCRIPTION Concrete floors in homes with basements are usually not structural. Basement and garage floor slabs rest on the ground and are usually poured after the house is built. Modern floors are typically three-inch thick slabs, although old ones may be as thin as 1/2 inch.

Slab-on-grade homes may have concrete floors that are part of the structure.

Common Problems with Concrete Floors

CRACKED/ BROKEN Floors may be cracked or broken. Replacement is not a priority, but is often done to make a basement or garage more usable. Broken utility lines are a possibility with slab movement on slab-on-grade homes. The movement may be settlement or heaving due to expansive soils, for example.

NO SLOPE TO DRAIN Many basement and garage slabs do not slope to drains. Re-sloping is rarely done because it is expensive and the problem of water on a floor is rarely serious.

SUSPENDED SLABS Suspended concrete floors are not common in homes. One exception is concrete porch slabs above cold cellars.

Suspended concrete floors above grade are common in high-rise and commercial buildings, and use steel reinforcing. They are heavier and more expensive than conventional wood floors, but can also be stronger and are more fire resistant. Suspended concrete floor systems are not evaluated during a home inspection.

6.0 Wall Systems

Walls carry the weight of the roof and floors down to the foundations, as well as providing a separation between inside and outside. Walls keep out the wind, rain, heat, cold, and noise, as well as providing us with privacy and support for interior and exterior finishes.

After a home is built, it may be difficult to identify the wall construction.

6.1 Materials

DESCRIPTION **6.1.1 Masonry Walls:** Common materials include brick, stone, concrete block, cinder block, clay tile and glass block. Masonry walls are typically comprised of two four-inch thick wythes (layers) of masonry. The outer wythe is often weather-resistant brick or stone. The inner wythe (layer) may be lower quality brick, concrete block or cinder block. The foundation must be wide enough to carry both layers of masonry.

Mortar used to bind masonry units together is a combination of cement, sand, and water. For more information on brick and mortar, see Section 3.2 in the Exterior chapter.

The masonry units may be exposed or covered with stucco, for example.

IDENTIFICATION In most cases, a solid masonry wall can be identified by the header courses (rows where the brick is turned end-wise to lock the inner and outer wythes of the wall together). This is done every five to seven courses (rows) up the wall. Sometimes every brick in the course is turned end-wise. Often, only every other brick is turned, and sometimes the pattern is random. In most cases, however, there are at least some of the units that are turned in every fifth, sixth or seventh course.

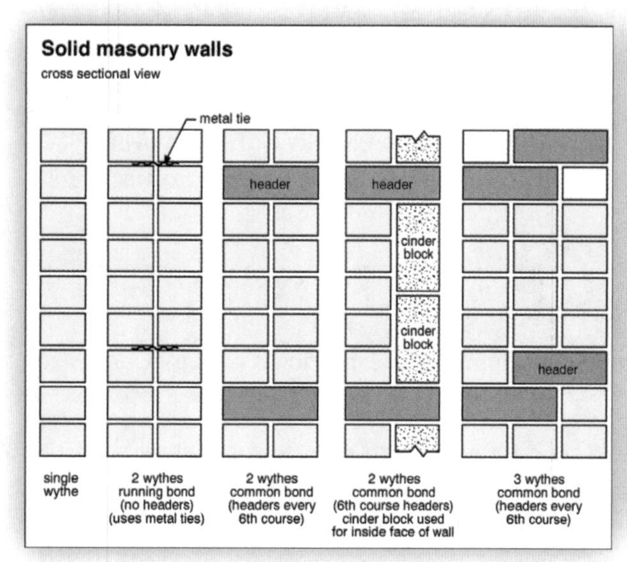

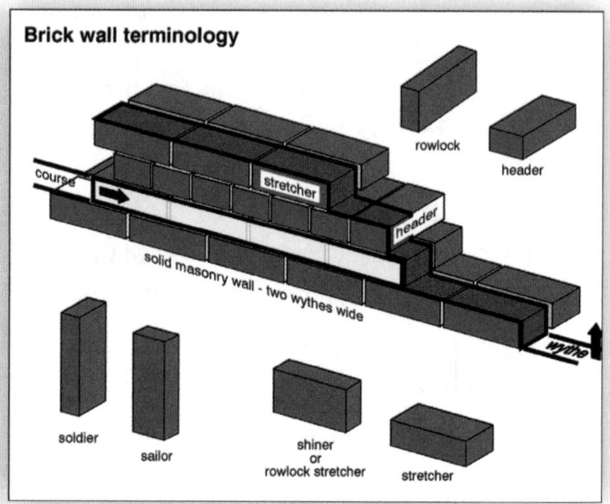

Metal ties or specially sized bricks can also be used to join the inner and outer wythes. In this case the wall will show no header courses, and it will not be apparent that it is a solid masonry wall.

Solid masonry walls have not been commonly used on single-family homes in many areas since the early 1970s. Areas prone to hurricanes are an exception.

Common Problems with Masonry Walls

DETERIORATED The wall may be weakened if the masonry or the mortar deteriorates. This may be the result of poor quality masonry or mortar, chronic moisture exposure or freezing.

CRACKS Cracks in brickwork may appear for several reasons. Cracks are clues, and their size, location, direction and rate of growth are all indicators of what is happening. Generally speaking, cracks through mortar joints are less serious than cracks through the brick or block, but there are exceptions.

LEAN/BOW Where the inner and outer wythes are not adequately secured together, the outer wythes can lean or bow outwards. The entire brick wall may lean or bow due to foundation settlement or the wall not having adequate lateral support. Walls may also be pushed out of plumb by vehicle impact, for example. If a wall leans, the ultimate danger is that it may fall. The more immediate danger, however, is that the rafters and joists resting on the wall may slip off as the wall moves out away from the building. Since the ends of joists may only rest on the wall by an inch or two, a little movement can create an unsafe situation. If joists or rafters slip off their supports, the framing system will collapse.

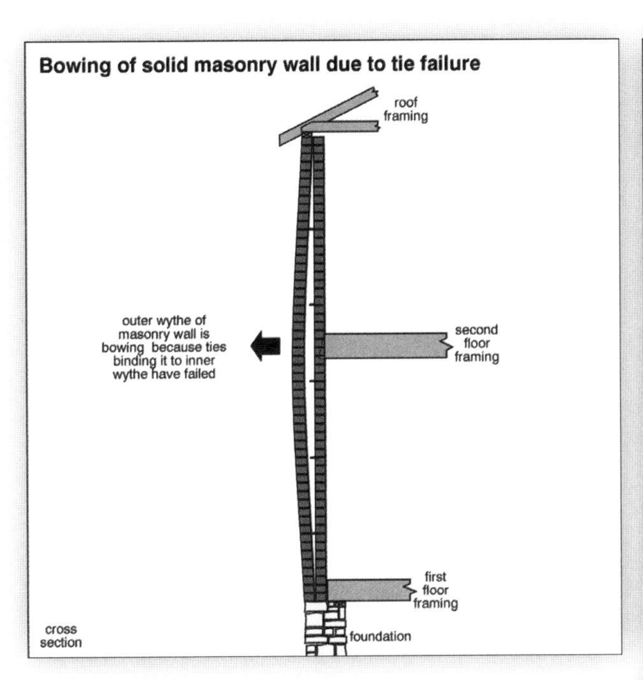

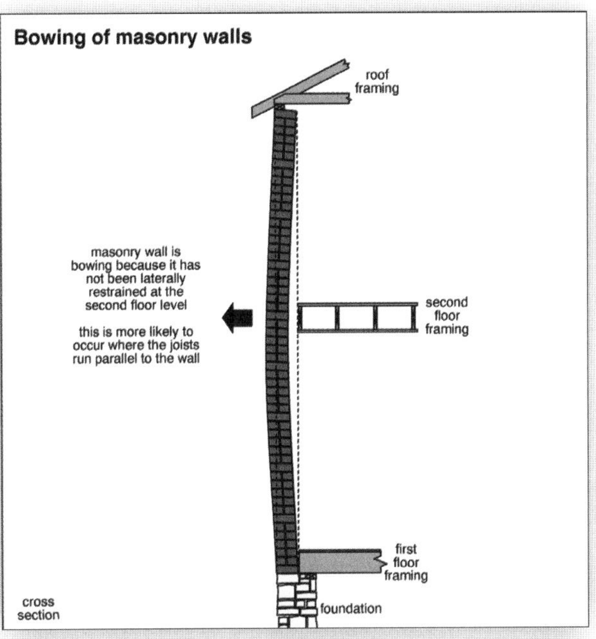

RAFTER SPREAD Spreading roof rafters may push the top of the walls out, resulting in an unstable situation.

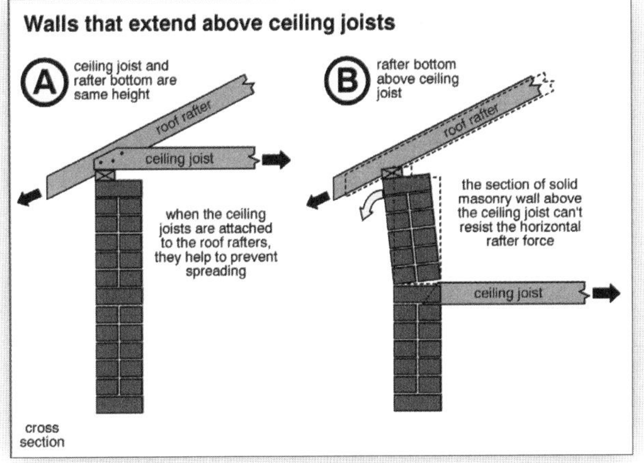

EXCESS CORBELLING Brick can be corbelled (offset) only about one inch beyond the brick below (i.e. one brick does not have to be set exactly on top of another). However, the total corbelling must not exceed one-third of the wall thickness to maintain stability.

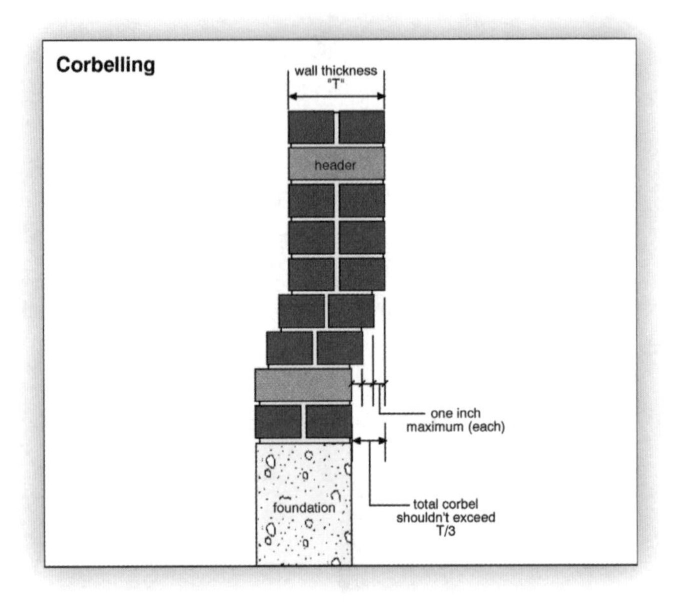

DESCRIPTION **6.1.2 Wood Frame Walls:** Load-bearing wood frame walls may be interior or exterior walls.

Some stud walls are load-bearing, others are not. Bearing walls should have a double top plate. Non-bearing stud walls may have only a single top plate. A single sole plate (also called sill plate or bottom plate) is provided in either case. None of this is visible once the home is finished.

Historically, 2x4 studs have been used, spaced 16 inches on center, although more recently, 2x6 exterior wall studs have become common as they provide more space for insulation between the studs.

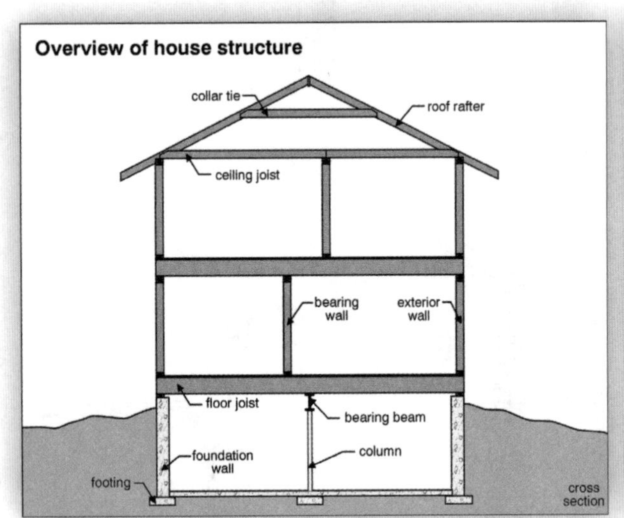

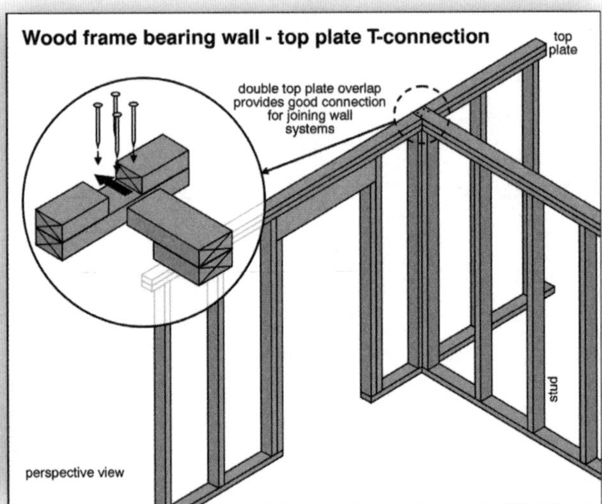

Common Problems with Wood Frame Walls

Rot, insect attack, mechanical damage, poor quality lumber, poor connections, design mistakes, poor workmanship and excessive spacing can all be problems.

POOR NAILING AND OPENING Inadequate nailing can lead to difficulties. Openings in walls may not be adequately framed. Wall sections above large openings for picture windows, for example, may sag if the openings are not bridged with appropriate support headers (some call these lintels).

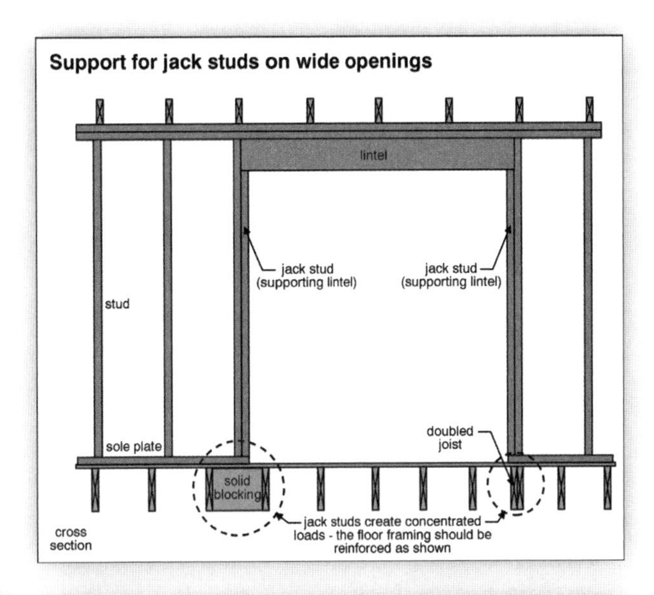

NOTCHES AND HOLES Holes and notches can weaken studs if they are too large. The illustrations below provide some guidelines.

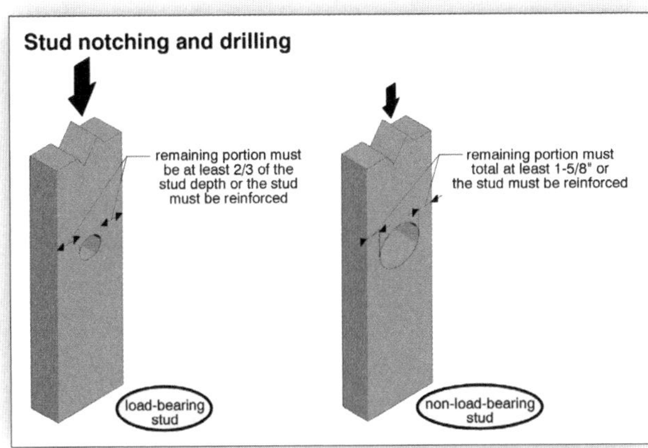

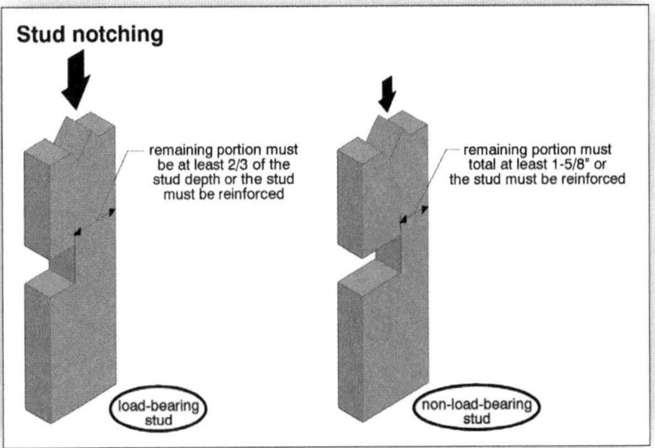

BUCKLING Some wood stud walls are susceptible to buckling under loads. This is particularly true if the walls are not braced with girts (blocking between studs near the mid-point) or if interior or exterior finishes are not provided. If finish is provided on one side of the wall, girts are not required.

Longer studs are more susceptible to buckling. This is easy to understand if you hold both ends of a yardstick and try and push the ends toward each other. The yardstick buckles very easily in the middle. This is more difficult with a six-inch ruler of the same material.

Where another floor level is to be added to a home, special consideration should be given to stud walls, which may not be strong enough to carry the added weight.

CONDENSATION IN COLD CLIMATES Rot or mold caused by condensation in exterior walls is a concern, especially where insulation is upgraded in older houses, and without effective air/vapor barriers. This cannot be detected during a visual inspection and it may be a long time before the damage is noticed. In some cases, peeling exterior paint suggests that wall condensation is a problem.

This is typically a seasonal problem in cold climates, with the condensation occurring during the winter months only. Warm moist air enters the wall from the house. As it passes through, the air cools. Cool air cannot hold as much water vapor as warm air. Condensation forms inside the wall as the air cools and gives off its water.

LOW QUALITY LUMBER Poor quality studs or studs that warp and bow can lead to uneven wall surfaces in new homes. The bowed or twisted studs have to be repaired or replaced.

GREEN LUMBER Building with lumber that is too wet or "green" can result in problems such as shrinking, warping, or bowing.

DESCRIPTION **6.1.2.1 Balloon Framing:** Balloon framing was common in the late 19th and early 20th centuries. This wood-frame construction technique used conventional studs and floor joists. However, the wall studs were continuous from the foundation up to the roof line. The construction process involves setting up the wall studs, and then hanging the floor systems from them. When completed, this resulted in a rigid structure. One disadvantage is that a fire can move very quickly up through the continuous stud spaces.

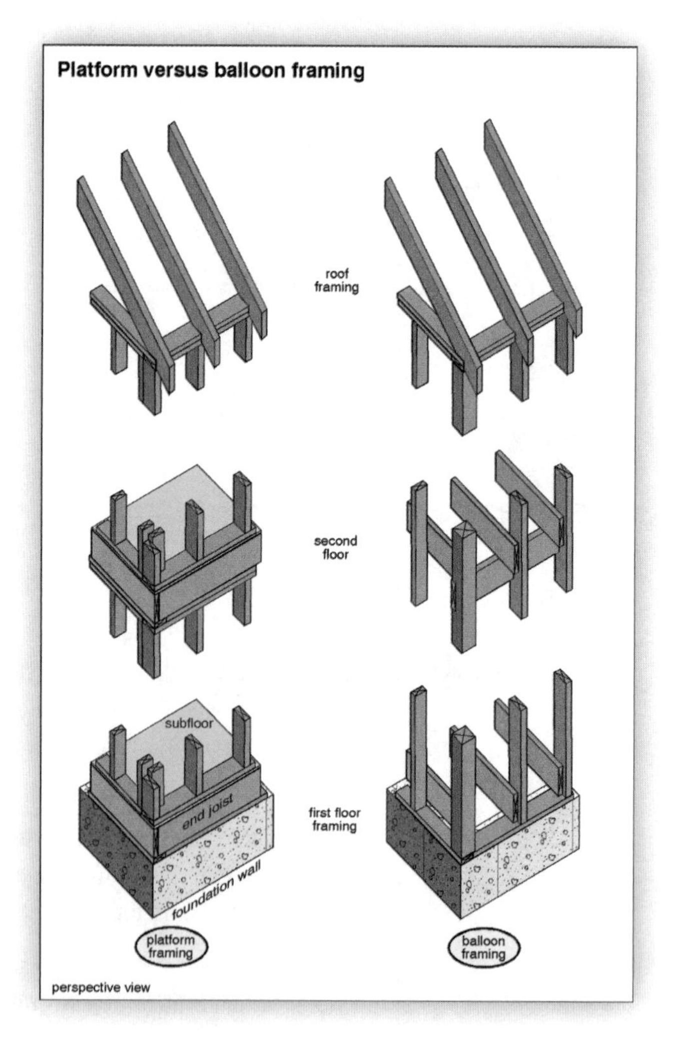

DESCRIPTION **6.1.2.2 Platform Framing:** Platform or Western framing is slightly different. A wood floor joist and subfloor system is provided on top of the foundations. One-story stud walls are built on the floor. If the house is two stories, a second floor platform is assembled on top of the studs, and then a second stud wall is built on top of this platform. This can be extended up to form a three-story house as well. The advantages of platform framing are ease of installation and lower material costs.

DESCRIPTION **6.1.3 Steel Frame:** Steel frame walls may be load-bearing, carrying the weight of the roof and floors down to the foundations. They may be interior or exterior walls. Steel frame walls may also be used as non-load-bearing partition walls. While wood framing members have traditionally dominated residential construction, the use of lightweight steel framing is increasing.

Structural framing elements are generally either C-shaped or U-shaped. C-shaped elements are designed as load-bearing elements, such as studs and joists, while the U-shaped pieces are tracks, or channels that hold the load-bearing components in place. In steel construction, tracks replace the sills and top plates used in wood-frame construction. Non-load-bearing walls are typically thinner, but are otherwise similar to load-bearing walls.

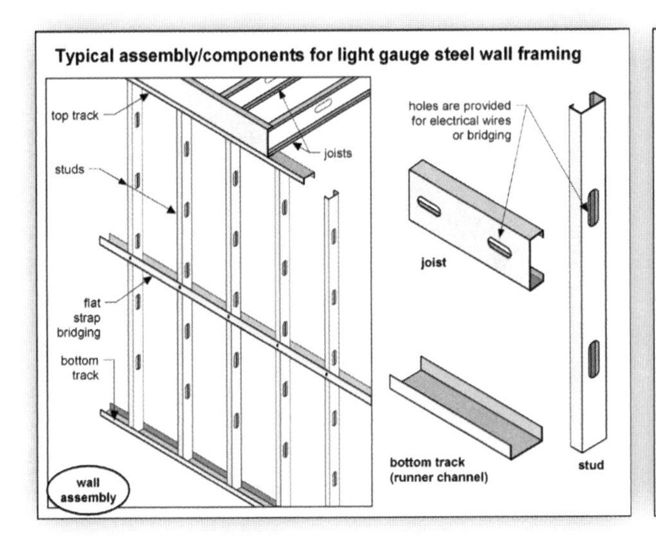

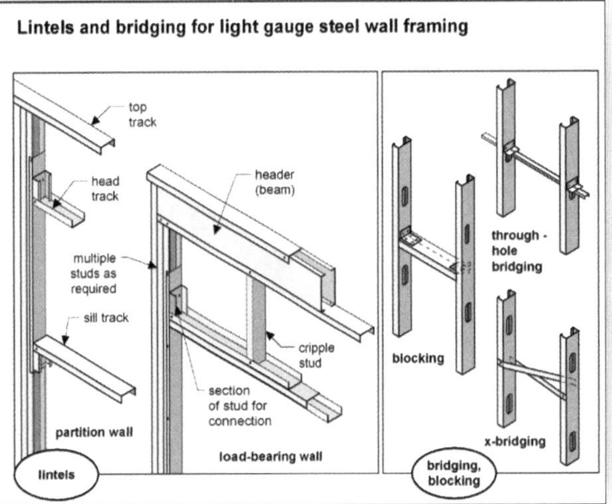

Common Problems with Steel Frame Walls

THERMAL BRIDGING As steel is much more conductive to heat than wood, the thermal efficiency of steel-framed walls is much less than that of a wood-framed wall. Steel framed walls may have half the insulating value of wood walls. The thermal bridges created by steel studs can be reduced through the use of insulated sheathing on the outside of the studs, and with the use of wider stud spacing.

CORROSION Some older steel frame walls did not adequately deal with thermal bridging issues, leading to condensation and corrosion of the steel studs. Corrosion may be an issue whenever there is a condensation or water leakage problem.

IMPROPER HOLES Steel studs usually come with pre-punched holes for plumbing and electrical wiring and should be installed so that these holes are aligned for easy installation of the mechanical and electrical systems. There are industry-specified requirements for other holes. Improper holes can weaken the wall.

REINFORCEMENT MISSING/ INADEQUATE Wood nailing strips are often required to allow door jambs and other trim to be nailed to the framing. Finishing screws may be used instead of nails. Walls have to be reinforced in some areas, such as when cabinets are to be secured to non-load-bearing steel studs.

DESCRIPTION **6.1.4 Brick/Stone Veneer:** A brick or stone veneer wall has a structural wood (or metal) frame inner wall, and a four-inch thick masonry outer section (veneer), which does not have any load-bearing responsibility. Typically, metal ties are used to secure the masonry to the wood frame wall, and there are no header courses in the masonry. The absence of headers identifies a veneer wall in most cases. Most solid masonry walls have headers.

Veneer walls have been the most common masonry walls in single-family homes in many parts of America since about 1970.

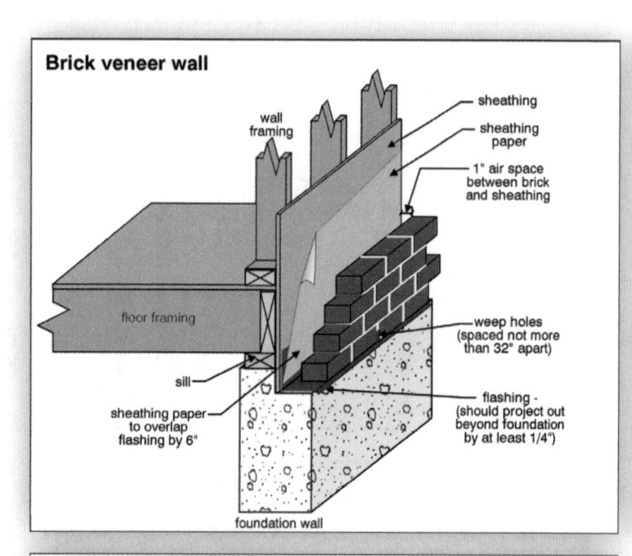

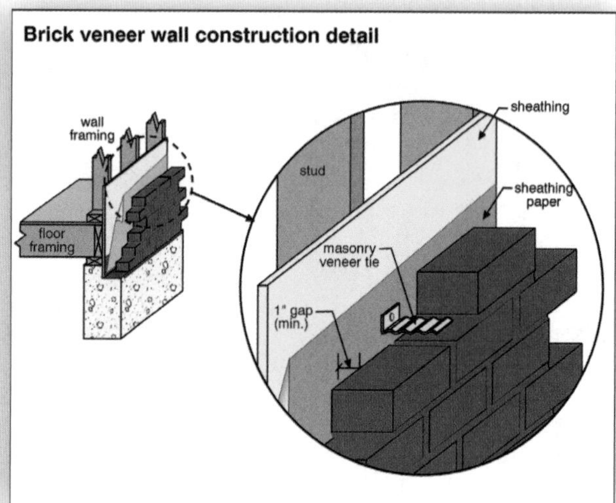

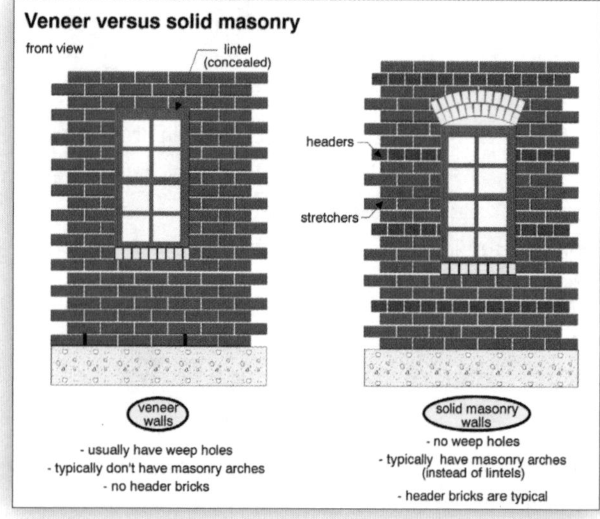

RAIN SCREEN PRINCIPLE Since the early 1970s, veneer walls have had weep holes provided at the bottom. A modern veneer wall uses a rain screen principle. This anticipates that wind driven rain will pass through a masonry wall, and as a result, a one-inch air space separates the masonry and the wood stud wall. Water runs down the inner face of the brick or the outer surface of the sheathing and drains out the bottom.

At the bottom row of masonry, every fourth vertical mortar joint (typically) is left open. A flashing at the bottom of the wall cavity directs water out through the weep holes. The flashing prevents the water from entering the foundation. Weep holes are also used above door and window openings.

Weep holes also allow pressure balancing on either side of the masonry. The air in the cavity behind the masonry is pressurized as wind blows against the wall, reducing the pressure differential across the masonry. This reduces the amount of water driven through.

A variation on weep holes is rope wicks in every fourth mortar joint in the bottom row of masonry. Where weep holes or wicks are noted, the wall is masonry veneer.

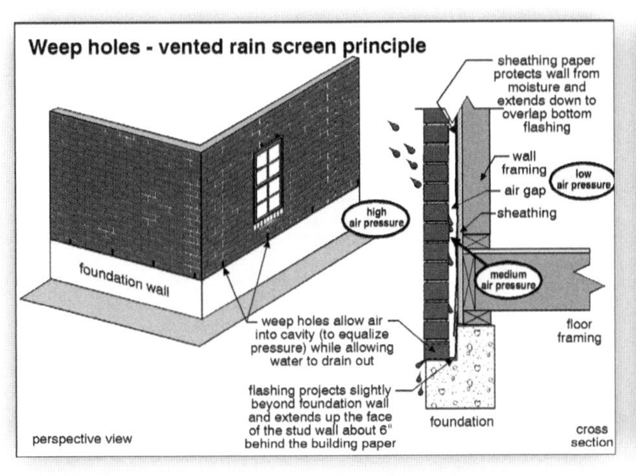

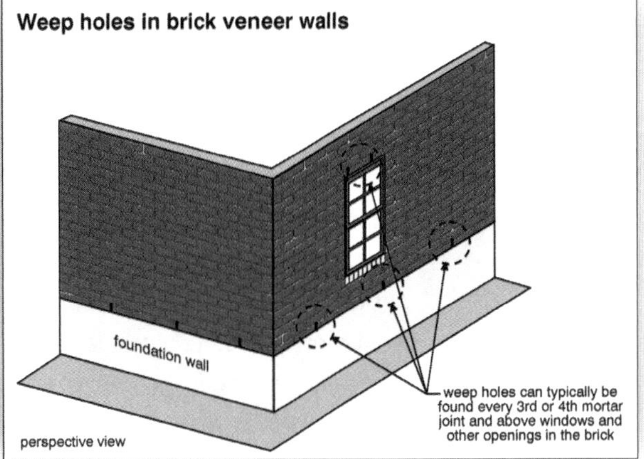

Common Problems with Brick or Stone Veneer Walls

FOUNDATIONS/ CONNECTIONS Although the veneer has no load-bearing responsibilities, it must sit on a foundation built to support the weight of the brick or stone. If the foundation is not substantial, the veneer wall may crack and/or settle away from the wood-frame wall. If the veneer is inadequately tied to the wood-frame wall, the masonry may bulge or pull away. This is an unsafe condition.

DETERIORATED Deteriorated masonry or mortar can lead to serious problems. In the worst cases, the veneer wall has to be rebuilt. Most brick is not designed to be in contact with the soil, and should be kept well above grade.

WEEP HOLES If weep holes are filled or omitted, water can collect in the wall cavity, damaging the sheathing and studs.

FLASHING Similar results occur if the flashing is inappropriate or the space between the masonry and sheathing is filled. The flashing cannot normally be seen during an inspection.

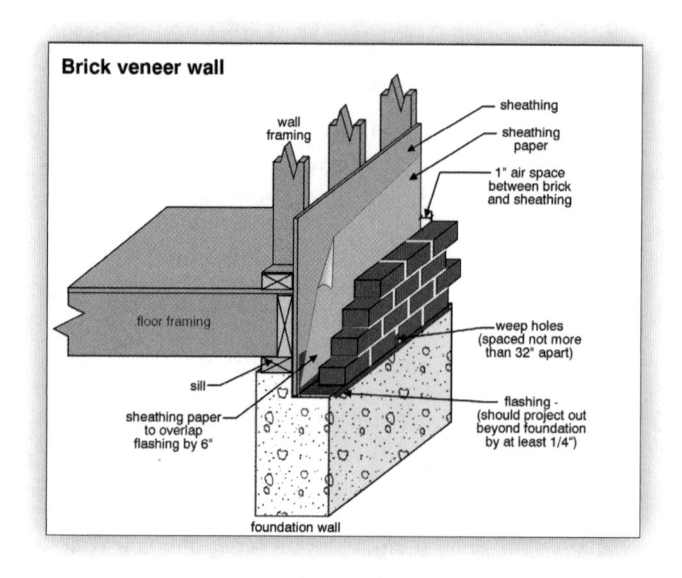

CORBELLING Excessive corbelling can make a wall unstable. (See Section 6.1.1)

METAL ANGLES In some cases, the masonry veneer is supported on steel angles bolted to the foundation. If there is any movement at all, the masonry may crack, bulge, or pull away from the wall behind.

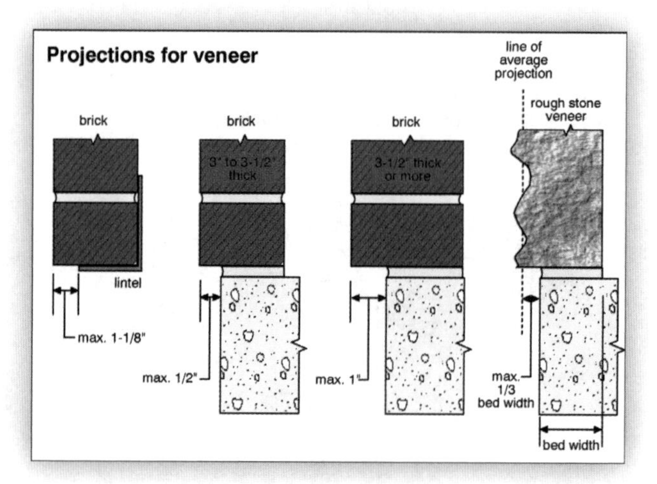

DESCRIPTION **6.1.5 Insulating Concrete Forms (ICFs):** Insulating Concrete Forms (ICFs) are either panels or interlocking blocks that are joined together to create formwork for concrete. The forms themselves are made out of insulation, either rigid foam, such as polystyrene, or a combination of concrete and foam insulation or wood chips. Plastic ties may be used to hold the inner and outer forms together. Once the forms are in place, concrete is poured into the forms, filling the spaces. Rather than remove the forms, as in conventional concrete work, they are left in place to act as insulation.

ICF walls are also used as foundation walls.

After a home is built, it may be difficult to identify the wall construction.

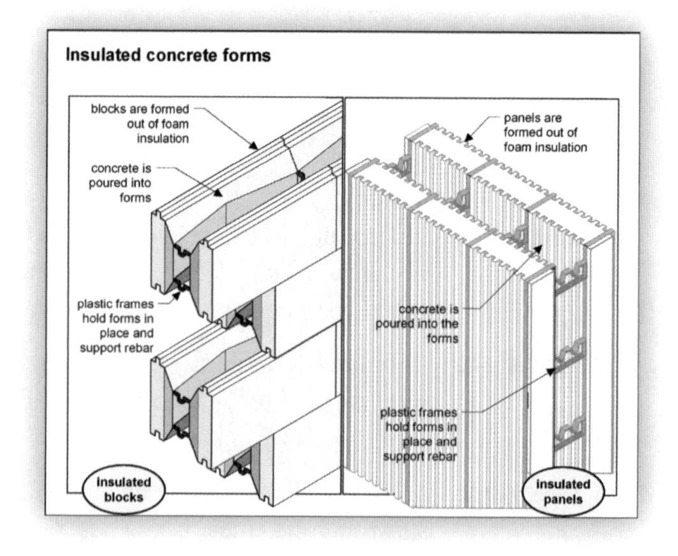

INSULATION ICF walls typically provide a total R-value of 22, about the same as a 2x6 stud wall. These walls also avoid thermal bridges (areas of high thermal conductivity) that are common in wood stud walls. ICF walls are also airtight, which is good for energy performance.

REINFORCEMENT ICF walls may include vertical and/or horizontal steel reinforcing bar, especially around window and door openings.

LEDGERS Where floors meet ICF walls, they may either rest on a sill plate on the top of the ICF wall, or bear on a ledger board secured to the ICF.

OPENINGS In most cases, wood framing is attached to the ICF at door and window openings to allow window frames and door jambs to be secured.

ELECTRICAL WIRING Electrical wiring and outlets generally require the inside form to be cut away. The shallow depth of the form means that wiring may require protection from mechanical damage, and receptacles need shallow boxes.

Common Problems with ICF Walls

WOOD DESTROYING INSECTS While polystyrene is not a food source for pests, some wood-destroying insects will nest in, or travel through, the foam. Some ICF products contain chemical protection, and some ICF installations use mechanical barriers to protect against infestation.

RENOVATIONS It is more difficult to create a new opening or alter an existing opening in an ICF wall than a wood frame wall because of the poured concrete.

6.1.6 Other Kinds of Walls

DESCRIPTION **6.1.6.1 Log:** Modern log homes utilize precisely cut logs, keyed together, with gaskets between logs, while older log structures are much rougher.

SIDINGS Many older log homes were covered with wood sheathing such as clapboard on the exterior as soon as the homeowners could afford it. Stucco was also used on the exterior in some cases and plaster was often applied on the interior. Some old log homes look quite different than they did when they were built. The foundations were typically stone, and wood shingles or shakes were often the roofing material.

CHINKING Chinking was traditionally used to fill the gaps between the logs. This was typically a mortar made of clay, sand and binders such as animal hair. Where gaps were large, stones would often be fitted in before the chinking was applied. Due to the considerable movement due to expansion and contraction of logs across the grain, chinking usually had to be redone every year, at least in part.

Common Problems with Log Walls

WOOD SHRINKAGE Traditional log construction today is a relatively expensive way to build. Further, wood tends to shrink and expand with changes in moisture content much more across the grain than it does with the grain. A log wall grows shorter as the wood dries and taller when the wood is wet. A wood stud wall will shrink and expand much less because the wood grain is vertical rather than horizontal.

If wood changes its moisture content from 19% to 5% (typical in a house), its length may change by 0.1% along the grain, but its width may shrink by 2.5% across the grain. This means an eight-foot long stud may only shrink 1/10 inch, while a stack of logs eight feet high may shrink by 2-1/2 inches. This can be a significant problem with windows, doors and other building components attached to a log wall.

CHINKING Regular maintenance is required in chinking the gaps between the logs in traditional log homes. The modern materials now available perform much better.

ROT/INSECT DAMAGE Rot is a common problem with logs at the bottom of the wall (where they may have been in contact with earth) on old homes. This is not likely to be a problem with modern log houses built on conventional modern foundations. Log homes are susceptible to insect damage, of course.

CONCEALED DAMAGE Where the logs have been covered with siding, concealed water damage is possible.

DESCRIPTION **6.1.6.2 Post and Beam:** This type of construction, with wood members much larger than conventional wood-frame construction, is not common, although it can be found on older country properties and was commonly utilized for barns, mills, churches and other large buildings. There are prefabricated kits available. Other names for this type of construction include timber, heavy timber or semi-mill construction.

This building style uses a small number of large wood beams and posts. This is very different from conventional framing that uses a large number of smaller wood studs and joists to carry the loads down to the foundations.

Traditionally, the heavy posts and beams were solid wood. In homes built today, built up or glue-laminated beams and posts are also used. In the original versions, the heavy wood posts were often flared out at the top to increase strength. A feature of these homes was the way the wood sections were connected. Very sophisticated mortise and tenon connections were utilized, as were dovetail joints. Many of the homes were assembled without nails, wood dowels often being used in their place.

The walls were often 2-inch thick planks, installed horizontally or vertically. In some cases these were load bearing, although for the most part they simply provided a weather tight skin.

These houses were expensive to build both in terms of materials and labor. Large pieces of good quality lumber have become harder to obtain. Because the wood components were very heavy, and sophisticated joint connections were used, construction was labor intensive.

Common Problems with Post and Beam Walls

LACK OF RIGIDITY Since the skeleton consisted of a few large components and relatively few connections, rigidity could be a problem, particularly where the sheathing did not perform a stabilizing function. Because of the intricacy of some of the connections, there was a good deal of room for error, and a poor understanding of load transmissions could lead to connection failures.

EXPANSION/ CONTRACTION The very large timbers undergo significant dimensional changes with changes in moisture content. These buildings are not static, expanding and contracting with changes in humidity. As timbers dried out, checking often developed. Checks are longitudinal cracks, parallel to the grain that widen as they get further from the heartwood. In many cases, this is not a structural concern, although a large check running horizontally through a beam does reduce its load carrying capacity. Where continuous checking in a post could lead to buckling, steel clamps are provided around the posts.

FOUNDATION Because of the skeletal nature of the framing, large concentrated loads were carried to the ground. Foundation systems were often too weak in areas of concentrated loads, and much stronger than they had to be in other areas.

CONNECTIONS These buildings rely on relatively few connections. Poorly made connections or damage by rot or insects can be more serious than on frame construction.

SPECIALIZED INSPECTION Since this type of construction is specialized, and not seen frequently, local authorities and professional home inspectors may not be familiar with it. In some cases, a specialist is engaged to comment on post and beam structures.

REPAIR Repair or replacement of components of post and beam construction is often difficult without compromising the aesthetic or architectural appeal of the home. The strength of structural components must be demonstrated using engineering calculations, rather than tables.

DESCRIPTION **6.1.6.3 Panelized:** Panelized describes a method of construction, rather than a specific system. In traditional framing, the individual components of the house, such as studs, joists and rafters, are brought to the site and the house is built from individual pieces. In panelized construction, large panels are built off-site, then assembled on-site and secured to the foundation. These panels may make up the floors, walls, ceilings and roofs of the home.

There are varying degrees of panelization. Panels may be simple structural sections, or they may include siding, insulation, wiring and even interior finishes. Panelized construction may utilize wood framing, steel framing, or a combination of the two. The panels often include upgraded insulation treatment and less thermal bridging than found in conventional construction.

Once the home is constructed, there is generally very little difference between a site-built home and a panelized home, although manufacturers maintain that the better working environment and quality control possible in a factory, results in better built homes.

DESCRIPTION **6.1.6.4 Structural Insulated Panels (SIP):** Structural Insulated Panels (SIPs) are one type of panelized construction. SIPs include the structural member, insulation, air barrier and exterior sheathing. These types of panels are sometimes called stress-skin panels because the wood outer layers act like the flanges of a steel I-beam. The insulation acts as the web. We end up with a strong structural member without using a lot of material.

Structural Insulated Panels are typically 3 1/2 to 5 1/2 inches of expanded polystyrene insulation sandwiched between 4-foot by 8-foot plywood or oriented strandboard (OSB) panels. The insulation is typically 1 1/2 inches smaller than the skin at the top and bottom, so the panels can receive sill plates and top plates. Some panels have recesses in the insulation at the sides to accept plywood or OSB pieces to join adjacent panels.

ELECTRICAL WIRING Many panels include hollow chases in the insulation to accommodate electrical wiring. Foam has to be removed to make room for electrical boxes.

OTHER MATERIALS Similar products are also made, replacing the wood with steel, aluminum, concrete and fiberglass. Insulation materials are most often expanded polystyrene, but can be polyurethane or other materials.

Common Problems with Panelized Walls

Rot, insect attack, mechanical damage, fire damage can all be problems with wooden components.

WOOD DESTROYING INSECTS While polystyrene is not a food source for pests, some wood-destroying insects will nest in, or travel through, the foam. Some SIP products contain chemical protection, and some SIP installations use mechanical barriers to protect against infestation.

DESCRIPTION **6.1.6.5 Rammed Earth:** As the name would suggest earth, or soil, is the primary component of a rammed earth wall. Native soil can sometimes be used, but a screened engineered soil is most often used. Ideal soils are about three parts sand to one part clay.

Forms are constructed on conventional foundations. The forms have plumbing pipes and electrical conduit placed prior to pouring the soil. A thick mixture of earth, cement and water is poured into the forms in layers (typically 8 inches thick). There is typically less than 5% cement and 5 to 10% water mixed into the soil. Each layer is compacted (to about five inches), and another layer is then added and compacted. Pneumatic tampers are typically used to compact the soil in the forms. The process is repeated until the wall is complete. An alternative approach uses a pump to shoot the mixture into one-sided forms with air pressure.

When the forms are removed, a rough surface is presented. This can be an architectural feature, or the walls can be covered with plaster on the interior and stucco on the exterior. Finished walls are typically 12 to 18 inches thick.

Common Problems with Rammed Earth Walls

POOR INSULATION Rammed earth homes are less practical in northern climates where the thermal mass of the walls does not provide good insulating performance. The insulating value of an 18-inch thick wall may be R-4 or R-5, well below modern standards in cold climates.

MOISTURE Like many building systems, moisture is the enemy. While rammed earth walls are not damaged by occasional moisture, durability may be an issue in wet climates. Some types of soil are also more moisture-resistant than others. Exterior sealants are used in some cases to protect the earth walls from moisture. Large roof overhangs and raised foundations help keep the walls dry.

DAMAGE Mechanical or moisture damage may result in missing or loose sections of the wall covering or the wall itself. Areas close to grade may be more vulnerable.

WINDOW SILLS Windows may be installed close to the interior or exterior wall face. From a performance standpoint, windows close to the exterior surface are preferred, since this eliminates a wide exterior window sill that will trap water.

DESCRIPTION **6.1.6.6 Straw Bale:** Straw bale walls can be load bearing structural members, carrying the second floor and roof loads, or the bales may fill in between or wrap around a wood post and beam frame. In either case, the bales provide the insulation as well as the base for interior and exterior finishes.

Straw is the stalk of grains such as wheat, barley, rye, oats and rice. Straw should not be confused with hay, which is grass that is food for horses! Horses would not appreciate being fed straw. Straw is generally considered a waste by-product of agriculture and a nuisance because it is slow to decompose.

Straw bales used for building weigh 50 to 90 pounds each. Small bales may be 14 inches by 18 inches by 36 inches. The largest bales may be 18 inches by 24 inches by 48 inches. The walls are typically 13 to 24 inches thick plus the thickness of the finishes on the inside and outside.

Bale walls sit on conventional foundations that, with some exceptions, should be as wide as the bales. There is usually a moisture barrier between the top of the foundation and the first row of bales. Vertical steel reinforcing bar (re-bar) projects 12 inches out the top of the foundation to secure the bales to the foundation. The re-bar is typically 1/2 inch diameter and is placed in the center of the foundation, every two feet along the wall length, and within 12 inches of all corners.

The bales are stacked like large bricks into a wall configuration, and are sometimes connected to each other with steel rebar, or wood or bamboo stakes. Water pipes in the bales are installed in continuous sleeves to protect the bales from damage due to leakage.

Stucco over wire mesh is the typical finish outside, and it can be used as the inside finish as well. Lime or clay based plasters may be applied directly to the interior of the straw bales without reinforcement. The inner plaster and outer stucco finishes add strength and rigidity, making the wall a stress skin panel.

STUCCO Exterior stucco should breathe. Stuccos with lime tend to be more permeable and allow walls to dry to the outside. Other stuccos are less permeable and do not allow moisture vapor to pass through. This restricts the drying potential of the wall, and may lead to mold or rot in the bales. Elastomeric stuccos like Exterior Insulation and Finishing Systems (EIFS) for example, are also impermeable and do not promote drying.

Common Problems with Straw Bale Walls

FIRE Fire vulnerability is roughly the same as for wood frame walls. Fire is actually less of a problem with straw bale than wood frame because it is harder to ignite. Straw bale walls do not have the natural chimneys that occur in wood frame walls. However, once the fire is established, straw bales contribute more fuel than wood frame construction. The slower-to-ignite issue may be more important for occupant safety.

ROT Straw bale walls are vulnerable to moisture problems, like most other exterior walls. Straw bale homes with flat roofs may be more prone to failure due to water damage from the roof. Flat roofs often accumulate water, and a leaking roof may provide a chronic water source into the walls.

BELOW GRADE Straw bale walls should be built well above grade level to prevent moisture damage. Raised foundations help keep the bales dry. Large roof overhangs also help keep the walls dry.

CRACKS Cracks in the stucco and any openings around wall penetrations are vulnerable points. The goal is to keep the moisture out of the home. Moisture content is usually limited to 20%. Some straw bale houses have moisture meters built in to monitor moisture levels in the bales.

DESCRIPTION **6.1.7 Party Walls:** Party walls or common walls separate two homes in the same building. Their main function is to prevent the spread of fire from one home to the next.

MASONRY Masonry party walls provide relatively good fire protection between the two houses, although they don't block sound very well.

WOOD-FRAME Wood-frame partition walls provide less fire protection, although they can be better from an acoustic standpoint. Some party walls are masonry part of the way up through the house, and wood-frame in the attic.

Common Problems with Party Walls

NONE IN ATTIC In some attached houses, there is no wall between the attic areas. This space can allow fire to spread quickly from one home to another. Modern construction rules do not permit this arrangement.

6.2 Arches and Headers (Headers are also called Lintels)

DESCRIPTION Arches and headers transfer the load above an opening in a masonry wall to the wall sections on either side.

LOADS IN MASONRY WALLS The arch or header supports a triangular section of masonry above the arch. The height of the triangle is roughly half the width of the opening. This means that a window with twenty stories of brick above requires only the same arch as a window with six feet of brick above.

There are several types of arches. Stone, brick and concrete are the most common materials used. Segmental arches are the most common, made up of several pieces. The arch typically has a rise of at least one inch for each foot of its span.

Jack arches have flat tops and bottoms and are often decorative but not functional. Steel headers typically support the arch. This is not a common type of arch.

Some arches have a larger masonry unit at the top/center. This is called a keystone, and is often the architectural focus of an arch and window system.

Headers are typically flat, and use the inherent strength of the material to transmit the load, rather than the arch principle. Headers (called lintels in some areas) may be steel, wood, stone or concrete.

Headers are made of a single piece, where arches are built from several pieces.

Common Problems with Arches and Headers

TOO FLAT OR TOO NARROW Failure in arches is common where the rise is very modest, or the arch is not quite wide enough to clearly span the opening. Another common problem with arches is slight movement of the walls on either side. This is particularly common where a window or door opening is close to the end of a wall. On one side of the arch, there may not be enough mass to resist the lateral thrust of the arch transferring its load to the wall beside. As the thin section of wall pushes outward, the arch drops.

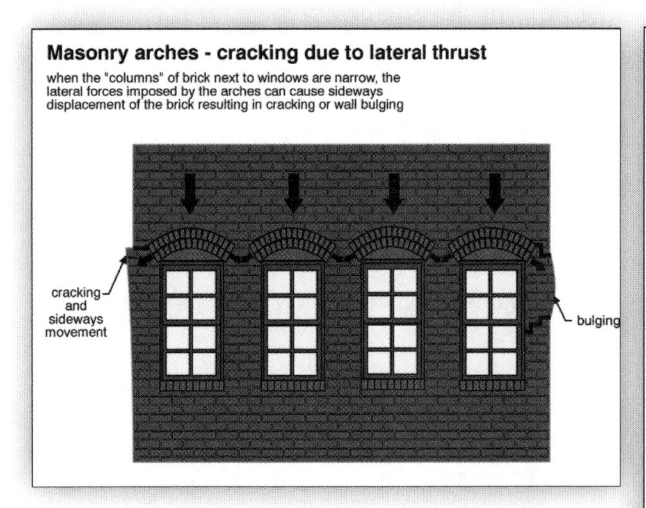

DETERIORATION/ LEANING Mortar or masonry deterioration can, of course, lead to failure. Building settlement may allow the arch to open up and drop. Another problem is forward movement of the arch out away from the building. This is usually caused by foundation movement or mortar and masonry deterioration. Corrective actions include rebuilding the arch or adding a header.

UNDERSIZED/ POOR END BEARING Headers may be undersized for the load. Inadequate end bearing of the headers may lead to failure. Steel headers (lintels) on masonry walls should extend at least six inches beyond the opening on either side. This cannot usually be seen.

RUST/ROT/ SPALLING / CRACKING Steel lintels are subject to rust. The rusting steel expands and may cause horizontal cracks in the mortar joints at the corners of the opening. Wood headers are susceptible to rot and insect attack. Concrete and stone headers are subject to cracking or spalling.

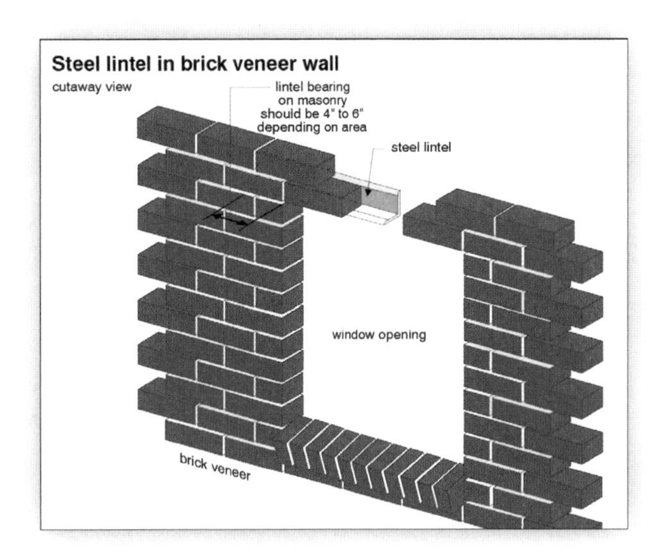

MISSING In amateurish construction projects, windows may be added to masonry walls or brick veneer walls with no arch or header provided. This will often work in the short term, but problems usually develop over time. Missing or inadequate headers should be replaced.

CAULKING Steel headers (lintels) supporting brick veneer should have no caulking between the steel and the brick above. Caulking may trap water and rust the steel.

7.0 Roof Framing

DESCRIPTION The roof framing is an assembly of wood or steel components. The roof framing ties the building together, adding rigidity and providing a surface for the roof covering. The roof framing also supports the ceiling finishes below. We will look at the individual components of roof framing systems.

7.1 Rafters – Wood

DESCRIPTION Rafters carry the loads from the roof sheathing, roof covering, wind, water, snow and ice. These loads are transmitted through the rafters to bearing walls or beams below. The term rafter is associated with sloped roofs. When these members are found on a flat roof, they are horizontal and called roof joists, although they do the same job.

Rafters can usually be seen overhead when standing in the attic. Some rafters support finished ceilings, creating a cathedral ceiling. In this case, insulation is often fit between the rafters.

Wood rafters are typically 2x4s, 2x6s or 2x8s, spaced 16 to 24 inches on center. Conventional rafters have been replaced by trusses in most modern home construction. The engineered trusses can span greater distances less expensively than conventional rafters.

When calculating the span of a rafter system, the horizontal span rather than the actual length of the rafter is used. Knee walls or purlins may provide intermediate support, reducing the span. Collar ties help keep rafters in place. Ceiling joists are horizontal members that often tie the bottoms of opposing rafters together, making a strong triangle.

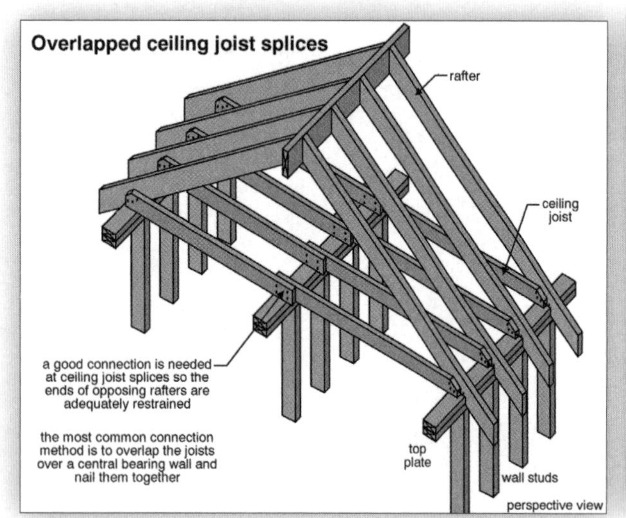

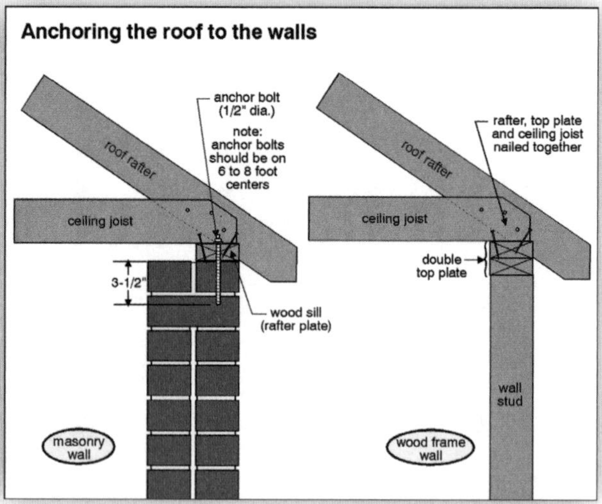

Common Problems with Wood Rafters

OVERSPANNED/ RAFTER SPREAD If rafters are overspanned or spaced too far apart, the roof will sag. If rafters are not adequately secured to the walls at the bottom edge, the rafters may spread apart. This is common on older houses, particularly with gable roofs. It is often noted at the eaves, because the soffits pull away from the house wall as the rafters spread. In other cases, the spreading rafters push the top of the wall outward. This can be very serious.

Rafters may also separate at the roof ridge if connections and support are poor.

ROT/INSECT DAMAGE/SPLIT Wood rafters are susceptible to rot, insect, fire and mechanical damage. Rafters may split under load.

CONDENSATION LEADS TO ROT Attics in cold climates with good insulation but poor ventilation may be susceptible to condensation problems. Condensation will attack the roof sheathing and the rafters. Left unchecked, this can lead to roof structure failure. Corrective action includes improved ventilation and replacing damaged wood. Mold often develops in attics as a result of condensation.

SAG–CONCENTRATED LOADS Concentrated loads may be a problem around roof dormers. The load from a dormer is transferred to the rafters on either side of the dormer. Unless these rafters are strengthened, the roof may sag around dormers.

In cold climates, roofs may fail because of a concentrated snow load. Split-level houses are susceptible to this problem, for example. It is not unusual for snow drifts to form on the lower roof, near the wall of the higher section. This leads to big loads on the rafters or trusses in these areas. The rafters may crack, sag or spread at the bottom. Trusses may collapse.

7.2 Roof Trusses – Wood

DESCRIPTION Roof trusses are engineered assemblies that perform the same function as rafters, collar ties, knee walls, purlins and ceiling joists. The roof truss carries the roof sheathing and shingles, and the live loads, transferring the roof loads to the outside or bearing walls. The bottom of the truss also supports the ceiling finish.

There are other engineered wood framing systems including wood I-joists, and other configurations. A design review of these is beyond the scope of a home inspection. The performance evaluation is similar to trusses and rafters.

Most trusses in homes are made of wood. The top and bottom members of the truss are called chords. The interior members of a truss are called webs. Truss members are fastened together with gusset plates. These may be made of plywood or steel. Different configurations of trusses have different strengths, and engineers can use the shape and component size that best suits them. Trusses are engineered systems. Trusses are normally spaced 24 inches apart, but this can vary, again depending on the spans and depth of truss desired.

There are two common truss types used residentially. The Fink or "W" has web members that form a "W". The Howe truss can be identified by vertical web members, including a vertical web running up to the peak. There are many variations of these found in residential construction.

In either truss type, the webs should be at least 2x4s, unless special engineering consideration has been given. Where the compression webs are longer than six feet, they are susceptible to buckling under heavy loads. Braces, such as 1x4s, should be fastened to the midpoints of these webs.

Where the bottom chord has a long span between support points, it may not be strong enough to carry the ceiling load. If the span is more than ten feet between support points, the bottom chord should be at least a 2x5. If the span is more than 12 feet, the bottom chord should be a 2x6. Again, special engineering consideration can result in deviations from these guidelines.

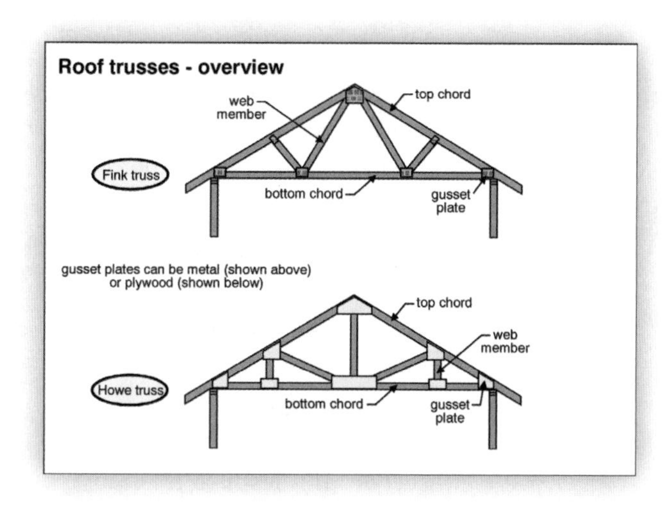

Common Problems with Wood Roof Trusses

Like any wood member, trusses are subject to rot, insect damage, mechanical damage and fire.

CUT Individual chords or webs that are cut or damaged can be a serious problem. Cutting a truss in one spot may seriously compromise the entire truss. Where trusses are cut to accommodate chimneys or other interruptions in the roof line, engineering consideration should be given.

FASTENING Trusses must be well secured to perform well.

OVERSPANNING Overspanning of trusses can lead to deflection and, in worst cases, roof collapse. Heavier roof material such as concrete tile, or greater snow loads than expected, due to unusual conditions or drifting may cause the problems. Overspanning cannot be identified during a home inspection, but evidence of deflection or failure is noted.

REPAIRS – DESIGN NEEDED Reinforcing overspanned or damaged trusses is more difficult than strengthening a rafter roof system. An engineer should design the repair.

LONG WEBS – BRACING NEEDED Trusses with web members longer than six feet may be subject to buckling. Braces should be added to the midpoints of the webs. One brace attached to each web with two nails should connect several webs in adjacent trusses. The braces should be at least 1x4s.

INADEQUATE CEILING SUPPORT Undersized bottom chords should be stiffened to prevent ceiling sag and cracking of ceiling finishes. Adding a second member to the bottom chord would normally be satisfactory.

TRUSS UPLIFT A phenomenon known as truss uplift is relatively common in cold climates. The temperature and humidity changes in the attic during the winter months affect the sections of the truss above the insulation level differently than the bottom chord, which is buried in the insulation. This results in an upward bowing of the bottom chord.

The result of truss uplift is that the center section of the bottom chord moves up, and gaps as large as 1-1/2 inches appear at the top of the interior walls, where they join the ceiling. The ceiling is picked up by the truss. It is also possible that the interior wall below will be lifted up, and separation will occur between the wall and the floor.

A common solution is to secure a molding to the ceiling (but not to the wall). As the ceiling moves up and down, the molding will slide up and down the wall, concealing the gap.

Another solution is to disconnect the ceiling finishes from the truss during construction and to clip the ceiling finishes to the wall. This allows the ceiling to bend very slightly, but not to crack.

Truss uplift is not a serious structural problem.

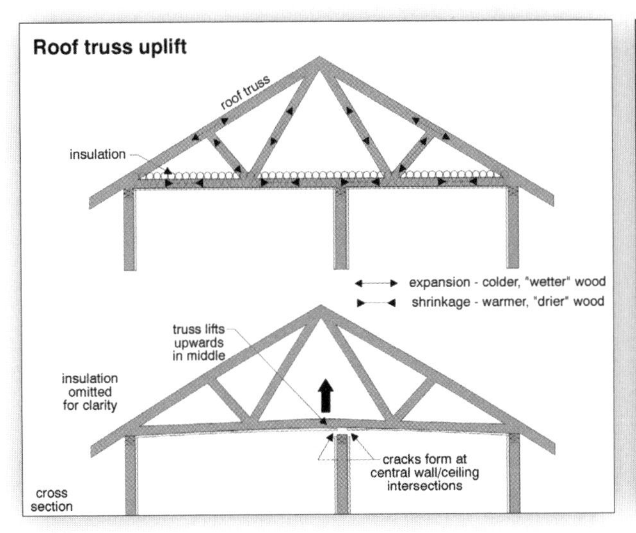

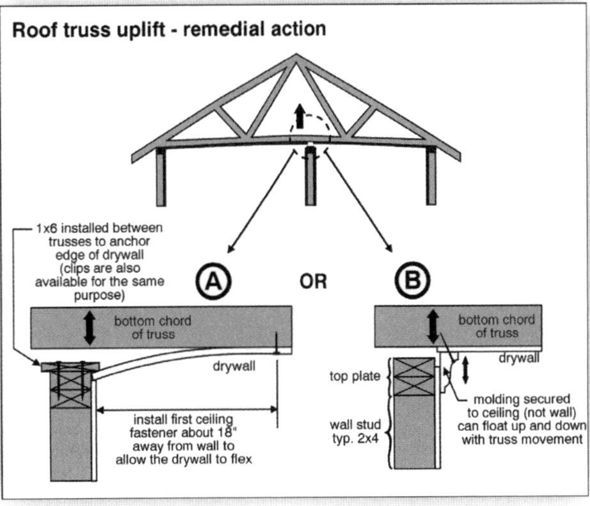

7.3 Steel Framing

DESCRIPTION Steel roof framing performs very much like wood framing. Like wood, steel roof framing may be manufactured trusses or site-assembled rafters and joists. The principles of wood framing also apply to steel roof framing, although continuous bridging on the rafters is often needed, either on the underside, or through the knockouts. The undersides of joists will twist and move unless they are restrained.

Wood sheathing materials, such as plywood, are screwed to the steel roof structure. Roofing materials are installed over this sheathing as normal.

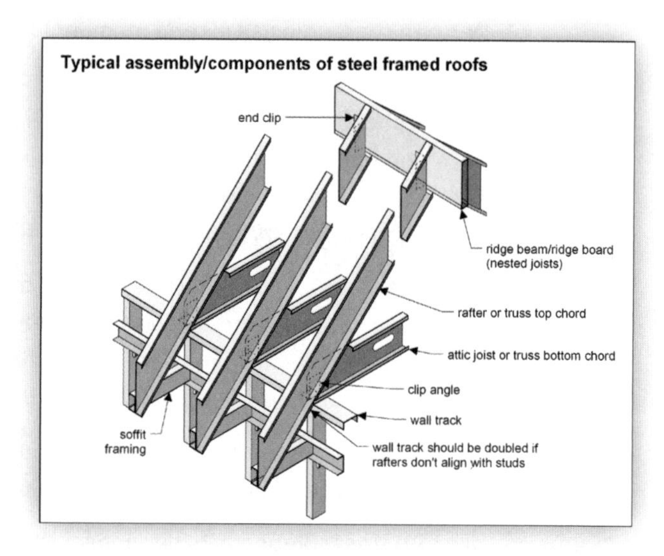

Common Problems with Steel Roof Framing

RUST Steel is, of course, vulnerable to corrosion with long-term exposure to moisture.

HOLES Any holes that are created should be at least 10 inches away from the end of the rafter, positioned in the middle of the rafter, and should not be wider than 1-1/2 inches and not longer than four inches, unless they are reinforced.

NO DESIGN REVIEW Steel roofs are engineered systems, and as with wood trusses, home inspectors do not assess their design.

7.4 Collar Ties

DESCRIPTION Collar ties may be installed to prevent rafter movement. These are typically wood members (at least 1x4s) installed horizontally across the attic space. They are connected at either end to opposing rafters. In some circumstances, metal straps may be used instead of collar ties to prevent uplift.

Common Problems with Collar Ties

MISSING, WRONG LOCATION OR POOR CONNECTION Missing collar ties can be added readily. Collar ties may be installed incorrectly or fastened poorly.

BUCKLED AND BROKEN When collar ties are installed to prevent rafter sagging, the compression from opposing rafters may buckle and crack the collar ties. Adding braces will prevent this. Broken collar ties can be replaced as needed.

7.5 Purlins

DESCRIPTION Purlins prevent rafter sag. These are wood components the same size as the rafters they support. They are nailed to the underside of the rafters and are supported, in turn, by 2x4 braces, which extend down, usually on an angle rather than vertically, to a bearing wall below. See illustration on next page.

Common Problems with Purlins

Like any wood component, purlins are subject to rot, insect and mechanical damage.

STRUTS – MISSING Braces or struts no more than four feet apart should support the purlins.

STRUTS – SLOPE Struts should be installed with a slope of not less than 45 degrees from horizontal. Any less than this and the struts will not properly transfer their load.

STRUTS – UNBRACED The struts themselves should be braced if they are longer than eight feet. A strip of lumber attached perpendicular to the struts will prevent buckling.

7.6 Knee Walls

DESCRIPTION Knee walls are intermediate supports that prevent rafter sag. These small walls in the attic are typically built with 2x4 wood studs. They run from the attic floor up to the underside of the rafters near their mid-point. In 1-1/2 or 2-1/2 story houses, knee walls form the walls of a room on the upper floor. These rooms often have a partly sloped ceiling as a result.

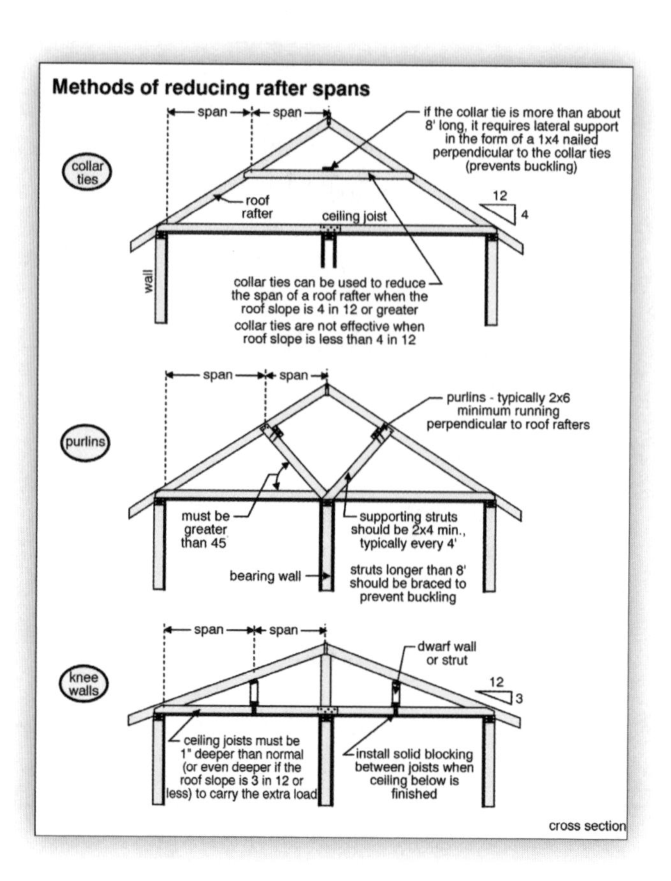

Common Problems with Knee Walls

POORLY SECURED/ WEAK FLOOR If the knee walls are not adequately secured to the rafters above or the joists below, they will move. If the floor joist system below is not strong enough, or there is no partition below, this can lead to deflection and damage in the ceiling below.

LOCATION If the knee wall is not near the mid span of the rafters, it may not be effective in preventing rafter sag.

DAMAGE/ROT/ INSECT DAMAGE Like any wood component, knee walls are subject to rot, insect and mechanical damage.

7.7 Roof Sheathing

DESCRIPTION Sheathing supports the roof covering, transmitting the loads from the covering and the live loads due to water, snow and wind to the rafters, trusses or roof joists.

Up until the 1950s, virtually all roof sheathing was wood plank. Plywood roof sheathing in 4-foot by 8-foot panels became popular in the 1960s, and waferboard panels arrived in the 1970s.

Plywood should be laid with the surface grain perpendicular to the rafters, trusses or joists. The eight-foot length should be across the rafters with each end supported by a rafter. The other edges should also be supported, typically by metal "H" clips located between rafters. These clips not only support the edges, but keep the sheets slightly separated to allow for expansion without buckling.

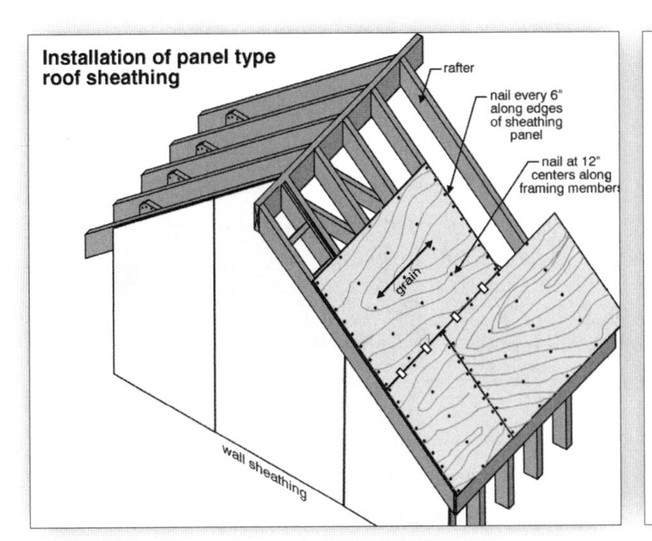

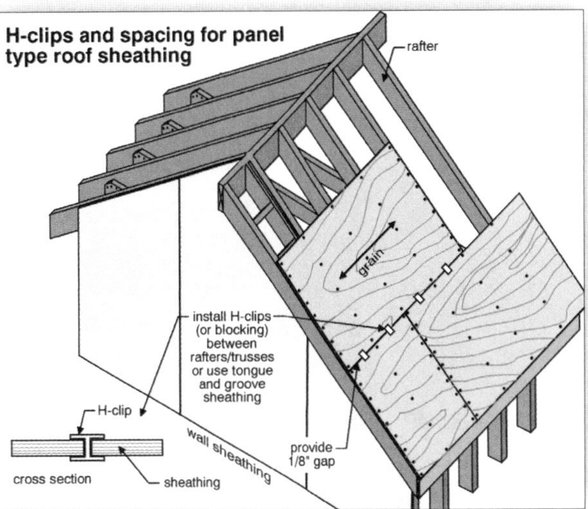

The thickness of the sheathing is determined by the spacing of the rafters and the live roof loads. Modern construction typically employs trusses or rafters on 24 inch centers and plywood sheathing 3/8 inch thick (or waferboard sheathing 7/16 inch thick). This leads to a fairly springy roof surface when walked upon. Unusually heavy loads or slight weakening of the plywood due to high moisture levels in the attic can lead to sagging of the sheathing between the supports. Normally this is not a structural flaw, although it is unsightly.

Common Problems with Roof Sheathing

DAMAGE/ROT/ INSECT DAMAGE Like any wood component, roof sheathing is subject to rot, insect damage and mechanical damage.

DAMAGE – CONDENSATION Condensation in an attic can cause problems. Plywood roof sheathing will begin to delaminate and waferboard sheathing will swell. This can cause loss of sheathing strength and render the nailing ineffective as nails are pulled out of the rafters or through the sheathing. In severe cases, the roof covering has to be removed and the sheathing replaced.

Concealed condensation in cathedral roofs is a common problem and considerable damage can occur before there are any visual clues.

MOLD Mold often appears when there has been condensation in the attic. Once the moisture is removed, the mold stops growing. Removal of the inactive mold is not necessary, although many homeowners remove it because of the stigma attached to mold.

TOO THIN Sheathing that is too thin for the application will sag under load. Aesthetically, this is often unacceptable, although sagging to the point of failure is unusual.

Sheathing thickness is determined in part by the spacing of the rafters or trusses below. Thicker sheathing is needed when the spans are greater. Sheathing thickness is also determined by the live loads from wind and snow as well as dead loads from roof coverings.

EDGE SUPPORT Unsupported edges of roof sheathing may lead to differential movement between two panels. This can lead to horizontal ridges appearing in the roofing. If the sheathing is unusually thick, edge support is not necessary.

FIRE RETARDANT TREATED (FRT) PLYWOOD Fire retardant treated (FRT) plywood was recognized as a problem in the late 1980s. Delamination and weakening of this plywood can lead to a loss of roof shingles and ultimately collapse. Where it has begun to fail, it should be replaced.

8.0 Masonry Chimneys

DESCRIPTION The structural function of a chimney is to carry its own weight down to the foundations and footings without moving. (We look at other chimney functions in the Roofing and Heating chapters.)

Common Problems with Masonry Chimneys

LEANING Chimneys that lean above the roof level should be braced or repaired as necessary, without delay.

FOUNDATION PROBLEMS Localized foundation settlement in a house around the chimney is fairly common, typically because the foundations were not large enough to carry the weight of the masonry. The chimney may eventually fall over, but the problem can become very serious before this point. A chimney that begins to lean or pull away may develop cracks or gaps, which allow smoke and heat to get near combustible materials, creating a fire hazard.

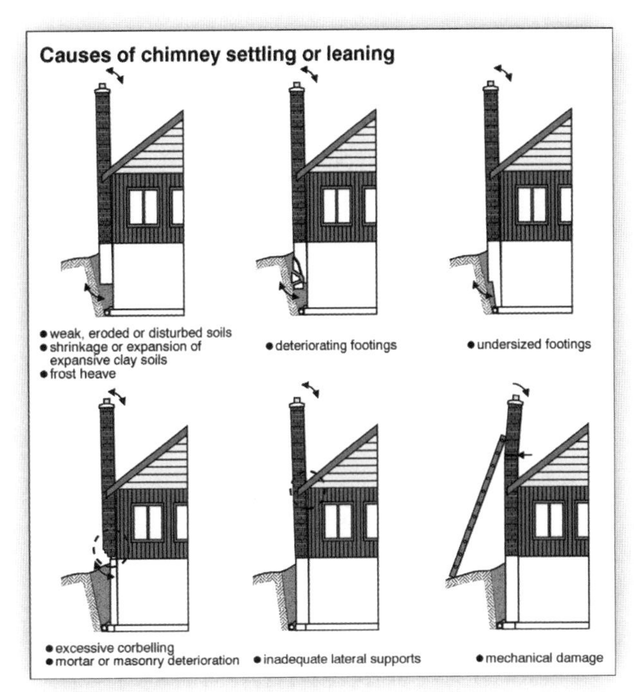

CRACKING/ DETERIORATED MASONRY OR MORTAR Cracking, spalling and deteriorated mortar are common problems with any exterior masonry.

CORBELLING Chimneys with excessive corbelling (one row of bricks projecting out and overhanging the row below) or undersized foundations are prone to movement. (See Section 6.1.1)

THREE SIDED Occasionally, chimneys are added to the outside of existing houses. Many of these are only three sided, using the house wall as the fourth side. This is usually considered unsafe although it may be acceptable where a brick veneer wall is made of solid masonry units and is spaced out at least 1/2 inch from combustible sheathing. On masonry walls, 12 inches of solid masonry must separate the flue from any wood joists or beams. A visual inspection cannot determine whether the installation is safe.

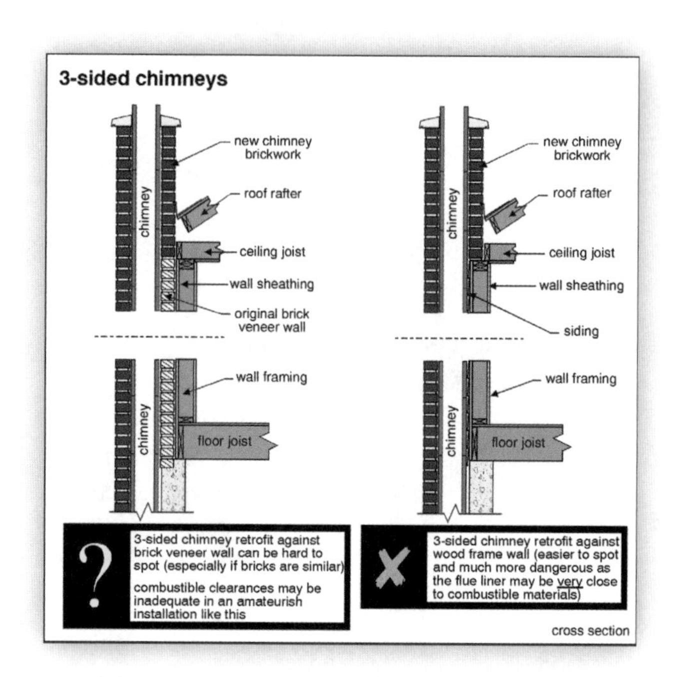

WOOD Wood building members should not contact masonry chimneys to avoid overheating.

CONTACTING CHIMNEYS Generally speaking, interior wood should be at least two inches from the chimney. On exterior wood, this can be reduced to 1/2 inch. Where it is necessary to frame into the chimney, there should be 12 inches of solid masonry between the wood and the flue.

FIREBLOCKING MISSING The space between masonry chimneys and wood framing can provide a channel for fire to move quickly up through house. Fireblocking at ceiling levels helps prevent this. The blocking material can be compressed fiberglass insulation or other non-combustible material. It is often difficult to see during a home inspection whether this has been installed.

9.0 Things That Cause Structural Problems

DESCRIPTION Let's look at some of the common things that go wrong with the structure. While there are some problems that are specific to one component (truss uplift problems, for example, are unique to wood roof trusses), there are two broad sources of problems – poor construction and things that attack the building.

9.1 Poor Construction

DESCRIPTION House components may fail because they were built with improper materials, or the materials were poorly assembled. Examples include undersized structural members like footings, beams and joists. Poor connection issues include inadequate nailing, missing or poorly installed joist hangers, bad post-to-beam joints, or using the wrong fasteners, like nails instead of bolts to secure a deck to a building.

There are hundreds of examples of poor construction practices common to homes.

9.2 Things that Attack Houses

DESCRIPTION Let's assume the home was properly built. We are not out of the woods yet! Lots can still go wrong, and often does. Some of the things that happen are universal, and some are specific. Rot and insects attack wood members but not concrete, for instance. We'll start with some things that apply to all or most homes, and then move to some that are regional.

DESCRIPTION **9.2.1 Rot Affects Wood:** All wood and wood-based building materials are subject to rot. Components that are more likely to get wet frequently are more likely to rot.

FUNGUS Rot occurs in wood under certain conditions of temperature, moisture and in the presence of oxygen (It's always present!). The decay is caused by fungus, which attacks the wood cells, causing the cells (and the wood as a whole) to collapse. The fungus that causes rot requires a temperature betwen 40° F. and 115° F. to be active. Above that temperature, the fungus can be killed and, below that temperature, the fungus becomes dormant, but can be reactivated once the temperature increases.

MOISTURE NEEDED Sufficient moisture is needed for rot to occur. When the moisture content of the wood exceeds approximately 20%, fungus spores that are naturally present in the atmosphere can be sustained and grow within the wood. Once the fungus is established, it will continue to grow and decay the wood as long as the wood remains wet. If the lumber is dried to below 20% moisture content, the rot will spread no further and will become dormant.

As the rot progresses, the wood cell walls collapse, leading to a loss of strength and the formation of cracks perpendicular to and parallel to the grain. The wood can often be broken off in small cubes.

OXYGEN NEEDED Oxygen must be present for rot to develop. This explains why wood submerged in water will not rot. Under normal circumstances in houses, there is always oxygen to support rot fungi growth.

Recommended Practices and Solutions for Rot

AVOID TRAPPED WATER Wood structures must be properly designed to resist rot. Wherever possible, the design should prevent cyclical wetting and entrapment of moisture. All joints should be free draining to dry quickly. Ledges, valleys and troughs where water can collect should be avoided. End grains of wood should be well protected, as they are capable of soaking up large amounts of water through capillary action.

ROT RESISTANT WOOD Some woods, including cedar and cypress, for example, are naturally resistant to decay fungi. Various wood treatments (such as pressure treating), can enhance the rot resistance of wood. In the case of pressure treating, copper arsenate salts (typically) are forced into the wood cells under pressure. It is these salts that give the wood a greenish tint. There are other treatments designed to provide resistance to rot, mold and insect attack. They can produce wood of different colors, including blue.

AVOID WOOD/ SOIL CONTACT Avoiding the direct contact of wood with soil will inhibit rot by helping to keep it dry. Good ventilation of porches and crawlspaces, for example, is also important in eliminating rot.

PREVENT LEAKS Appropriate flashing details at joints that promote good drainage, and a well-maintained protective coat of paint or stain, will also help to fight rot. Leaking roofs and gutters, if uncorrected, can create an ideal environment for the establishment of rot fungi. Similarly, wood in the area of kitchens and bathrooms can be susceptible to rot if there are leaking pipes or fixtures.

DESCRIPTION **9.2.2 Insects Attack Wood:** Insects can do serious damage to wood structures. Termites do the most damage because they eat the wood, but there are many insects that damage wood by nesting in it. These include carpenter ants and powder post beetles.

Home inspectors do not perform pest inspections as part of a home inspection. But they do look for evidence of the structural damage that results. The evidence is often hidden or very subtle.

DESCRIPTION **9.2.3 Fire Attacks Wood and Steel:** Fire damage to a building can be severe or cosmetic. As a very general rule, major structural members with less than 1/4 inch of char do not require re-supporting. This, of course, depends on the size, orientation and function of the member. Where there is doubt, specialists can be consulted.

Another type of fire damage should be considered. Where wood structural components are too close to fireplaces, furnaces, etc., the wood around them may begin to char as it overheats. This can occur at temperatures as low as 250° F. This will allow the wood to ignite easily if exposed to higher temperatures even briefly. Charred wood around heat generating appliances is a danger sign that should not be ignored.

Although steel does not burn in the sense that wood does, it loses its strength quickly when exposed to fire. Steel members typically fail before wood components in a fire.

DESCRIPTION **9.2.4 Rust Attacks Metal:** Rust or corrosion affects most metals to some extent. Rusting steel is a common house problem with respect to posts and beams as well as fasteners like nails, screws and bolts. Unprotected steel rusts when exposed to water. Steel that is expected to be wet can be painted or treated with rust inhibitors such as galvanizing (adding zinc to the steel to resist rust). Hot dip galvanizing is more effective than electroplate galvanizing, although neither guarantee that there will be no rust. Stainless steel is more corrosion resistant than galvanized steel but is not common as a building material. There are different types of stainless steel.

EXPANDING RUST Rust can cause metal components to weaken but can also damage other materials. Steel expands as it rusts, exerting tremendous force. If the steel is embedded in concrete, the damage can be significant. Steel reinforcing bars can break (spall) concrete and steel railings can damage concrete porches, decks and balconies, for example.

DESCRIPTION **9.2.5 Mechanical Damage Affects All Building Materials:** Wood and steel are more susceptible than concrete, but damage is possible in any of these.

Mechanical damage to wood members can take several forms. It may be split, broken or crushed during handling or while the building is under construction. It is common for some wood in a home being built to suffer minor mechanical damage. The extent and location of the damage determine whether replacement or repair is needed. The entire system must also be considered. If the wall, roof, or floor system is significantly over-designed, one damaged member may not be critical.

NOTCHES AND HOLES Similar consideration is given to mechanical damage caused by cutting, notching or drilling holes in wood members. Again, there are several criteria that help determine whether corrective action is warranted.

IMPACT DAMAGE Impact damage may be from vehicles, animals or people. The damage can be trivial or devastating.

DESCRIPTION **9.2.6 Ground Movement – Earthquake and Soil Conditions:** No matter how well the home is built, when the ground below moves, damage is likely. Earthquakes are significant problems in some parts of North America. Erosion, landslides and underground streams undermining buildings are examples of less dramatic ground movement. Homes built on weak soils may fail catastrophically. Expansive soils can also cause dramatic building damage. Another kind of soil movement specific to cold climates is frost heave, where the soil below or beside the building damages concrete floors and walls.

Construction techniques can improve the chances of successfully withstanding damage, but there are no guarantees with nature. During an earthquake, the house should act as a unit, with the foundations, floors, walls, and roof moving together. Problems arise when these move independently of each other.

RISK FACTOR Unreinforced masonry buildings and structures are more vulnerable to earthquake damage than wood frame homes. Wood frame homes with shearwalls are better than ordinary wood frame buildings. Homes with the structural components tied together and tied to the foundation are better than conventionally framed houses. Single story homes are better than two story homes.

COMMON PROBLEMS Failure modes during earthquakes typically include things like posts moving off piers, beams moving off posts, cripple walls falling off foundations, and masonry chimneys collapsing.

TWO STRATEGIES The two critical strategies in reducing earthquake damage are tying the house structural components together and using shearwalls to minimize racking of the structure.

TYING HOMES TOGETHER Special fasteners are used, both during new construction and in upgrading existing homes. The hardware includes sill anchors (mechanical wedge-type in retrofit situations), hangers, hold downs (tie downs), post caps, straps and hurricane clips (hurricane ties). Wood members can also be used to tie components together.

SECUREMENT The fasteners may be nailed, bolted or embedded in concrete. Engineers, manufacturers and designers have differing opinions about the type, size, location and number of fasteners required in any situation. The goal is to tie the building together to prevent lateral movement or overturning. The sills should be tied to foundations or floor slabs, posts should be tied to piers, beams should be tied to posts, floors should be tied to sills, walls should be tied to floors and sills, and roofs should be tied to walls.

BRACING POSTS Adjacent posts in sub-grade areas may be supported with 2x4 diagonal braces to help resist lateral forces.

SHEARWALLS Shearwalls help wood frame walls resist racking caused by the strong lateral forces that occur during earthquakes. Shearwalls are typically 3/8 to 1/2 inch plywood or waferboard. They must extend the full height of the wall to be effective. Shearwalls are typically the exterior walls of a wood frame home. Some interior walls on large homes may also be shearwalls.

DETAILS The plywood or waferboard panels may be installed on the inner or outer faces of stud walls. They are not needed on both. The panels are installed vertically, except on cripple walls less than four feet tall. Gaps of roughly 1/8 inch are left around all edges of panels to allow for expansion due to changes in moisture content. Without these gaps, the panels may buckle when they swell.

SECUREMENT Panel edges are nailed every four to six inches, depending on the designer and the situation, and every 12 inches in the field of the panels. All four edges of panels must be backed by something solid such as sills, studs, rim joists, top plates or blocking.

HOLD DOWNS Hold downs are provided at each corner of the home and at each end of every shearwall. Hold downs are heavy L-shaped brackets that secure the shearwall to the foundation. Hold downs are usually secured with bolts.

CRIPPLE WALLS Cripple walls are short wood frame walls that span from the foundation to the first floor. They are vulnerable to earthquakes because they have little resistance to lateral forces. Cripple walls can be converted to shearwalls from the inside by adding plywood or waferboard panels to the studs. Stud spaces are typically vented into the sub-grade area with 1/2 inch diameter holes at the top and bottom of each stud cavity.

STRAP APPLIANCES DOWN Heavy appliances such as water heaters, furnaces, refrigerators, washing machines and stoves should be strapped to the building to keep them in place.

SPECIAL GAS VALVES Gas valves that shut off automatically if the gas line ruptures can be provided near the gas meter in earthquake prone areas.

CHIMNEYS Unreinforced masonry chimneys are common on old homes and there is no easy way to improve their resistance to earthquake. Some people put 3/4-inch plywood on attic floors to prevent bricks falling off chimneys from coming through ceilings into the home.

DESCRIPTION **9.2.7 Hurricane and Tornadoes:** Earthquakes impose lateral forces on homes, for the most part. Hurricanes exert lateral forces and uplift forces. While similar to earthquakes in some respects, hurricanes, tornadoes and other high winds present separate problems.

RISK FACTOR Hurricanes are regional issues, and there are other wind-related problems such as twisters and tornadoes that are also somewhat regional. The southeastern United States is the most prominent hurricane area in North America. Several devastating hurricanes have occurred in this area and building officials, insurance companies, builders and homeowners all look at homes differently as a result.

Considerable investigation and research has been done after hurricanes, and much has been learned about the mechanisms of failure. Hurricanes usually carry heavy rains and much of the damage from hurricanes is caused by water. Wind is not the only issue, but often creates the openings that allow water into homes. Wind carried projectiles are another problem.

KEY ISSUES Many believe the three key issues in hurricane resistance for homes are: the roof sheathing must be well secured to the roof framing, the roof framing must be well secured to the walls, and openings including doors and windows must be protected from flying debris.

DECK NAILING Roof sheathing should be nailed at six-inch centers along panel edges and at 12-inch centers in the field. Sheathing at overhangs is often nailed at four-inch centers because wind forces can be greater here.

HURRICANE CLIPS Hurricane clips or straps are used to secure roof framing to walls. Straps are also used to fasten wall top plates to the walls themselves.

OPENINGS Openings can be protected through special impact resistant doors and windows, or shutters, plywood covers or some other shielding protection on the outside.

ROOF BRACING Truss roofs can be strengthened with wood braces on the webs and the chords. Gable end walls have proven vulnerable to hurricane winds, and are often strengthened with braces in the attic.

WIND RESISTANT SHINGLES Asphalt shingles are often blown off roofs during hurricanes and other high winds. Manufacturers have been making efforts to increase the wind resistance of roofing materials. Some areas call for mopped-in asphalt underlayment beneath shingles where the risk of shingle loss is significant.

CONCRETE TILES Concrete tiles have also blown off roofs in hurricanes. These are worse than asphalt shingles because the heavy tiles become dangerous projectiles. Improved installation techniques include full mortar beds for concrete tiles.

HIP ROOFS Designers are being encouraged to move from gable roofs to hip roofs, since hips are less likely to fail. Hip roofs have no vertical gable wall to 'catch the wind'.

GARAGE DOORS Garage doors have been a problem because they blow in easily. Stronger doors, hardware and tracks are a partial solution.

NO GUARANTEES As with earthquakes, homes can be built to improve their chance of surviving serious winds, but nature is so strong that there are no guarantees.

DESCRIPTION **9.2.8 Flood:** Flood damage can be severe and may be the most serious impact of hurricanes and earthquakes.

Homes in flood prone areas may be built on stilts to reduce the risk of damage or loss of building, but there are few absolutes with flooding, as with other natural forces.

Electrical

INTRODUCTION

Electricity has become an important element of every North American home. It provides lighting, heating and power for electric motors and electronics such as controls and computers. Our homes would not be nearly as comfortable or as convenient without electricity.

On the other hand, electricity is dangerous. It has to be installed and used properly to be safe. Electricity is tricky because it is invisible, it is complicated and it can kill.

1.0 The Basics

DESCRIPTION Electricity can provide us with heat, light and power as invisible electrons move in a circuit through wires and appliances. We can control whether it gives off mostly light or mostly heat by using light bulbs or electric heaters. Electricity can also drive electric motors with fast changing magnetic fields.

Where does electricity come from?

Electricity is provided by utilities. It can be generated by moving water (e.g. Niagara Falls generates hydroelectric power) burning fossil fuels like coal or from nuclear reactions, for example. As we look for more environmentally sensitive ways to generate electricity, solar, wind and geothermal power sources are becoming more common. Batteries may be used to store and deliver power.

Electricity is distributed through communities by a grid of overhead and/or underground wires. Electricity can be alternating current or direct current. Our discussion will focus on alternating current, since that's what we find in homes.

Let's start with a brief description of four common electrical terms:
V = Voltage, measured in volts. This represents the electrical force that is available.
I = Current, measured in amps (amperes). This represents the amount of electricity flowing.
R = Resistance, measured in ohms. This is a measure of the opposition to electrical flow.
P = Power, measured in watts (1 kilowatt is 1000 watts). This represents the rate at which work is done.

The table below shows the relationship between these four terms.

Table 1 – Electrical Basics			
V=Voltage (volts)	**P**=Power (watts)	**I**=Current (amps)	**R**=Resistance (ohms)
Formulas: **V=IR** **P=VI**			

1.1 Voltage

DESCRIPTION Electricity flows because there is a pressure (volts) being applied to a circuit, supplied from the local utility. Utilities provide 240 volts to homes, in two 120-volt bundles.

1.2 Current

DESCRIPTION The electric current in a circuit, measured in amps (or amperes), is the rate of flow of electricity that results when a light bulb, heater or appliance is turned on. The amount of current is a result of the amount of pressure (volts) and the resistance to flow (ohms). The larger the pressure, the greater the flow. The larger the resistance, the smaller the flow.

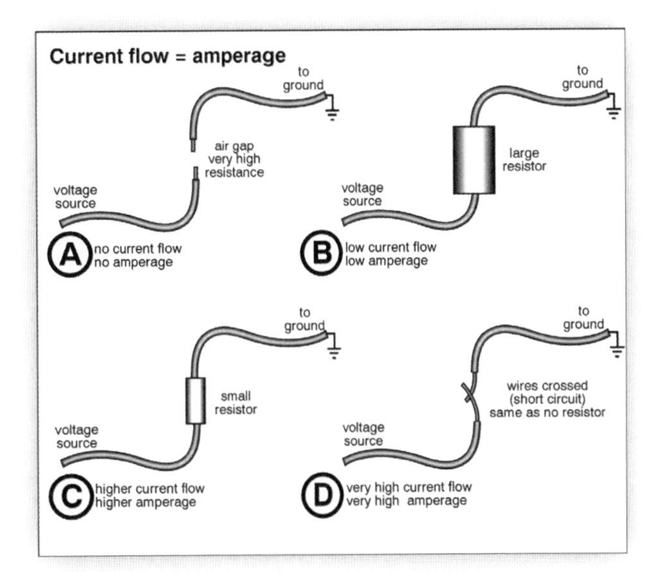

CONTROLLING THE FLOW Two dangerous things can go wrong with the flow of electricity:

1. Too much flow results in overheating and possibly a fire. We can get too much electricity flowing if too many appliances are plugged into one circuit. There are other ways too much electricity can flow, but let's leave it at that. If everything works properly, fuses and circuit breakers turn the electricity off when too much electricity flows.
2. Electricity may flow where it is not supposed to. This is where people get electrical shocks. It happens when you drop the hairdryer or radio into the bathtub, you stick a key into an electrical outlet, or you drive a nail into a live electrical wire, for example. A flow of less than one amp can kill you.

1.3 Resistance

DESCRIPTION Resistance, measured in ohms, prevents electricity from flowing. We use resistance to control whether electricity flows, and if so, how much. Things that slow down or resist electrical flow are called resistors or insulators. Things that allow electricity to flow easily are called conductors.

CONDUCTORS Good electrical conductors have relatively low resistance. Conductors are useful for moving electricity from one place to another. Most metals including copper and aluminum wiring are good conductors. Aluminum is not quite as good as copper, but is less expensive. Water is a very good conductor, which is why it's dangerous. When electricity contacts water, it often flows where it shouldn't. The human body is a pretty good conductor, which is unfortunate for us.

INSULATORS HAVE HIGH RESISTANCE When we don't want electricity to flow, we use things with lots of resistance. These things are called insulators. Air, glass, wood, rubber and most plastics are good insulators. Homes use copper wire (a conductor) to move electricity around. We wrap the wire in a plastic insulator, so the electricity stays within the wire, making it safe to touch.

1.4 Power

DESCRIPTION Power is measured in watts or kilowatts (1000 watts), and is calculated by multiplying the voltage (volts) times the current (amps). A house with a 240-volt power supply and 100 amp main fuses has 24,000 watts. This is commonly referred to as 24 kilowatts (because one kilowatt is 1000 watts). A 1200-watt hair dryer plugged into a 120-volt circuit will result in a 10-amp electrical current flow.

KILOWATT-HOURS 1 kilowatt (kW) is 1000 watts (W). Electrical consumption in your home is measured in kilowatt-hours (kWh). If you use 1000 watts (1 kilowatt) for one hour, you consume one kilowatt-hour (kWh). This is how we buy electricity from the utility. The electric meter records kilowatt-hours used in the house. If each kWh costs ten cents and we use 500 kWh in a month, our electrical bill for that month is $50.

NEXT STEPS Let's have a quick look at wire size, fuses and circuit breakers before we start to look at the house system in more detail.

1.5 Wire Size (Gauge)

DESCRIPTION We use wires to move electricity around the house because wires are good conductors. The amount of current (amps) a wire can safely carry is determined largely by its diameter. A larger wire can carry more current. Typical household circuits are designed to carry 15 amps, and 14-gauge copper wire will do this safely. The illustration shows common wire sizes and the typical size of fuse or breaker that is used to protect them. Aluminum is not as good a conductor of electricity, and a larger wire has to be used to carry the same amount of electricity as copper. It's very confusing, because larger wires have a smaller number gauge. We think electricians do this to make it hard for us.

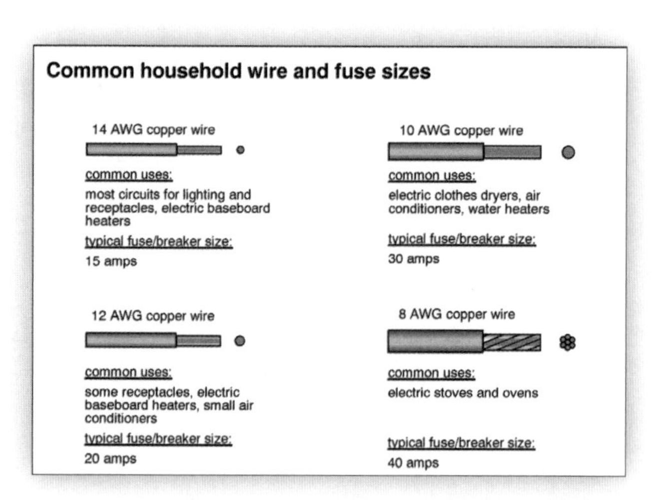

1.6 Breakers and Fuses

DESCRIPTION When too much electricity flows, things can overheat and we might have a fire. Fuses and circuit breakers turn off the electricity when there is too much flow. They are the lifeguards of the electrical system. Let's look at a normal household circuit.

A 14-gauge wire with 120-volt pressure can safely carry about 15 amps before things get too hot. We put a fuse or breaker at the beginning of the circuit to shut the circuit off if more than 15 amps flow. A 1200-watt hair dryer will cause about 10 amps to flow. If we plug a 1200-watt curling iron into the same circuit, another 10 amps will flow. Now we have 20 amps flowing and the wire is going to get too hot. That's when the circuit breaker should trip or the fuse should blow. Losing power is a nuisance, but it prevents a fire.

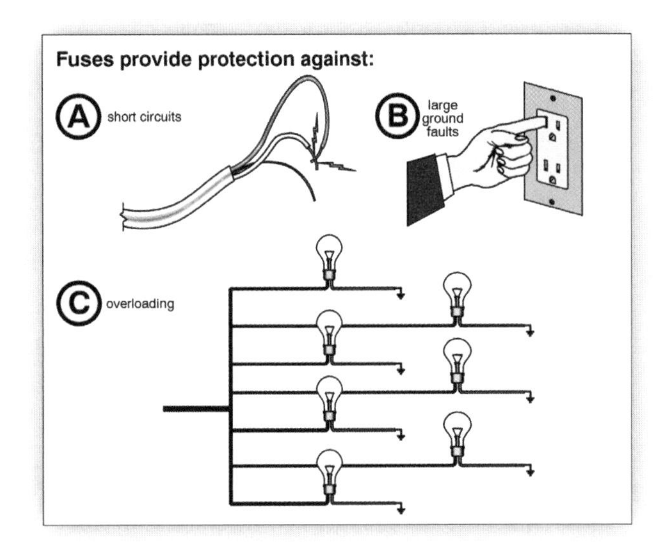

OVERCURRENT PROTECTION DEVICES The fancy name for circuit breakers and fuses is overcurrent protection devices. Both fuses and breakers perform the function equally well. A circuit breaker can be turned back on like a switch after the overload situation is corrected. A fuse 'blows' and has to be replaced. Most modern electrical work in homes uses circuit breakers.

NEXT STEPS For the rest of this section, we'll look at electricity in the home. We'll start with how electricity gets into the house and spend some time on the panel before looking at the wire carrying electricity through the house. We'll finish with the switches, light fixtures, junction boxes and electrical receptacles at the end of the circuit.

Some people think of electricity as a tree. The trunk is the bundle of electricity coming into the house from the utility. The trunk is split into branches at the panel. You can think of each circuit in the home as a tree branch. Each circuit typically has some lights, switches and receptacles. You can think of these as the twigs on each branch.

2.0 Service Entrance

2.1 Service Drop and Laterals: Getting Electricity to the House

DESCRIPTION – SERVICE DROP AND SERVICE LATERALS

A typical house has 240-volts, brought in through overhead (service drop) or underground wires (service laterals) from the utility. There are three wires. The live black and red wires each bring 120 volts to the home, and the white wire is neutral. It does not bring any voltage to the home, but completes the circuit.

These wires may be copper or aluminum. The potential between the black and white wires is 120 volts, between the red and white is 120 volts, and between the black and red is 240 volts. (Incidentally, the "red" wire often has black sheathing, just to make things confusing). The size of the service entrance cable determines how much electricity is available to the house.

The service drop and service laterals are typically the responsibility of the utility. Everything beyond this point is the responsibility of the homeowner. Service drops connect to the service entrance conductors, which are typically in conduit running down the outside of the building.

Underground service wires (laterals) are in a conduit, typically buried one and a half to three feet deep. The conduit comes up to the electric meter on the outside of the building. From the electric meter, the conduit goes into the building.

Overhead service drops may be attached to the side of the building, and come down to the electric meter in a conduit (or cable), again along the outside of the building. On shorter buildings, they sometimes come in above the roofline and enter an electrical mast that sticks up above the roof. The wires go into the mast, which forms a conduit, again running down the outside of the building.

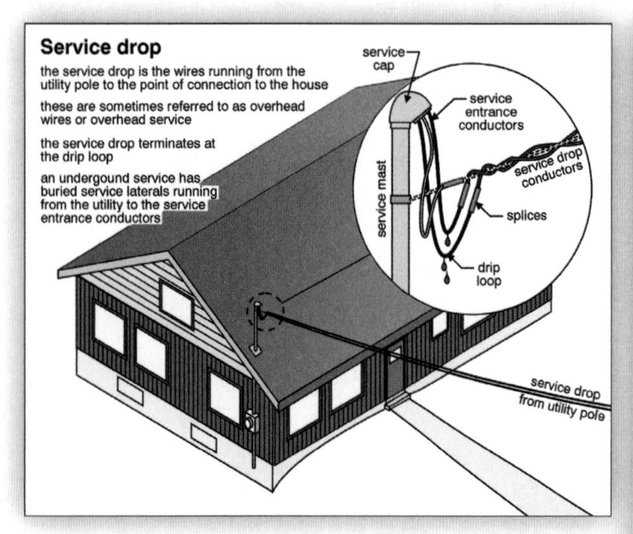

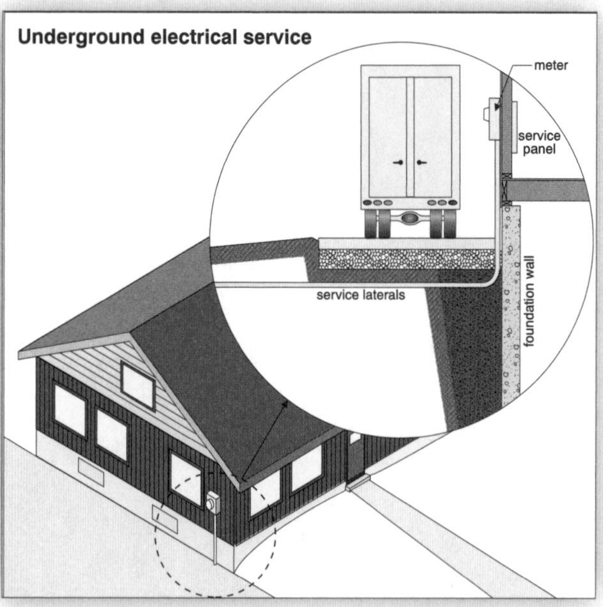

120-VOLT AND 240-VOLT CIRCUITS Typical household circuits are 120-volt. Some 120-volt circuits use a black wire and white wire. The others use a red wire and a white wire. Large appliances that need lots of electricity, like stoves, clothes dryers, water heaters and air conditioners, use 240-volt circuits. They use a black wire, a red wire and a white wire, typically.

SERVICE SIZE The size of the electrical service to the house (100 amps, 200 amps, etc.) is determined by the size of the wires coming to the house. We'll talk more about this shortly.

Common Problems with Service Drops and Service Laterals

What can go wrong as we bring electricity to the house? There are three common problems – damage, improper location, and moisture problems. We will focus on the overhead wires, because there's not much we can see of underground wiring coming into the house. Remember, problems with the service drop are usually the responsibility of the utility.

DAMAGED WIRE Wire can be damaged by tree branches or may deteriorate due to weathering. Where damage such as frayed insulation is noted, the utility (electric company) should be notified.

CLEARANCE Wires that are too low can be hit by vehicles. You don't want your moving truck taking out your electrical service before you move into the house. Overhead wires should be about 12 feet above ground level. We don't want people leaning out windows or standing on decks to be able to touch these overhead wires. Wires should be kept at least three feet away from windows, and roughly ten feet above decks. Again, where clearance is not adequate, the utility should be notified.

WATER Water on the overhead wires is not a problem. However, once the water gets into the conduit that goes into the home, it is a problem.

POOR CONNECTION TO SERVICE ENTRANCE CONDUCTORS The service drop wires may not be well-connected to the service entrance conductors. This can interfere with the house electrical service and create a dangerous situation.

2.2 Service Entrance Conductors

DESCRIPTION The overhead service drop is typically the responsibility of the utility. These wires connect to the service entrance conductors, which are the responsibility of the homeowner. This hand-off point from the utility wires to the homeowner wires is sometimes called the service point. The service entrance conductors are typically in a metal or plastic conduit that runs down the outside of the house. The conduit protects the wires from mechanical damage and moisture. Some homes have a service entrance cable rather than a conduit.

DRIP LOOP A drip loop prevents water entering the service conduit. The service wires form a loop below the service head, which allows water to drip off the wire. That keeps the water out of the conduit.

CONNECTION TO BUILDING Remember the service drop has to be at least 12 feet above the ground. On tall buildings, the service is connected to the side of the building. The service entrance conductors form a drip loop and then enter a conduit that runs down the side of the building. On shorter buildings, the drip loop attaches to a service mast (conduit) that extends above the roof and carries the service entrance conductors down along the outside of the building.

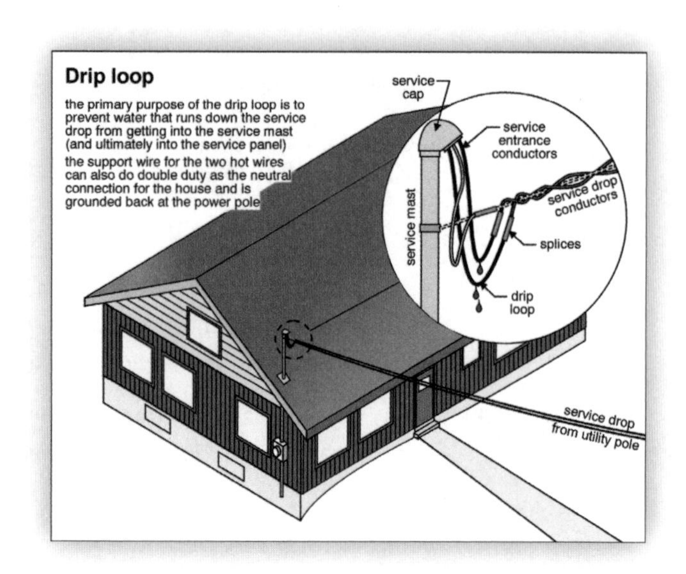

METERS The service conduit carries the service entrance conductors through the electric meter so we can pay for our electricity. Meters are typically on the outside of the home close to the front of the building to facilitate meter reading by a utility representative. Modern systems are eliminating the need for a human meter reader.

INSIDE BUILDING Once inside the building, the conduit must be kept as short as possible, ideally going straight into the box. This avoids exposing the conduit to mechanical damage.

Common Problems with the Service Entrance Conductors

DRIP LOOP MISSING/ INEFFECTIVE Sometimes the drip loop is missing or does not create a low spot for water to run off the service entrance wires. This results in water getting into the conduit, which can run into the service box or panel inside the house, causing rust and poor electrical connections.

SERVICE CAP NOT WATERPROOF The service entrance conductors have to enter the conduit through a weather-tight cap. Water can cause rust and poor connections. Where there is evidence of water penetration, repairs should be made.

MAST DAMAGED/ TOO SHORT/POOR LOCATION The service mast above the roof has to be well secured and free from rust or rot. Weaknesses here should be corrected promptly to maintain the integrity of the electrical service drop and service conductors. The mast should be tall enough (at least three feet typically) to keep the wires clear of the roof, so they will not interfere with re-roofing or maintenance activities. We also try to avoid having overhead wires running across roofs. We don't want someone up on the roof cleaning the gutters or repairing a leak to touch these wires.

POOR FLASHING AT ROOF Where the mast penetrates the roof surface, the opening should be protected with a flashing that prevents water getting into the roof structure. Where this is not effective, there may be water damage to the building.

DAMAGED/ POORLY SECURED The conduit should be intact and well secured to the building. Rust, cracks, loose connections and deformities in the conduit should be corrected.

COVERED BY SIDING The service mast or conduit should not be covered by siding, so it will not be damaged inadvertently and so it can be inspected easily.

POOR SEAL AT METER/WALL The conduit should be sealed at the meter and where it passes through the wall to prevent water penetration.

2.3 Service Size

DESCRIPTION The service size is determined by the size of the wire coming from the street to the home. It's often hard to determine the wire size, since it is in a conduit. The size of the main fuses or breakers is a good indication of service size.

As the power enters the house, it goes into a service box, which has two fuses or two circuit breakers (or one big breaker). One is for the black wire and one is for the red. No breaker or fuse is used on the neutral wire. The size of the fuses or breakers should match the wire capacity. (100 amps, 200 amps, etc.) See Table 2 below for ratings of various service entrance wires.

A service box with fuses might have two 100-amp fuses. This indicates a 100-amp service, not 200 amps. You can't add them together. One of the fuses protects the black wire and the other one protects the red wire.

The rating stamped on the meter box or on the service box is not always a good indicator of the electrical service size.

HOW MUCH ELECTRICITY IS ENOUGH? Every house gets 240 volts. The amount of electricity available is described by the number of amps the system can safely deliver. 100 amps is a common electrical service for an average home. Larger houses or houses with big electrical demands like electric heat might have 150 or 200 amp services. The largest residential electrical service we typically see is 400 amps. Some older homes have 60-amp services. While this may be serviceable for some homes and lifestyles, 100 amps is commonly considered a minimum.

Table 2 – Typical Service Entrance Sizes

Minimum Wire Size USA		Service Size (amps)	Minimum Wire Size Canada	
Copper	Aluminum		Copper	Aluminum
4	2	100	3	2
2	1/0	125	2	2/0 (1/0)
1/0	2/0	150	1/0	3/0
2/0	4/0	200	3/0	250 MCM

Note: Variations are possible, depending on type of wire, temperature rating, etc.

ELECTRICAL

Table 3 indicates what typical electrical appliances need to operate. The size of the service needed for the house depends on the number of electrical appliances. Some of the appliances that can tax an electrical service include electric heaters, saunas, and hot tubs. It is the simultaneous use of appliances that causes problems, and this is dependent on lifestyle. Larger families are likely to use more electricity at the same time, and may need a larger electrical service than a smaller family in the same house.

Table 3 –Typical Power and Current for Household Appliances

	Watts	Amps
Stove and oven	9600	40
Clothes dryer	5000	20
Central air conditioner	5000	20
Electric water heater	3000	12.5
Kettle	1500	12.5
Toaster	1200	10
Microwave oven	1500	12.5
Coffee maker	1200	10
Dishwasher	1200	10
Iron	1500	12.5
Portable electric heater	1500	12.5
Window air conditioner	1200	10
Central vacuum	1500	12.5
Hair dryer	1800	15
Portable vacuum cleaner	1400	12
Washing machine	500	4.2
Furnace fan	250	2
Blender	360	3
Refrigerator	700	6
Television	120	1
DVD player	20	0.2
Stereo	120	1
Desktop computer with monitor	180	1.5
Laptop computer	60	0.5
60 watt incandescent light	60	0.5
14 watt compact fluorescent light	14	0.1
1/4 horsepower motor	700	6
1/2 horsepower motor	1000	8

The Common Problem with Service Size

100 amp services are common and the minimum acceptable for most homes. How much electricity you need depends on the size of the house, and the number of electrical appliances.

SERVICE TOO SMALL A house with an undersized electrical service is not a safety concern, but it is an inconvenience. An electrical service that is marginally sized may suffer blowing of the main fuses or breaker. The breakers can simply be reset by the homeowner, but fuses usually have to be replaced by the utility or an electrician. The entire house is often without electricity while waiting for a service call. This is one reason modern installations use a main breaker rather than fuses.

Changing the service size typically means new wires from the street to the house, new conduit, a new meter and usually a new service box. Replacing underground wires is more expensive than replacing overhead wires.

Most modern homes have a combination panel that incorporates the service box (with the main circuit breaker) with a panel housing the breakers that go to the individual circuits. When a service in an existing home is upgraded, a combination panel is typically installed. A good installation includes a panel with room to add more circuits in the future.

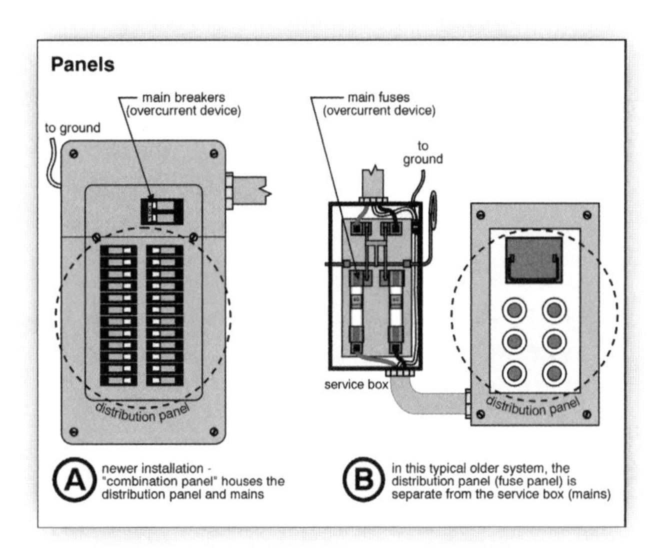

2.4 Service Box (Service Equipment)

DESCRIPTION The service box includes a circuit breaker that can be used to shut off all the power in the house (newer), or a switch with a handle located on the outside, and the service fuses inside (older). This is your emergency shut-off for all the electricity in the home. The service box may stand alone, although in modern homes, a combination panel (service panel) is common. This includes the breakers for the individual branch circuits.

HOUSE POWER LEFT ON The main switch or breaker is not shut off during a home inspection, since it would shut down the entire house. This can disrupt clocks, timers and computers, for example, and can result in damage to some motors and compressors.

Home inspectors don't remove the cover for the main breakers in a combination panel for safety reasons.

Not all homes have a single service box. Some have a number of different points where electricity can be turned off. In many areas, up to six different disconnect points are acceptable to turn off all the electricity in the house.

Common Problems with the Service Box

UNDERSIZED BOX The service box rating must be at least as large as the service entrance wires, and the fuses or breakers inside. For example, if a house has a 150-amp service, a box rated for only 100 amps is not acceptable.

UNDERSIZED BREAKER OR FUSE The fuse or breaker rating should match the wires' current rating (ampacity) to ensure an adequate supply of electricity to the home and to ensure proper protection for wires. If improperly sized, the main fuses or breakers should be replaced.

MISMATCHED FUSE SIZES The two main fuses in the service box should be the same size to properly protect the wires and ensure the supply of electricity to the home is adequate. If they are not, an electrician should be engaged to correct the situation.

POOR CONNECTIONS/ EVIDENCE OF OVERHEATING Poor connections may lead to overheating and should be corrected. In some cases it is necessary to replace the service box itself.

DAMAGED/ POORLY SECURED If the main switch or breaker handle is inoperative or damaged, it should be replaced. Similarly, if the box is rusted or damaged, it should at least be checked by an electrician. The service box should be re-secured to the wall if it is loose, to prevent poor electrical connections.

RUST Moisture in the box leads to rust, which damages the box and can result in unsafe electrical conditions.

POOR ACCESS OR LOCATION The service box should be accessible and in a dry location. The service box should be roughly five feet above the floor and have three feet clear in front of the box. Service boxes should not be located in clothes closets, bathrooms or stairwells.

NEXT STEPS Before we move on to talk about the panel that breaks the trunk of the tree up into branches, let's have a look at a safety system called grounding.

2.5 System Grounding

DESCRIPTION The purpose of grounding is to give electricity a safe place to go if it gets out of control. When people touch live electrical things, they get an electrical shock, and in some cases they die. Grounding helps prevent that.

Until roughly 1960, grounding was only found at the service panel. Since then, it has been used on all branch circuits, including lights and electrical outlets. A ground wire is a wire that provides a safe path for stray electricity.

Generally speaking, the grounding wires are connected to metallic parts of an electrical system that are not supposed to carry electricity. These metal components (panels, switch boxes, light boxes, etc.), are close to electricity, and if something goes wrong, the metal cabinet could become live. A person touching the cabinet would get a shock. Connecting the ground wire to the metal cabinet ensures that if someone touches the cabinet, he or she will not get a shock, even if a live wire inside is touching the cabinet.

WHERE DOES THE ELECTRICITY GO? The stray electricity quite literally goes to ground, where it dissipates harmlessly. In most houses, the electrical system is grounded to the metal water supply piping and/or one or more eight-foot metal rods (Grounding Electrodes) driven into the ground. This allows stray electricity to get into the ground. Where grounding is through metal supply piping, the ground wire (Grounding Electrode Conductor – GEC) should be connected to the supply piping near its point of entry into the house. If connected downstream of the water meter or a water filter, a jumper wire is provided across the meter or filter to maintain the connection to ground even if the device is removed.

OTHER GROUNDING ELECTRODE SYSTEMS Other grounding configurations include a well casing, a long copper wire or bar encased in the concrete footing, and a metal plate or ring buried in the ground. None of these is visible and they are not evaluated during a home inspection.

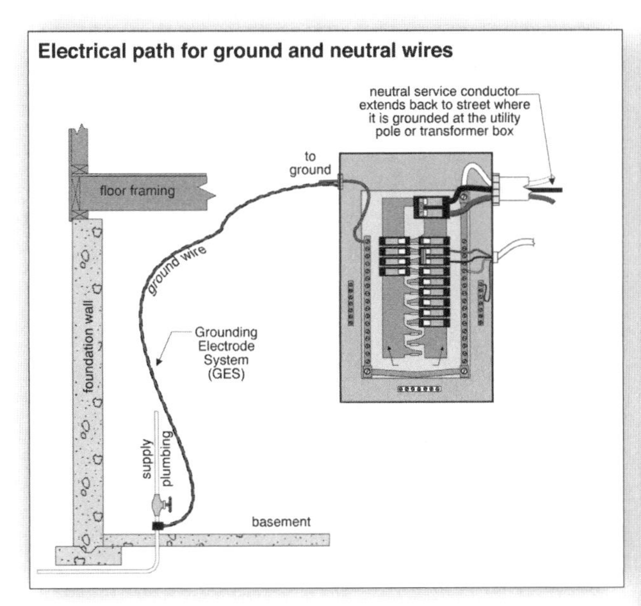

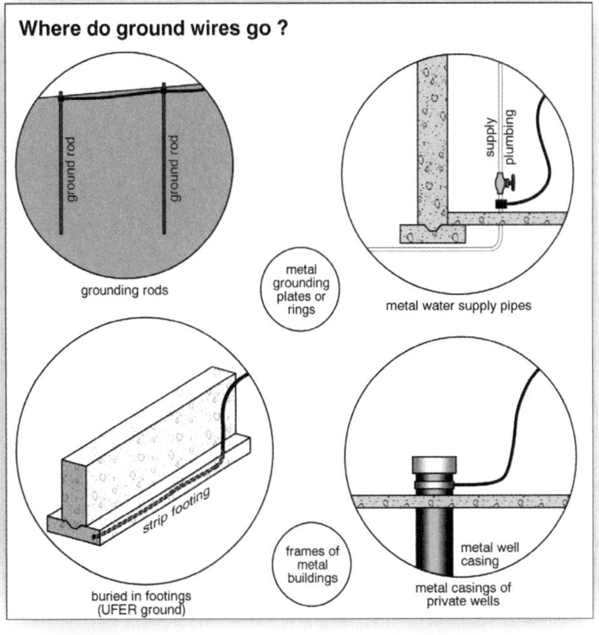

Common Problems with Grounding

MISSING The system ground is missing in some cases. It may have been omitted from the original installation, or removed during electrical or plumbing work; or the original ground may have been left behind when the service panel was relocated. Adding a new ground wire is not usually difficult or expensive.

WIRE TYPE/ SPLICES The ground wire may be too small for the service size, the wrong material, or there may be splices. Connections in ground wires are generally discouraged for fear of a bad connection.

INEFFECTIVE GROUNDING The system ground may be ineffective. If the connections are poor or the wires damaged, the quality of ground is suspect. If there is a splice in the ground wire, a potentially weak connection exists. Ground wires are sometimes ineffective because they are secured to pipes that are no longer in service. This is common on galvanized steel plumbing pipes that are abandoned. If the plumber did not move the ground wire over to the new piping, the grounding system will be defeated. By the same token, connecting a ground wire to plastic supply piping is not effective, since plastic is not a good electrical conductor. The ground wire (GEC) may also be too small.

Checking the quality of the grounding system is beyond the scope of a home inspection.

LACK OF BONDING The grounding system has to be continuous. The ground wire has to be bonded to other wires that rely on grounding. The ground wire, the service box, and the neutral wire should be electrically bonded together at the service box, but often are not. This situation should be corrected promptly. Again, the continuity of the system is not verified during a home inspection.

BONDING AND GROUNDING These terms are similar, confusing and often used interchangeably. Strictly speaking, a ground wire connects to ground. Bonding means connecting things electrically so they have the same electrical potential. The things may have a potential of 120 volts, zero volts, or anything else, as long as both are the same. The idea is we don't want electricity flowing between the two. When we bond something to a ground wire, everything is effectively grounded.

BONDING PIPING SYSTEMS Metal pipes for water and gas can become live electrically if something goes wrong. In many areas, the hot water cold water and gas piping are bonded together and connected to the system ground to the house to reduce the risk of electrical shock from piping.

GROUND WIRE DOWNSTREAM OF WATER METER Connecting the ground wire to the plumbing system downstream of the water meter is not considered effective because stray electricity may not be able to get past the meter to ground, especially if the meter is removed for repair! This can be easily corrected by relocating the ground wire upstream of the meter, or providing a jumper wire around the meter.

NEXT STEPS Now we'll look at the main panel where electricity gets distributed throughout the house.

3.0 Service Panel

3.1 Panel (Panelboard in Electrical Code Terms)

DESCRIPTION Electricity is carried from the service box to the service panel. Modern systems use a combination panel where the service box and service panel are in one box. The black and red wires are each connected to a live connection bar (called a bus bar – a current-carrying metal bar with several connection points) and the white wire is connected to the neutral bus bar. Each branch circuit is connected to one of the two bus bars through a fuse or circuit breaker that protects that circuit.

TYPICAL HOUSEHOLD CIRCUIT (120-VOLT) The black or red branch circuit wire for an individual circuit is connected to its own small breaker (or fuse). The current flows through the bus bar, through the breaker or fuse, and into the black or red wire for the circuit. The electricity flows out, completes its circuit, running through whatever fixtures or appliances are in use on the circuit, and comes back through the white (neutral) wire. The white circuit wire is connected to the neutral bar, which is attached to the service entrance white wire.

It doesn't matter whether power is taken from the black or the red bus bar. The result is the same; a 120-volt branch circuit has been established. The typical 14-gauge copper wire is protected by a 15-amp breaker.

NUMBER OF CIRCUITS Panels may have room for anywhere from four to 40 circuits. 240-volt circuits for large electric appliances are established by combining a 120-volt black circuit and a 120-volt red circuit.

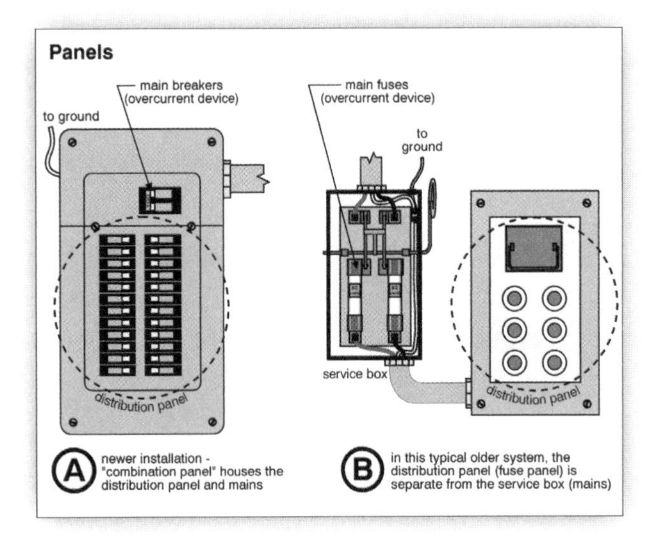

AUXILIARY PANEL (SUBPANEL) When the service panel is filled, an auxiliary panel can be added. This does not bring more power into the house; it simply allows for more branch circuits. It's like adding more branches to the tree without increasing the size of the trunk.

ELECTRICAL

Common Problems with Panels

DAMAGED/ LOOSE/RUST Where the panel is damaged mechanically or by water, it should be replaced. Water in the panel causes rust and possible connection problems. Poorly secured panels should be re-secured to the wall.

OBSOLETE PANEL Old ceramic fuse-holders, which may or may not be in a metal cabinet, are considered obsolete and unsafe. These should be replaced. These panels, which may be found on walls or ceilings, have exposed terminal connections, and it is easy to accidentally touch a live wire while changing a fuse.

PANEL COVER MISSING OR DAMAGED Covers should be provided or replaced as needed. Loose covers should be re-secured to reduce the risk of electric shock. Power should be disconnected prior to removing the cover.

UNPROTECTED PANEL OPENINGS There should be no openings in the panel that allow someone to reach in and touch a live electrical component. This may occur where the panel has room for more circuits, or where a fuse block has no fuse. Wherever this situation exists, the opening should be covered or the fuse block fitted with a fuse. Installing a blown fuse on a spare circuit to fill an opening is acceptable.

Unprotected panel openings may also occur at the sides of the panel, where circuit wires typically leave the panel. Any openings in the side of the panel should be blanked off.

UNDERSIZED PANEL Where the panel rating is smaller than the service size, the panel must be replaced with a larger one.

POOR PANEL LOCATION Panels are not allowed in clothes closets, bathrooms or stairways, for example.

POOR ACCESS TO PANEL The panel should be accessible with the center of the panel roughly five feet above the floor. The three-foot area in front of the panel should be kept clear for service access.

CROWDED WIRING IN THE PANEL Panels should not be overfilled with wire. Excess wire in the panel can lead to poor connections and overheating. This can happen if installers do not trim the wire to the right length inside the panel.

DAMAGED OR ABANDONED WIRE IN THE PANEL Damaged wire should be replaced. Abandoned wire in the panel may lead to overcrowding or confusion about what is live and what is not. It should be removed.

OVERHEATED PANEL WIRING Evidence of overheating including discoloration or melted wire insulation should be investigated by an electrician immediately. It may be the result of a loose connection, mechanical damage, moisture or overloading.

PANEL WIRING POORLY SECURED Most wiring leaves the panel through the side of the box. Wiring should be well secured where it leaves the panel. A cable connector is used to make sure the wire is not exposed to the sharp edges of the hole in the box, and to secure the wire so that if someone pulls on the wire, it will not loosen the connections inside the panel. Where these connectors are missing, they should be provided.

DOUBLED-UP CIRCUITS DOUBLE-TAPS, DOUBLE-LUGS People often add circuits as a house expands or as electrical needs grow. In some cases, circuits in the panel are doubled by adding a second wire to the terminal screw for one breaker or fuse. This double-tapping or double-lugging is not permitted and should be corrected. The most common solution is adding an auxiliary panel. Replacing the existing panel with a larger one is acceptable but more expensive. This makes sense if the existing panel is damaged or very old.

Some manufacturers have a special circuit breaker designed to hold two wires. Some authorities do not accept these types of breakers. Securing three wires under one terminal screw is never acceptable.

UNDERSIZED WIRE FEEDING AUXILIARY PANEL Where an auxiliary panel is used, the wire from the service panel to the auxiliary should be protected by breakers or fuses in the main panel. The wire size should be large enough to carry the load from the auxiliary panel. If the auxiliary panel is rated at 60 amps, the wire feeding it should also be rated at 60 amps. This would be a 6-gauge copper wire.

INAPPROPRIATE BONDING AT THE AUXILIARY PANEL The ground wire and neutral wire should not be bonded together in an auxiliary panel. This may turn the grounding wire into a current-carrying wire inadvertently, creating a dangerous situation.

SUSPECT PANEL Some electrical panels have been the subject of some controversy and there have been recalls.

3.2 Fuses and Breakers

DESCRIPTION Fuses and breakers perform the same function. They are the brains of the electrical system and shut off the circuit when too much current is flowing. A circuit breaker can be turned back on after the overload situation is corrected. A fuse has to be replaced.

DANGEROUS PRACTICES People sometimes get frustrated with fuses blowing. They do not understand that this is signaling a serious problem. Bypassing a fuse is a very dangerous practice. It is foolish to wrap a blown fuse with foil or put a penny in a fuse block. This may cause a fire.

OVER-FUSING One disadvantage of fuses is that it is easy to use the wrong size fuse. It is unfortunate that 15, 20, 25 and 30-amp fuses all fit into the same fuse block. An oversized fuse or breaker will not shut off the circuit in time to prevent overheating. Circuit breakers are typically not changed by the homeowner, and are less likely to be incorrectly sized.

FUSE REJECTORS Fuse rejector washers are small plastic rings that are inserted into the fuse block. There are different rejectors for 15, 20, 25 and 30 amp fuses. Fuse rejectors prevent the wrong fuse from being screwed into the fuse block.

TYPE C FUSES Here's another way to prevent over-fusing: Type C screw-in (plug) fuses are non-interchangeable. This means that the wrong size fuse will not fit into the fuse holder.

OTHER TYPES OF FUSES Fuses rated at 15, 20, 25 and 30 amps are glass screw-in type fuses. Larger fuses are always cartridge type with a metal collar at each end. Cartridge fuses are also available in smaller sizes.

TIME DELAY (TYPE D) FUSES When electric motors start up, they draw a lot of electric current for a very short time. In some cases this can lead to nuisance fuse blowing. Special time delay (Type D) fuses allow this extra electricity for a very short time. This is okay, because things will not overheat in a second or two. Circuit breakers have this time delay feature built in.

TYPE P FUSES Type P fuses have an added safety feature. The low melting temperature of this fuse senses heat build-up around the fuse, which may be caused by a poor connection between the fuse itself and the fuse holder. Poor connections can overheat and cause fires with current flows that are too small to blow a fuse.

WHICH CIRCUIT IS OFF? Most circuit breakers trip by moving the switch to the middle position, others simply switch to the off position. It is usually very easy to see which circuit breaker has tripped. The circuit is re-activated by simply 'switching' the breaker off and on again. With fuses, it is not always easy to see which one has blown. On glass fuses, you can usually see if you look closely through the glass, but on a cartridge type fuse it is often difficult to know.

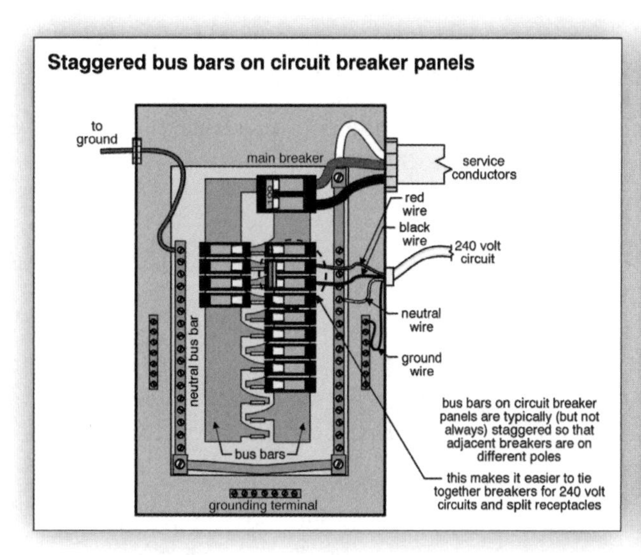

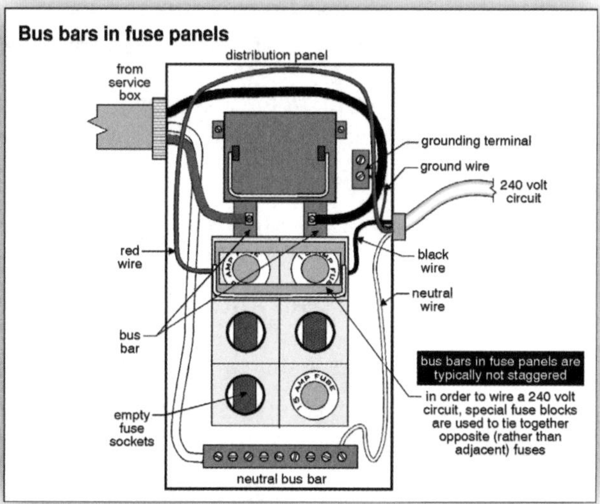

Common Problems with Fuses and Breakers

OVER-FUSING The most common flaw with fuse panels is fuses that are the wrong size for the wire. This unsafe condition should be corrected promptly to prevent overheating of the wire. The illustration below shows the appropriate size of fuse for given wire sizes.

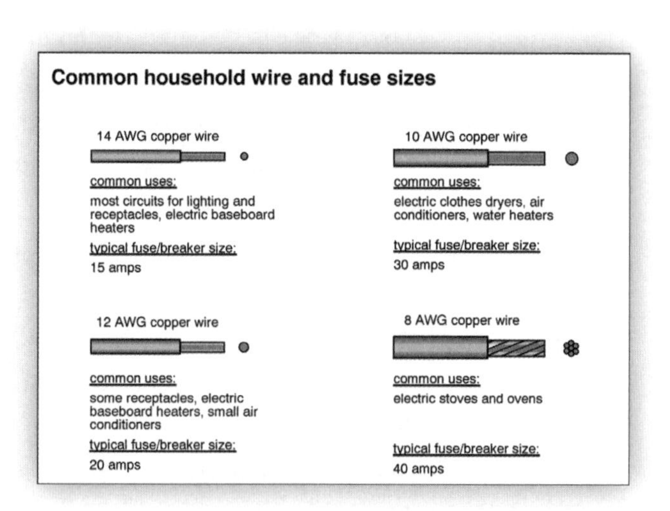

DAMAGED OR LOOSE A broken or damaged fuse holder or circuit breaker may not operate properly and should be replaced. Poorly secured fuse holders or circuit breakers may result in poor connections and should be re-secured or replaced.

DOUBLED-UP CIRCUITS (DOUBLE-TAPS, DOUBLE-LUGS) (TEXT REPEATED FOR CLARITY) People often add circuits as a house expands or as electrical needs grow. In some cases, circuits in the panel are doubled by adding a second wire to the terminal screw for one breaker or fuse. This double-tapping or double-lugging is not permitted and should be corrected. The most common solution is adding an auxiliary panel. Replacing the existing panel with a larger one is acceptable but more expensive. This makes sense if the existing panel is damaged or very old.

Some manufacturers have a special circuit breaker designed to hold two wires. Some authorities do not accept these types of breakers. Securing three wires under one terminal screw is never acceptable.

3.3 240-Volt Circuits and Multi-wire 120-Volt Circuits

DESCRIPTION Heavy duty appliances use 240-volts. These include electric ranges, ovens and cook tops, clothes dryers, electric furnaces and heaters, air conditioners and water heaters. Here, the black wire and red wire are both used in the circuit. For most of these appliances, a white neutral wire is also used.

Multi-wire 120-volt circuits use cables with the black, red and white conductor. At some point in the circuit, these split into two 120-volt circuits. These circuits can be used to reduce the amount of wire that has to be run throughout the house. These are common for dishwashers and garbage disposals, for example. They may also be used at kitchen receptacles. The top half of the receptacle can be on one circuit and the bottom half can be on another. This allows the two appliances to be plugged in to the same outlet without blowing a fuse or tripping the breaker. These circuits have two fuses or breakers, just like 240-volt circuits.

Two breakers (or fuses) are needed; one for the black wire, and one for the red wire. These two breakers (or fuses) should be linked so that if one is switched off (breaker) or pulled out (fuse), the other must be switched off or pulled out with it. This is a safety feature to prevent electric shocks. If only one part of the circuit was turned off, there would still be power to the other part. It would not be safe to work on the system.

Circuit breakers should have mechanical ties or links to make sure both are turned off. There are also special double circuit breakers with a single handle. With fuses, double fuse holders are used that must be pulled out together to disconnect the circuit.

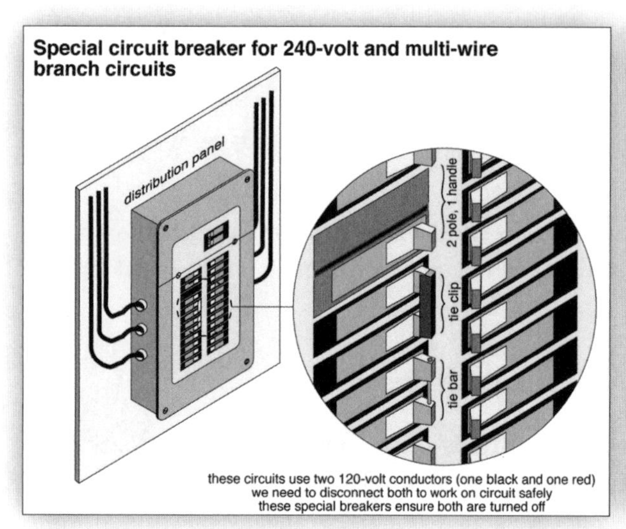

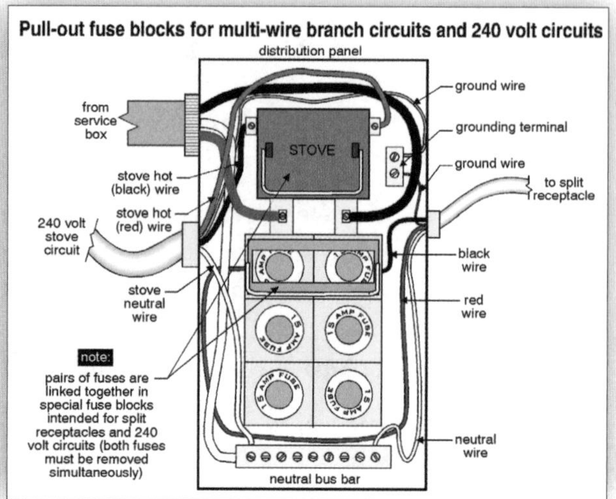

The Common Problem with Multi-wire Circuits

MISSING LINKS FOR BREAKERS OR MISSING PULLOUTS FOR FUSES The most common issue with 240-volt circuits and multi-wire 120-volt circuits is the absence of the device to make sure both circuits are turned off. In most cases, this important safety improvement is inexpensive.

NEXT STEPS Before we move on and look at the wiring throughout the house, we are going to look at a couple of other devices that help circuit breakers and fuses make houses safer – ground fault circuit interrupters and arc fault circuit interrupters. The names are confusing but the concepts are simple.

3.4 Ground Fault Circuit Interrupters

DESCRIPTION These safety devices have been around since about 1970. They improve the safety of regular circuit breakers and fuses by reducing electric shock hazards. Instead of looking for too much current flowing, they look for current going where it's not supposed to go. They shut the power off when as little as .005 amps are leaking. Under normal circumstances, the same amount of current is flowing at any point in the circuit. If there are five amps flowing out through the black wire, there should be five amps coming back through the white wire. If there is a difference, current is escaping somewhere, and this is dangerous. The GFCI shuts down the circuit when it measures different currents in the black and white wires.

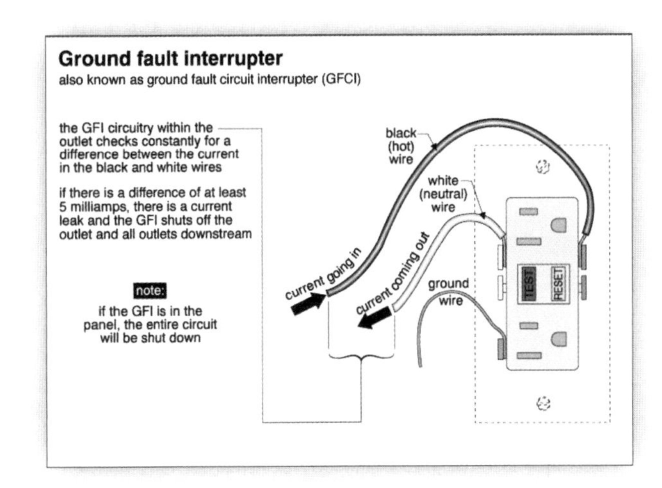

Modern electrical codes require ground fault protection where there is the potential for water to come into contact with electricity. This includes receptacles for bathrooms, kitchen countertops, wet bars, laundry tubs, spas and hot tubs, whirlpool baths, swimming pools, unfinished basements and outdoor receptacles.

Protection may be provided by GFCI circuit breakers or receptacles. GFCI circuit breakers at the panel protect the entire circuit. GFCI receptacles protect only that outlet, and the downstream outlets on that circuit. Note: we use the terms receptacle and outlet interchangeably, as most home owners do.

While electrical codes require these devices in new work, they do not require them on existing installations, although the extra protection afforded by these devices is desirable. Code requirements for GFCIs have changed several times since they were introduced in 1970.

IDENTIFICATION Ground fault circuit interrupter breakers at the panel can be identified by the Test and Reset buttons. Ground fault interrupter receptacles can also be identified by the Test and Reset buttons.

Common Problems with Ground Fault Circuit Interrupters

MIS-WIRED In addition to the normal problems that may be the result of mis-wired electrical receptacles, a mis-wired GFCI receptacle may not shut off the circuit as expected. A common problem is the reversal of the "line" and "load" connections on the back or sides of the outlet. Newer GFCI receptacles will not reset if the wiring is done improperly. Correcting this problem is quick and inexpensive.

MISSING GFCIs may not be provided in new work as required by local jurisdictions. Replacing conventional breakers with GFCI breakers is not difficult, although GFCI breakers are more expensive.

TEST FAULTY/ INOPERATIVE GFCIs have a test button that simulates a ground fault situation. Pressing this button will cause the breaker to trip if it is working properly. If the test button does not trip the breaker, the device may have to be replaced. Since this test turns off the power to everything connected to the circuit, many home inspectors do not perform this test.

There may be no power to the GFCI. A specialist should be engaged to investigate.

3.5 Arc Fault Circuit Interrupters

DESCRIPTION Arc Fault Circuit Interrupters (AFCIs) help protect against fires by detecting arcing. Arcing is an electrical problem that occurs when electricity jumps from one conductor across an insulator to another conductor. Light and heat are generated as the current passes through the insulator, which may be air or a solid insulating material. Arc faults are common where electrical cords are damaged, or where outlets are not properly installed.

GFCIs are designed to prevent electrical shock. AFCIs are designed to prevent fires. GFCIs look for electricity that is not where it's supposed to be by measuring current running through wires. AFCIs look for overheating by monitoring the waveform of the circuit voltage.

Arc faults are dangerous because the heat generated may ignite nearby combustible material, starting a fire. Arc fault currents are often too small to trip a breaker or blow a fuse. A GFCI will not detect arc faults. An AFCI breaker protects the entire circuit.

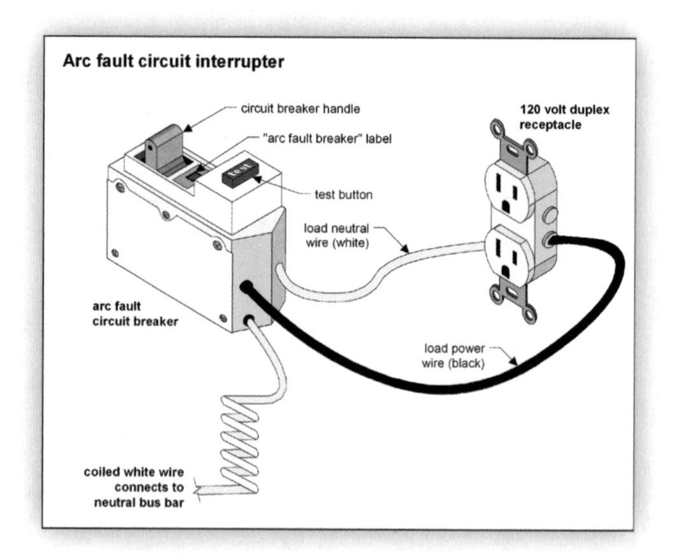

WHERE NEEDED In houses built since roughly 2001, AFCIs have been required on circuits serving bedrooms. In some areas, codes have extended this requirement to other areas in the house, such as living rooms, dining rooms and hallways. They do not have to be added to existing installations.

Common Problems with Arc Fault Circuit Interrupters

MISSING AFCIs may not be provided in new homes as required by local jurisdictions. Replacing conventional breakers with AFCI breakers is not difficult, although AFCI breakers are more expensive than conventional breakers.

FAULTY AFCIs have a test button to simulate an arcing situation. Pressing this button will cause the breaker to trip if it is working properly. Since this turns off the power to everything connected to the circuit, many home inspectors do not perform this test.

4.0 Branch Circuit Wiring

4.1 Branch Circuit Wire: (Distribution Wiring)

DESCRIPTION The wire carrying electricity from the panel to the fixtures and appliances is typically copper, although aluminum was commonly used from the mid-1960s to the late 1970s. Each post-1960 cable is made up of two conductors and one ground wire. Pre-1960 installations did not include a ground wire in each branch circuit. (Notes: Dates are approximate. We use the terms wire and conductor interchangeably.)

The conductors are wrapped with color-coded plastic insulation. On older wiring, the insulation was rubber. The ground wire is not insulated. This group of three wires is typically wrapped in a plastic or nylon sheathing. Older sheathings were paper, cloth and rubber. Flexible metal cable and rigid metal conduit are also used as sheathing.

BLACK AND WHITE WIRE One conductor has black insulation and is the live or hot wire. The other conductor has white insulation and is referred to as the neutral. Neither wire should be touched when there is power to the circuit. The black and white wires carry the current. The voltage available is 120 volts, and the current flow is less than 15 amps.

GROUND WIRE (EQUIPMENT GROUNDING CONDUCTOR – ECG) The ground wire is normally idle. If there is a problem, the ground acts as an escape route for the electricity, inducing the current to flow through this wire to the ground, rather than into a person, causing an electrical shock. Grounded distribution wiring was introduced to residential electric systems in the late 1950s.

THREE CONDUCTOR CABLE 240-volt circuits and multi-wire 120-volt circuits have an additional live or hot wire, as we have discussed. This cable contains a black, red, and white insulated wire as well as an uninsulated ground wire.

WIRE GAUGE The normal wire size is 14-gauge. This is capable of carrying 15 amps safely. A fuse or circuit breaker rated at 15 amps should always be provided on a 14-gauge copper circuit. In some cases, 20-amp circuits serve kitchen or other outlets. The copper wire size for these circuits should be 12-gauge.

DEDICATED CIRCUITS (INDIVIDUAL BRANCH CIRCUITS) All 240-volt appliances get dedicated circuits. This includes things like stoves, water heaters, air conditioners, clothes dryers, hot tubs and saunas. Some 120-volt appliances also get a dedicated circuit. This includes such things as the furnace or boiler, dishwasher, food waste disposal, compactor, central vacuum system, microwave oven, refrigerator, freezer, washing machine, whirlpool bathtub, and electric heaters. Split receptacles (outlets where the top and bottom halves are on separate circuits) are also usually on dedicated circuits. Exterior outlets are often on one dedicated circuit. A home inspection will not identify which circuits are dedicated. These are determined when the electrical circuits are labeled.

NOT A SAFETY CONCERN Dedicated circuits are rare in older houses and it is very difficult to verify during a visual inspection. It is not a major expense to rearrange this, and the issue is not one of life safety, simply a matter of convenience. Without dedicated circuits for each of these appliances, there is the possibility of nuisance fuse blowing or circuit breaker tripping with several appliances in use simultaneously.

REFRIGERATOR AND FREEZER The reason a refrigerator or freezer gets a dedicated circuit is to prevent food spoilage. If it is on a circuit with other appliances, the fuse or breaker may be blown as a result of a problem with another appliance. The fuse or breaker may not be replaced immediately if the homeowner doesn't know that the refrigerator or freezer is also on this circuit. As a result, food may be spoiled. Again, home inspectors will not pick this up.

FURNACE OR BOILER The heating system should be on a dedicated circuit. If the heating system was to shut down due to an overload from another appliance, the house would be without heat. This can result in freezing if the home is unoccupied for some time.

HEAVY CURRENT DRAW Some appliances need dedicated circuits because of their heavy electrical draw. Putting additional outlets and lights on the circuit may lead to regular shut-downs.

Common Problems with Branch Circuit Wiring

DAMAGED Wire that is damaged or has been overheated should be replaced. Wire that is nicked is smaller in diameter at that spot. The smaller the wire, the more difficult it is for electricity to move through. (The resistance is higher.) This can lead to localized overheating, and eventually a fire.

OPEN SPLICES Connections should be made inside panels or junction boxes. Exposed connections are not safe and should be corrected.

CABLE CONNECTORS MISSING OR INEFFECTIVE Wire should be protected from the metal edges of panels and boxes with appropriate cable connectors. This is usually done with bushings, grommets or cable clamps. These devices not only protect the wire from the sharp edges, but they secure the wire, so something pulling on the wire will not cause a loose connection. Missing or ineffective connectors should be replaced.

LOOSE OR DAMAGED Wiring which is poorly secured should be re-secured as necessary to protect it from mechanical damage and reduce the risk of electric shock. The wire should be secured where it enters a panel, junction box or fixture. The wire should be secured within 12 inches of the box, and every four and a half feet to five feet thereafter.

If cable staples are used, only one wire should be secured under each staple. Staples should be the appropriate size for the wire. Inappropriate stapling can damage the cable, risking overheating or electric shock.

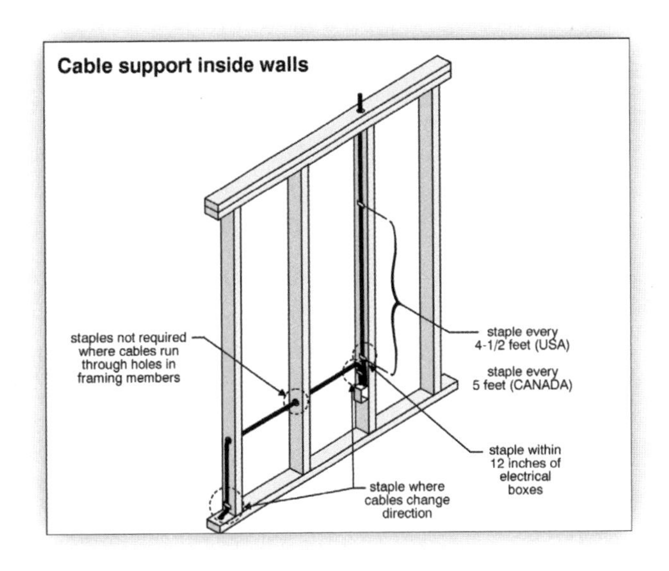

EXPOSED TO DAMAGE Wires should not be exposed to mechanical damage. Wires should be run through joists in unfinished basements, rather than on the underside, where they are more likely to be damaged. Wires should be set well back from any nailing surface in stud walls, to avoid a nail being driven into the wires. Alternatively, steel plates should be used to protect the wires from nails or screws.

Wire should not be run along interior surfaces of walls, floors or ceilings in finished areas.

EXPOSED IN ATTIC Ideally, the joists should be drilled and the cables should be run through them. Although very common, it is considered poor practice to secure the cable to the top of the joists.

DON'T WALK THROUGH INSULATED ATTICS Walking through an insulated attic where you can't see what you are stepping on is very dangerous because wiring is often run along the top of the attic for joists or trusses. That's why home inspectors don't do it, and you shouldn't either.

DAMAGED INSULATION The wiring may be damaged by rodents. Mice and squirrels in the attic, for example, can damage wiring insulation and create a fire hazard. This is often difficult to detect without pulling back the insulation. Where pests are known to have been in a home, an electrician should inspect the wiring.

UNPROTECTED SURFACE WIRING Where wiring is run on the surface of walls, baseboards or other interior finishes, it should be protected from mechanical damage with a rigid covering.

TOO CLOSE TO DUCTS AND PIPING Wiring should be kept at least one inch away from heating ducts and hot water piping to avoid overheating the wire. Insulation can be used to separate these materials.

UNDERSIZED WIRE Wire that is too small for the appliance it serves, or for the rest of the circuit wiring, should be replaced to reduce the risk of overheating.

EXTENSION CORDS USED AS PERMANENT WIRING Extension cords should not be used as permanent wiring, and should never be stapled to walls, floors or trim. Cords should not run under carpets or go through doorways or windows. These practices are fire hazards.

ABANDONED WIRING Wires that are not in use should be removed or the wire ends should be terminated in junction boxes to prevent confusion and electrical shocks.

IMPROPER EXTERIOR WIRING Exterior wiring should be suitable for outdoor use. There are different types of exterior wire for above grade and below ground use. Exterior wiring should be protected from mechanical damage and special exterior junction boxes are required.

Smaller electrical wires (14-gauge, 12-gauge and 10-gauge) are made up of a single solid conductor. Larger wires (8-gauge and larger) are made up of a number of strands of smaller conductors. These stranded wires are much stronger in tension than solid conductors. Solid conductors (10-gauge and smaller) cannot be run as overhead unsupported wiring because the metal may fatigue. Solid conductor overhead wiring should be replaced.

OVERLOADED CIRCUITS While it is difficult to tell from a visual inspection, the number of lights and outlets (receptacles) on any given branch circuit should be such that the circuit will not draw more than the circuit rating (typically 15 amps) under normal circumstances. At a maximum, 12 lights and/or outlets should be connected to each circuit. The practical limitation, however, is if one of the outlets is used for a hair dryer, which may draw close to 15 amps, it is wise to connect the circuit only to other outlets which will be used for very low-drawing appliances such as clocks, radios, televisions, computers or lights. Most circuits serve a combination of electrical receptacles and lights.

TERMINOLOGY DOUBLE-TALK Electricity is confusing, there's no getting around it. Here's an example of what electrical purists call things: Black and red wires are live and are called 'ungrounded' conductors. White wires are neutral and are called 'grounded' conductors. Ground wires are the emergency system and are called 'grounding' conductors. That's just cruel.

4.2 Knob-and-Tube Wiring

DESCRIPTION Knob-and-tube wiring was used in homes until approximately 1950. While different than the wiring that is used now, it is not necessarily inferior. This wire gets its name from the ceramic knobs that secure it and the ceramic tubes that protect the wire as it passes through wood-framing members such as floor joists.

SEPARATE BLACK AND WHITE The black and white wires in knob-and-tube systems are run separately, in two distinct cables. In modern cables, the black wire, white wire and ground wire are all wrapped up in a single cable. It was felt originally, that having the black wire and white wire separate was safer, since there was very little chance of the black and white wires ever touching, creating a short circuit. This has not proved to be a big problem with modern cables.

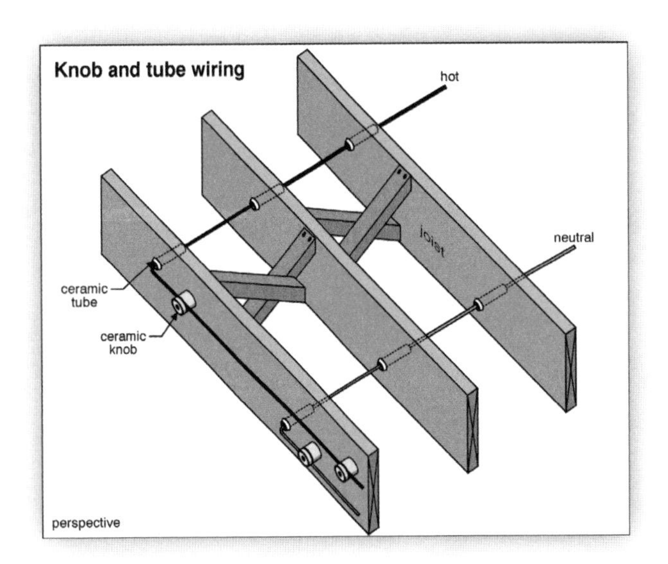

NO JUNCTION BOXES Another difference between knob-and-tube wiring and modern cable is that with knob-and-tube wiring, electrical junction boxes were not used to connect wires. In modern construction, wires must be connected inside a closed box. Knob-and-tube connections were made by twisting the wiring together, soldering the wires, and wrapping the connection in rubber, then in electrical tape. While no longer a common practice, if properly done and not disturbed, these connections will serve indefinitely.

NO GROUND WIRE Another difference between knob-and-tube wiring and modern cable is the absence of a ground wire. As mentioned earlier, knob-and-tube wiring was used up until 1950. From the 1950s to roughly 1960, two-conductor cable was popular, although no ground wire was included. Since roughly 1960, ground wires have been incorporated into the two-conductor cable, and electrical receptacles included a third slot (for the grounding pin) thereafter.

WIRE INSULATION Another distinction between knob-and-tube wiring and some modern cables is in the insulation. The knob-and-tube wiring used rubber insulation and cloth sheathing around the wiring. In modern cables, each wire has plastic insulation typically, and the entire cable is wrapped with another layer of plastic. Over the years, these sheathing materials have included cloth, paper, rubber, metal and plastic.

BRITTLE INSULATION Breakdown of the insulation on knob-and-tube wiring is often the reason it is replaced. This is frequently the result of overheating or mechanical abuse.

REPLACEMENT While knob-and-tube wiring must be recognized as old, it is not necessary to replace it as a matter of course. It should be inspected and evaluated on an individual basis.

Common Problems with Knob-and-Tube Wiring

POOR CONNECTIONS Problems with knob-and-tube wire almost always result from amateurish connections made after original installation. Since original connections were made without junction boxes, many home owners felt they too could make connections to knob-and-tube wiring without junction boxes. This is an unsafe practice, particularly since the chance of making a splice as good as the original connection is very remote. In any case, this violates modern electrical rules.

DAMAGE Since knob-and-tube wiring is invariably old, it has been subject to more home handymen, more mechanical abuse (such as items stored on top of the wire in the basement or attic), and is more likely to have suffered wear and tear. Pinched wiring and damaged insulation is a problem, particularly in unfinished basements, where the wiring is exposed.

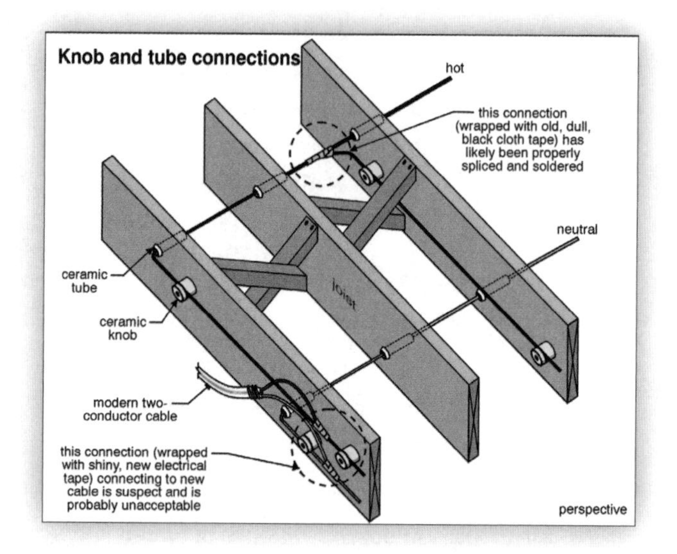

BRITTLE Another problem is brittle knob-and-tube wire insulation, which may occur if the wire has overheated in the past as a result of over-fusing, a poor connection or damaged cable. Often the wire becomes brittle in high heat areas, such as panels and junction boxes. In exposed areas, where inspection is easy, there is usually good air circulation and little heat build-up. The wires are least likely to be brittle in these areas.

Brittle wire insulation may be a problem where the wire is buried in attic insulation. This is common in attics where insulation has been upgraded.

CIRCUITS EXTENDED Since older electrical systems had few circuits by today's standards, the chances of each knob-and-tube circuit having been extended over the years are very good. While this is not necessarily a problem, the additional loads and the possibilities of poor connections make an argument for replacing older knob-and-tube wiring. This is often cost-effective during remodeling.

TWO FUSE CIRCUITS (FUSED NEUTRALS) In all modern systems, there is only one circuit breaker or fuse at the beginning of each circuit. There is a very good reason for this. When we want to work on a circuit, we have to turn it off. Using the fuse or circuit breaker is a common way to do that. If the fuse or breaker is at the end of the circuit, turning it off will leave the entire circuit live until we get to the breaker. That makes it very dangerous to work on the system.

Another problem specific to knob-and-tube wiring is the presence of two fuses on a single circuit. Both the black and white wires have fuses on some very old panels. This means there is a fuse at the beginning and at the end of the circuit. If the fuse on the neutral wire blows, the fixtures and appliances on this circuit will not work. It is not safe, however, to work on the circuit! Power is still available through the circuit, right up to the blown fuse. A person could get a shock in this case. By the way, one fuse on each circuit is perfectly adequate.

We can replace these old panels to solve the problem, without having to replace the knob-and-tube wiring throughout the house.

INSURANCE DIFFICULTIES Some companies will only provide insurance after an inspection and approval of the knob-and-tube wiring by the local authorities. Many companies will not offer insurance at all on houses with knob-and-tube wiring.

REPLACE WHEN REMODELING It is much less expensive to replace wiring in a home when remodeling a home. Walls, ceilings and floors are opened up and accessible. Many homes with knob-and-tube wiring have the wiring replaced as individual rooms are remodeled. It's very common to find pre-1950s homes with a combination of knob-and-tube and modern wiring.

4.3 Aluminum Wire

DESCRIPTION Aluminum wiring was commonly used from the mid-1960s until about 1978. It was introduced because it was less expensive than copper. It was recognized from the start that aluminum wiring is not quite as good a conductor of electricity as is copper. As a result, 12-gauge aluminum was used in place of 14-gauge copper for a 15 amp household circuit. Other wire sizes were also suitably increased. This was fine.

THERMAL EXPANSION Some other properties of aluminum, however, were not recognized and did cause problems. Firstly, aluminum has a higher co-efficient of thermal expansion than copper. This means that when the wire heats up (as all wire does when electricity flows) the aluminum tends to expand more than copper. This leads to the wire trying to move out from under the terminal screws at connections. This phenomenon is called "creep" and can lead to poor connections and subsequent overheating.

SOFT Secondly, aluminum is softer than copper, and electricians used to working with copper would often nick aluminum wiring inadvertently. Nicking the wire, of course, reduces its diameter, and its ability to carry electricity. Localized hot spots can develop where the wire has been nicked. Further, if the wire is bent after it has been nicked, it will often break.

INSULATING OXIDE Lastly, the oxide of aluminum that forms on the wire is a very poor electrical conductor. All metals rust or oxidize. The greenish copper oxide that forms on copper wiring is no problem because it is a good electrical conductor. The oxide that forms on aluminum can lead to higher resistance and higher temperatures.

CU-AL & CO/ALR As a result of these difficulties, special components, designated CU-AL or AL-CU, were introduced. These components can be used with either copper or aluminum wiring. These included wire connectors (wire nuts), electrical receptacles, circuit breakers, stove blocks, etc. In most cases, these improvements were satisfactory. However, electrical receptacles and light switches continued to be a problem. The subsequently designed receptacles and switches were designated CO/ALR. This designation means Copper/Aluminum Revised.

One alternative to using special components is to join the aluminum wires to short "pig-tails" of copper wire just before they connect to outlets, distribution panel terminals, and so on. The connection between the aluminum and copper wire is made with a connector known to be appropriate. There are connectors specifically approved for this purpose.

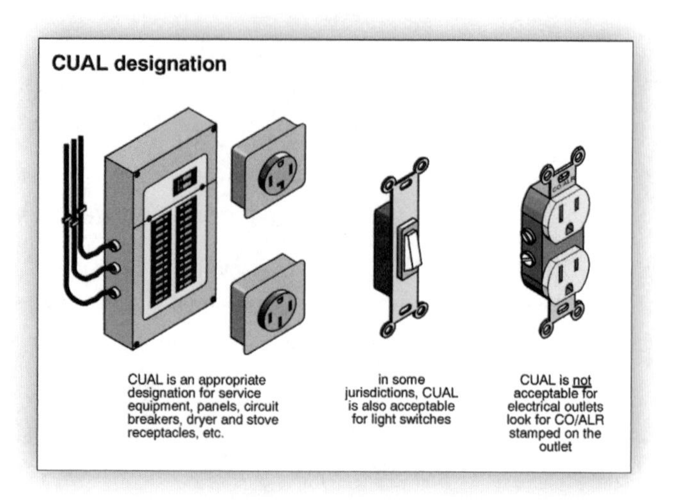

SPECIAL SYSTEMS There were some special systems developed to connect copper and aluminum wire. Many are no longer available and installations are typically evaluated individually by an electrician.

ACCEPTABLE As long as proper connectors are used, and the connections are made without damaging the wire, aluminum wiring is considered safe. It is permitted for use by electrical codes, although it is not commonly used in homes due to the adverse publicity it received during its early problem years. It is still used commonly by utilities in street wiring and for service entrance cables. In some areas, aluminum is still commonly used for 240 volt appliances like ranges and air conditioners.

Common Problems with Aluminum Wiring

PANEL/BREAKERS/ RECEPTACLES/ CONNECTORS – NOT PROPERLY RATED Where special devices or connectors have not been provided for aluminum, they should be added. It is often difficult to know whether the small twist-on connectors are appropriate. The safest thing is to replace them with those known to be appropriate. For example, the small twist-on connectors are so small that they are not marked CU-AL. They are now color-coded, but on older ones it is difficult to know whether or not they are appropriate. Since they only cost a few cents each, it makes sense to replace them with those known to be the correct type. Some experts do not consider twist-on connectors to be appropriate for use with aluminum wire.

INSPECTION BY SPECIALIST RECOMMENDED The examination of every electrical connection in the home is not part of a home inspection. The provision of special aluminum compatible connectors is not an expensive undertaking. We recommend that the specialist check all the devices in the home of aluminum wiring and make improvements as needed.

OVERHEATING Aluminum wires that show evidence of overheating should be further investigated by a specialist. There may or may not be a significant problem.

ANTI-OXIDANT MISSING Connections on large gauge aluminum wires are typically coated with a special grease to prevent corrosion. Where this is missing, aluminum oxide may build up and the wires may overheat.

NEXT STEPS We've talked about everything right up to and including how we get electricity through the house. Now we'll have a look at the endpoints where it gets used.

5.0 Outlets, Lights, Switches And Junction Boxes

5.1 Outlets (Receptacles)

DESCRIPTION Electrical outlets are used to plug in portable lights, appliances, heaters, etc. Most outlets are duplex, meaning that we can plug in two appliances. They are usually located in walls, but can also be installed in ceilings and floors in special cases. An adequate number of convenient receptacles is a distinct advantage for today's lifestyles. Situations that require extension cords are inherently dangerous.

THE RULES KEEP CHANGING The rules around electrical outlets change regularly. Most existing houses will not comply with the most current code requirements. While improvements are possible, this is not considered a defect.

POLARIZED Until 1960 most receptacles were ungrounded. They had only two slots in them, one connected to a black wire and one connected to a white. Outlets typically have the two slots in different sizes, (polarized receptacles) so that a polarized appliance could only be installed in the proper orientation. The smaller slot is designed for the black wire (hot or live wire) and the larger slot is connected to the white (neutral wire).

LIGHT SOCKET POLARITY Polarity is important on some appliances. In some cases, polarity is important for safety. In others it is important for proper operation of the appliance.

A lamp is a good example of an appliance that has a polarized plug for safety reasons. There are two electrical components of the light socket that may be live electrically. The threaded collar around the socket is one half of the connection, and the brass button at the bottom of the socket is the other connection. A person is much more likely to touch the threaded collar that comes up to the top of the socket when replacing a light bulb, so it is safer to make that the white (neutral) connection. The black (live) connection at the bottom of the socket is less likely to be touched.

Some home entertainment systems require polarized connections to operate properly.

BLACK TO BRASS Many modern outlets have a brass colored screw on one side to which the live (usually black) wire is connected. The white (neutral) wire is connected to the silver colored screw on the opposite side, and the ground wire is connected to the ground screw (usually green) near the end of the outlet.

PUSH-IN, BAYONET OR DAGGER Some modern outlets do not have screws on the sides to hold wires in place, but have holes in the back, into which the wires are fitted. These are called bayonet, dagger or push-in type connectors, because of the way the wire is inserted. These outlets were particularly troublesome when used with aluminum wire.

TAMPER RESISTANT Tamper-resistant receptacles are designed to prevent children from inserting things like paper clips or keys into the receptacle. An internal mechanism will block such attempts unless both prongs of a plug are inserted into the outlet at the same time.

GROUNDED OUTLETS The grounding of electrical outlets, which became popular after 1960, affords additional protection. The ground wire is a third wire that normally conducts no electricity. It is an escape route for stray electricity, in case something goes wrong with the appliance or receptacle. When an appliance malfunctions, a cord is damaged, a connection comes loose or a receptacle is faulty, a person touching a live electrical component may get a shock. The ground wire provides a safe path for the electricity, so it does not flow through a person touching the system.

Grounded receptacles are only useful for appliances with grounded plugs. There are very few home appliances with grounded plugs. These include refrigerators, washing machines, microwaves, waterbed heaters, some computers, some small kitchen appliances and some power tools, for example. Grounded plugs also control polarity, since appliance plugs can only be put into outlets one way.

GFCIS AS AN ALTERNATIVE A ground fault circuit interrupter (GFCI) on an ungrounded circuit will improve the safety of the system. Many electrical authorities will now accept ground fault circuit interrupters as an alternative to grounding in existing homes. GFCIs can be installed at the panel or as GFCI receptacles. Some authorities may not accept GFCI receptacles. For more information about how ground fault circuit interrupters work, see 3.4 in this chapter.

20-AMP RECEPTACLES FOR KITCHENS 20-amp receptacles are protected by a 20-amp breaker and the wire size for 20-amp circuits is 12-gauge, rather than 14-gauge. 20-amp receptacles are easy to identify because the larger (neutral) slots are T-shaped. These receptacles are also common in laundry areas and bathrooms where high-current small appliances are common – kettles, toasters, hair dryers, etc. Receptacles rated at 15 amps may be found on 20-amp branch circuits.

Common Problems with Outlets (Receptacles)

UNGROUNDED Where only two-prong appliances are used, this does not pose a hazard. However, where three-prong plugs (grounded appliances) are used, the outlet should be grounded. A special ground wire can be added, but this is expensive and rarely done. The ground fault circuit interrupter provides improved safety, but it is not quite a replacement for grounding.

POOR LOCATION Outlets should not be installed horizontally in floors or countertops unless they are a special type suitable for this application. Moisture can create an electrical hazard. For the same reason, outlets should not be located on countertop surfaces, facing up.

Outlets should not be close to a source of water unless protected by a ground fault circuit interrupter. They should not be directly above kitchen sinks or bathroom basins, for example, where appliance wires may touch water. Outlets should not be above electric baseboard heaters or close to other heat sources, where appliance wires may touch hot surfaces.

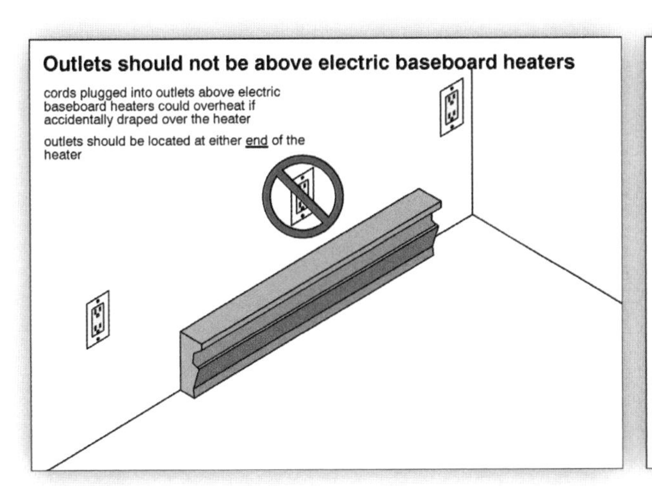

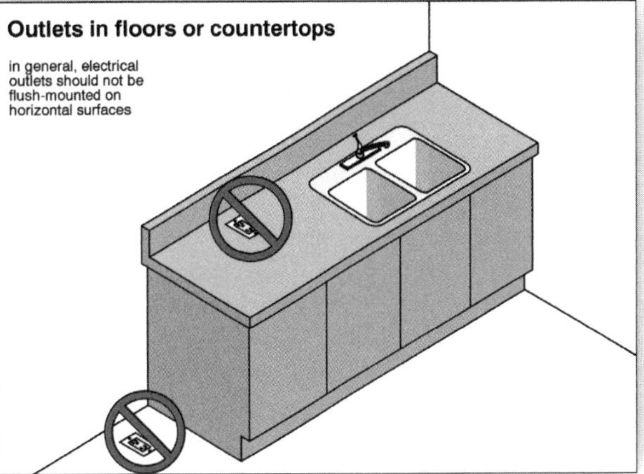

REVERSED POLARITY OUTLETS Modern outlets have a large slot (neutral) and small slot (hot). If the wires are connected improperly, this is referred to as reversed polarity. A reversed polarity outlet can compromise the safety of an electric appliance. A grounded appliance may have its grounding made ineffective by reversed polarity.

With reversed polarity outlets, it is possible for some appliances to have their housing become live in the event of a malfunction. It is also possible for some electrical equipment to operate improperly with reversed polarity. This may include a home computer, a stereo system, etc. Corrective action simply involves connecting the wires to the correct terminals on the outlet (black wire to the brass terminal and white wire to the silver terminal).

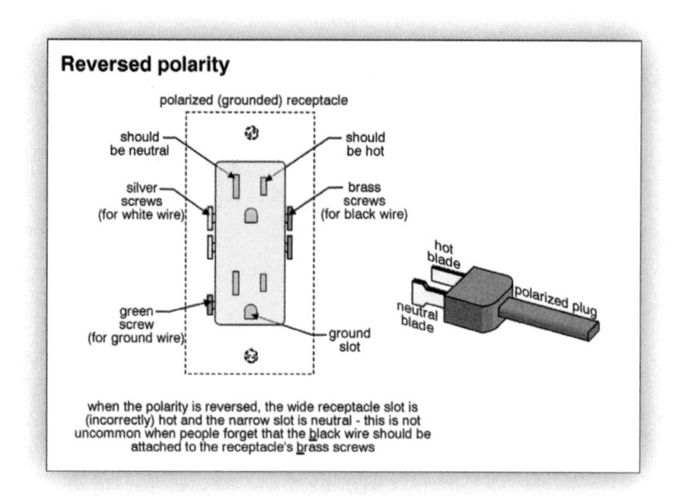

NUMBER OF OUTLETS There should be receptacles wherever people are likely to plug things in. In new construction, there should be an outlet within six feet horizontally of any point along the wall (in finished living spaces). Translated, this means there should be an outlet every 12 feet along the wall. In new kitchens, there should be an outlet within two feet or three feet of any point along the counter.

Older homes will not typically have as many outlets as modern lifestyles demand. Common sense says there should be outlets wherever you need them. If you have lots of extension cords, you need more outlets.

BATHROOMS Outlets should be within three feet of basins, but not directly above the basin. In modern construction, bathroom outlets should be protected by GFCIs.

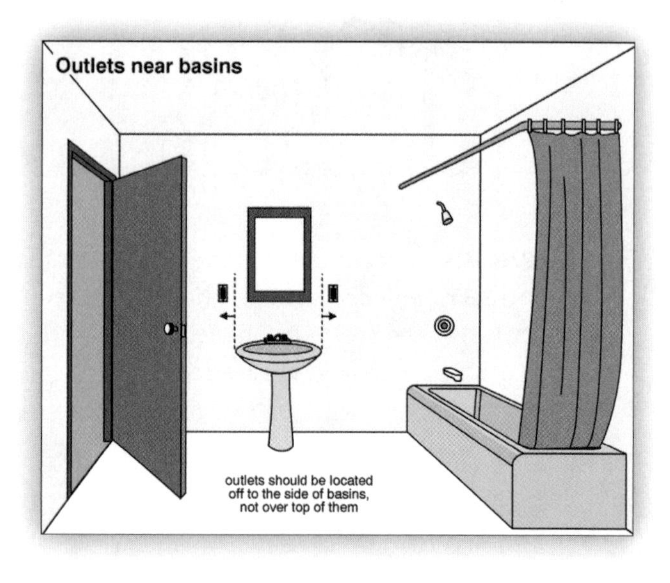

LOOSE/ DAMAGED/ WORN/ OVERHEATED As outlets wear, they may not hold plugs securely in place. Electrical outlets that are loose or damaged should be repaired or replaced. Similarly, cover plates should be replaced when damaged. Where there is evidence of overheating, a specialist should be engaged to investigate.

WEATHER-TIGHT OUTLETS NEEDED Special weather-tight outlets are required outdoors or where water may contact the outlet.

COVER PLATE MISSING/ DAMAGED Damaged or missing cover plates should be replaced.

WON'T WORK If an outlet is inoperative, it is possible that:

1. The outlet itself is defective.
2. The wires inside the box at the outlet are not properly connected. (Intermittent problems usually mean a loose connection.)
3. There is a problem in the wire between the panel and the outlet (perhaps at another box upstream).
4. There is a blown fuse or tripped breaker in the panel.
5. There is a poor connection or damaged wire in the panel.
6. The power has been turned off.

5.2 Lights (Luminaires in Electrical Code Terms)

DESCRIPTION Installed lighting may take the form of traditional ceiling-mounted fixtures, recessed lighting, combination lights and fans, or any number or architectural options. There are several types of lighting fixtures including incandescent, fluorescent, LED (light emitting diode) and halogen.

Common Problems with Light Fixtures

DAMAGED/ POORLY SECURED/ OVERHEATING Damaged light fixtures may present a fire or shock hazard and should be replaced. Light fixtures should be well secured to junction boxes. They should never be supported by the wiring. Light fixtures should be arranged so that they are not susceptible to overheating. Some fixtures require clearance from combustibles to prevent overheating, and some can only be installed in certain orientations.

MISSING When light fixtures are removed, sometimes open junction boxes are left with live wires in them. This is not safe and the box should be covered.

Lights should be provided for all exterior entrance doors, so people can enter safely at night.

WON'T WORK Inoperative lights may be the result of –

1. A burned out bulb.
2. A faulty light fixture.
3. A poor connection in the box.
4. A flaw in the wiring leading to the box.
5. A problem with the switch controlling the light.
6. A problem with the wire between the panel and the switch.
7. A blown fuse or tripped breaker.
8. A poor connection within the panel.

If the problem is not simply a burned out bulb or a blown fuse, you may need an electrician to resolve the difficulty.

FLICKERING LIGHTS Flickering lights may indicate dangerous conditions including poor connections. These should be investigated promptly by an electrician.

POT LIGHTS (RECESSED LIGHT FIXTURES) SHOULD BE CHECKED Unless they are specially designed for the application, recessed light fixtures should not be installed in areas where insulation will blanket the fixture, impeding normal heat dissipation. This may lead to overheating and is a common problem on the upper floor of the house. Special fixtures typically have a designation that includes the letters IC (Insulation Contact or Insulated Ceiling). These are often not visible to the home inspector. Where pot lights are used in an insulated cavity, an electrician should be engaged to verify the safety of the system.

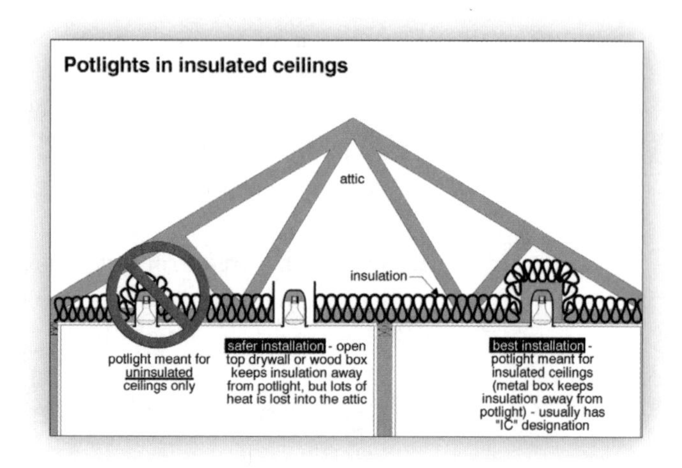

DAMP AREAS NEED SPECIAL FIXTURES Lights used in areas where exposure to water may occur, should be of a special type. This includes lights in shower stalls, saunas and outdoor light fixtures. Again, the home inspector may not be able to determine whether the lights are appropriate for the application.

STAIR LIGHTING SHOULD BE CONTROLLED FROM THE TOP AND BOTTOM Light for stairwells, except for unfinished basements, should be switched at the top and bottom. This eliminates the need to walk up or down poorly lit stairs.

HEAT LAMP PROBLEMS Heat lamps at ceiling level should be located beyond the swing of any doors. If a door is partially open below a heat lamp, a towel or article of clothing flung over the top of the door can be ignited, causing a fire.

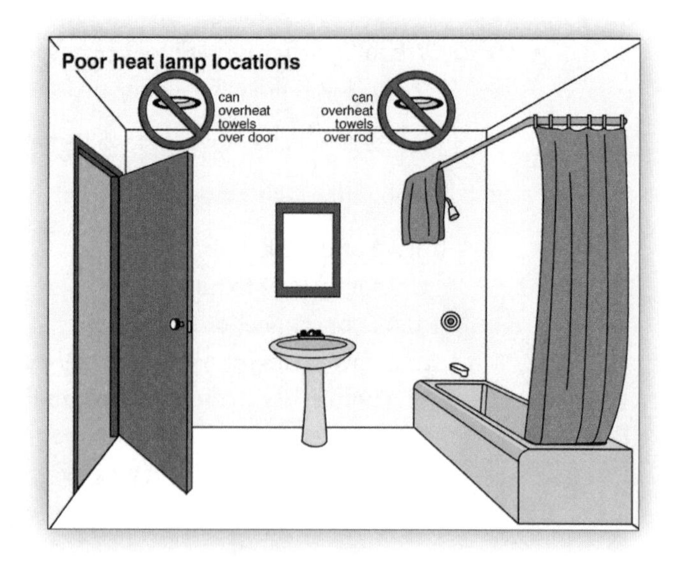

GROUNDING MISSING Lighting fixtures, outlets, switches and junction boxes should be grounded. Remember, we said grounding was important to carry stray electricity to a safe place, so we don't get an electric shock. Home inspectors don't determine whether light fixtures are properly grounded.

OBSOLETE Very old-style porcelain light fixtures, used without electrical boxes, are not safe and should be replaced. Live electrical connections are exposed on these fixtures.

EXPOSED TO MECHANICAL DAMAGE Light fixtures in closets are a convenient feature, but the lights must be kept clear of areas where they may be damaged, or where storage may be directly against the light bulb. Lights should not be installed above or beside shelving units in closets, for example. Lights on the wall above the closet door are usually safe. Incandescent bulbs should be fully enclosed, ideally.

5.3 Switches

DESCRIPTION Switches may control lights, receptacles, exhaust fans or other installed equipment, such as furnaces and boilers. Ideally, light switches should be placed in areas where they can be easily reached when entering a room, or approaching a set of stairs.

THREE-WAY SWITCHES Three-way switches are required in order to control lighting from both the top and bottom of most stairways. Despite their name, there are two switches that control one set of lights. They are also common at either ends of hallways.

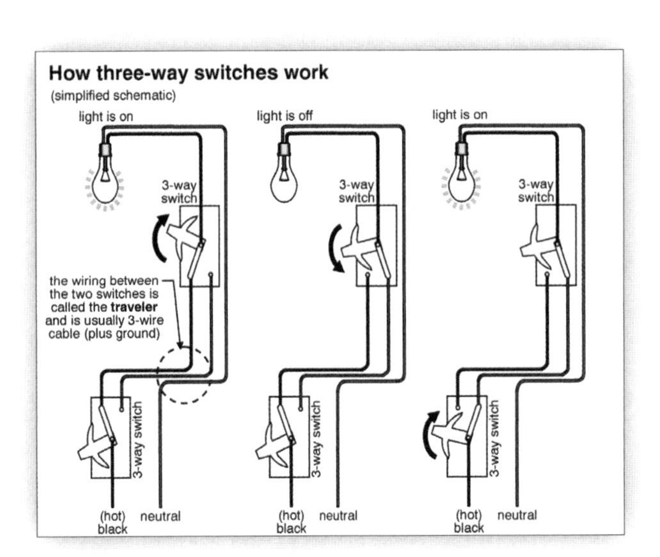

Common Problems with Switches

DAMAGED/ LOOSE/OBSOLETE Damaged or loose switches or cover plates should be repaired or replaced. The old push button switches (with two circular buttons which push into the switch and pop out) are generally considered unsafe and should be replaced. Reproduction switches of this type are now approved and available in North America for the architectural purist.

IMPROPER OPERATION Any switch that works only intermittently or that causes the lights to flicker should be replaced promptly.

POOR LOCATION Traditionally, switches were located about five feet above the floor. Where access for the disabled is important, switches are typically about four feet above the floor.

Switches in bathrooms should be as far as possible from basins, bathtubs and showers, ideally five feet or more.

IMPROPER STAIRWELL LIGHTING Stairwell lighting should be switched both top and bottom.

SWITCH OR COVER PLATE MISSING/ DAMAGED Damaged or missing switches or cover plates should be replaced.

WON'T WORK An inoperative switch may be:

1. A problem within the switch mechanism.
2. A problem with the connections of the wire in the box at the switch.
3. A flaw in the wire between the panel and the switch (including boxes upstream of the switch).
4. A problem downstream in the circuit from the switch that makes it seem like the switch is faulty.
5. A blown fuse or tripped breaker in the panel.
6. A damaged or poorly connected wire at the panel.
7. A burned out light bulb.

An electrician should be contacted to locate and correct the problem.

5.4 Junction Boxes

DESCRIPTION Junction boxes are used to contain and support switches, outlets and lights. They can be metal or plastic, and come in a large variety of shapes and sizes. Junction boxes may also simply contain wire connections. Junction boxes not only protect the connection itself, but secure the wires coming into the box and hold them in place. All modern connections should be made inside a junction box.

Common Problems with Junction Boxes

MISSING Where electrical connections are made with no junction boxes, the danger of electrical shock and fire is increased. With the exception of the early knob-and-tube wiring, all connections should be in junction boxes.

LOOSE Junction boxes should be properly secured to framing members, and wires should be secured to the box, otherwise there is potential for strain on the wires, which may result in loose connections.

SPECIAL OUTDOOR BOXES NEEDED Special water-resistant junction boxes are required on building exteriors. This applies to other damp locations as well.

CROWDED Every junction box is rated for a certain number of wires of a certain size. Where boxes are overcrowded, there is a danger of overheating and pinching wires.

NOT ACCESSIBLE All electrical junction boxes should be accessible for servicing. This means they cannot be covered by plaster, drywall or paneling, for example.

COVER PLATE MISSING OR DAMAGED All junction boxes should be provided with cover plates to prevent people touching live electrical connections.

5.5 Appliances

Some appliances have special electrical situations or needs. A few of those are discussed here.

CEILING FANS The blades of ceiling fans should be at least seven feet above floor level so that people do not get injured. The fan blades themselves should be 12 inches below the ceiling. Heavy fans should be supported independently of the electrical box.

AIR CONDITIONERS The outdoor component of an air conditioning system should have an electric disconnect in a weathertight box. This makes it safe for servicemen to make sure the power is off before working on the equipment.

GARBAGE DISPOSALS The cord for a garbage disposal should be no shorter than 18 inches and no longer than 36 inches. It should have a drip loop and in many areas must be armored cable.

DISHWASHERS The cord for a dishwasher should be between three feet and four feet long.

FURNACES AND BOILERS There should be a disconnect switch within sight of the heating unit.

WHIRLPOOL BATHTUBS HYDROMASSAGE TUB OR CIRCULATING BATHTUB These should be protected by a ground fault circuit interrupter. The pump motor should be accessible.

Heating

INTRODUCTION

THE PURPOSE OF A HEATING SYSTEM IS OBVIOUS. HOW WELL A HEATING SYSTEM PERFORMS IS NOT SO OBVIOUS. A WELL-DESIGNED HEATING SYSTEM IS LARGE ENOUGH TO PROVIDE ADEQUATE HEAT ON THE COLDEST DAY, IS RELIABLE, IS INEXPENSIVE TO INSTALL AND OPERATE (EFFICIENT), IS QUICK TO RESPOND TO ITS CONTROLS, CAN HEAT ALL PARTS OF THE HOME EQUALLY OR DIFFERENTIALLY, AND IS SAFE. THERE IS NO ONE HEATING SYSTEM THAT PERFORMS ALL OF THESE FUNCTIONS PERFECTLY.

OUR DISCUSSION IN THIS CHAPTER WILL ASSUME THAT WE ARE IN COLD CLIMATES WHERE HEATING IS NEEDED SEVERAL MONTHS A YEAR.

1.0 Heating Objectives

Simply put, the goal is to generate and distribute heat through the home. The heat is often generated centrally, in a furnace or boiler, and is distributed by air through ducts or by water in pipes. If the heat from the gas, oil, or electricity is transferred to air, the system is called a furnace. Where water is the heat transfer medium, this is a boiler. Any fuel can be used with either distribution system.

We can also generate heat in each room and have no distribution system. The most common example is electric baseboard heaters.

2.0 Generating Heat

2.1 Fuel

DESCRIPTION Several fuels can be used to generate the heat. Oil, natural gas and propane are fossil fuels that are burned. Wood is also burned. Electricity generates heat by passing current through coils or wires. Heat pumps and solar heating for example collect existing heat and release it into the home. Fuel choices are based on fuel availability, cost, efficiency (how much of the heat generated can be used), and the cost and durability of the heating equipment.

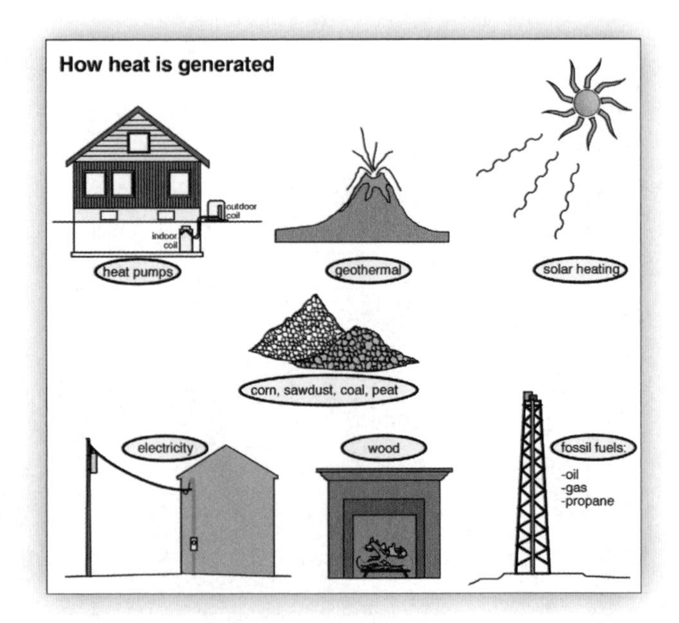

Let's look at some of the fuel delivery systems.

2.2 Gas (Natural Gas or Propane)

DESCRIPTION

2.2.1 Natural Gas Piping: Homes with natural gas have underground piping that delivers gas to the house from a utility's distribution network.

BURIED PIPING

Underground piping can be steel, copper or plastic. Where steel piping is used underground, it should be protected from rusting with coatings or wraps that cover the pipe underground and up to six inches above grade. Some areas also require cathodic protection (a sacrifice material that rusts to protect the gas piping).

Where plastic pipe is used underground, the plastic should not be visible or exposed to mechanical damage. Risers that extend above grade should be metal. A copper tracer wire is typically laid with the pipe to help the gas company find it later, when someone wants to dig in the area. The wire should be visible on the above grade section of the pipe.

PIPING IN THE HOME

Gas piping indoors should be steel, copper or corrugated stainless steel tubing (CSST). The steel tubing is coated with a PVC plastic exterior. Copper is not permitted in some areas because sulfur in the natural gas can react with the copper.

PIPE SUPPORT

Gas piping should be well supported, and there should be no strain on the connections. The gas piping should not be used to support appliances. The illustration here shows support requirements for steel piping.

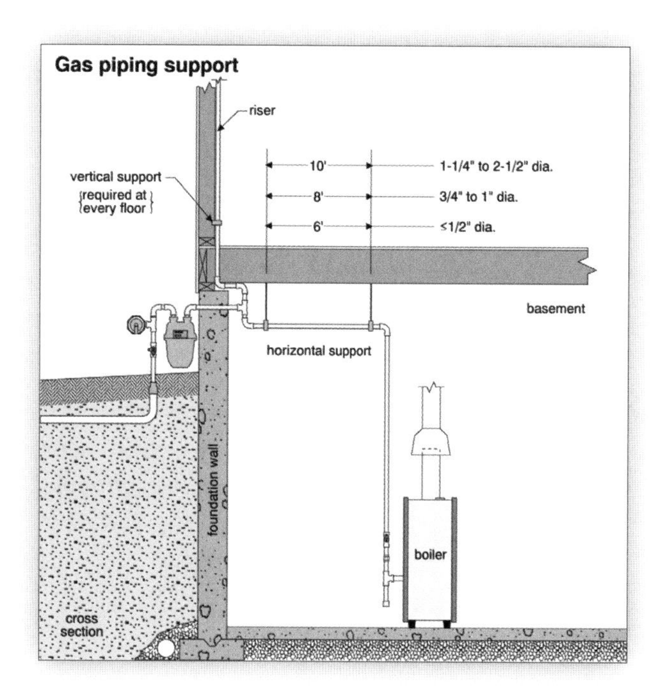

METERS

Meters may be inside or outside the house. Most gas meters on new construction are on the exterior, since this is more convenient for the utility and is arguably a safer location. Meters usually have an isolating valve so that the gas can be shut off. The meter and shut-off valve should always be accessible, both for the convenience of the gas company and for safety. Meters should be protected from mechanical damage from vehicles.

Meters may have a regulator to provide the right gas pressure for the home. These discharge gas into the atmosphere through a relief vent. Regulators should vent to the outside, at least three feet from sources of ignition, windows, doors and appliance intakes or exhausts, and at least ten feet from mechanical air intakes.

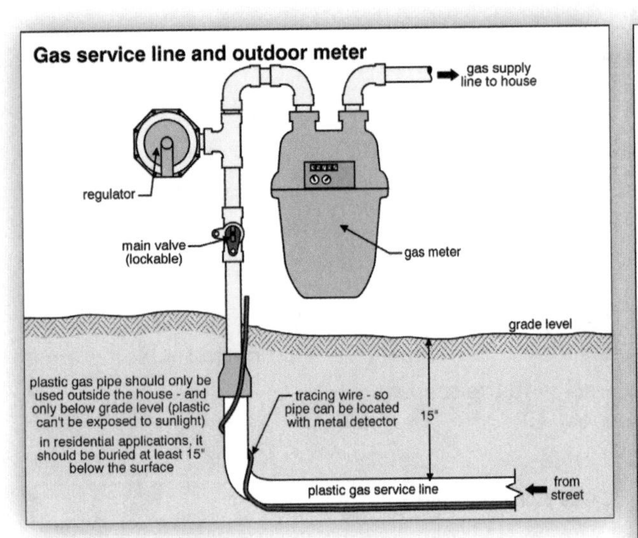

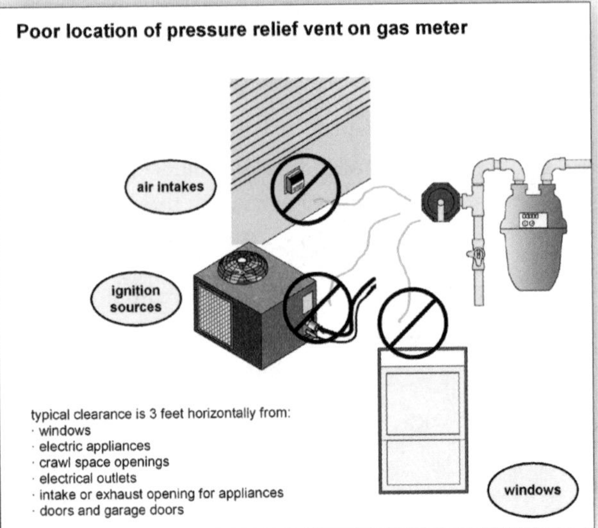

APPLIANCE CONNECTIONS Where appliances are connected, there should be a shut-off valve in the same room for each appliance, as close to the appliance as practical. This allows things to be shut off quickly in the event of an emergency. Piping connections should not be in concealed areas (walls, attic, etc.).

Appliance connectors (flexible metal piping) can be used in some areas. Direct connection is considered superior, except where earthquake is a concern. Connectors, for the most part, should be two feet long, although range or dryer connectors can be three feet long. The connectors should not pass through walls, floors or ceilings, and should be immediately preceded by a shut-off valve.

Where there are gas outlets for barbecues or fireplaces, the valves should be outside the hearth and in the same room as the appliance.

GROUNDING AND BONDING Gas piping should not be used to ground the electrical system; however, metal gas piping is typically bonded to supply piping (usually at the water heater) or something else that is connected to ground. The bonding prevents the gas piping from becoming a dangerous electrical conductor if a live wire touches the piping.

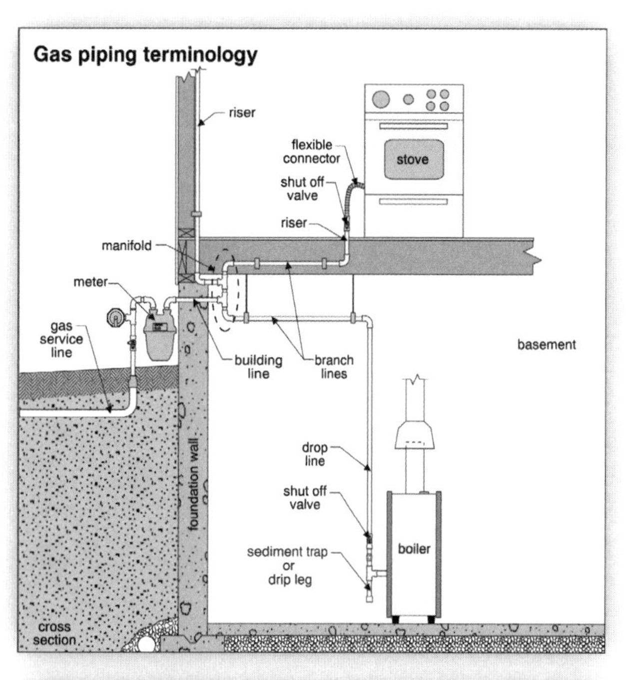

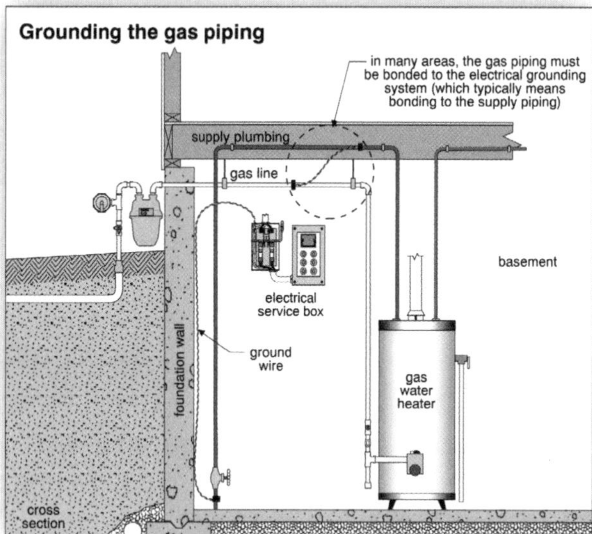

SEDIMENT TRAP Many jurisdictions require a vertical pipe extension called a sediment trap (also known as a dirt pocket or a drip leg) below the elbow where the horizontal pipe feeds an appliance. Any foreign material or moisture in the gas coming toward the appliance will drop into the dirt pocket/drip leg, rather than turn and head into the burner.

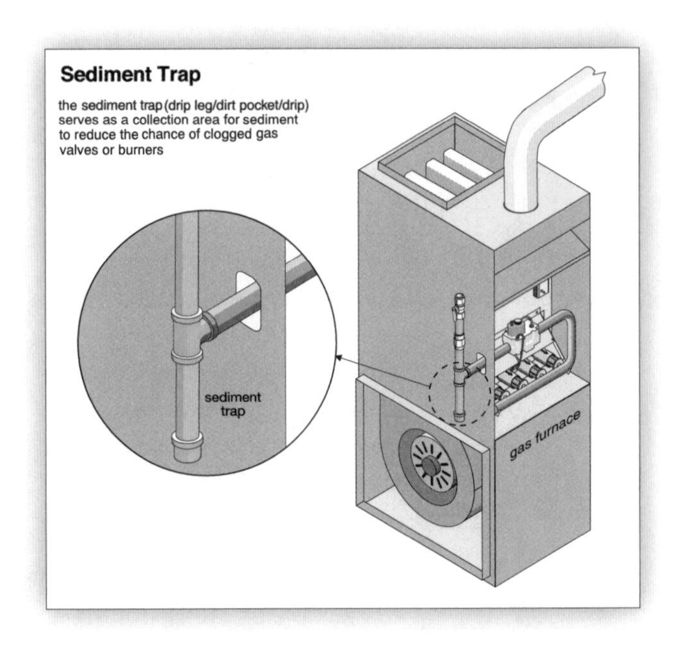

Common Problems with Gas Piping

LEAKS Any gas leak is a potentially life threatening situation. If a leak is noted, all occupants should leave the house immediately and contact the gas company. No switches, telephones including cell phones, door bells, or anything else that might cause a spark should be operated.

Leaks are usually noted by the odor. Natural gas is odorless, but a perfume is added to it so we can smell a leak.

INAPPROPRIATE MATERIAL Plastic gas piping should not be exposed above ground or inside the building. In some areas, copper gas piping is not permitted.

INADEQUATE SUPPORT Where gas piping is not well supported, improvements should be made promptly.

SEDIMENT TRAP (DIRT POCKET/ DRIP LEG) MISSING Sediment traps catch foreign material before they get into burners. Missing sediment traps should be provided by a specialist.

2.2.2 Propane Tanks : Propane and natural gas are very similar, but their delivery methods are different. Natural gas is carried to the home through a utility network of pipes. Propane is delivered by truck to a propane storage tank outdoors on the property. Propane is stored as a liquid that turns into a gas as pressure is released. Many people are familiar with propane used on gas barbecues. The tanks are only filled to roughly 80% capacity, allowing room for expansion.

Propane tanks may be installed above ground or below grade. We will focus on above grade tanks here, since underground tanks cannot be seen. Propane tanks should be approved for their use, and should be mounted on any stable surface. They should be protected from mechanical damage.

SERVICE PIPING/ YARD LINE Pipe running from the tank to the furnace is buried 12 to 18 inches under the ground. It is typically copper or polyethylene. Copper is not permitted in all jurisdictions. The service piping may be run underground in a PVC sleeve, for example for added protection.

TANK LOCATION Tank location is determined in part by the size of the tank. Most tanks are at least 10 feet from buildings, property lines and sources of ignition. Tanks should not be covered by roofs, awnings or overhangs, since relief valves discharge propane straight up.

JURISDICTIONS MAY HAVE THEIR OWN RULES Requirements for installation including location and materials used can vary significantly among municipalities. Propane tank and service line installations are usually subject to permits from local authorities.

Common Problems with Propane Tanks

TOO CLOSE TO BUILDINGS OR IGNITION SOURCES Tanks should typically be 10 feet from walls, windows, air conditioners, appliance intake vents, etc. A specialist should be consulted where there is uncertainty.

UNDER ROOF/ AWNING/ OVERHANG Propane tanks should not be installed below any structure. Propane that is being vented may collect, creating an explosion hazard.

DESCRIPTION **2.2.3 Gas Burners:** Gas burners can be either propane or natural gas, so we will treat them as the same. A gas burner is fed from an electrically operated valve that allows gas to enter the burner where it is mixed with air and ignited. The most common gas burners are, ribbon burners, monoport burners and ring burners. Since gas is dangerous, there are several safety devices associated with burners.

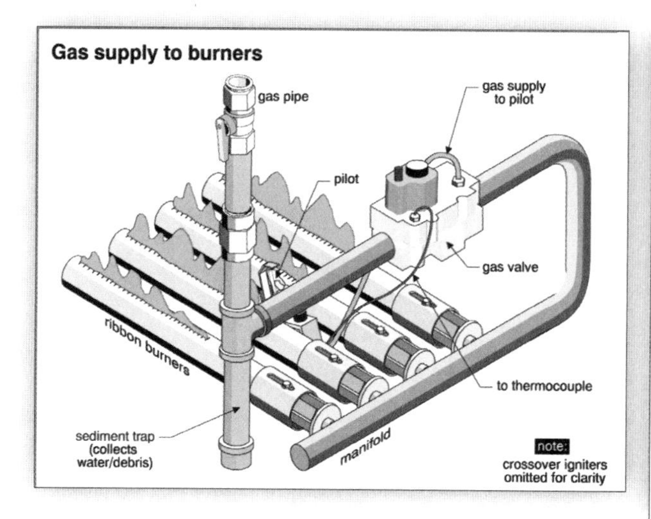

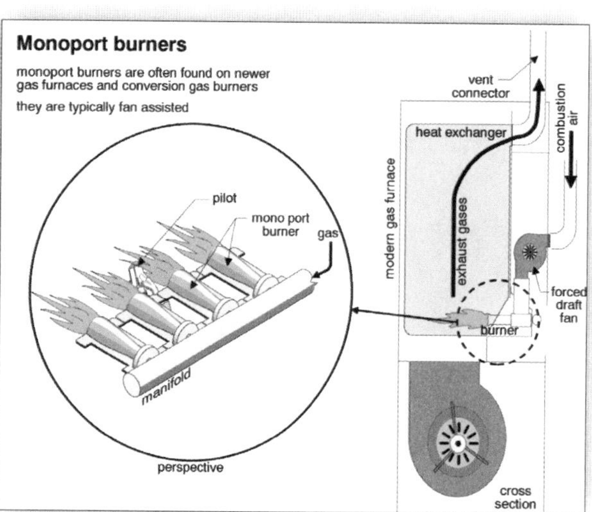

TWO-STAGE FURNACES (MODULATING) FURNACES Traditional furnaces only have one speed. They are either on or off. Many modern furnaces can operate at a low and a high firing rate. This improves efficiency and helps to reduce heating costs. These may be referred to as two-stage or modulating furnaces.

Common Problems with Gas Burners

DIRTY/ MISALIGNED/ RUSTED Burners get dirty and the small orifices (particularly on ribbon burners) plug with debris. Burners also become misaligned and the flame may not point in the right direction. Burners can also rust, especially if humidifiers or air conditioners above leak into the furnace, or if the exhaust gases condense in the furnace.

INCOMPLETE COMBUSTION Natural gas needs lots of air to burn properly. The restricted air supply results in incomplete combustion, higher heating costs, and, in some cases, condensation problems. In severe cases, carbon monoxide poisoning may occur.

FLASHBACK On some heating systems (particularly with ribbon burners) "flashback" is a common problem when the system first starts up. Some of the ignited gas spills out of the front of the heating system. Heat shields, provided on most systems, prevent any serious damage under these conditions; however, in extreme cases, control wiring and other components of the heating system may be scorched.

DESCRIPTION **2.2.4 Gas Valve:** The gas valve contains most of the brains of the heating system. The electrically operated valve opens and allows gas into the combustion chamber, after making sure it is safe to do so.

Common Problems with Gas Valves

INOPERATIVE The most common problem is failure to operate. Gas valves always fail in the closed position for obvious safety reasons. They are fail-safe devices. Failure to open may be the result of safety devices doing their job.

GAS LEAK Gas leaks are not common but are serious. If natural gas is smelled, the occupants should leave the house immediately and contact the utility from outside the home. No telephones including cell phones, computers or other devices that may generate a spark should be used in the home.

DESCRIPTION **2.2.5 Heat Shield:** A heat shield, found on most conventional forced-air furnaces is a metal plate designed to prevent the flames from coming out the front of the burner. The heat shield is not normally removed during a home inspection.

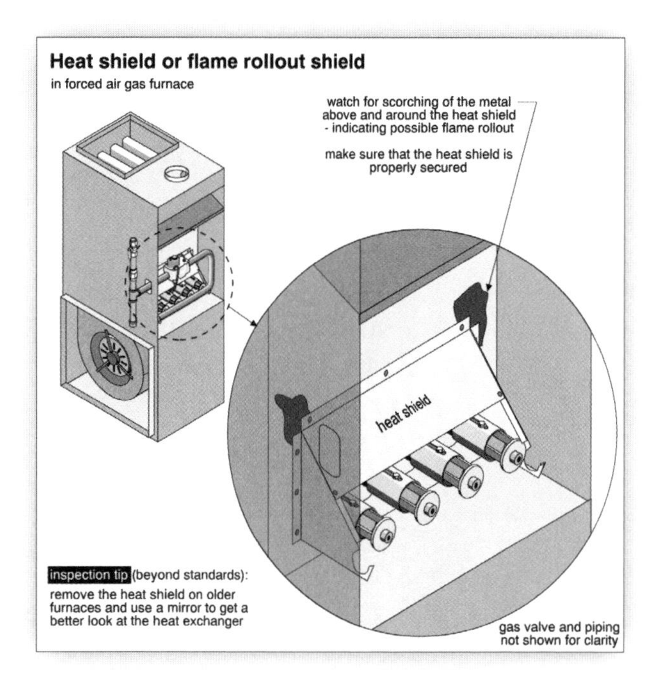

MISSING/OUT OF PLACE/RUST The heat shield may be loose, out of place, rusted, or missing. Where there is evidence of scorching on the heat shield, a service specialist should be engaged to investigate.

DESCRIPTION **2.2.6 Ignition Systems:** Ignition systems light the burner and may be pilot, spark or hot surface systems. There will be no heat in the house if the ignition system is defective. It is unusual for home inspectors to find problems with ignition systems, since the heating system will not operate. Troubleshooting heating systems is not within the scope of a professional home inspection.

DESCRIPTION **2.2.6.1 Pilot/Thermocouple:**

Many older gas-fired heating systems have a continuous pilot. The pilot lights the burner when the gas valve opens. The thermocouple makes sure the pilot is on before allowing the gas valve to open.

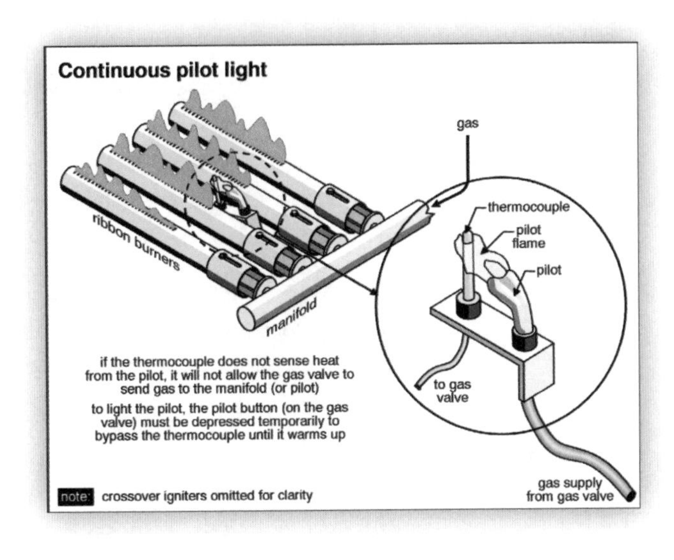

DESCRIPTION **2.2.6.2 Intermittent Pilot/ Electronic Ignition:** Newer systems have an inter-mittent pilot that is ignited by a spark plug. Pilot ignition is verified by a thermocouple. If the pilot does not light after a few attempts, the heating system shuts down.

High efficiency gas systems typically use a hot surface ignition system instead of a pilot. These systems have a flame sensor to shut down the system if ignition is not detected.

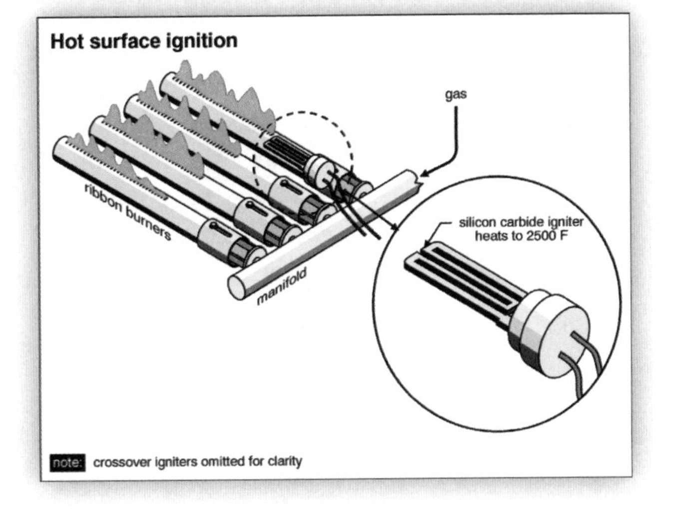

2.3 Oil

DESCRIPTION **2.3.1 Oil Tanks and Piping:** Fuel oil for heating systems is typically stored in a steel or fiberglass tank, which may be either inside or outside the building, above or below ground.

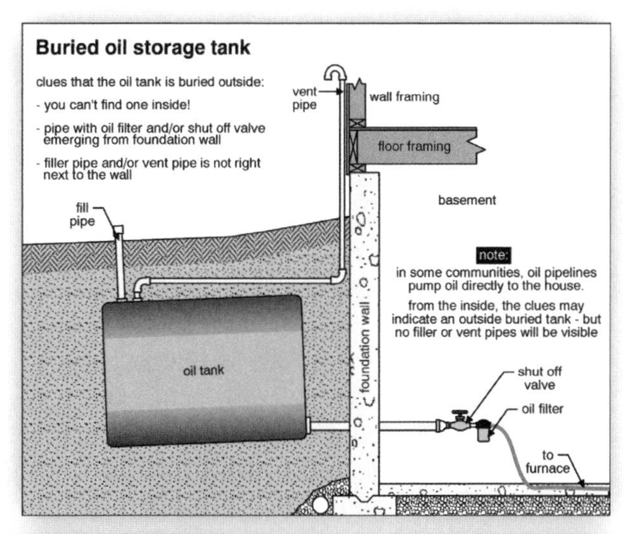

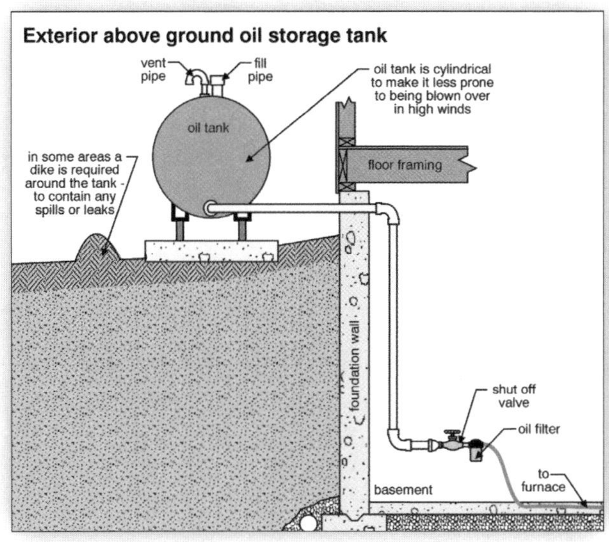

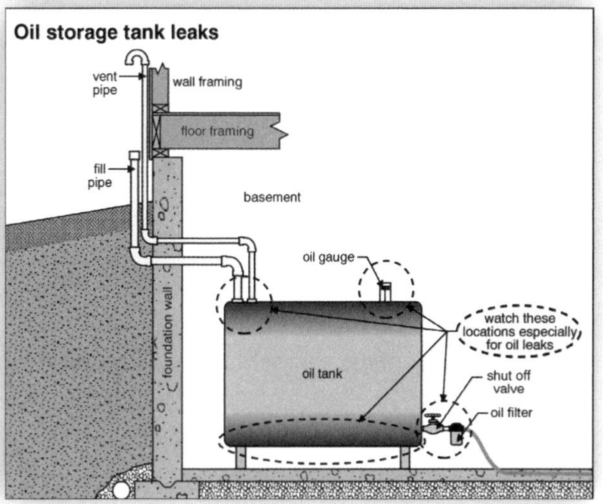

Common Problems with Oil Tanks

LEAKS Leaks can occur in the tank, filter and oil line leading to the burner. Leaking filters and lines can be easily repaired or replaced; however, a leaking tank is typically replaced.

POOR LOCATION For safety reasons, oil tanks should be kept away from sources of combustion such as oil burners. Outdoor tanks should not be subject to constant wetting from water running off the roof, and should be protected from mechanical damage by vehicles.

WRONG TYPE Some tanks are meant for use indoors, others are meant for use outdoors. An indoor tank installed outdoors may fail prematurely.

CONDENSATION Rusting occurs due to water in the tank (often from condensation). Water is heavier than oil and settles to the bottom of the tank. This is where most of the damage occurs. It is best to keep the tank full during the summer months to minimize condensation.

SUSPECT SUPPORT Oil tanks may fail because their legs rust and collapse due to moisture.

UNDERGROUND TANK? The presence of an underground tank cannot always be confirmed. A specialist should be consulted regarding the presence and condition of the tank. This is important because of the risk of soil and groundwater contamination from a leaking tank, whether in use or abandoned.

DESCRIPTION **2.3.2 Oil Burners:** Oil burners consist of a fan to force air into the combustion chamber, a pump to force oil into the combustion chamber, a nozzle to convert the oil to a fine mist, and an ignition system to ignite it.

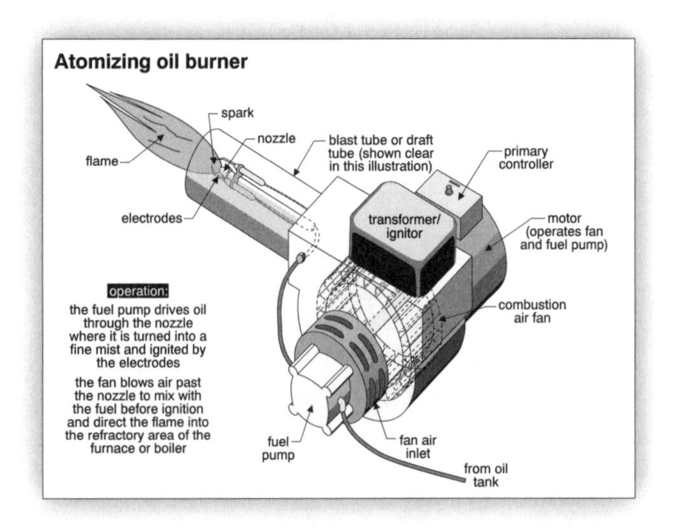

Common Problems with Oil Burners

POOR ADJUSTMENT Poorly adjusted burners result in increased heating costs. Burners starved for air are costly to operate and may generate dangerous carbon monoxide. Oil burners should be serviced annually. Old systems should have an annual efficiency test as part of regular servicing.

LEAK A leaking oil burner may be a safety risk and an environmental hazard.

DESCRIPTION **2.3.3 Combustion Chamber Refractory:** Refractory is found in oil fired boilers and furnaces, which burn hotter than gas heating systems. It contains the flame in a controlled area. It may be a similar material to firebrick found in fireplaces and, in some cases, is made of firebrick. Its purpose is to protect the other heating system components from direct contact with the flame.

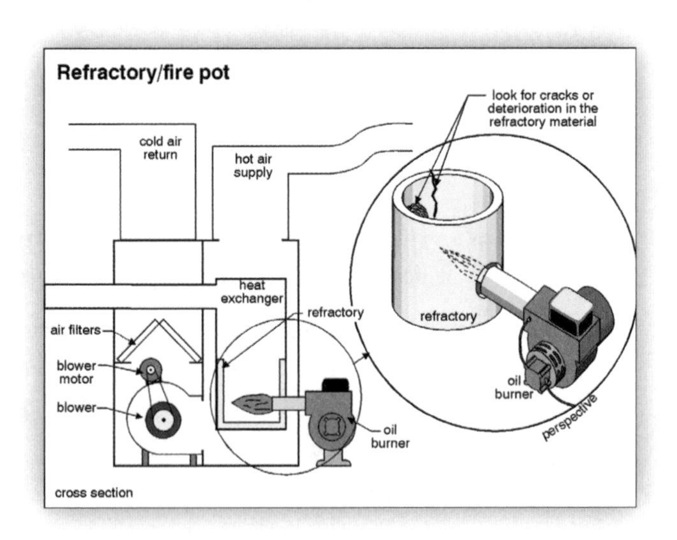

The Common Problem with Combustion Chamber Refractory

DETERIORATION Refractory deteriorates with time and exposure to flame, and requires repair or replacement from time to time. It is often not visible without dismantling the system or breaking a mortar seal. Deteriorated refractory can lead to overheating and the risk of fire.

DESCRIPTION **2.3.4 Primary Control:** The primary control prevents the burner from operating if it is not safe. The control may be mounted on the exhaust flue or on the burner. When installed on the flue, the device looks for heat in the exhaust flue. If the oil burner is pumping oil into the burner area and the primary control senses no heat in the exhaust pipe, it concludes that the oil is not being ignited and it shuts off the pump. We don't want to accumulate a large pool of oil in the combustion chamber and then have it ignite violently later.

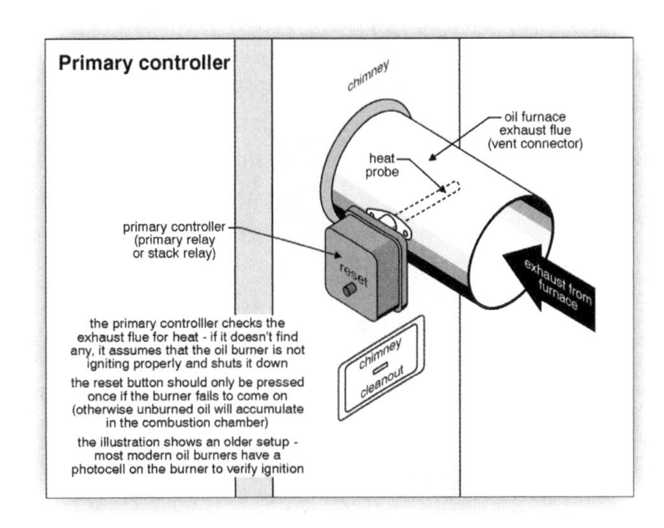

Newer oil burners use a cadmium sulfide 'eye' or photocell on the burner that verifies ignition by looking for light at the burner rather than heat.

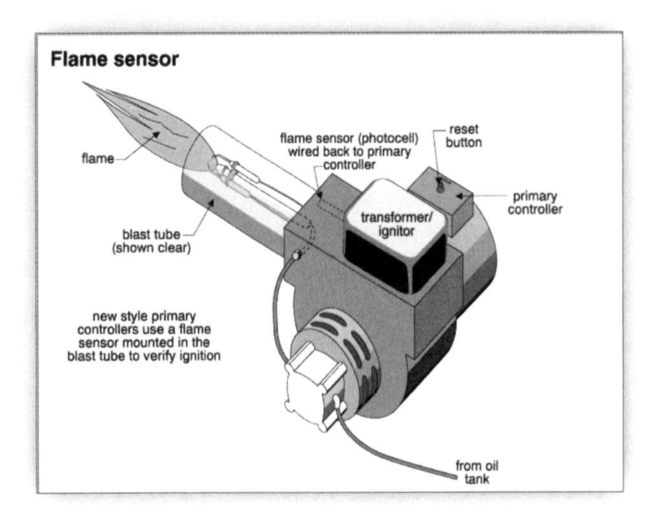

Most primary controls have a reset button on them. It should be pressed only once if the furnace fails to ignite. Pushing the reset button several times could allow an unsafe accumulation of oil in the combustion chamber.

The Common Problem with Primary Controls

INOPERATIVE A heating system may be inoperative because of a defective primary control. It is beyond the scope of the professional home inspection to determine the cause of an inoperative heating system.

2.4 Combustion Air and Dilution (Draft) Air

DESCRIPTION All fuel-burning systems need air to mix with the fuel. If the burner is in an enclosed room or closet, ventilation should be provided. This is often done with louvers in the furnace room door. Natural draft appliances also require extra dilution or draft air to ensure the exhaust gases will be carried up the chimney. As a rough rule, 15 cubic feet of combustion air and 15 cubic feet of draft air are required to burn one cubic foot of natural gas in a conventional furnace.

NATURAL DRAFT APPLIANCES MORE SUSCEPTIBLE TO PROBLEMS Oil burners also need combustion air but have fewer problems, because the oil burner has a strong fan that draws air into the burner. Conventional gas furnaces rely on natural draft and are more susceptible to problems. Many newer gas furnaces have a fan that pulls air into the burner, reducing the need for draft air. These systems are less susceptible to draft problems than natural draft furnaces.

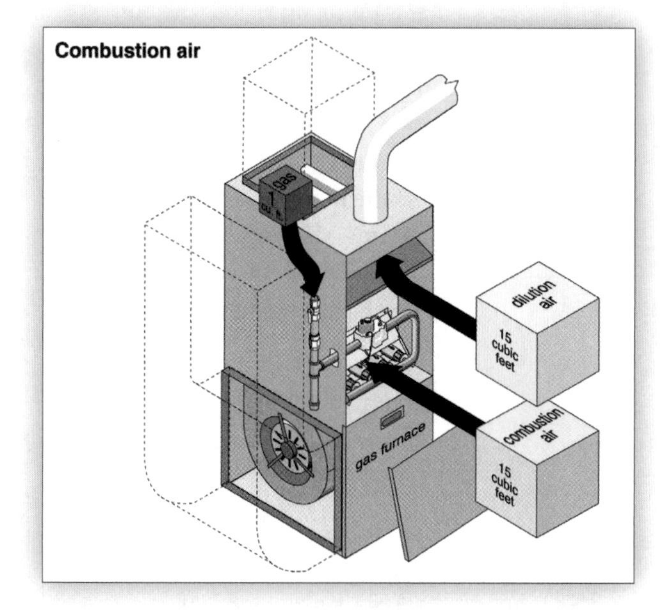

HIGH EFFICIENCY FURNACES Some high efficiency furnaces bring outside air for combustion directly into the burner through a closed pipe. This reduces heating costs because we are not wasting indoor air that we have heated to room temperature for combustion. Pressure sensors in the furnace verify air supply before the burner is allowed to fire.

The Common Problem with Combustion Air

INADEQUATE COMBUSTION/ DILUTION AIR The most common problem is a lack of combustion and dilution air, often because the heating system is in an enclosed room or closet. There may also be a problem when combustion air is drawn from outdoors, if the inlet is obstructed. The heating system may not operate if there is a lack of combustion air. The system may operate inefficiently, and there may be a risk of combustion products spilling into the living space, creating a life safety issue.

2.5 Venting – Getting Rid of the Exhaust

DESCRIPTION

2.5.1 Draft Hood (Draft Diverter): Conventional gas heating systems have a draft hood or draft diverter in the exhaust system. This hood allows room air to be drawn into the exhaust system to help the exhaust gases go up the chimney and out of the house. This draft or dilution air helps cool the exhaust gases as it mixes with them. It also ensures there will be enough draft to keep things moving up and out of the chimney.

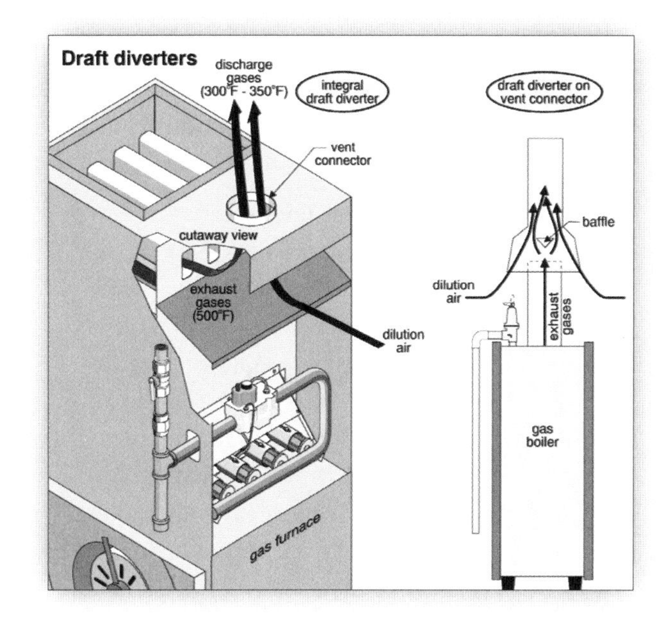

Common Problems with Draft Hoods/Diverters

OBSTRUCTED/ NEGATIVE AIR PRESSURE IN HOME

If the chimney is blocked or if the house air pressure is lower than the outdoor air pressure, exhaust gases may spill out of the draft hood, creating a dangerous situation for the occupants. This is often called backdrafting or spillage.

DESCRIPTION

2.5.2 Barometric Damper (Draft Regulator): Oil burners and some gas burners have a barometric damper (draft regulator) in the exhaust flue. This damper allows house air to be drawn into the exhaust flue to help exhaust gases go up the chimney. The barometric damper is safer than the draft hood, in that the damper will close if the pressure in the exhaust flue is higher than in the home. This prevents exhaust gases entering the living space.

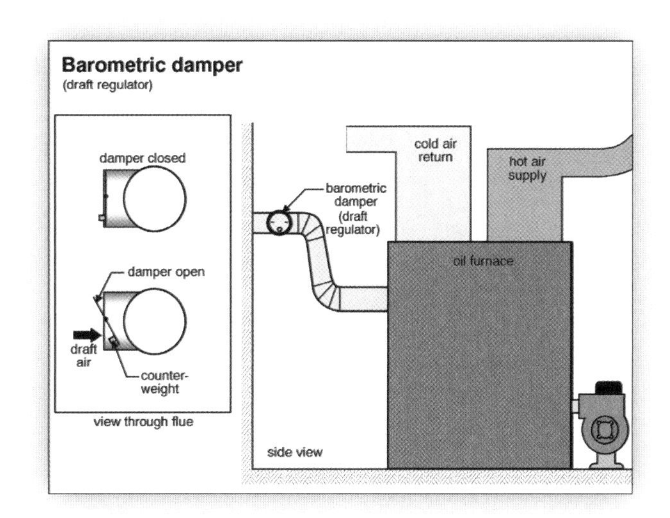

Common Problems with Barometric Dampers

RUST/ ADJUSTMENT Many primary controls have a damper that is in a harsh environment – the exhaust flue. It is common for dampers to be rusted, damaged or out of adjustment. The damper may be stuck and may not move at all. If the damper does not swing freely, service is required to ensure the heating system operates safely and efficiently.

DESCRIPTION **2.5.3 Vent Connector:** The vent connector carries the hot exhaust gases from the furnace or boiler to the chimney. It is typically a single-wall galvanized steel pipe, four inches to ten inches in diameter. Vent connectors for oil heating systems have to deal with higher temperatures than gas systems. Vent connectors for gas systems typically require a six-inch clearance from combustibles, and vent connectors for oil systems need nine inches or more.

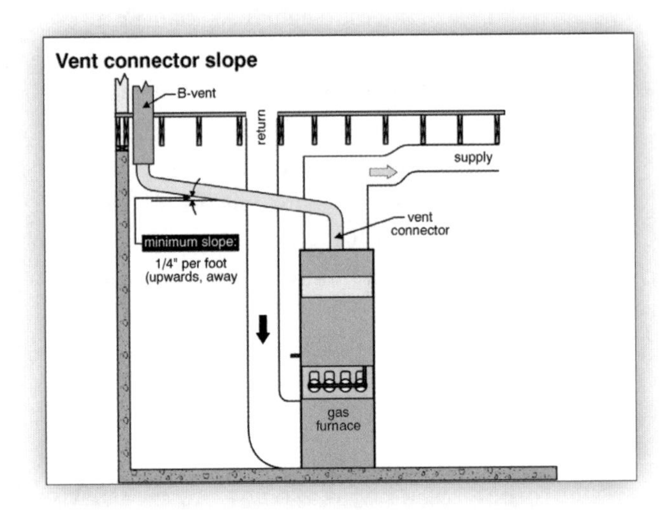

Modern high efficiency gas heating systems remove so much heat from the combustion products that the exhaust gases are cool enough to be carried in plastic pipes and discharged out through the side of the building, rather than up through a chimney.

Common Problems with Vent Connectors

POOR CONDITION AND LOCATION Problems include poor connections and corroded metal. Flues should not extend into the chimney far enough to obstruct the flow of gases out of the flue and up the chimney.

LENGTH Vent connectors that are too long may cool the exhaust gases, causing condensation and poor draft problems. Exhaust flues from oil furnaces for example, should be no more than ten feet in length.

SLOPE/ CONNECTIONS Vent connectors should slope up toward the chimney to allow exhaust gases to flow easily (at least one-quarter inch per foot). Individual sections of the vent connector must be well secured, typically with three screws. Vent pipes must be well supported to maintain a proper slope and to reduce stress on connections.

SIZE An undersized vent connector may restrict the flow of exhaust gases. An oversized vent connector may allow exhaust gases to linger and not move up and out the chimney.

EXHAUST SPILLAGE – BACKDRAFTING Conventional furnaces need air to maintain draft up the chimney, in excess of the air needed for combustion. Where this is not available, exhaust gases may not go up the chimney. Exhaust gases spilling from the exhaust flue, draft hood or burner area, may present a life threatening situation. This problem requires immediate action.

CLEARANCE TO COMBUSTIBLES – VENT CONNECTOR Exhaust gases can be 300°F - 700°F. A minimum of nine inches clearance should be provided for oil furnaces and special collars should be used where the exhaust flue (vent connector) passes through a combustible material. Gas furnace flues should be at least six inches from combustibles (Oil burns at higher temperatures than gas). There is a risk of fire where combustible clearances are not maintained.

INAPPROPRIATE MATERIAL Plastic venting is acceptable for some gas heating systems but not all. The venting material must be suitable for the application to ensure the heating system operates safely.

DESCRIPTION **2.5.4 Chimney:** Most gas and oil heating systems require a chimney. Electric heating systems do not, since there are no products of combustion. Chimneys are typically masonry or metal. High efficiency systems with relatively cool exhaust have plastic vent pipes rather than a chimney. There have been recalls on High Temperature Plastic Vents (HTPVs) for mid efficiency gas furnaces.

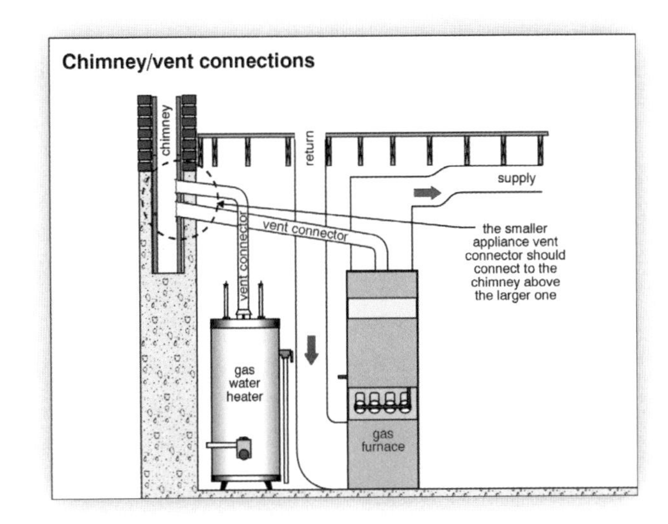

DESCRIPTION **2.5.4.1 Masonry:** Brick chimneys may be lined or unlined. An unlined chimney has brick or concrete block on the interior. While this may be suitable for many oil furnaces, it is not suitable in most areas for gas furnaces or boilers, because condensing exhaust gases can damage the chimney. Check what is acceptable in your area. The liner can be metal, clay tile, or asbestos cement pipe. Where more than one appliance vents into a chimney, the smaller appliance should connect above the larger one.

SHARED CHIMNEYS In attached housing, it is common for two houses to have one chimney. Chimneys may have more than one flue. Each home may have one or two flues. When repairs to the masonry are required, the cost is often shared. Where this situation exists, the neighbor should be consulted prior to starting chimney work.

Common Problems with Masonry Chimneys

DETERIORATION Chimneys may deteriorate on the interior or exterior. Brick and mortar problems are common, especially near the top of chimneys or on the inside where condensation occurs as exhaust gases make their way up the chimney. The danger is exhaust gases getting back into the house. If the chimney is connected to a wood burning fireplace, there is also a risk of a house fire.

LINER NEEDED If mortar, sand or pieces of brick are found in the base of the chimney, a liner should be considered to prevent further chimney deterioration. A specialist should be consulted.

POOR VENT CONNECTION The vent connector should be well secured to the chimney to prevent leakage of exhaust gases in the home.

SHARED FLUES Two appliances sharing a single flue is not usually a good situation because exhaust from one appliance may come into the home through the vent for the other. A furnace and a fireplace, for example, should not share a flue. There are some circumstances where flues can be shared safely.

DEBRIS IN CHIMNEY Chimney flues without metal liners should have a clean-out door at the base of the chimney to remove debris. If debris accumulates in the bottom of the chimney, it could block the flue, causing exhaust gases to back up into the house.

COMBUSTIBLE CLEARANCES/ FIREBLOCKING Masonry chimneys should be kept at least two inches away from combustibles including wood framing. While there are exceptions, this is a good general rule. Fireblocking should be provided at each floor level so that a fire cannot quickly spread from floor to floor around the outside of the chimney. Non-combustible insulation is commonly used for fireblocking.

DESCRIPTION **2.5.4.2 Metal:** Metal chimneys for gas furnaces are typically Type B vents. Metal chimneys for oil furnaces are heavier Type L vents. Wood-burning appliances including fireplaces can also have metal chimneys. These are typically double- or triple-wall systems that see much higher temperatures than gas or oil vents.

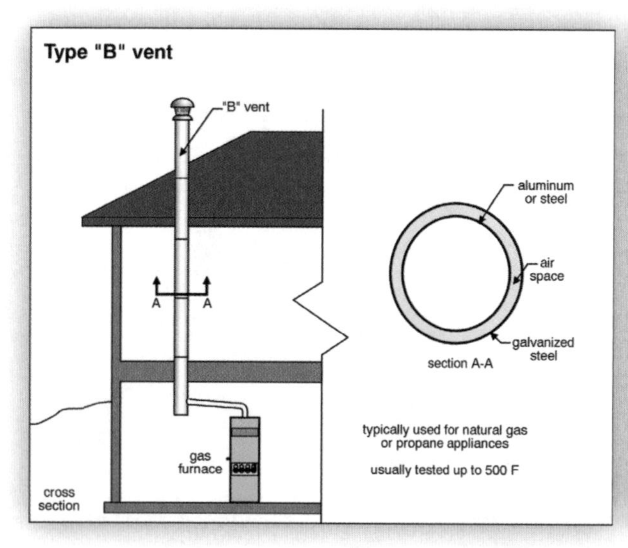

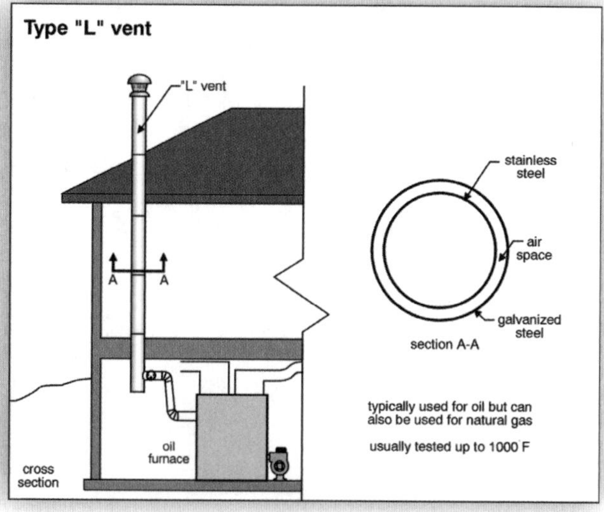

Common Problems with Metal Chimneys

RUST/CORROSION With time, the corrosive exhaust gases can deteriorate the interior of a metal chimney. Rust can also develop on the exterior of a metal chimney. Metal chimneys more than ten years old should be inspected regularly by a specialist.

POOR CONNECTIONS/ SUPPORT AND MISSING CAP Other problems with metal chimneys include poor connection of sections, poor support for the chimney and missing rain caps. Products of combustion may find their way into the home.

INADEQUATE CLEARANCE FROM COMBUSTIBLES Type B and Type L vents require a one-inch clearance, and the special heavy metal chimneys used for wood-burning fireplaces typically require a two-inch clearance. Inadequate clearances may lead to overheating and fire.

3.0 Turning the Heat On and Off

All heating systems have controls to adjust the house temperature.

3.1 Thermostat

DESCRIPTION The function of a thermostat is to turn on the heating system when the temperature is lower than the setting, and shut the system off when the set temperature is reached.

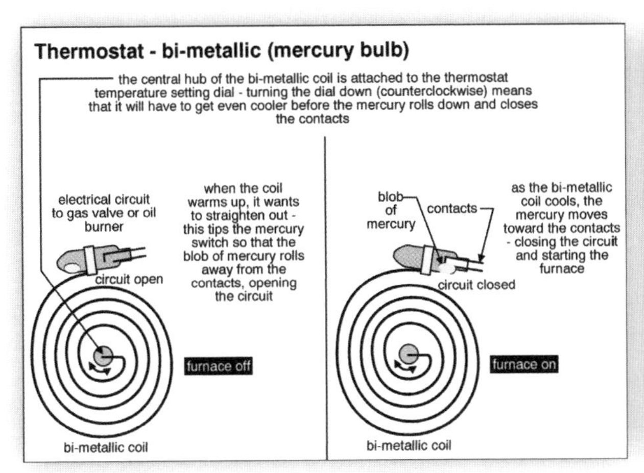

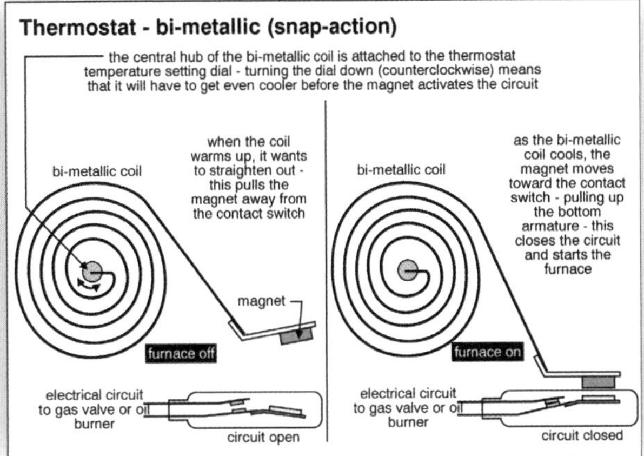

LOCATION The location of a thermostat is important for comfort. It should not be near a heat source such as a fireplace or a heating duct in the wall behind the thermostat. The thermostat should not be behind doors, on outside walls, in drafty areas or on walls that get direct sunlight. All of these can fool the thermostat into thinking the house is warmer or cooler than it actually is. Relocating a thermostat is not a difficult job.

PROGRAMMABLE OR SET-BACK THERMOSTATS Many modern thermostats are programmable and allow the temperature to be lowered when the occupants are away or sleeping. The maximum set-back should be less than ten degrees Fahrenheit, since cooler temperatures create higher relative humidity levels, which can result in condensation problems.

HEATING AND AIR CONDITIONING CONTROL Air-conditioned homes typically have one thermostat to control both heating and cooling.

BLOWER CONTROL Some furnace thermostats have a control for the blower (furnace fan) on forced-air systems. They either run the blower when the furnace operates or run the blower continuously. Continuous operation is often used with a good quality air filter to provide constant cleaning of the house air.

Common Problems with Thermostats

MALFUNCTIONS/ DAMAGE/ ANTICIPATOR PROBLEMS Thermostats can function improperly if they are dirty, not level, or improperly calibrated. They can also suffer mechanical damage. Most thermostats contain an anticipator – a device that prevents overshoot. If the heating system shuts down when the set temperature is reached, residual heat will overheat the home. The anticipator shuts the system off just before it reaches the set point, to avoid overheating. The anticipator must be calibrated to the specific furnace or boiler. If it is not, overshoot or short cycling may occur, resulting in an uncomfortable home.

POOR LOCATION The thermostat should not be placed where it may get a false reading of the room temperature. This will make the house uncomfortable and may increase heating costs.

4.0 Moving the Heat Through the House

We've been talking about how we can generate heat. Now let's talk about how we move the heat through the house. We'll look at furnaces, and then at boilers. We will also describe steam heating and electric systems.

Furnaces use ducts to move heated air. Boilers use radiators to move heated water. Hot water radiant systems move heat through concealed pipes. Electric systems can be furnaces, boilers, radiant systems within floors or ceilings, and space heating including electric baseboard heaters.

5.0 Furnaces

DESCRIPTION Furnaces distribute their heat by warming the house air as it passes through the furnace. The furnace fan draws cool air in from the rooms through the return ducts. The air is warmed as it passes over a hot metal box called a heat exchanger. The warm air is pushed out to the rooms through the supply ducts. The house air can be thought of as moving in a loop, passing by the furnace every few minutes to be reheated.

Gas and oil furnaces have three major components: a heat exchanger, a burner, and a blower. Electric furnaces have a heating element rather than a burner to generate the heat.

Furnaces are typically in a cabinet. There are also operating and safety controls, and an air filter in the furnace. Gas and oil furnaces have a vent to get rid of the exhaust products. Some furnaces have accessories such as humidifiers or central air conditioning systems. Electronic air cleaners may replace conventional filters.

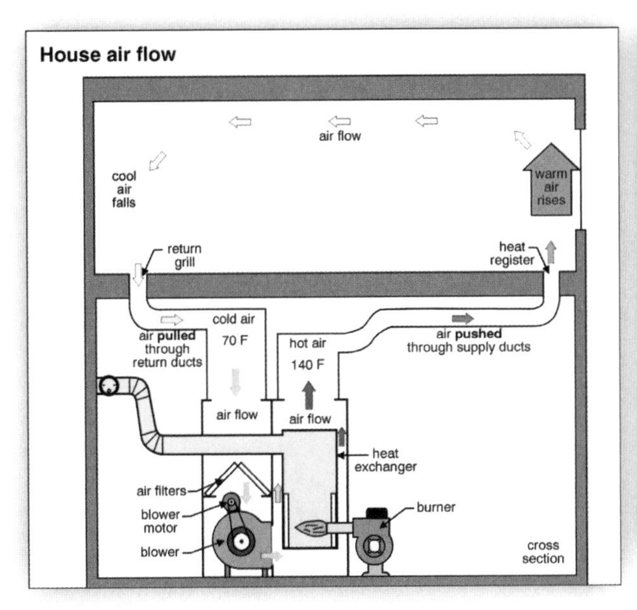

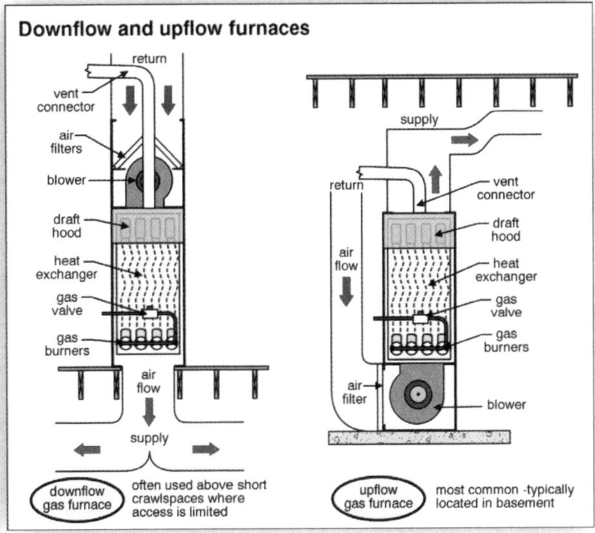

5.1 Electric Furnaces

DESCRIPTION Electric furnaces are similar in some ways to a hair dryer. Cool air is blown over a heating element. Since there is no combustion, there is no need for a burner, heat exchanger or vent system. These are replaced by electric elements sitting directly in the air stream. The blower simply forces house air across the heating elements, and the warmed air heads out through the supply ductwork.

Electric furnaces have multiple heating elements. A typical element is five kilowatts (5,000 Watts). Heating elements in electric systems are much like light bulbs. They burn out from time to time, and we can't predict when this will happen. Most electric furnaces have a sequencer to turn on the heating elements one by one, so that they don't create a large electrical surge.

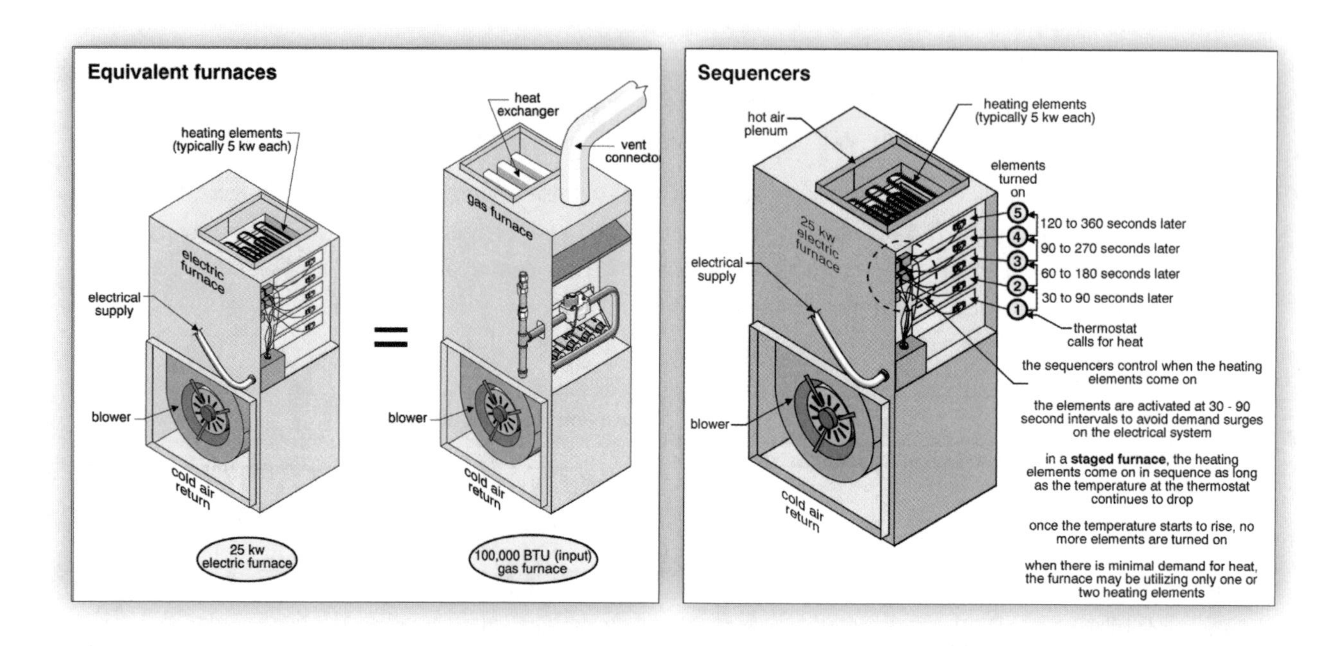

ELECTRIC PLENUM HEATER Some heating and air conditioning systems have an auxiliary electric plenum heater. Electric plenum heaters often do not work in conjunction with the furnace. The plenum heater will first try to satisfy the heating demands of the house. If it cannot keep up, the plenum heater shuts down and the furnace comes on.

Common Problems with Electric Furnaces and Heaters

INOPERATIVE The most common problem is a lack of heat due to a failed heating element, sequencer or control. In some cases the electric supply has been interrupted by a tripped breaker or blown fuse. The blower may also fail.

WIRING FAILURE The wires leading to heating elements and various controls sometimes overheat in electric furnaces. Any evidence of burned wires or components should be evaluated by a specialist.

5.2 Gas and Oil Burners

To review these burners, see Section 2 of this chapter.

5.3 Heat Exchanger

DESCRIPTION The heat exchanger is the most critical component of a gas or oil furnace. It separates the house air that is being heated from the burning fuel. The heat exchanger can be thought of as a metal box with fire on the inside and house air on the outside. House air picks up heat from the walls of the box. The burning fuel never comes in direct contact with the house air. This is an indirect-fired heating system.

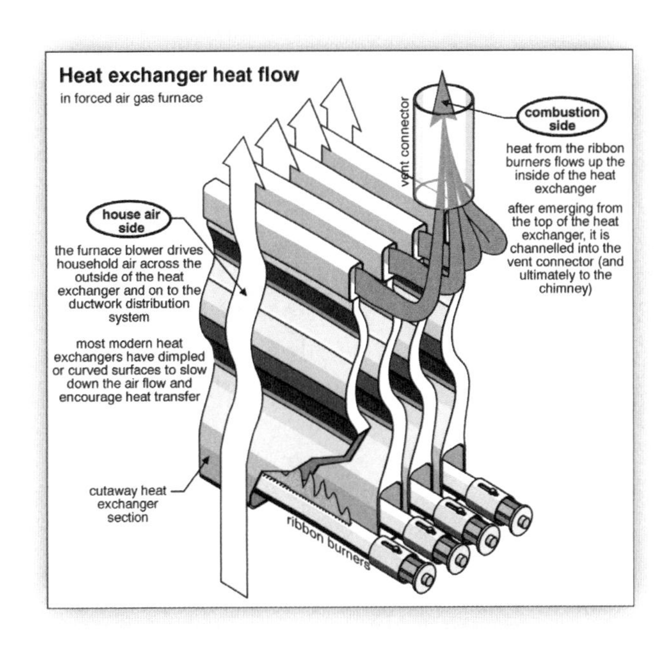

Common Problems with Heat Exchangers

HOLE OR CRACK IN THE HEAT EXCHANGER The exchanger is the heart of the furnace. It fails in one of two ways – it rusts through or it cracks. Either way, the products of combustion may escape through the heat exchanger and into the air supply to the house. This can be life-threatening, because the products of combustion may contain carbon monoxide, a poisonous gas. On some furnaces the heat exchanger can be replaced. Commonly, the entire furnace is replaced when the heat exchanger fails. A crack or hole in a heat exchanger is usually not visible, and typically will not be identified during a home inspection.

LIFE EXPECTANCY Heat exchangers in conventional furnaces have an average life expectancy of 18 to 25 years. The life expectancy of heat exchangers in high efficiency furnaces is somewhat less. We'll look at high efficiency furnaces shortly.

LEAKING HUMIDIFIERS Defective humidifiers, leaking condensate trays from air conditioning systems or moisture from damp basements can cause heat exchangers to rust prematurely.

CORROSIVE ENVIRONMENTS There are some environments where chemicals in the air are also corrosive to a heat exchanger. Swimming pool chemicals, paint strippers and the chemicals found in hair dressing salons for example, will rust a heat exchanger quickly. In a corrosive environment, a furnace with a specially protected heat exchanger is recommended.

MANUFACTURING DEFECT Some manufacturers have a reputation for heat exchangers with short life expectancies.

CLOGGED Some heating systems have very small heat exchanger passages. Over time and with incomplete combustion and condensation, these can become obstructed. This reduces the efficiency of the heating system and in some cases the heating system will shut down and there will be no heat. Flushing the heat exchanger is part of regular maintenance for some heating systems.

5.4 Blowers and Blower Motors

DESCRIPTION Furnaces have a blower to pull air into the furnace through the return ductwork, move the air across the furnace heat exchanger to warm it up, and push the heated air through the supply ductwork to heat the house.

The motor can be mounted within the blower to drive it directly. Some motors are external to the blower, driving the blower with a pair of pulleys and a belt. Belts and pulleys need regular maintenance and adjustment.

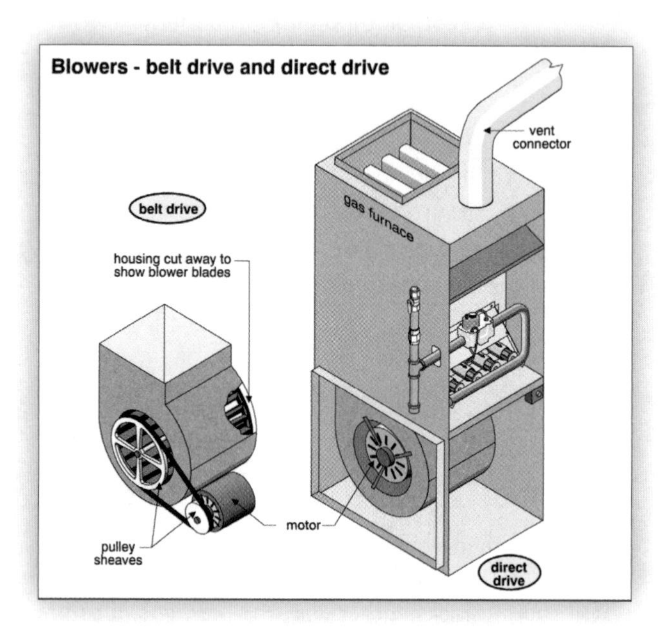

MULTI-SPEED BLOWERS AND HIGH EFFICIENCY MOTORS Motors may have one single speed, or multiple speeds. One speed may be used to deliver warm air, and a lower speed used to continuously circulate air throughout the house. Some more expensive fan motors (ECM or Electronically Commutated Motors) are more efficient (use less electricity), but are more expensive than traditional (PSC or Permanent Split Capacitor) motors. ECM motors have the additional advantage of a larger range of operating speeds than conventional motors.

Common Problems with Blowers and Blower Motors

BURNED OUT MOTORS, WORN BEARINGS, DIRTY The most common problems are burned out motors and worn bearings. If furnace filters are dirty or missing, blowers get dirty and move less air, making the furnace work harder and the house less comfortable. Dirt can also cause the blower to get out of balance. This will cause excessive noise and vibration. Sometimes, vibration causes the entire blower unit to become loose. In other cases, the blower bearings may fail.

BELT-DRIVEN FAN ADJUSTMENT Belts may slip, reducing air flow and squealing. When the belt breaks, the fan stops and the furnace may overheat and shut down.

5.5 Operating and Safety Controls

DESCRIPTION **5.5.1 Fan/Limit Switch:** Many forced-air furnaces have a fan/limit switch. This switch has two functions. The first is an operating function. It tells the blower to come on when the furnace is warm enough to provide warm air at the registers.

The fan/limit switch does not shut off the fan when the burner is shut off. Since there is some residual heat in the heat exchanger, the fan keeps blowing until the fan/limit switch determines that the air coming out of the registers would feel cool.

The safety function of the fan/limit switch is to shut off the burner if the furnace overheats. These are typically set at 200°F. Older fan/limit switches are mechanical, and newer units are electronic. The illustration shows a mechanical fan/limit switch.

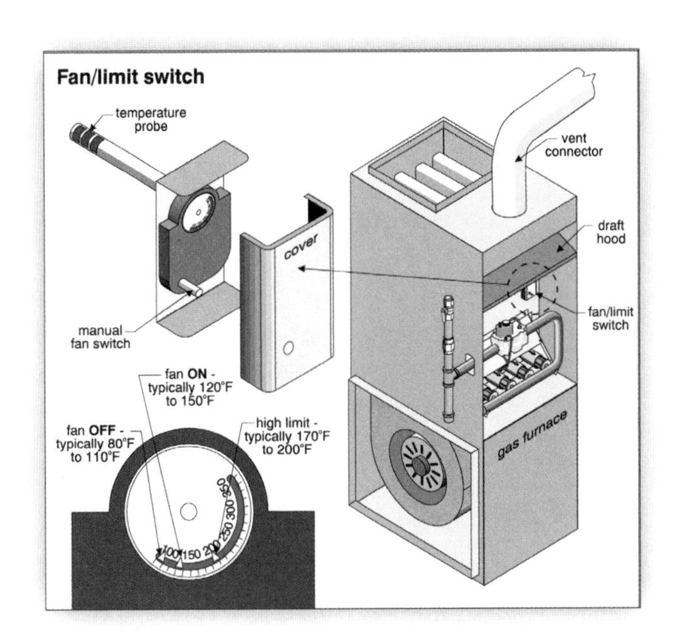

Common Problems with Fan/Limit Switches

SETTINGS Sometimes, fan/limit switches are out of adjustment, causing the furnace or the blower to short cycle (turn on and off at short intervals). Other causes of short-cycling include thermostat and heat exchanger problems.

If the limit setting is too high, or the switch is defective, the furnace may not shut off when it overheats. In some cases, this can cause a fire by igniting dust inside the ductwork or combustible materials nearby. The fan/limit switch should be checked during regular furnace servicing.

DESCRIPTION **5.5.2 Proving Ignition:** Depending upon the type of furnace, there is also a safety device to verify ignition. It would be unsafe to allow unburned gas accumulating in a furnace. A potentially explosive condition would exist. Older gas furnaces have a continuously burning pilot, which ignites the gas when the main gas valve opens. A thermocouple (heat sensor) verifies that the pilot is running. If the pilot goes out, the thermocouple will not allow the gas valve to open.

Some gas furnaces have an intermittent pilot that is ignited by a spark. Again, there is a flame sensor to ensure that the spark successfully ignited the pilot. If it does not, the gas valve will not open. A third option is hot surface ignition (also called electronic ignition), where there is no pilot. A flame sensor again makes sure that the system is operating safely.

Oil burners are typically spark-ignited. Heat or flame sensing devices (primary control) stop the burner from dumping fuel into the system if the burner is not firing.

Common Problems with Ignition Proving Systems

INOPERATIVE These systems are fail-safe devices. They may fail mechanically or electrically, but either way, they will not allow the burner to operate. The pilot valve may fail or the pilot orifice may become obstructed. It is also common for the thermocouple to fail, preventing the furnace from firing. The spark-ignited systems may have problems with the spark plug. The igniter may crack and fail to work on a hot surface ignition system. The implication of all of these is no heat for the home. It is beyond the scope of a professional home inspection to determine why a heating system is not working. A specialist should be engaged.

DESCRIPTION **5.5.3 Handling Condensate:** On high efficiency heating systems, the products of combustion (exhaust gases) are cooled to the point where condensation forms. This condensate (water) must be collected and drained away with a condensate line. Sometimes, the drain lines are plugged or poorly installed.

Some municipalities require the condensate to be neutralized before it goes into the drains. It is somewhat acidic and may deteriorate city piping. Neutralizing kits are available through furnace manufacturers.

CONDENSATE PUMP If a condensate line cannot flow by gravity to a drain, a condensate pump is used. The pumps are relatively inexpensive but can be a high maintenance item.

Common Problems with Condensate Systems

LEAK/CLOGGED/ FAILED PUMP/ POOR DISCHARGE POINT The most common problems are leaks that may be the result of clogged or disconnected condensate lines. Failed condensate pumps can also result in leaks. Depending on where the water goes, there may be damage to the furnace or surrounding area. Neutralizing salt baths may also be clogged, resulting in backup and leakage.

DESCRIPTION **5.5.4 Back Draft Sensor – Spillage Switch:** Some furnaces have a spillage switch to detect exhaust products escaping out of the front of the burner. This safety device shuts off the burner if spillage (back drafting) is detected.

Common Problems with the Spillage Switch

INOPERATIVE/ DAMAGE/ DISPLACED The spillage switch may be inoperative, damaged, or out of position as the result of impact. If the spillage switch does not work, the furnace will not operate and the house will have no heat.

DESCRIPTION **5.5.5 Air Proving Switch (Differential Switch):** Furnaces with induced draft fans have a sensor that makes sure air is moving through the intake, combustion and venting system before the burner is allowed to fire. These sense the pressure differential across the fan, making sure there is good airflow.

Common Problems with the Air Proving Switch

INOPERATIVE/ DAMAGE/ DISPLACED The switch may be inoperative or damaged. If the heating system does not work, the switch may be doing its job, because it has detected a problem with the airflow, and shut the system down.

5.6 Filters

DESCRIPTION Furnaces need a filter to clean the air before it enters the furnace. Filters protect the furnace, keeping it clean, and help maintain good air quality throughout the house.

AIR FILTER There are several types of air filters that clean the return air before it goes into the furnace and out through the registers. This cleans the house air and helps keep the furnace clean. Conventional air filters sit in the return air plenum, just upstream of the blower. It is not unusual to find filters installed backwards or missing.

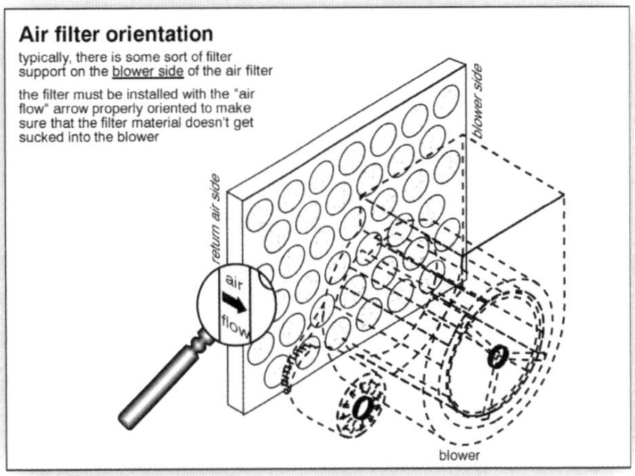

Air filter orientation

typically, there is some sort of filter support on the blower side of the air filter

the filter must be installed with the "air flow" arrow properly oriented to make sure that the filter material doesn't get sucked into the blower

return air side

blower side

air flow

blower

ELECTRONIC AIR FILTER Electronic air filters (also called electronic air cleaners) clean the air better than conventional mechanical filters. Because they can help to remove pollen and cigarette smoke particles, these are good for people with allergies. The units have a preliminary mechanical filter to remove larger airborne debris. The smaller particles that get through the filter are electrically charged and then collected on plates of opposite polarity. When one hears an intermittent sparking or crackling noise, the unit is functioning properly.

Activated charcoal filters to help absorb odors are often included with electronic air filters. These are usually downstream of the electronic filter collector plates.

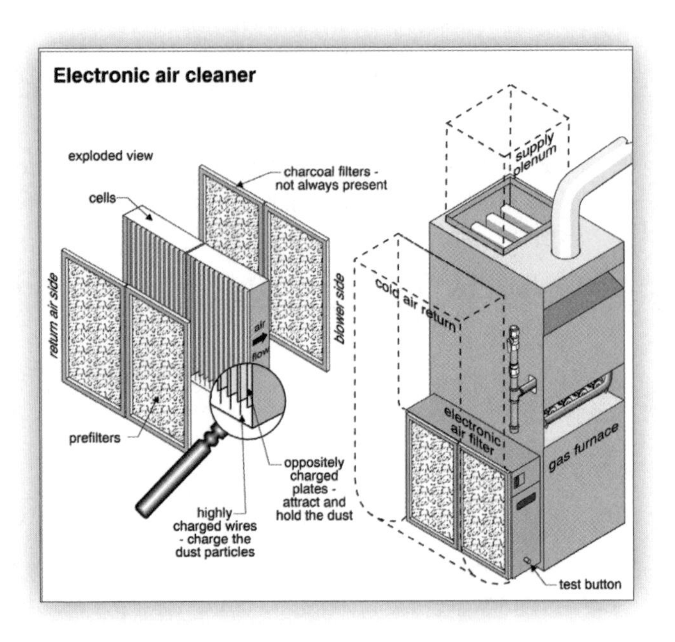

Common Problems with Air Filters

DIRTY Some are cleanable while others are disposable. Regardless of the type, they should be checked monthly. Clean filters improve the comfort of the home, help to reduce heating costs and protect the heating and cooling equipment.

IMPROPER ORIENTATION When the removable components are put back in the ductwork, care must be taken to ensure that they are installed in the right orientation. An arrow indicating airflow should point toward the blower.

MISSING It is not unusual for the filter to be missing altogether. Dirty filters are sometimes removed with the deferred intention of buying a new filter.

INOPERATIVE ELECTRONIC AIR CLEANER From a visual inspection it is not always possible to determine whether an electronic air filter is working properly. In some cases, the power supply has been interrupted and simply needs to be reactivated. The implication is poor air circulation or a dirty furnace.

5.7 Humidifiers

DESCRIPTION Many furnaces have a humidifier to add moisture to the house air through evaporation, combating the dry winter air in homes. There are several types of humidifiers.

HUMIDIFIER TYPES Drum-type humidifiers are common. They are simple and fairly inexpensive. They should be mounted on the return air ductwork with a bypass duct to the supply plenum. They should not be directly above the heat exchanger. We don't want water rusting the furnace heat exchanger when the humidifier leaks.

TRICKLE HUMIDIFIERS Trickle (cascade) type humidfiers that allow water to fall over a special pad are usually highquality units. The water that is not evaporated is collected and flows to a drain.

ATOMIZING AND STEAM HUMIDIFIERS Atomizing humidifiers and steam generating units are high quality and are rarely seen residentially. Due to their design, the inner workings cannot be inspected during a visual examination.

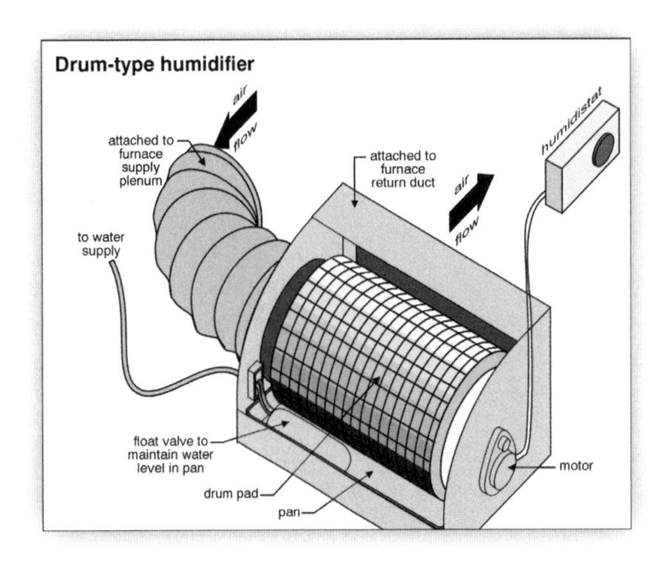

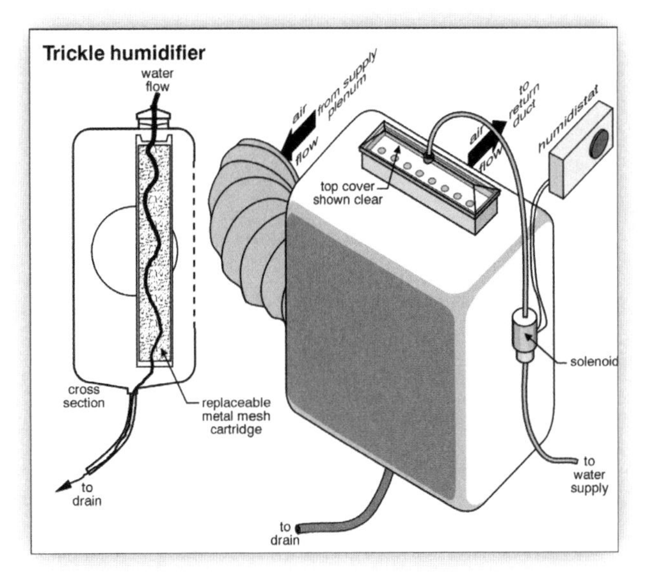

Common Problems with Humidifiers

TOO MUCH HUMIDITY If too much humidity is added, condensation forms on windows and on other relatively cool house surfaces. Condensation can also form inside wall and ceiling cavities, causing rot and mold.

HUMIDITY LEVELS Unfortunately, the ideal humidity level for the house is not the same as the ideal humidity level for people. People like higher levels than are desirable from the house's perspective. To prevent condensation and mold, the following should be observed:

Outside House Temperature	Humidity Level
20 degrees F.	15%
-20 to -10 degrees F.	20%
-10 to 0 degrees F.	25%
0 to +10 degrees F.	35%
+10 and above degrees F.	40%
Summer months	Off

FAULTY HUMIDISTAT, LEAKS, SEIZING Drum humidifiers have several common problems. The control or humidistat may be defective or poorly adjusted. The water reservoir may overflow due to poor adjustment, or float or valve problems. This may rust the furnace. The tray sometimes overflows because mineral deposits foul the automatic water supply valve, causing it to stay open even when the tray is full. Leaks at the water supply line or valve are also common.

The drum pad itself gets clogged with mineral deposits, seizing the drum, which in turn burns out the motor. Replacement parts for these humidifiers are not expensive.

DUCT DAMPER – WRONG POSITION A humidifier duct damper should be provided if there is an air conditioner connected to the furnace. This damper should be kept closed during the cooling season to prevent air conditioner coil ice-up due to short-circuiting of the airflow.

POOR LOCATION Humidifiers should be installed on the return air duct, not the supply plenum above the heat exchanger. Humidifiers often leak, and water entering the furnace heat exchanger can cause rust.

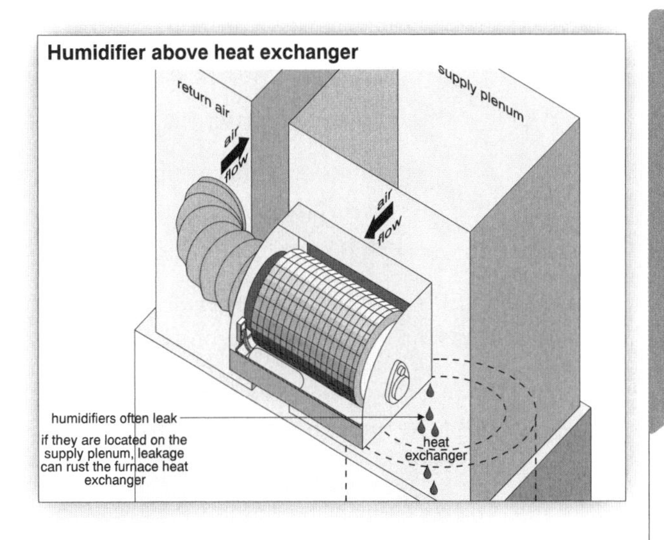

5.8 Ducts, Registers and Grilles

DESCRIPTION Furnaces have two sets of ductwork: one to supply the air to the rooms in the house, and a second to return air to the furnace. Every room in the house should have at least one supply air register. Ideally, each room would have a return air register; however, most houses have fewer return air grilles. Return air systems are often centrally located in hallways and at the bottom of stairwells.

Common Problems with Ducts, Registers and Grilles

MISSING/ INEFFECTIVE SUPPLY REGISTERS Some rooms have no heat. Some registers are poorly located. Supply registers should be located near exterior walls, below windows. However, it is often not cost-effective to relocate existing registers. Some registers provide very little heat. The ductwork may be obstructed, damaged or disconnected. The result is an uncomfortably cool room.

MISSING/TOO FEW/UNDERSIZED RETURN POINTS Ideally, every room with a supply register should have a return air grille; however, this is almost never the case. In many older homes there are one or two centrally located return air grilles. Rooms with supply air registers and no return air grilles should have doors with a one-inch gap at the bottom to allow air from the room to get to the return air grille when the doors are closed. The total supply register area should equal the total area of the return air grilles. It is common in older homes to find inadequate return air. This leads to uncomfortable rooms and higher heating costs.

MISSING/ INOPERATIVE GRILLES Supply registers and return grilles are often missing or painted shut. They are easily replaced.

DIRTY/BROKEN Return air ductwork often accumulates debris. Older return grilles in floors are often broken and may not safely support people or furniture.

POOR LOCATION Ideally, the supply registers should be located on an outside wall below a window (the coolest part of the room), and the return register should be located on an opposite wall (the warmest part of the room). In some houses, return air registers were provided near the supply air registers.

Some of these systems short-circuit in that the warm supply air is simply drawn back into the return air register, with little heat going to the room itself. Sometimes, simply blocking off the return air register will improve heating in a room considerably.

Some homes have supply registers near the ceiling. This is a less than ideal arrangement since warm air wants to rise, and all the heat will be at the ceiling. This is not usually cost-effective to change.

POOR LOCATION IN BASEMENT Supply registers in basements are often located in the ceiling, which is not ideal. Many people install supplementary electric baseboard heaters rather than relocate the registers.

UNSAFE LOCATION – GARAGE Supply air registers or return air grilles should not be provided in garages, since automobile fumes may be drawn into the house air.

OBSTRUCTED The house will be uncomfortable and heating costs will be higher if the air flow is obstructed. Carpeting and furniture should be kept clear of air flow paths. Ductwork may also be disconnected or incomplete, although this is difficult to determine visually.

HEATING DUCTS IN CONCRETE Slab-on-grade houses with forced-air heat often have heating ducts embedded in the concrete foundations and slab. Sometimes the ducts are partially collapsed during the concrete pouring process. Moisture in and around the slab can flood the ducts and rust the metal duct walls. The water standing in the ducts becomes a health hazard. Rusted duct walls can come loose and collapse. Any of these will restrict at least some air flow through the system. Ductwork in poured slabs and foundations is, of course, difficult to inspect and repair.

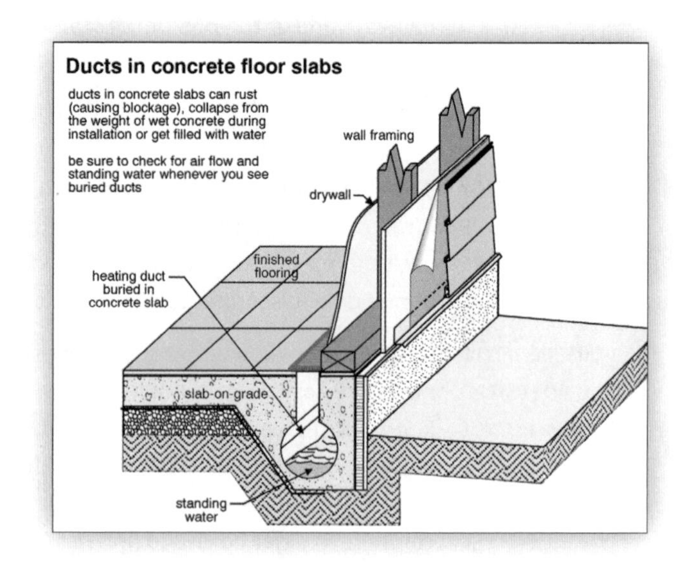

OTHER DUCT PROBLEMS Common problems with supply ducts and registers are disconnected or obstructed ducts, dirty ducts, ducts sized adequately for heating but inadequate for air conditioning, ducts sized for conventional furnaces, but inadequately sized for high efficiency systems, and unbalanced ductwork (too much air coming through one register and not enough air coming through another).

INOPERATIVE ZONE DAMPERS Some sophisticated warm-air heating systems are zoned. Thermostats in various areas of the house control dampers which open and close, directing air to the areas where heat is needed.

Motorized dampers in residential installations are often neglected and inoperative. The problems may be in the controls or the dampers themselves. In many systems, they are abandoned or removed.

5.9 Furnace Efficiencies

Both furnaces and boilers are classified by their efficiency.

DESCRIPTION

5.9.1 Conventional Efficiency Systems: Until the mid-1970s, all systems were of similar (conventional) design and efficiency. Almost all had an operating (steady state) efficiency of approximately 80%. When the system was operating, 80% of the heat produced from burning the fuel went into the house. The other 20% went up the chimney. The systems are not 80% efficient over the entire heating season.

Since a furnace has to provide enough heat during the coldest day of the year, it is oversized every other day of the year. Consequently, systems do not run continuously during the winter.

OFF-CYCLE LOSSES

When a conventional furnace is not operating, warm house air is escaping up the chimney. Even when the system is operating, a good deal of warm air is lost up the chimney, just maintaining adequate draft for the exhaust gases. On gas-fired systems, some fuel is wasted keeping the pilot on. Also, when a boiler or furnace is starting up or cooling down, it is not operating at full efficiency. If you combine the off-cycle losses with the start-up and cool-down losses, and add in the 20% losses during normal operation, the average seasonal efficiency of a conventional boiler or furnace is about 55% to 65%. That means 35% to 45% of the heat from the fuel is lost. With the advent of more efficient furnaces and boilers, this system became known as a conventional system. Conventional systems were phased out in the early 1990s.

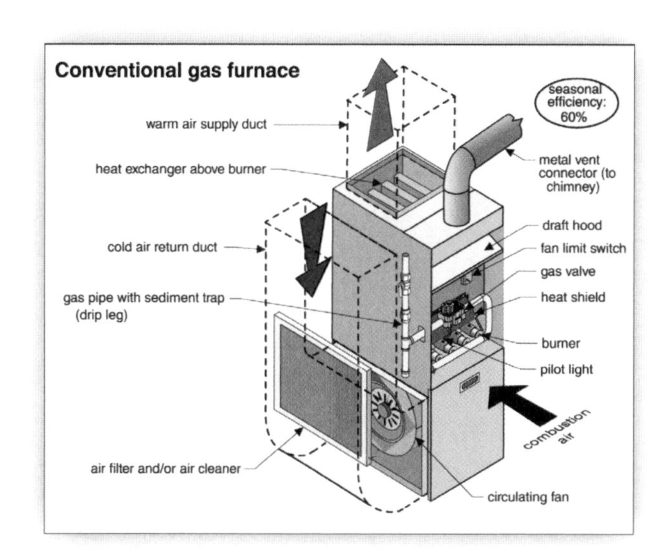

DESCRIPTION

5.9.2 Mid-efficiency Systems: Most mid-efficiency furnaces are conventional units (although some have a secondary heat exchanger) with modifications to reduce off-cycle losses. The enhancement is often an induced draft fan in the exhaust, which only operates when the burner is on. Alternatively, a motorized vent damper may be used in the exhaust to prevent heat from escaping up the chimney when the system is shut down. Both of these strategies prevent heat loss to the outdoors when the system is idle.

Continuous pilots on gas systems are replaced with intermittent pilots. This avoids wasting fuel when the systems are not working. These improvements combine to almost eliminate the 20% off-cycle losses.

Mid-efficiency systems are not much more efficient when operating than conventional systems. However, their seasonal efficiency is much higher – typically 80%. This is a 20% improvement over conventional systems. We are only losing 20% of the heat from the fuel. Mid-efficiency sytems are being replaced with high efficiency systems in the first part of the 21st century.

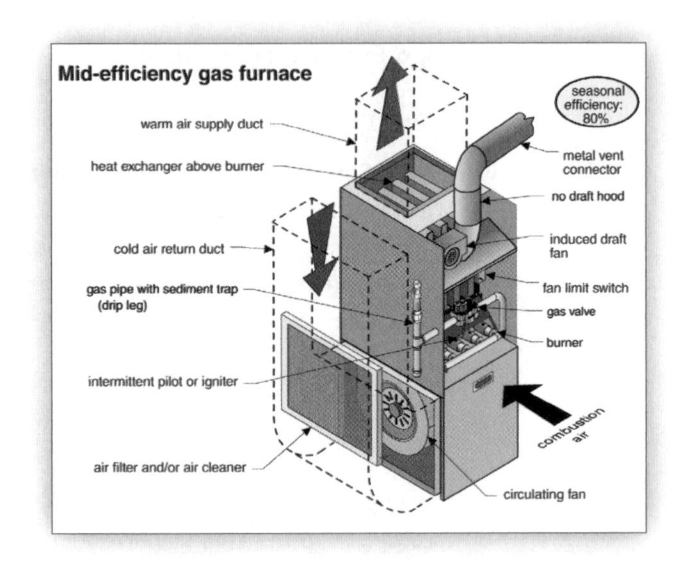

DESCRIPTION

5.9.3 High Efficiency Systems: High efficiency furnaces go a step further. They are also known as condensing furnaces because the exhaust gases are so cool they condense water. (One of the main products of combustion of burning natural gas is water.) These furnaces can withstand the slightly corrosive condensate and have a drainage system to collect it and carry it away.

While a conventional furnace has a single heat exchanger, high efficiency units may have two or three heat exchangers. High efficiency systems keep the hot exhaust gases in contact with the heat exchanger longer so that more heat is transferred to the house air or water.

High efficiency systems also limit the off-cycle losses, just like mid-efficiency systems. They have a seasonal efficiency in the 90% range, with some over 95%.

Since there are more components in a high efficiency system, there is more to go wrong and repair and maintenance costs are typically higher than a conventional furnace. At the very least, annual servicing is required. Many believe their life expectancy is also shorter.

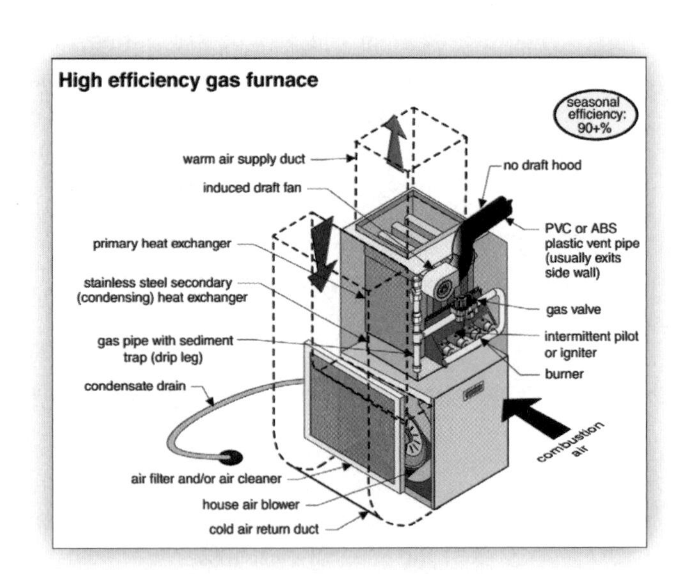

5.10 Combination Heating Systems (Integrated Mechanical Systems)

DESCRIPTION Combination heating systems use the domestic water heater to heat the house. The hot water in the tank can either flow to the plumbing system or to a fan coil unit to heat the house. The fan blows house air across the coil filled with hot water, picking up heat. The warm air is distributed to the house through ductwork.

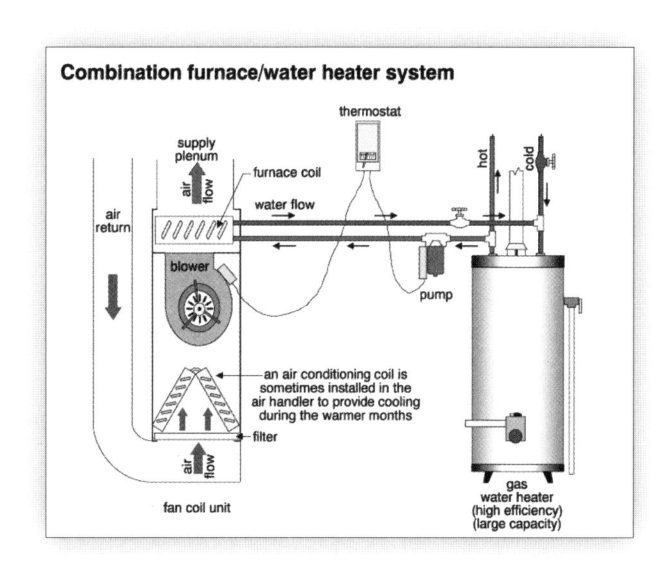

Water from a boiler can heat the home (through radiators or radiant floor heating, for example), and can also be used to heat the domestic hot water in a tank. These are often called indirect systems.

Common Problems with Combination Heating Systems

INADEQUATE HEAT Combination forced air systems tend to have modest capacity. Some systems have proved to be undersized for heating a home.

TEMPERING VALVE (MIXING VALVE) NEEDED As a result of inadequate heat problems, some homeowners turn up their domestic water temperature to as high as 170°F. This may result in scalding at plumbing fixtures. It may also result in pressure relief valves leaking on hot water tanks. If the units are to be operated at such high temperatures, mixing (tempering) valves to cool the domestic hot water are required. These valves mix cold water with the hot to lower the temperature.

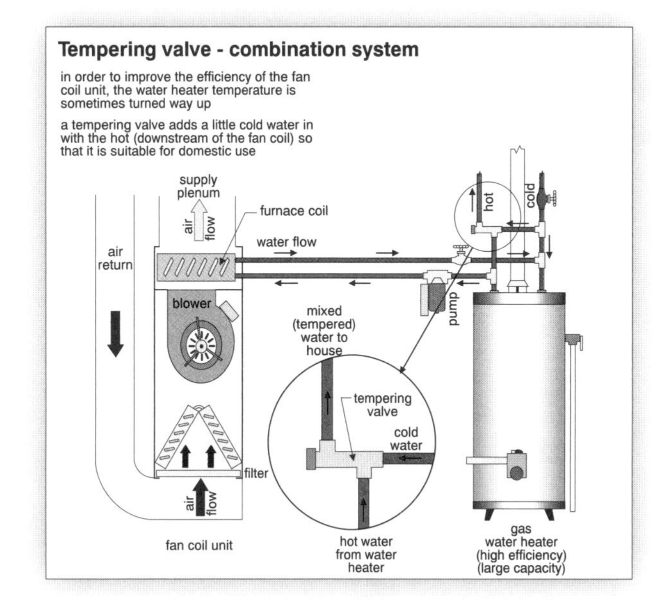

Some jurisdictions insist that the systems be designed so that the water temperature can be no more than 140°F and the design water temperature of the air handler is 130°F. This means that more airflow is needed to heat the house. The ductwork in many houses is not designed to handle these high volumes of air. This may make these systems a questionable solution for existing houses. Also, these systems appear to be more practical in climates where the heating demand is relatively small compared to the domestic hot water demand.

NEW TECHNOLOGY – SUSPECT

These systems have not been around for several decades, but early experience has shown some reliability problems. We have seen some early failures of water heaters that are working much harder than they used to.

Pumps and tempering valves add some complexity. Controls can be an issue. Other problems include leaking or clogged coils. Failures result in no heat for the house.

5.11 Furnace Life Expectancy

Life expectancies depend on many things, but there are some averages.
Conventional and mid-efficiency furnaces – 18 to 25 years
High efficiency furnaces – 15 to 20 years
Combination heating systems – 5 to 10 years

6.0 Hot Water Boilers (also called Hydronic Heating)

DESCRIPTION

Boilers heat the home by moving hot water through pipe loops. Heat is distributed at radiators, convectors or baseboards.

Hot water heating systems are called boilers, but they do not actually boil the water; they only heat it to a maximum of roughly 180°F. Steam heating systems, discussed in the next section, actually do boil the water.

A boiler consists of a burner, a heat exchanger and typically a pump. The burner generates heat within a combustion chamber. The heat exchanger allows the heat from the flame to heat the water that circulates through the house.

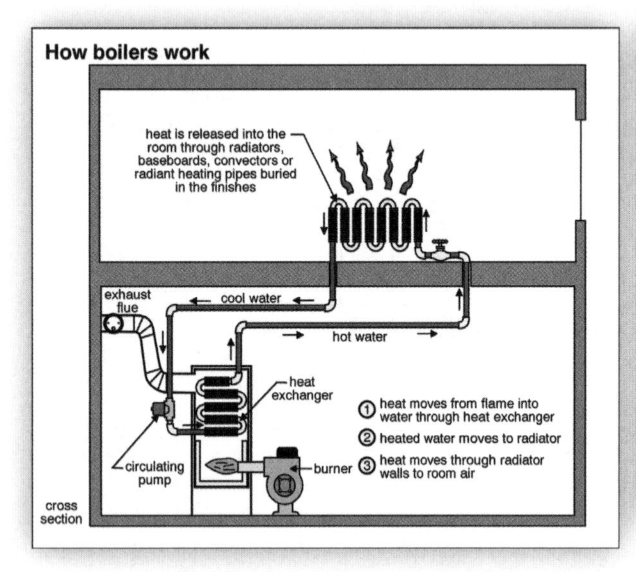

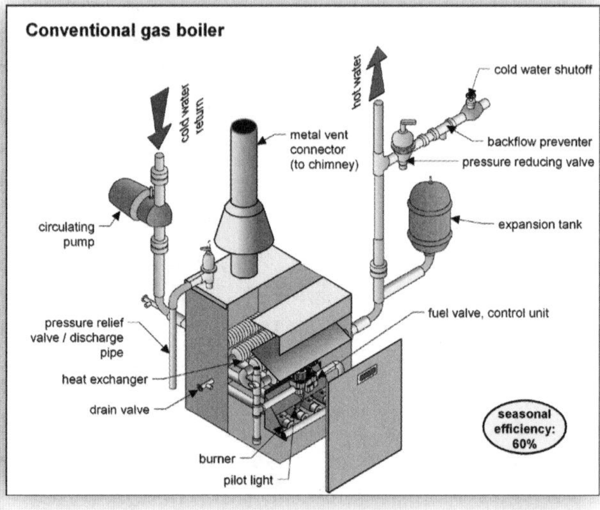

HEATING

6.1 Electric Boilers

DESCRIPTION Electric boilers have electric heating elements rather than a heat exchanger. They work much like an electric water heater or a kettle, although they don't actually boil the water.

Electric boiler

temperature/pressure gauge
automatic air vent
hot water to radiators
high limit control
pressure relief valve
cold water return
drain valve
boiler
circulating pump
sequencers
heating elements
power supply

6.2 Gas and Oil Burners

We have discussed gas and oil burners in previous sections. We won't repeat those discussions here.

6.3 Heat Exchanger

DESCRIPTION With the exception of electric systems, all boilers have two major components: a heat exchanger and a burner. The heat exchanger, which is the heart of the boiler, has products of combustion on one side and the water to be heated on the other. The flame heats the metal heat exchanger, which in turn heats the water. Heat exchangers are made of cast iron, steel or copper.

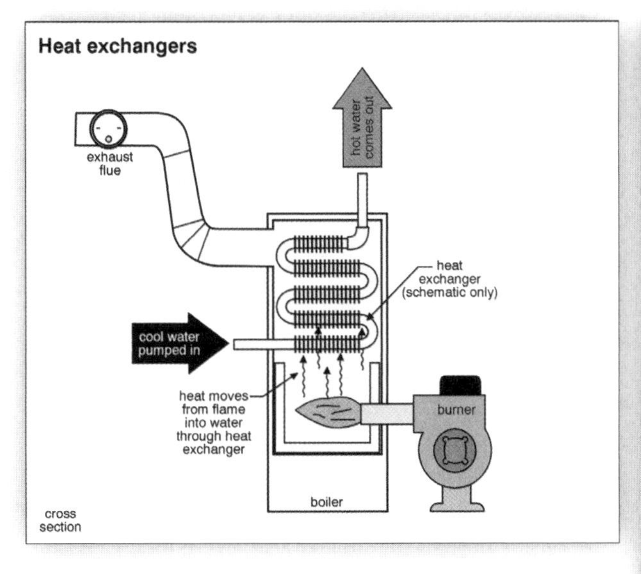

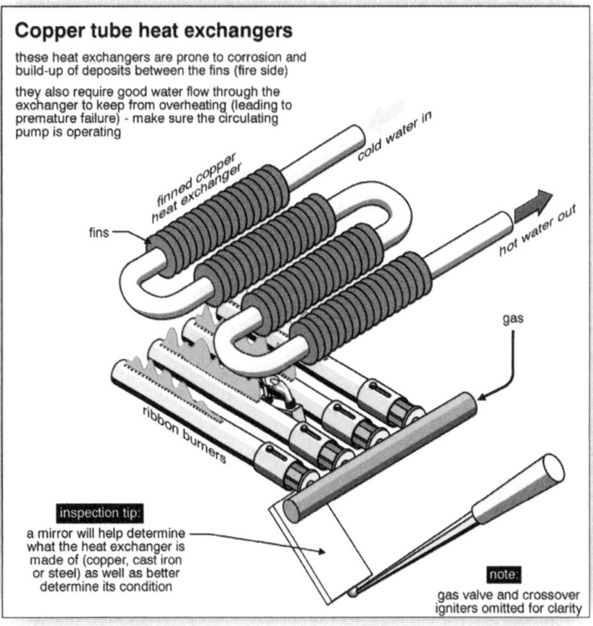

Common Problems with Heat Exchangers

RUST/ CRACKS/HOLES When a heat exchanger fails, it rusts through or cracks and water leaks into the combustion chamber and/or out of the boiler. The boiler usually shuts down and there is no heat for the home. The boiler is typically replaced when the heat exchanger fails.

OBSTRUCTED Corrosion on the fire side of the boiler can lead to clogging, which restricts the flow of exhaust products out of the house. This can be a dangerous situation with products of combustion getting into the home through the draft hood.

6.4 Pump

DESCRIPTION Older systems relied on gravity and convection to move water through the house but most systems now have a circulating pump. The pump may run continuously, or intermittently when the water in the boiler is above a certain temperature. Others operate whenever the boiler is operating.

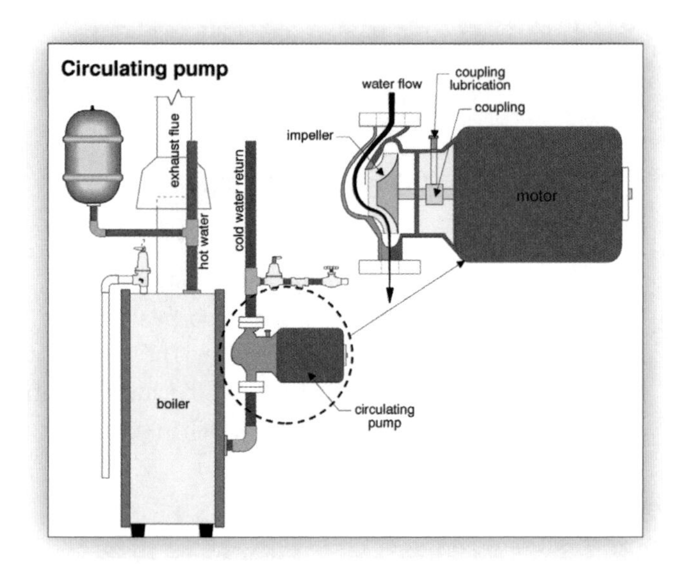

Common Problems with Circulating Pumps

LEAK/ INOPERATIVE/ NOISY/HOT The most common problems associated with circulating pumps are leakage and inoperative pumps caused by worn pump bearings, burned out pump motors and defective temperature sensors. Pumps that are about to fail may be noisy or hot to the touch.

In some cases the heating system will not operate if the pump fails. In other cases the heating system may continue to operate somewhat inefficiently.

6.5 Expansion Tank

DESCRIPTION Modern boilers are closed systems. The water in the system is under pressure. As the boiler heats up, the water expands and begins to fill an expansion tank, compressing the air in the tank. The air provides a cushion that prevents excessive pressure build-up. This expansion tank is usually near the boiler.

The air in an expansion tank eventually gets absorbed into the water, and expansion tanks have to be drained when they become waterlogged.

Some expansion tanks have a diaphragm or bladder that separates the water and the air. The air is never absorbed into the water and unless the diaphragm fails; the tank will theoretically never become waterlogged, reducing maintenance.

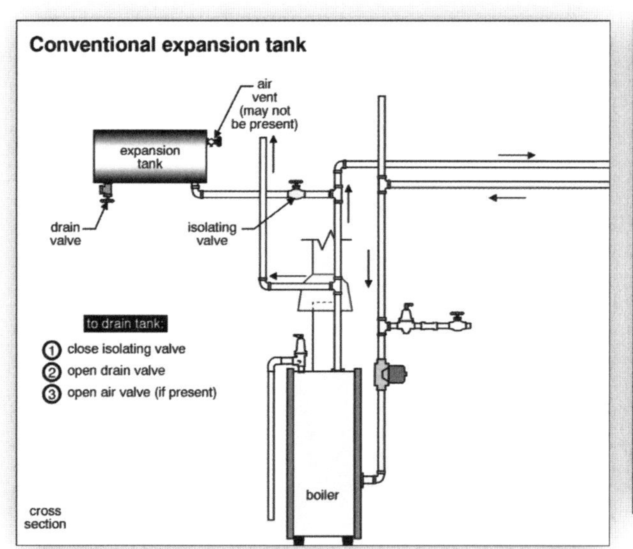

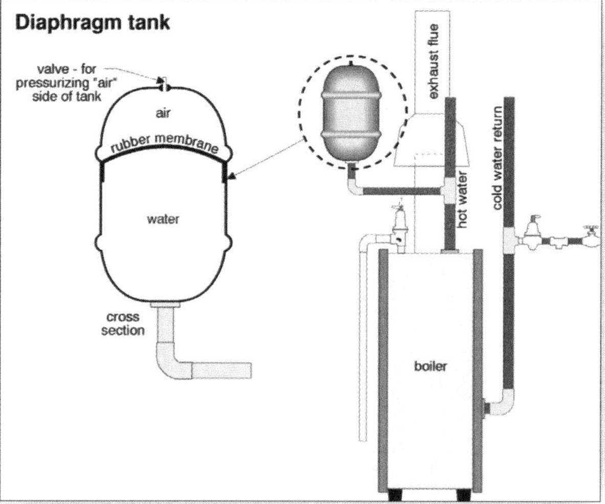

Common Problems with Expansion Tanks

TANK WATERLOGGED If the expansion tank has no air in it, it has no capacity to accept more water and is said to be waterlogged. When the boiler heats the water, the pressure rises and the pressure relief valve operates. A leaking or dripping pressure relief valve may mean a waterlogged expansion tank.

LEAK/RUST Expansion tanks are typically made of steel and can rust and eventually leak.

6.6 Operating and Safety Controls

Hot water heating systems have several controls to ensure safety and proper operation.

DESCRIPTION

6.6.1 Pressure Reducing Valve (Water Make-up Valve): On modern systems, water is automatically added to the system through a pressure reducing valve as needed. The valve connects the boiler to the house plumbing system. It is typically set at 15 psi (pounds per square inch). If the pressure in the heating system drops below 15 psi, the pressure reducing valve allows water in from the plumbing system. When the plumbing system is drained, there is a risk of unhealthy water from the heating system draining back into the plumbing system. Modern systems include a backflow preventer to keep this from happening.

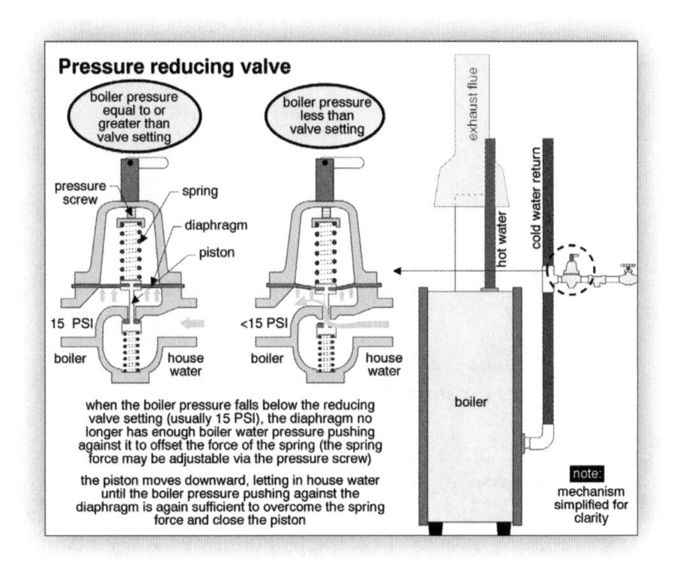

Common Problems with Pressure Reducing Valves

LEAKS The most common problems with pressure reducing valves are leakage and improper adjustment.

DEFECTIVE If the boiler is cold, the pressure gauge on the boiler should indicate roughly the same pressure as the pressure reducing valve (12-15 psi). If the two numbers are not the same, the pressure reducing valve may be out of adjustment or the pressure gauge may be wrong. There may also be a closed valve between the pressure reducing valve and gauge.

SYSTEM NOT FILLED WITH WATER? Sometimes the top floor of the home is cool, and radiators are not hot. If no water discharges after opening a radiator bleed valve on the top floor, the system is probably not full of water. There may not be enough pressure to push water up to the top of the home to fill the upper radiators. The pressure reducing valve may have to be adjusted or replaced.

DESCRIPTION **6.6.2 Backflow Preventer:** The backflow preventer only allows water from the plumbing system to flow into the heating system. We don't want the dirty heating water from the boiler to get into our drinking water.

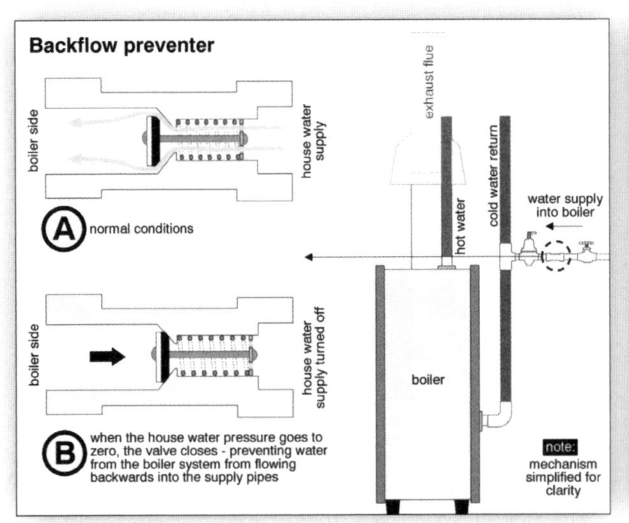

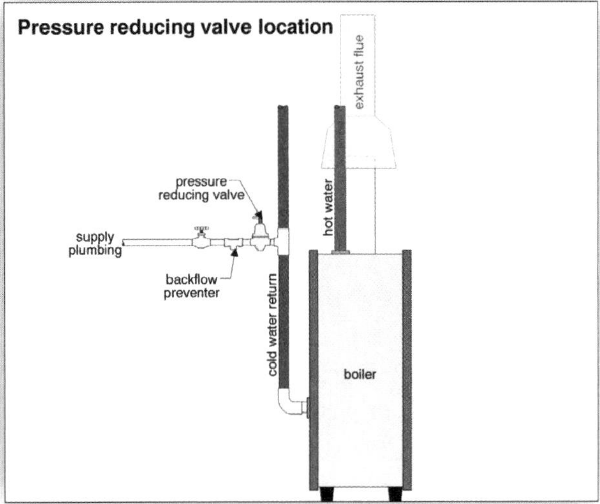

Common Problems with Backflow Preventers

MISSING/LEAKING A missing backflow preventer may represent a health hazard. The most common problem with backflow preventers is leakage.

DESCRIPTION **6.6.3 Low Water Cut Out:** Low water cut outs are provided on large boilers. They are designed to shut the heating system off if the boiler water level drops below a safe level. This prevents the boiler from burning itself up.

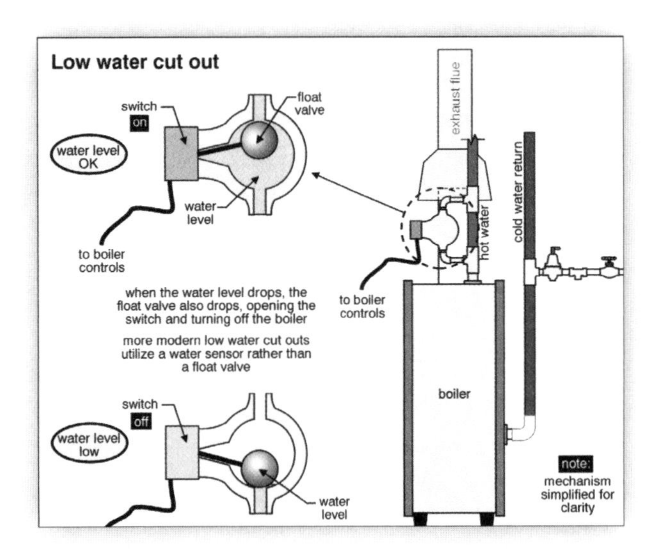

Common Problems with Low Water Cut Outs

LEAK/ INOPERATIVE Like most safety controls, the most common problem is leakage. It is also possible the low water cut out is inoperative, although this would not be discovered during a home inspection. This system should be tested during regular servicing.

DESCRIPTION **6.6.4 High Temperature Limit:** The high temperature limit is a safety device that shuts off the boiler if the water temperature reaches roughly 200°F. The high temperature limit prevents the water from boiling. Boiling water builds up pressure, which may rupture the boiler or piping or possibly cause an explosion. This is not tested during a home inspection.

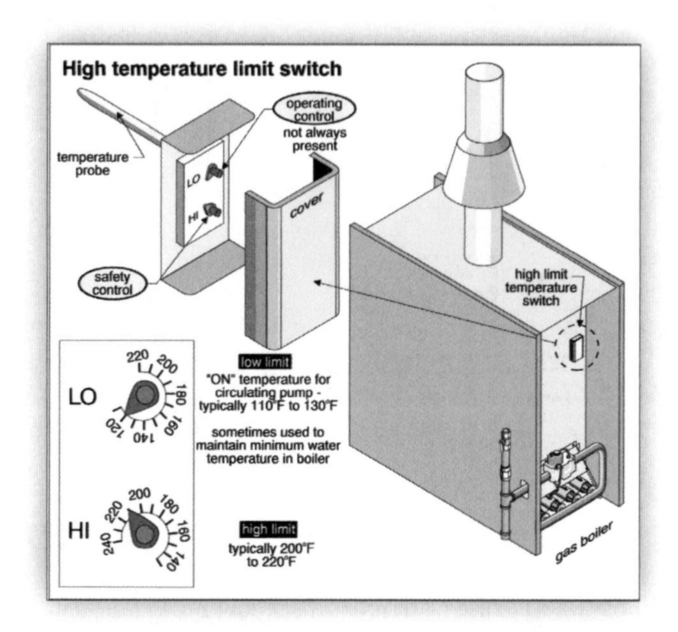

Common Problems with High Temperature Limit Switches

LEAKS/ DEFECTIVE/ ADJUSTMENT High temperature limit switches often leak where they are connected to the heating piping. The switch itself may require adjustment or repair. An inoperative high temperature limit switch may result in an unsafe situation, although they are designed to fail-safe and prevent the heating system from operating if they are defective. The high temperature limit is not tested during a home inspection.

DESCRIPTION **6.6.5 Pressure Relief Valve:** All boilers should be provided with pressure relief valves. The valves are typically set at about 30 psi. If the pressure in the boiler gets too high, this valve will allow the pressure to escape safely by releasing water. This device should be tested by a technician during regular servicing since it is not tested during a home inspection.

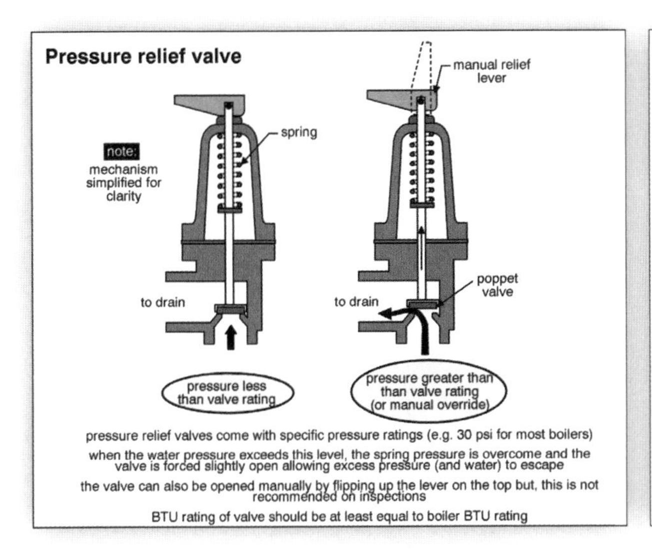

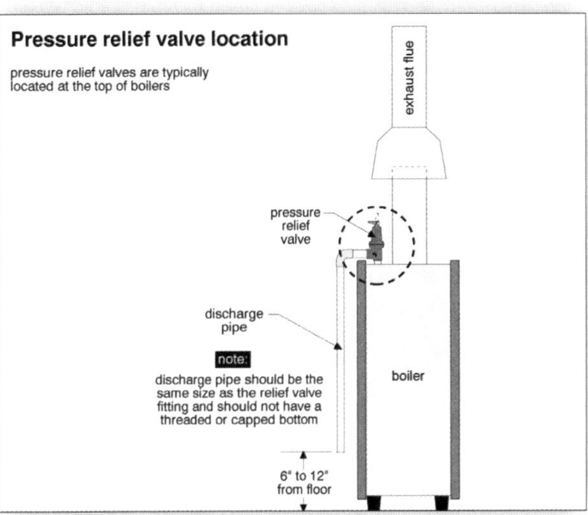

Common Problems with Pressure Relief Valves

POOR DISCHARGE POINT Because the water discharging from a pressure relief valve is very hot, the discharge should be piped down to six to 12 inches above the floor. This reduces the risk of scalding anyone nearby. If no pipe has been connected to the relief valve, there may be a dangerous situation.

LEAKS Pressure relief valves often leak. Sometimes this is due to a defective valve seat or debris caught on the valve seat. These nuisance problems are easily rectified. A leaking pressure relief valve may suggest a waterlogged expansion tank that allows pressure to build up in the system when the water is hot.

CAPPED OFF Sometimes, pressure relief valves that leak chronically are capped off. This should never be done, as the relief valve is an essential safety device.

6.7 Piping and Radiators, Convectors and Baseboards

DESCRIPTION Water heated in the boiler is distributed through the house. Cast iron radiators are common in older homes.

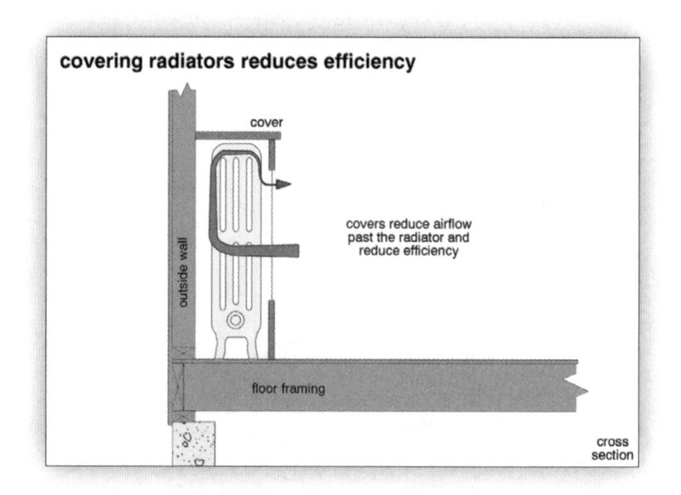

CONVECTORS Hot water convectors are an alternative to radiators. Convectors may be cast iron or copper tubing with aluminum fins. Radiators are typically 24 to 36 inches high. Convectors take up less space, usually being less than 12 inches high.

BASEBOARDS There are low profile baseboard hot water distribution systems. The piping can be steel, copper or polybutylene (PB).

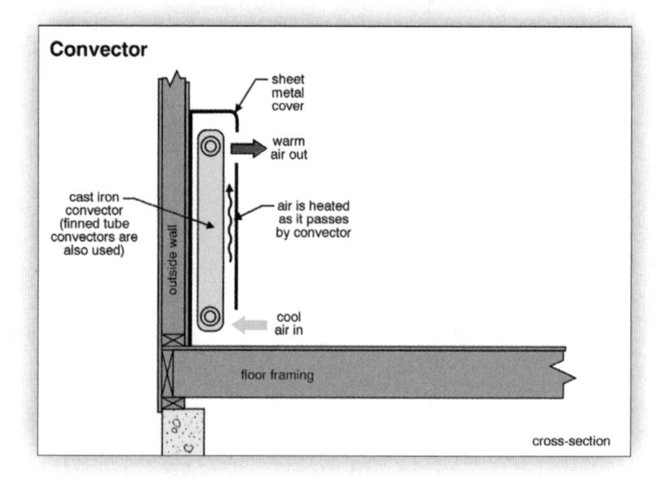

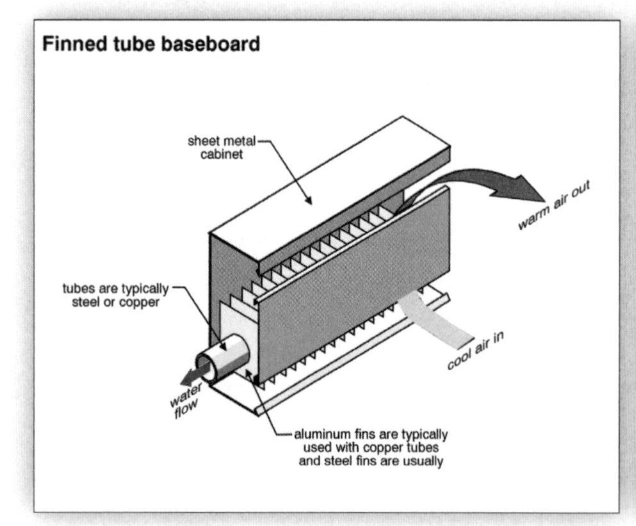

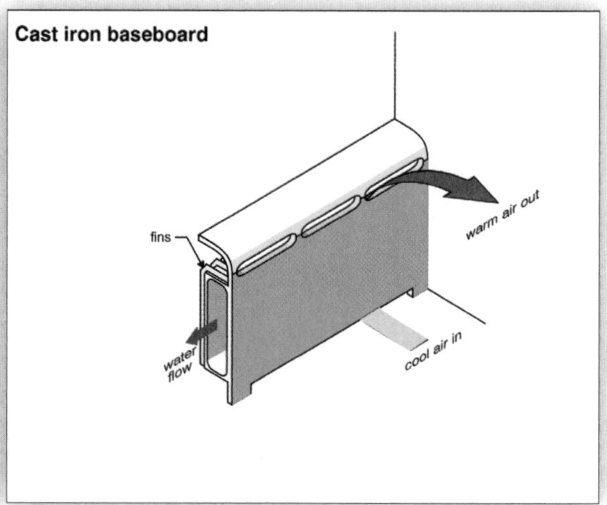

Common Problems with Radiators/Convectors

MISSING At least one radiator or convector should be provided in each habitable room. These are sometimes removed to make room for kitchen cabinets, for example. It is often easier and less expensive to install an electric baseboard heater than to re-install a radiator. The same is true if relocating a radiator. It may be best to remove it and replace it with electric heat.

AIR IN THE SYSTEM If air is trapped in a radiator, the radiator will not heat properly, because the radiator does not fill with water. Trapped air can be released through the bleed valve. If the radiators on the top floor of a home are not filled with water because there is not enough pressure in the system, these radiators will be cold. Adding more water to the system by changing the setting of the automatic water makeup valve usually resolves the problem.

LEAKS Other problems include leaks caused by failed packing at the control valves, or cracking of the radiator itself if the water in the system freezes.

MIXED SYSTEM Cast iron radiators and convectors take a long time to heat up, and a long time to cool down. This helps to produce even heat. Light weight convectors heat up and cool down quickly. Either system is fine, because the thermostat moderates the heat. However, uneven heating and comfort problems may be noticed where radiators and convectors are mixed in the same house.

OBSTRUCTED Radiators and convectors respond more slowly if air movement around them is obstructed. Some radiator covers reduce both effectiveness and efficiency. If radiators cannot give their heat off to house air that circulates freely, they may direct heat through the outside walls, effectively wasting it. Reflective materials (aluminum foil-faced insulation boards, for example) behind radiators help direct heat into the living area.

DESCRIPTION **6.7.1 Piping:** The piping on most hot water heating systems is black steel (not galvanized); however, some modern systems have copper or plastic piping, either polybutylene (PB) or cross-linked polyethylene (PEX). This piping distributes water to and from the boiler to the radiators or convectors. The piping may also be used as part of a radiant heating system.

Common Problems with Piping

CORROSION Steel piping corrodes, but the rate of deterioration is slow as the water within the heating system is rarely replaced. The water becomes chemically inert and the rusting process is slow. Draining the water from a heating system every summer is not recommended, since the pipes will deteriorate more quickly if the water is changed regularly.

FAILED FITTINGS Polybutylene (PB) piping is used in some hot water heating systems. Although there have been some issues with polybutylene plumbing piping and failed plastic fittings, this has not been a big issue on hot water heating systems. There are however, issues to be aware of with PB in baseboard systems.

POLYBUTYLENE BASEBOARD SYSTEMS – LEAKS

The use of polybutylene (PB) piping for hot water heating in a baseboard convector configuration is not considered good practice. The connections are prone to leakage due to the cycling of pressure and water temperature. The piping is rated for 180°F, and the water temperature can exceed that.

DESCRIPTION

6.7.2 Control Valves and Bleed Valves: Most radiators or convectors have a control valve that can be used to adjust the rate of water flow through the unit. This can be used to balance the heat in the home.

BLEED VALVES

A small bleed valve is located near the top of the radiator. This allows trapped air in the radiator to be removed. Bleeding the radiators is part of annual maintenance.

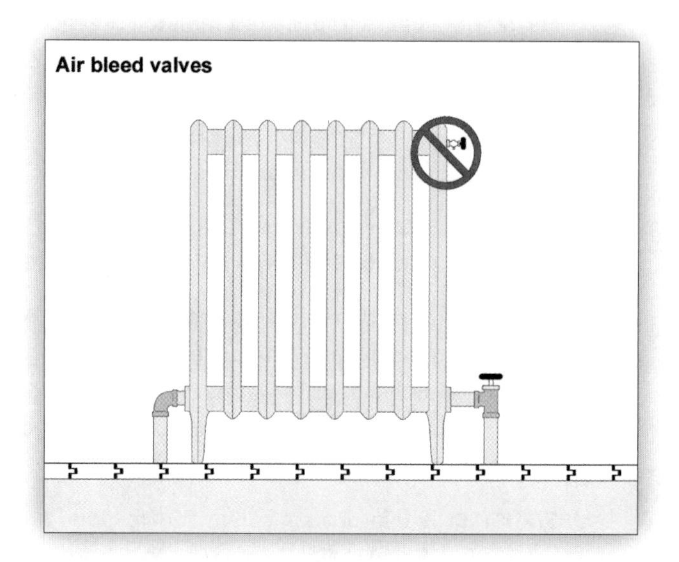

Common Problems with Control Valves and Bleed Valves

CONTROL VALVE – LEAKS/ INOPERATIVE

Control valves are rarely used and, consequently, they often leak when they are turned. These valves are not operated during a home inspection. These valves are often inoperative or at least very difficult to move.

Even undisturbed valves are prone to leakage over time. The damage from a leaking valve can be extensive.

BLEED VALVE – DAMAGE/SEIZED/ LEAKS

Bleed valves are delicate and easily broken. The very small valve openings can be obstructed by dirt or paint. They are prone to seizing or leaking; however, they are easily replaced. This requires at least partial draining of the system. Inoperative bleed valves don't allow air to be removed from radiators, and heating may be inadequate.

DESCRIPTION

6.7.3 Zone Valves: Some sophisticated hot water heating systems have different areas of the house controlled by different thermostats. These thermostats operate motorized valves that open and close to direct hot water to specific areas of the house.

Another way to get zone control is with multiple circulating pumps. The thermostats control different pumps, directing water to specific zones, on demand.

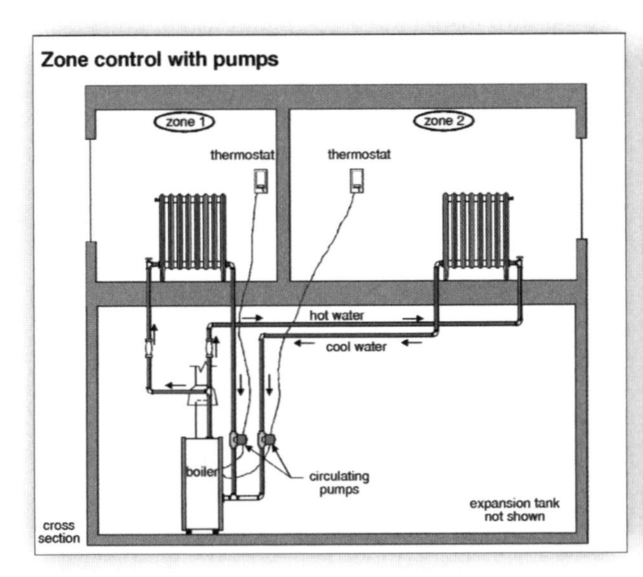

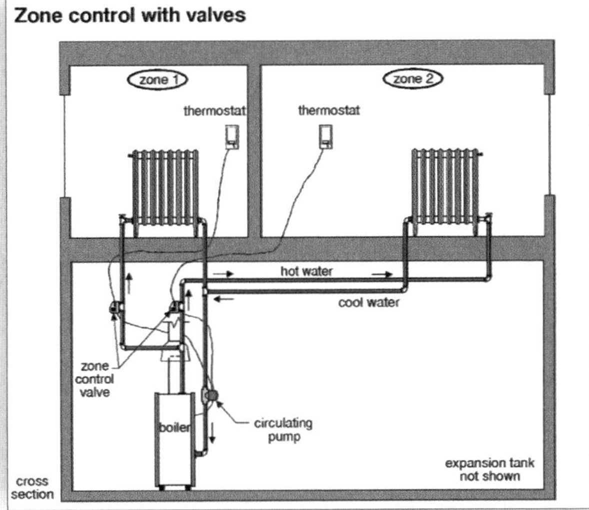

The Common Problem with Zone Valves and Pumps

INOPERATIVE Maintenance on these valves is frequently neglected and they are often abandoned. Pumps may be inoperative because the pump itself has seized or because the electric motor has failed. It is not possible during an inspection to verify the proper operation of zoned systems.

6.8 Radiant Hot Water Systems

DESCRIPTION Some hot water heating systems employ piping buried in floors or ceilings. The piping heats the floor or the ceiling, which in turn radiates the heat into the room. The pipes have traditionally been galvanized steel, black steel, or copper, although flexible plastic tubing is now used.

The pipes may be buried about three inches below the surface of concrete flooring and are typically four to 12 inches apart. Piping may also be set between the subfloor and flooring, often held in place with a special grid. In some cases, a foil reflector helps direct heat up into the room. Radiant piping can also be placed below the subfloor, running between the floor joists.

The temperatures in radiant heating systems are typically much lower than conventional radiator or convector systems. Water temperatures are typically maintained around 115°F, so that flooring is not overheated.

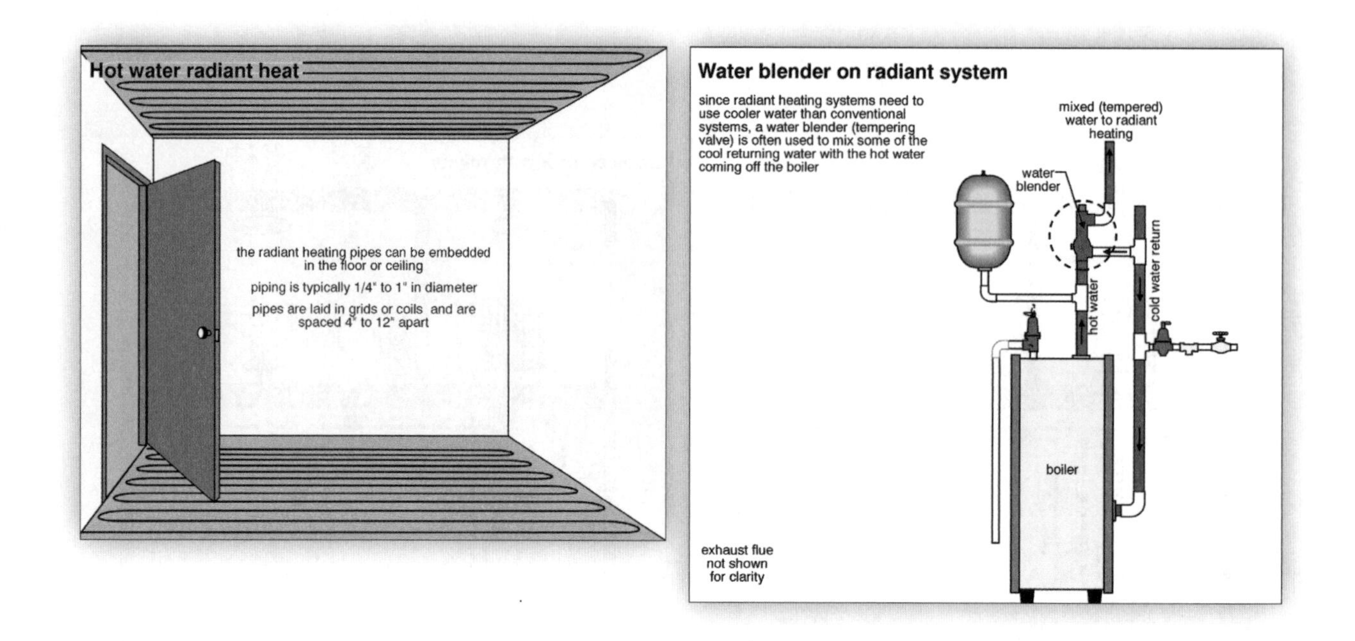

Many radiant systems have several discrete loops feeding different parts of the home, fed from a single manifold at the boiler. This approach is sometimes called a home run.

POLYBUTYLENE (PB) AND PEX Polybutylene (PB) piping is used in radiant heating systems extensively in some areas. Cross-linked polyethylene (PEX) piping is also used for radiant heating systems.

Common Problems with Radiant Hot Water Systems

LEAKS/ OBSTRUCTIONS Leakage can be a significant problem with hot water radiant systems. When a leak occurs, it is usually easily located due to the obvious water damage, unless the leak is below the basement or slab-on-grade floor. The piping can be crimped or obstructed, although this is less common. It may be difficult to find the problem.

TOO DEEP/ POORLY SPACED Heating pipes can be buried too deep (more than three inches) in concrete floors, resulting in slow response to the thermostat and some heat loss. There may be unwanted fluctuations in temperature. Hot spots and cold spots are often noted if pipes are too far apart (more than eight to 16 inches).

BREAKS/LEAKS These systems are susceptible to building settlement, and especially with steel or copper, the pipes can be broken as the house moves.

OXYGEN PERMEATION THROUGH PB PIPING CAUSES RUSTING When non-oxygen barrier polybutylene (PB) tubing is used in a hot water heating system, oxygen may pass through the tubing into the boiler water. This can cause the boiler to rust and fail prematurely. The condition of the boiler interior cannot be determined by a visual inspection. It is recommended that a heating specialist evaluate the system to determine whether improvements are needed. These could include adding a chemical to the system to discourage corrosion or adding a second heat exchanger system to separate the boiler water from the water circulating through the system. The heat exchanger option is costly but needs less maintenance.

CONDENSATE SYSTEM – LEAKING/ CLOGGED High-efficiency boilers have condensate that must be collected and disposed of, just like high-efficiency furnaces. In some jurisdictions, the condensate must be neutralized, so that the city piping is not attacked by the slightly acidic water. A leaking or clogged condensate system may damage the boiler or the home.

6.9 Boiler Efficiencies

DESCRIPTION Conventional boilers are roughly 60% seasonally efficient. More modern mid-efficiency boilers are roughly 80% seasonally efficient. There are very few high-efficiency boilers with efficiencies of up to 90%.

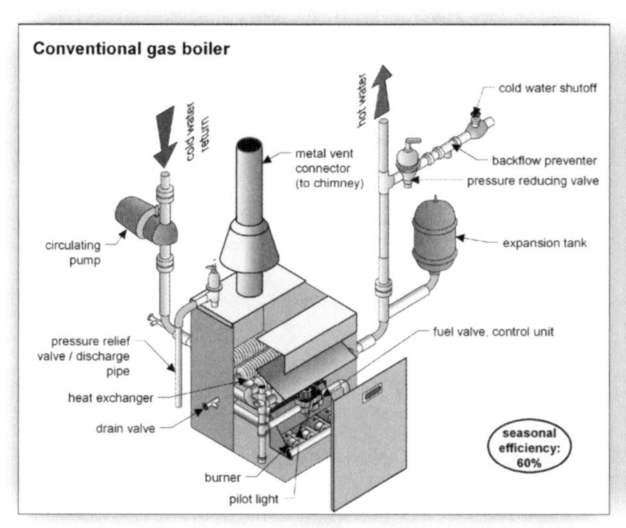

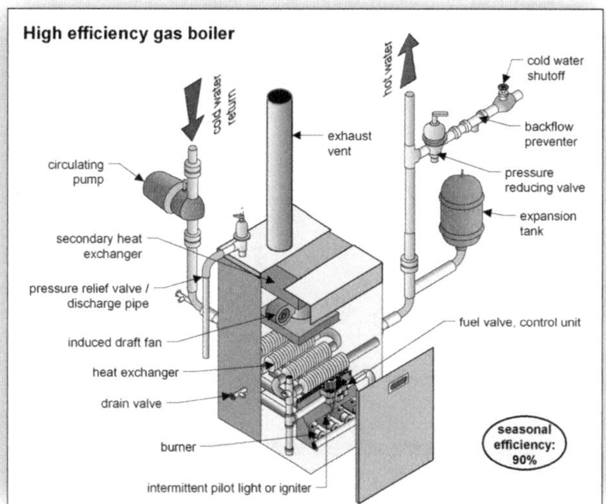

6.10 Boiler Life Expectancy

Conventional and mid-efficiency cast-iron boilers – 25 to 50 years
Conventional and mid-efficiency steel boilers – 20 to 35 years
Conventional and mid-efficiency copper boilers – 15 to 25 years

7.0 Steam Boilers

DESCRIPTION Steam boilers are similar to hot water boilers, typically made of cast iron or steel. As with hot water boilers, cast iron systems last longer than steel. Generally speaking, a hot water boiler may be expected to last slightly longer than a steam boiler made of the same material. Typical fuels are gas or oil, similar to a hot water boiler.

Unlike hot water heating systems, the radiators, piping and the top section of a steam boiler are filled with air when the boiler is at rest. When the boiler comes on and steam is generated, the steam moves through the system displacing the air. The air is released through air vents on the radiators or on the piping system. As the steam hits the relatively cold surface of the radiators, it condenses, giving up its heat to the radiators. The heat is transferred from the radiators into the room, similar to a hot water system. The condensed water flows back to the boiler to be reheated.

Steam systems are specialized, very complicated, and there are many variations. A complete inspection of the steam heating system is beyond the scope of most home inspections.

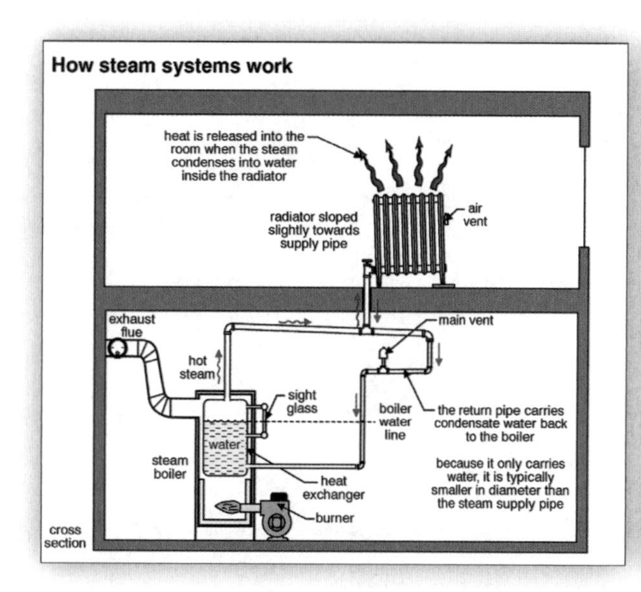

How steam systems work

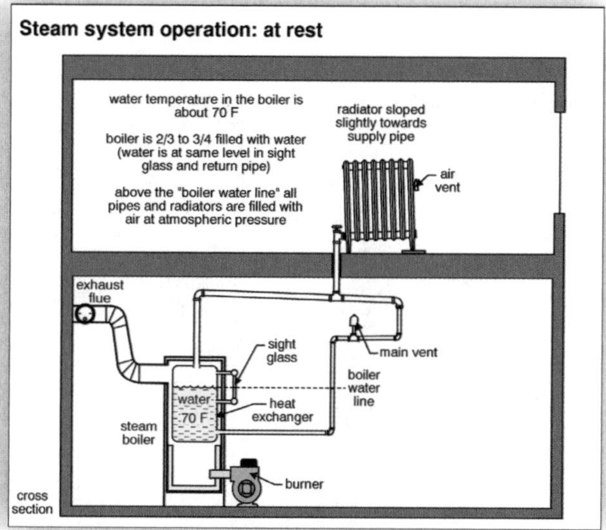

Steam system operation: at rest

ONE-PIPE SYSTEMS A one-pipe steam system has a single pipe attached to each radiator. Steam moves through this pipe to the radiator, and the condensate flows back to the boiler through the same pipe. One-pipe systems cannot be converted to a hot water system without the addition of a second pipe.

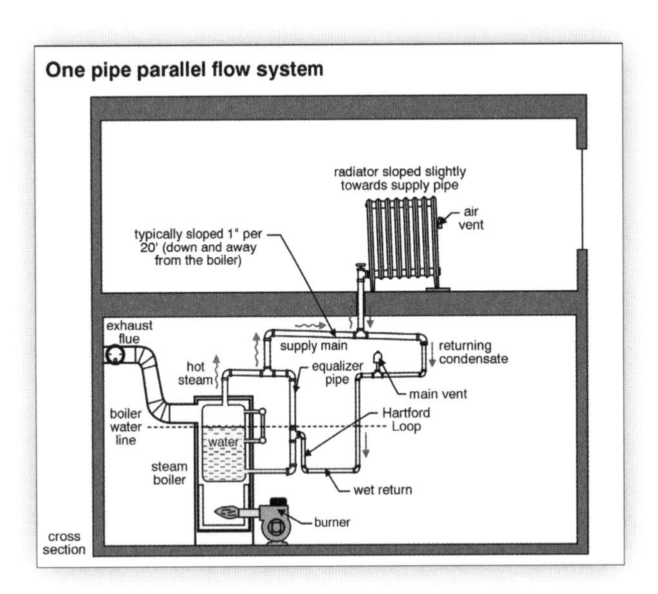

TWO-PIPE SYSTEMS The two-pipe system has one pipe for carrying steam to the radiator, and a smaller pipe for returning condensate water to the boiler. Two-pipe systems can be converted to hot water, which may yield more efficient heating, and better control. Conversion can be tricky, and problems can be encountered if the work is not done professionally. A specialist should be consulted.

Two-pipe systems are considered more economical to operate than one-pipe systems.

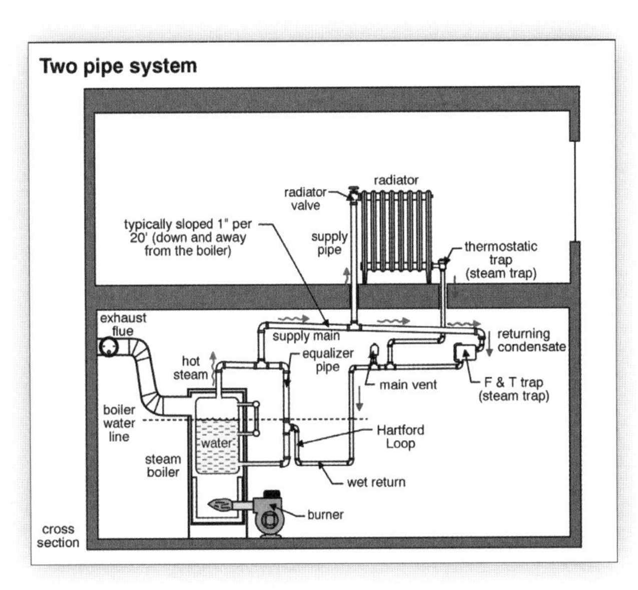

RADIATORS The radiators are typically provided with a control valve that can be opened or closed, and may have an air vent or a steam trap. Sophisticated and relatively expensive supply valves are thermostatically controlled, and may allow zone control of the heating. Steam radiators can be much hotter than hot water rads.

PRESSURETROL The steam boiler has three primary safety controls. The pressuretrol is both an operating device and a safety device. It triggers the burner when the thermostat is calling for heat and when the steam pressure is low, and cuts the burner out when the pressure is high. The pressuretrol is the first device that should shut off the burner with rising steam pressure. Rising steam pressure can be very dangerous, leading to a steam explosion.

LOW WATER CUT OUT The low water cut out shuts off the burner if the boiler water level drops too low. It can be mounted inside or outside the boiler. Externally-mounted low water cut outs typically have a blowdown valve that allows them to be tested. Some manufacturers recommend monthly testing.

PRESSURE RELIEF VALVE The pressure relief valve senses the steam pressure at the top of the boiler and discharges steam to relieve pressure if it gets too high.

OTHER CONTROLS Other controls include water level and pressure gauges to monitor the operation of the system. There is also a manual or automatic water make-up valve so that water can be added to the system.

HARTFORD LOOP The Hartford Loop and equalizer pipe prevent the water level in the boiler from dropping as a result of a leak in a return pipe or a pressure imbalance between the supply and return piping side of the boiler. The Hartford Loop is somewhat redundant to the low water cut out, but is required in many jurisdictions.

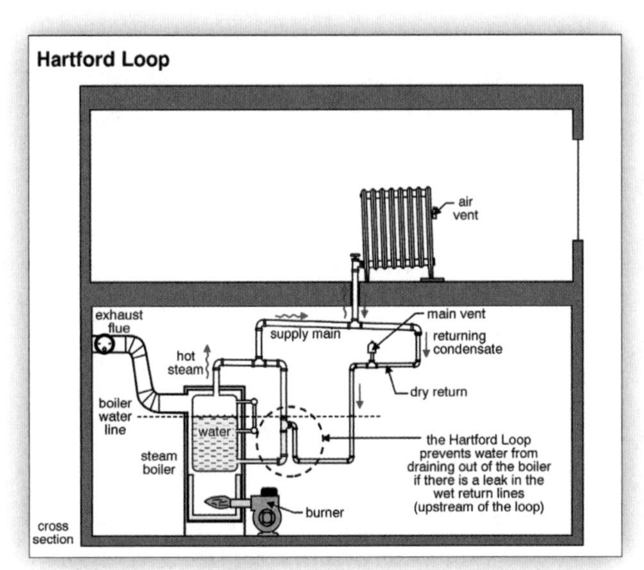

SUMMARY A steam boiler should be fully serviced by a specialist on a regular basis. It is important that the homeowner know how to maintain the system and that the maintenance procedures be followed.

Common Problems with Steam Heating Systems

Steam heating systems have many of the same components as hot water boilers, and are subject to many of the same problems. There are also some problems specific to steam systems.

AIR VENTS Obstructed air vents will prevent the system from heating up. Air vents stuck in the open position will be inefficient and can be dangerous as steam is released directly into the room.

LEAKS If the water level in the system drops, the boiler may crack as it overheats. If the system floods with water, the piping and radiator systems may allow water to leak out.

STEAM TRAP If the steam trap fails in the open position, the system will be inefficient and the house will be uncomfortable. Similarly, if the steam trap is clogged, steam may be unable to move properly through the pipes and radiators.

LOW WATER CUT OUT PROBLEMS If the blow-off for the low water cut-out is not tested regularly, the cut-out may not operate properly and may fail to shut the boiler off in a low water situation. This is an unsafe situation.

PIPE SLOPE If the pipe slope is incorrect due to poor installation or building settlement, the system can be very noisy and heat distribution can be very uneven.

HIGHLIGHTS ONLY These are only the common problems associated with steam systems. The list is by no means exhaustive. Since steam boilers are, for the most part, older, the availability of parts can be a problem. A specialist should be engaged to inspect and maintain a steam heating system.

8.0 Electric Heat

We have touched on electric furnaces and boilers in the Furnace and Boiler sections. Here we will look at space heaters and radiant heat.

8.1 Electric Space Heaters

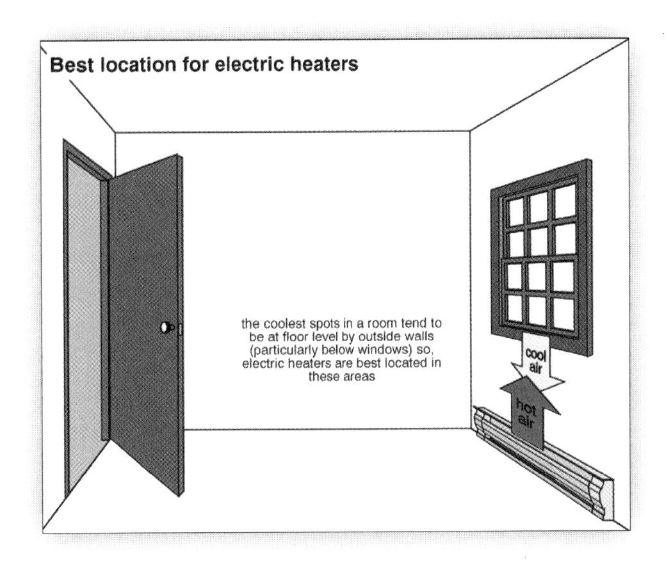

DESCRIPTION Some houses are heated entirely by electric heaters. Others use electric heat as a supplement to the main heating source. With the exception of electric furnaces and boilers (which are discussed elsewhere), electric heating systems are individual rather than central. In other words, the heat is generated within the room or space to be heated, and there is no distribution system – piping or ductwork. The most common type of electric room heater is the baseboard heater. Heaters with fans can also be installed in the floors, walls and ceilings, for example. The best place for a heater is in the coolest part of the room.

THERMOSTAT The thermostat can be directly on the units or mounted on a wall in the room. Wall thermostats may control one or more heaters. Wall mounted thermostats tend to be the preferred (and more expensive) method as they are easier to reach and, according to some, more accurate.

Common Problems with Electric Heaters

OBSTRUCTED Floor mounted heaters may be covered with rugs or mats, particularly during the summer. Blocking the airflow may lead to overheating.

COMBUSTIBLE CLEARANCES The manufacturer's recommendations for clearance from combustible materials should be followed. Draperies, for example, should typically be kept eight inches above the heaters. Alternatively, the drapes can be three inches in front of the heaters as long as they are at least one inch above the floor.

Electrical receptacles should not be installed on the wall above an electric heater because appliance cords may touch the heater and overheat.

DAMAGE Electric heaters are vulnerable to mechanical damage, such as bent fins, and are prone to rust when installed in damp or wet areas. Rust, dirt and damage can impair performance and lead to failure.

WIRED INCORRECTLY Heaters designed to operate at 240 volts can be incorrectly wired at 120 volts. They will not work as efficiently as they should. This will not normally be picked up on a home inspection.

INOPERATIVE – RUST/DAMAGE/ OVERHEATING Rust, damage and overheating will ultimately lead to an inoperative heater. Generally, this requires replacement of the heater. Where evidence of overheating is noted, a specialist should be consulted promptly.

8.2 Electric Radiant Heat

DESCRIPTION Electric radiant systems are common in ceilings and floors. Wires may be embedded in the ceiling or laid in the floor. Some systems employ pre-wired panels or mats. The ceiling or floor will be warm but not hot to the touch when operating. Many radiant floor systems make the floor more comfortable but may not be intended to be the only heat source in the room.

With any radiant heating system, care must be taken not to damage the system when drilling holes or mounting things such as light fixtures. Special patching materials are available for treating cracks and other flaws in heated ceilings.

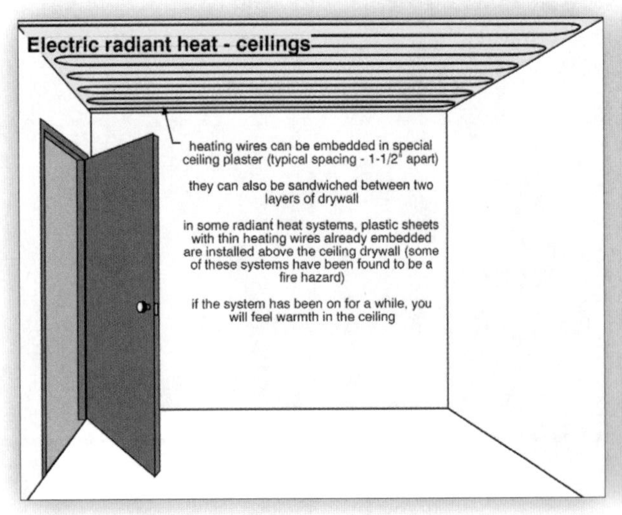

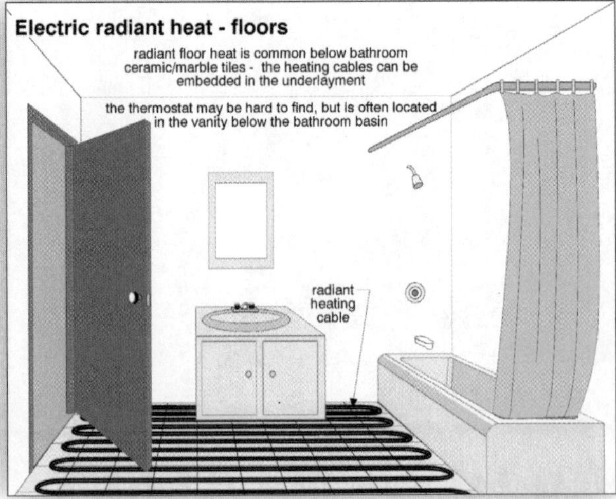

Common Problems with Electric Radiant Heating

INOPERATIVE In radiant heating systems, if the distribution wire itself malfunctions (breaks), it is often difficult to locate the problem in the wiring. There is special equipment to locate the problem. In many cases however, these systems are abandoned when they fail, and are replaced with electric baseboard heaters.

SHADOW EFFECT One common complaint about radiant heating systems is the shadow effect. Since radiant heat works the same way as sunlight, some people's legs feel cool if, for example, they are sitting at a dining room table for several hours. The table shades their legs from the direct radiant heat.

9.0 Failure Probability

Every boiler or furnace contains several components that may cause the system to stop operating. For example, if an inexpensive thermocouple fails on a gas-fired furnace, the pilot will shut off. With the pilot shut off, the furnace will not operate. This is easy to repair. We think of failure as having to replace the whole furnace or boiler, for example.

HEAT EXCHANGERS FOR FURNACES AND BOILERS For most furnaces and boilers, terminal failure is usually a crack or a hole in the heat exchanger. Since most of the heat exchanger is not visible, the heat exchanger cannot be fully inspected during a home inspection. Because a home inspection is not technically exhaustive, the likelihood of failure is based on probability rather than testing or equipment tear-down.

A conventional gas-fired furnace, for example, contains a heat exchanger having an average life expectancy of 18 to 25 years. There are, however, manufacturers of gas-fired, forced-air furnaces whose heat exchangers have a reputation for failing sooner.

RETROFIT ISSUES FOR HIGH EFFICIENCY FURNACES Most high efficiency furnaces require more air flow across the heat exchangers than conventional furnaces. Replacing a conventional furnace with a high efficiency furnace can be tricky. Older, smaller ductwork and/or an air conditioning coil can restrict air flow, increasing the temperature rise within the furnace. This can result in premature failure of the heat exchangers and void the warranty. This condition may not be identified in a home inspection.

LIFE EXPECTANCY OF STEAM BOILERS Steam boilers are typically old and most are considered near the end of their life. Steam boilers have a heat exchanger, like hot water boilers and when this fails, the system is typically replaced.

LIFE EXPECTANCY OF ELECTRIC SYSTEMS Electric furnaces and boilers contain electric heating elements and controls for the elements. Every single component can be replaced. With age, however, electric systems get to a stage where replacement of the entire unit makes sense due to lost reliability and a lack of available replacement parts. Electric boilers have a water jacket that will eventually rust. Although there are not great statistics on these units, a life expectancy of 20 to 25 years may be reasonable.

With individual electric heaters, failure probability is not meaningful, since replacing individual heaters is not a significant expense. Electric heating elements are like light bulbs. Their life expectancy is not well defined, and their failure can't be predicted.

Cooling/Heat Pumps

INTRODUCTION

THERE ARE MANY TYPES OF AIR CONDITIONING AND HEAT PUMP SYSTEMS; HOWEVER, THEY ALL WORK ON THE SAME PRINCIPLE. THEY MOVE HEAT FROM A RELATIVELY COOL SPACE TO A RELATIVELY WARM SPACE. IN THE SUMMER, THEY TAKE HEAT FROM THE HOUSE AIR AND TRANSFER IT TO THE EXTERIOR. THIS HEAT MAY BE TRANSFERRED TO THE OUTSIDE AIR, A BODY OF WATER, OR INTO THE GROUND. IN THE HEATING SEASON, HEAT PUMPS REVERSE THE PROCESS, MOVING HEAT FROM THE OUTSIDE AIR, GROUND, OR WATER, INTO THE AIR INSIDE THE HOME.

1.0 Air Conditioning

1.1. Air Cooled

REFRIGERANT TAKES HEAT FROM HOUSE AIR

1.1.1 Description and Components: Air-cooled air conditioning systems are the most common. They have two main components: the evaporator, which may be in the ductwork immediately above the furnace or in a fan coil in the attic, and the condenser, which is outdoors. The refrigerant (a liquid/gas that moves the heat) enters the evaporator as a cold liquid. It removes heat from the house air, which is blown across the cooling coil by a fan. The refrigerant changes state from a liquid to a gas.

HOUSE AIR IS COOLED AND DEHUMIDIFIED

As the house air cools, water in the house air condenses, reducing humidity levels. This dehumidifying helps make the house more comfortable. Air conditioning systems both cool and dehumidify the house air.

GETTING BACK TO THE REFRIGERANT

The refrigerant, which is now a gas, moves outdoors to the condenser unit. The compressor squeezes the gas, raising the temperature above the outdoor air temperature (This is the magic! We can squeeze the gas coming from the house and make it hotter than the outdoor air). The hot gas enters the condenser coil and a fan blows outdoor air across the coil, removing heat from the gas. As it cools, the refrigerant condenses into a liquid. The liquid moves indoors and goes through a pressure-reducing device, which cools the liquid below the temperature of the house air. The liquid passing through the evaporator coil is evaporated into a gas again, removing more heat and humidity from the house. The cycle continues.

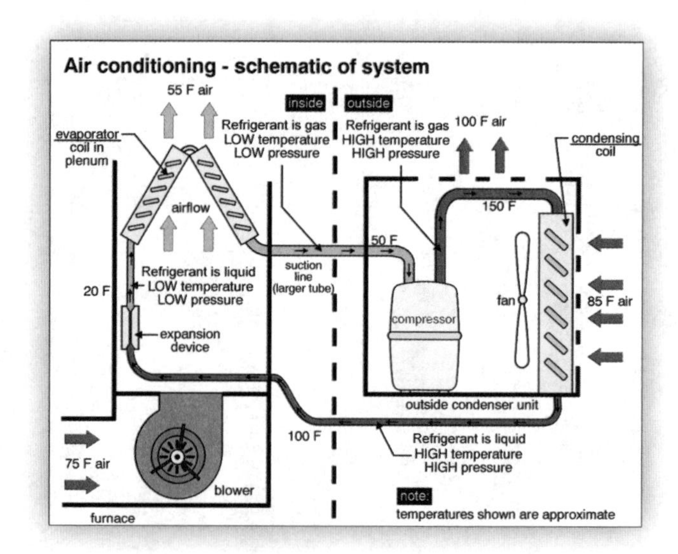

DESCRIPTION **1.1.2 Compressor:** The compressor is a pump that moves the refrigerant through the system and compresses the refrigerant when it is a gas, raising its temperature significantly. The compressor is the heart of the system. It is usually located outdoors in the condenser cabinet.

Older compressors are piston-type. Scroll-type compressors are used in many new systems.

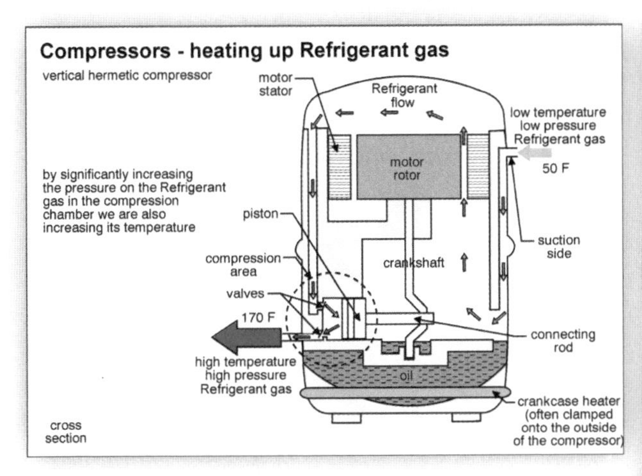

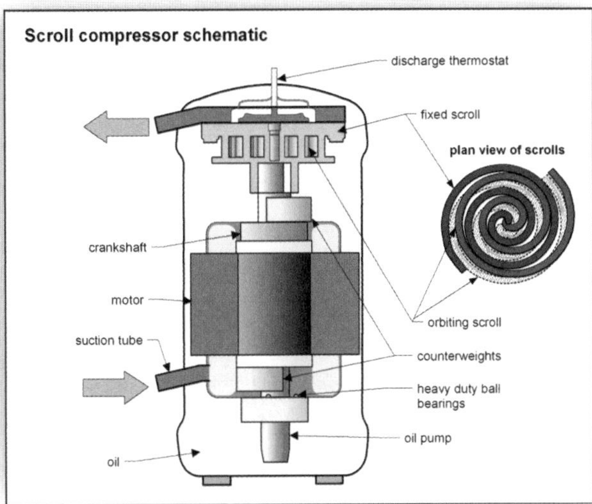

EASILY DAMAGED Severe damage can occur to air conditioning compressors if they are turned on when the outside temperature is below 65° F (16° C). Some compressors contain a small heating element (crankcase heater) that must be on for 12 to 24 hours prior to the compressor starting up. The heater ensures there is no liquid refrigerant mixed in with the lubricating oil. If the heater has not been turned on, or if the outside temperature is low, the compressor cannot be tested.

Common Problems with Compressors

OLD The life expectancy of a compressor is typically 10 to 15 years in moderate climates and as little as 8 to 10 years in hot climates. It is not uncommon for a compressor to constitute 30% to 50% of the cost of an entire system. The compressor age typically cannot be determined during a home inspection.

INOPERATIVE Depending on the unit age, replacement of a failed compressor may not be cost effective. If the unit is so old that replacement parts are not readily available or if the system uses an older refrigerant, it may be better to replace the entire condenser unit, rather than just the compressor.

NOT LEVEL The compressor (located outdoors in most systems) should be level (within roughly ten degrees). The compressor or the refrigerant lines may be damaged if the unit is out of level.

ELECTRICAL DISCONNECT – MISSING There should be an outdoor electrical disconnect that can be seen from the compressor unit so that the outdoor unit can be turned off for safe servicing.

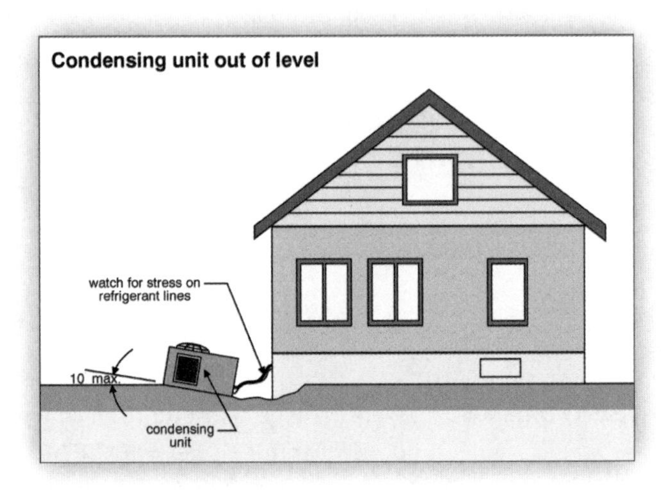

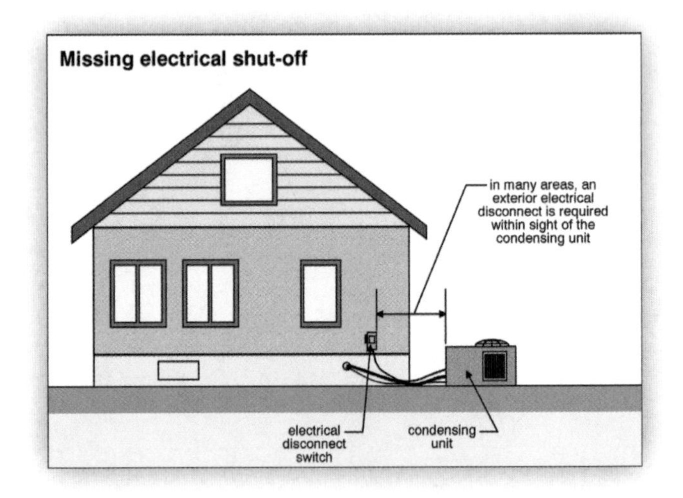

APPLIANCE EXHAUST TOO CLOSE TO CONDENSER Hot air discharging from a water heater exhaust vent or clothes dryer vent can affect the operation of air conditioning systems. These should be kept several feet from the condenser.

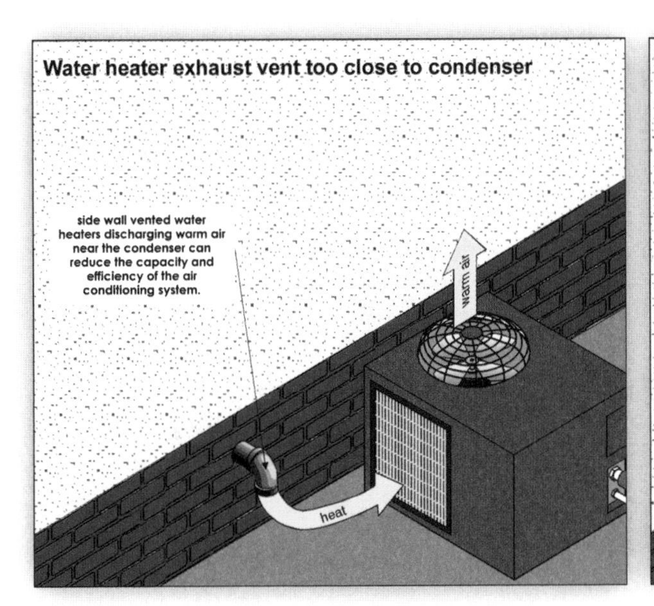

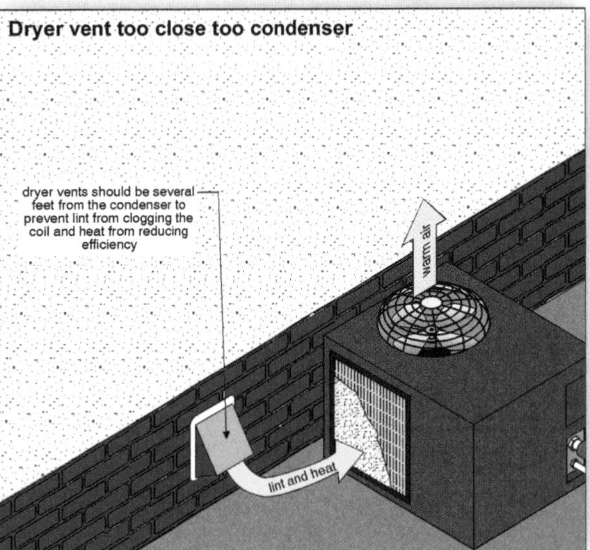

NOISY There are several causes of noisy compressors. A service specialist should be engaged to diagnose and correct the problem.

DESCRIPTION **1.1.3 Indoor and Outdoor Coils:** The indoor (evaporator) coil sits in the ductwork downstream of the heat exchanger in a gas or oil furnace, or in the attic in a fan coil unit, typically. The evaporator coil moves heat from the house air to the refrigerant in the coil. The outdoor condenser coil moves heat from the refrigerant to the outside air.

Coils are normally made of copper or aluminum tubing with very thin fins to enhance the heat transfer. The fins are delicate and easily damaged by power washers for example.

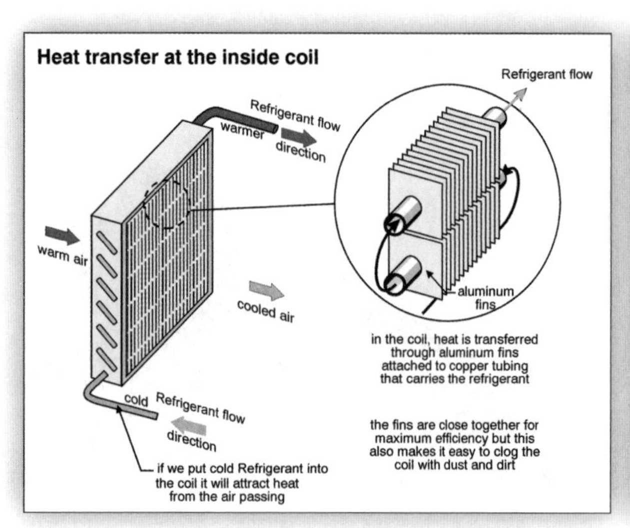

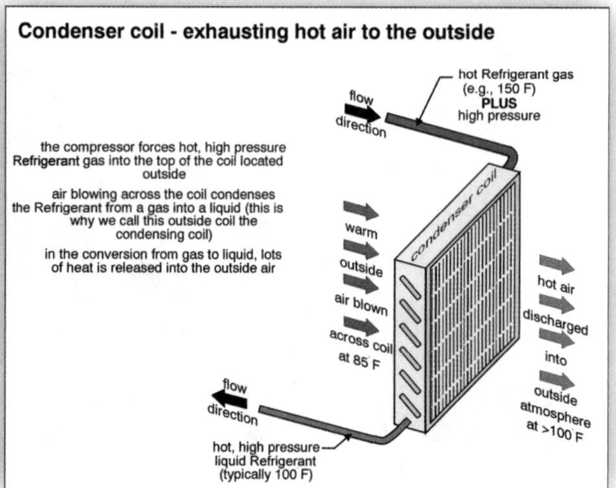

Common Problems with Coils

CORROSION, BLOCKAGE OR DAMAGE Coils are subject to corrosion, blockage and damage. Dirt or other foreign matter can inhibit airflow across the coil. Grass clippings from lawn mowers can clog condenser coils. Damaged fins reduce efficiency and increase operating costs.

LEAKAGE Leaking refrigerant reduces efficiency and comfort while increasing costs. In a worst-case scenario, the system will not work. Leaks are difficult to identify visually. They are most often picked up during regular servicing.

HIGH/LOW TEMPERATURE DROP ACROSS COIL The air temperature should drop 14° to 22° F as it moves across the indoor (evaporator) coil. If heat transfer is inhibited by dirty or damaged coils, the temperature drop will be less, indicating poor performance. Dirty coils may be the result of a missing house air filter or poor maintenance.

If airflow is restricted by a dirty air filter for example, the air may not move quickly enough across the coils and may get too cold. The temperature drop may be more than 22°, also indicating poor performance. In severe cases, the coil may ice up.

Improper temperature drops may also indicate refrigerant level problems.

POOR LOCATION OF OUTDOOR (CONDENSER) COIL Outdoor coils should be several feet from clothes dryer vents and furnace or water heater vents coming out through the wall. Coils should not be located under decks or surrounded by trees or shrubs, since this will restrict the airflow, adversely affecting performance.

DESCRIPTION **1.1.4 Attic Drip Pan:** Where the air conditioning coil is in the attic, a drip pan should be provided as an extra safety precaution. When the condensate tray overflows, the drip pan provides a second line of defense.

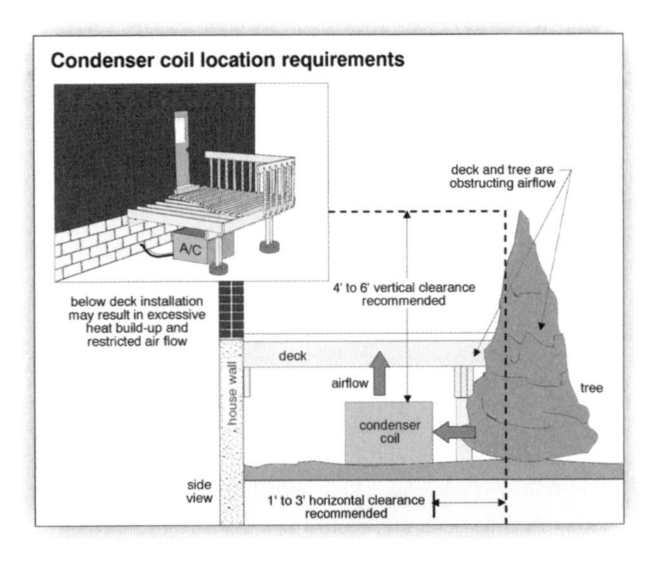

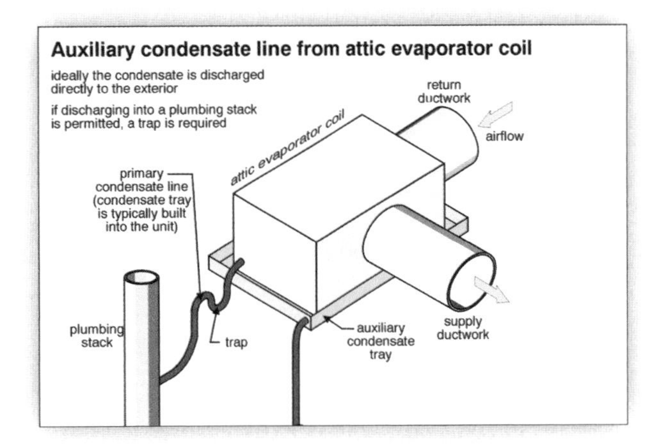

Common Problems with Attic Drip Pans

MISSING/ LEAKING While they are not always installed, drip pans can prevent a lot of damage. However, a leaking or clogged drip pan is as bad as a missing drip pan.

NO SECONDARY DRAIN The drip pan should have its own drain line. A common drain line between the condensate tray and drip pan may cause a flood if it plugs. In this case, there is no second line of defense.

POOR DRAIN DISCHARGE LOCATION Some drains discharge into the plumbing stack. This may allow sewer gases to back up into the house through the air conditioning system.

DESCRIPTION **1.1.5 Indoor and Outdoor Fans:** The fans move air across the coils, picking up or giving off heat. The cooled air is distributed throughout the house by the indoor fan. The indoor fan is often also the furnace fan (usually modified for increased airflow). On independent systems, a separate fan is provided.

The outdoor fan moves air over the outdoor coil. This cools and condenses the refrigerant, which has been heated to above the outdoor air temperature by the compressor. The outdoor fan is in the condenser cabinet.

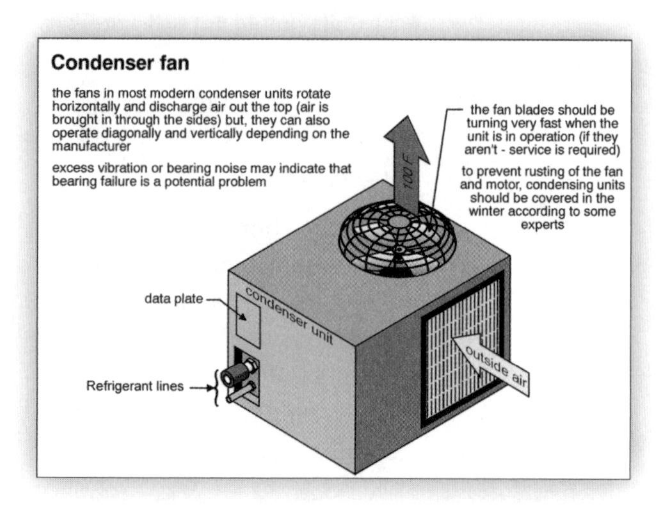

INDOOR FAN PROBLEMS Fan bearings and motors can wear out. On belt driven fans, the belt tension can be incorrect or the pulleys may be improperly set up. Missing air filters allow the blower (fan) to get dirty. Fans that are unbalanced can be noisy, especially attic fans as the noise is transmitted through the rafters and ceilings. Bad bearings can also make the fan noisy. Fans may be inoperative due to belt or pulley problems, a failed electric motor, or interrupted electrical supply.

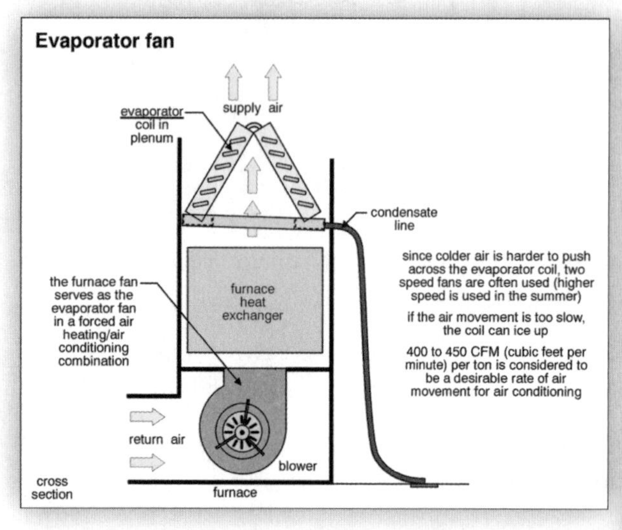

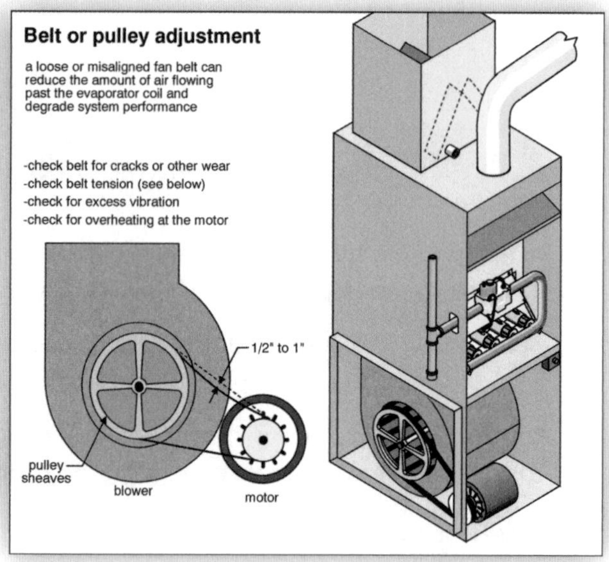

FAN SIZE If the indoor fan is too small, airflow through the house will be weak. The air at the registers may be cool, but the velocity will be too low. An oversized fan will give strong airflow, but the air will not be as cool as it should be. The system may also be noisy.

DAMAGE AND WEAR Outdoor fans are exposed to the elements, and blades can be damaged by foreign matter. Also, motors and bearings can wear out. Corrosion is also an issue.

OBSTRUCTED The outdoor fan can wear out prematurely if the intake air or the exhaust air is obstructed. This will also greatly reduce efficiency. It is important to keep the area around the outdoor unit free of obstructions.

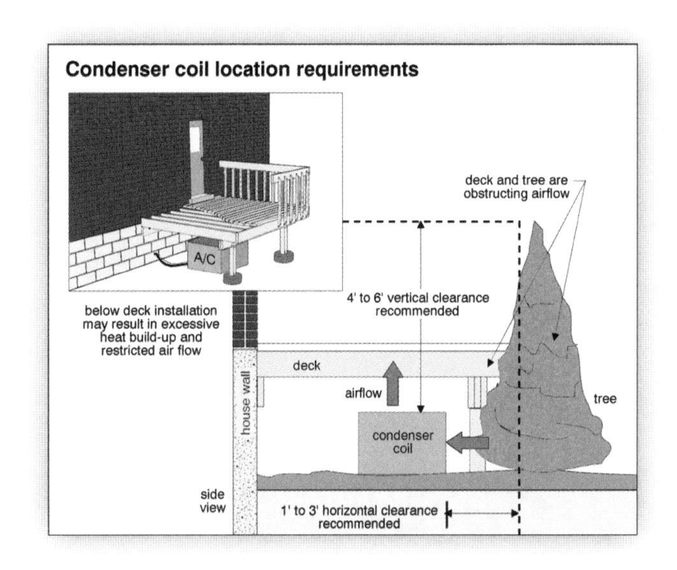

DESCRIPTION **1.1.6 Refrigerant Lines:** The copper refrigerant lines move the refrigerant between the condenser and the evaporator. Refrigerant lines are normally arranged in pairs, with the larger diameter line carrying gas and the smaller one carrying liquid. The larger refrigerant pipe containing cool gas is typically insulated to prevent condensation and increase efficiency.

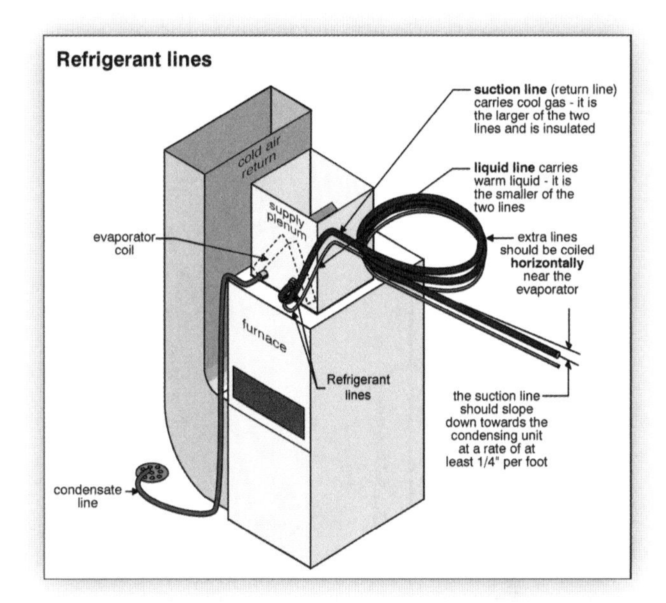

Common Problems with Refrigerant Lines

DAMAGE/ LEAK/CORROSION The most common problems with refrigerant lines are mechanical damage, leakage and corrosion. Refrigerant lines are frequently damaged where they pass through the house wall. Leaking refrigerant lines are usually identified by oil deposits on the line.

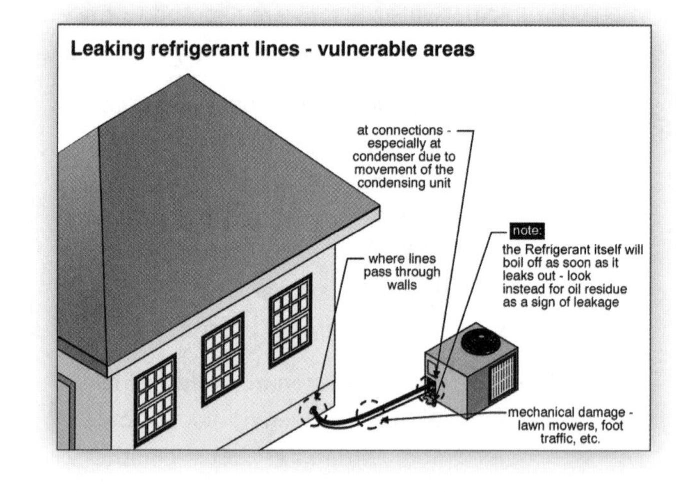

INSULATION MISSING/ DAMAGED Insulation on the outdoor larger (suction) line may be missing or damaged, significantly reducing the efficiency of the air conditioning system. If insulation is missing on the larger line indoors, condensation may be a problem.

DESCRIPTION **1.1.7 Condensate System:** When an air conditioning system or a heat pump is cooling, house air passing across the cold evaporator coil condenses as it cools. The condensation is collected in a tray below the coil. A condensate line carries the water from the tray to a floor drain or sink in the house, or to the outdoors. The piping should be arranged so that siphoning cannot occur.

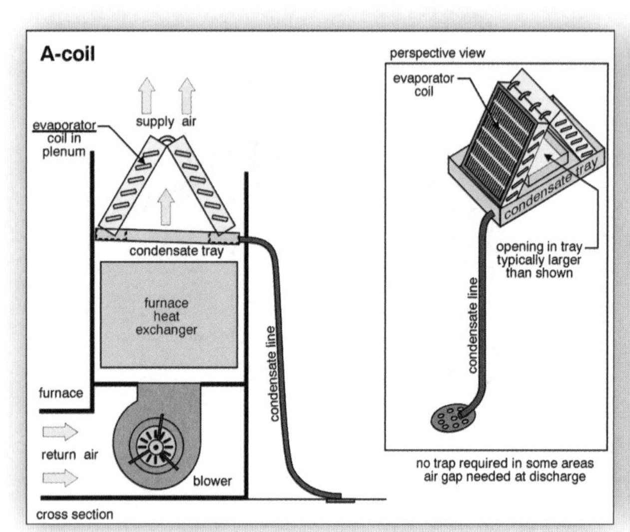

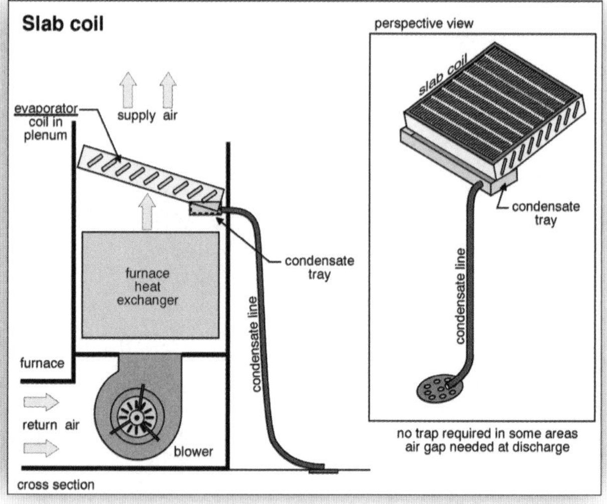

If the water cannot flow by gravity, a condensate pump moves the water to a suitable location. The condensate should not discharge directly into a plumbing vent or stack, or onto a roof.

Common Problems with Condensate Systems

TRAY LEAKING/ OVERFLOWING While the condensate tray is not visible, there is sometimes evidence of a problem. Water stains may be seen below the evaporator coil indicating a cracked or broken condensate tray, a condensate tray that is not level, or a plugged condensate tray that is overflowing.

Where the air conditioner is installed above a furnace, it is important that the condensate tray function properly. Water dripping on a furnace heat exchanger can rust it prematurely, necessitating furnace replacement.

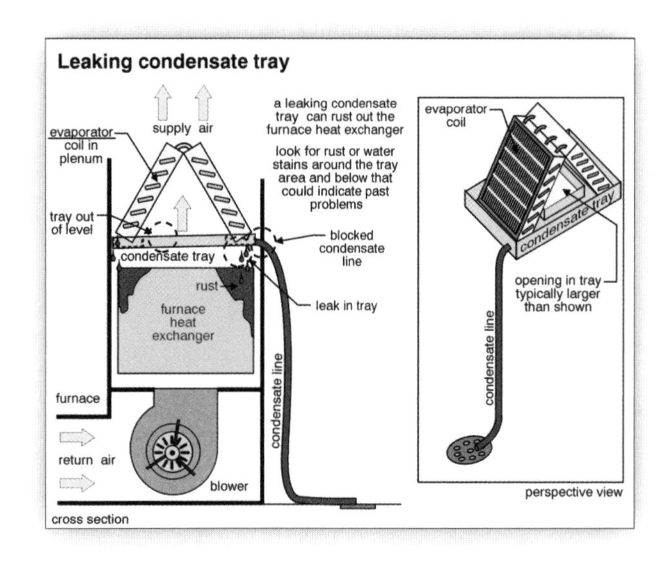

PIPE – MISSING/ LEAKING/ CLOGGED The condensate line that takes the condensation from the tray may be leaking, missing or plugged.

PUMP PROBLEMS Inoperative condensate pumps are a common problem. These are typically low-cost pumps that are easily replaced.

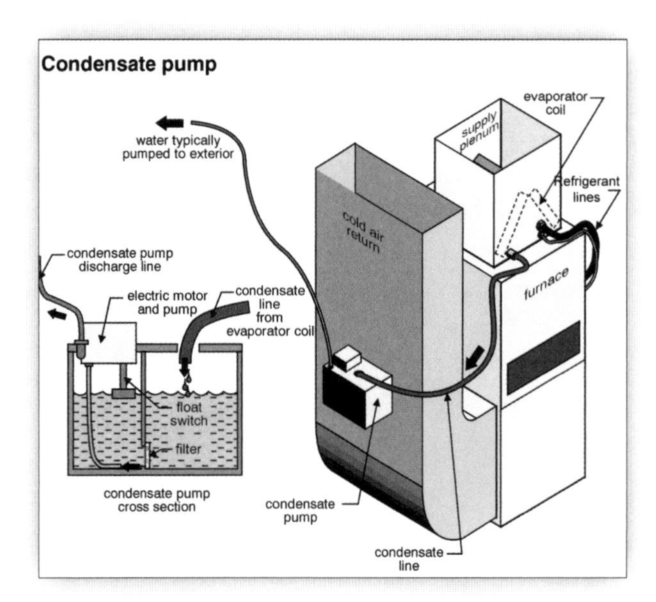

POOR DISCHARGE LOCATION FOR CONDENSATE Condensate should not discharge into plumbing fixtures where siphoning problems may develop. Condensate should not discharge into the space below a floor slab or into a plumbing stack, in most cases. Condensate should not run down the outside of the building wall because the wall may be damaged.

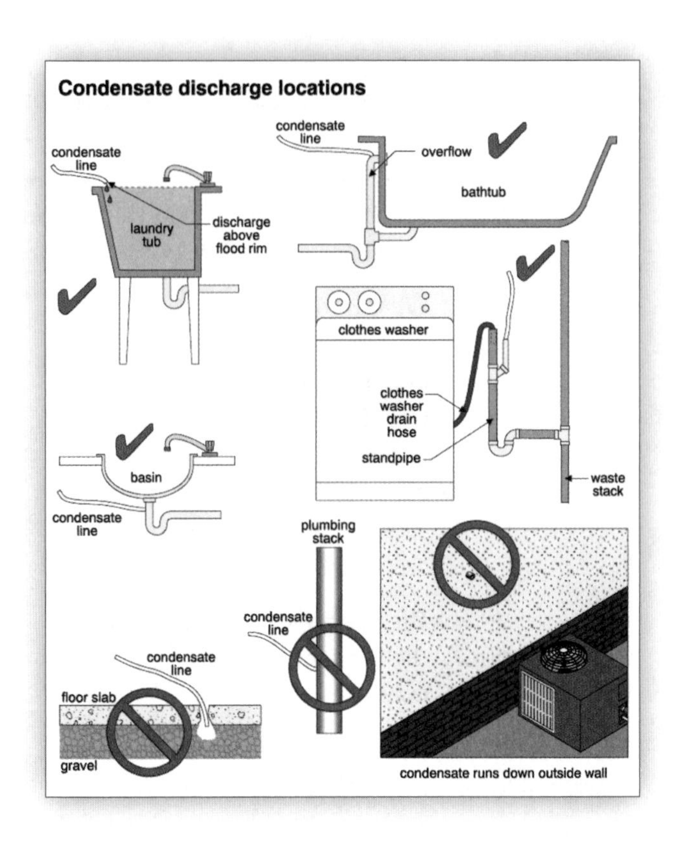

PUMP INOPERATIVE In some cases the condensate is pumped up to a drain. Water damage may occur if the pump fails.

DESCRIPTION **1.1.8 Duct System:** The ductwork distributes the cooled air throughout the house. Ductwork can be incomplete, disconnected, obstructed or dirty. Supply and return registers can be missing, damaged, inoperative or covered with furniture or carpets. Ductwork designed for heating systems may be undersized for cooling. When air conditioning or a heat pump is added to an existing system, the duct size may limit the size of the air conditioning or heat pump. On poorly matched systems, the airflow at the registers will be weak. In most cases, major ductwork modifications are not cost-effective.

Common Problems with Duct Systems

HUMIDIFIER DAMPER MISSING/OPEN Humidifiers on furnaces can cause air conditioning problems. The most common bypass humidifiers are mounted on furnace ductwork near the air conditioner. A section of ductwork runs between the supply and return ductwork, with the humidifier in the duct. A damper should be provided to shut off the airflow through this duct during the cooling season to prevent short circuiting of the airflow. If there is no damper, or it is left open in summer, the air conditioner will suffer. At best, efficiency will be reduced. At worst, the evaporator coil will ice up.

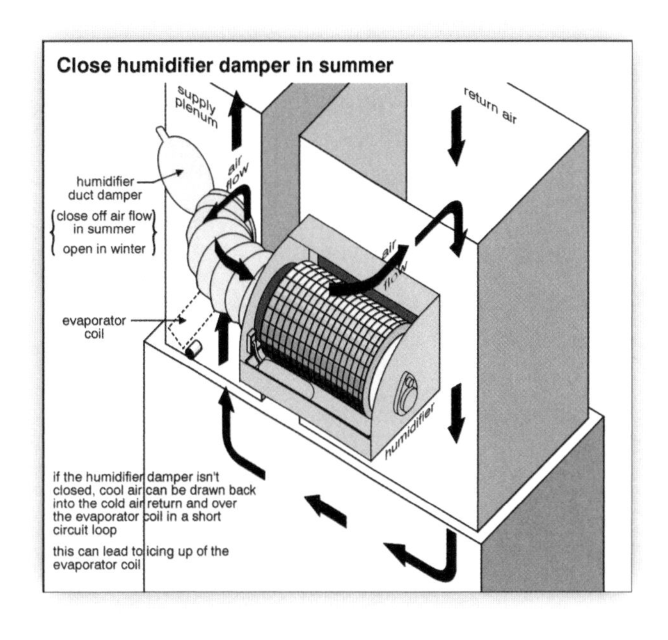

BALANCING Where heating and cooling systems share the same ductwork, rebalancing of the distribution system is usually necessary when switching between heating and cooling. The rooms requiring the most cooling don't always need the most heating. Rebalancing is usually done by moving dampers in the ductwork and by adjusting the supply registers and return grilles.

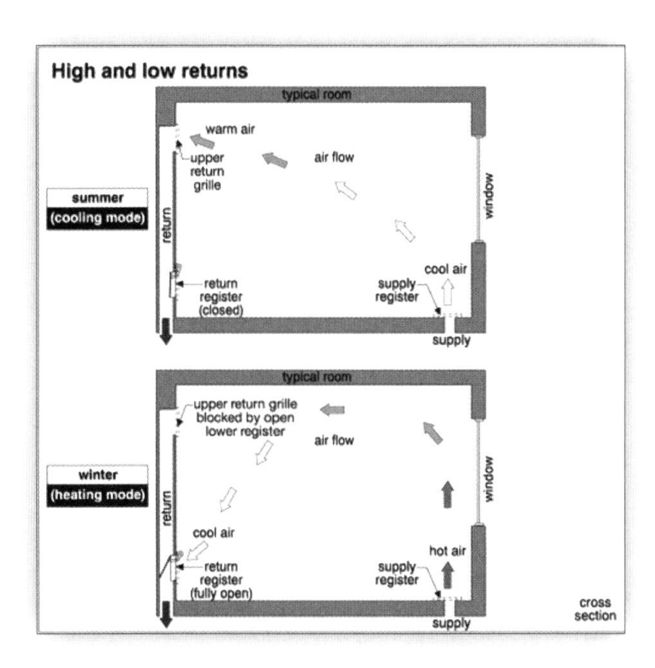

DAMAGED Ductwork may be crushed, separated or obstructed, either during original construction or subsequently.

MISSING Some rooms may have no air conditioning. This is typical in additions and garages that have been converted to rooms. They may have no heating ductwork and be heated by electric baseboards. Since there is no ductwork, there is no air conditioning to this part of the home.

DUCTS IN CONCRETE FLOOR SLABS

Slab-on-grade houses often have ducts embedded in the concrete foundations and slab. Sometimes the ducts are partially collapsed during the concrete pouring process. Moisture in and around the slab can flood the ducts and rust the metal duct walls. The water standing in the ducts can become a health hazard.

Rusted duct walls can come loose and collapse, restricting airflow through the system. Ductwork in poured slabs and foundations is difficult to inspect and to repair.

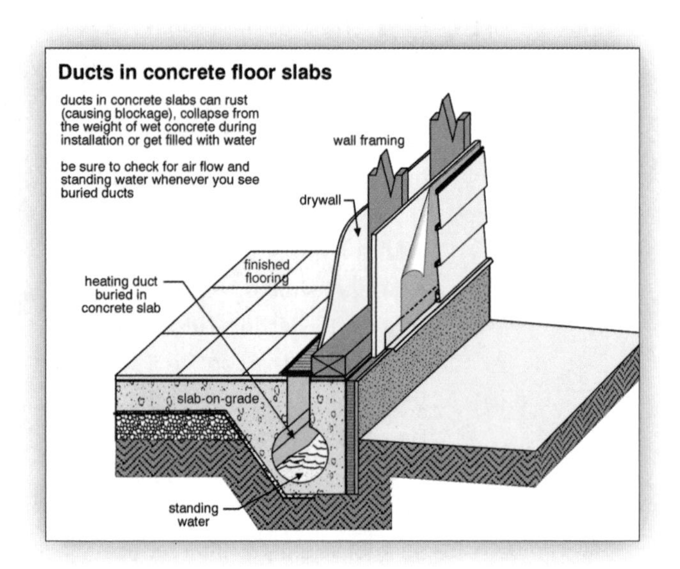

INSULATION OR VAPOR BARRIER MISSING ON ATTIC DUCTS

Attic ductwork should be insulated to prevent heat transfer in the attic. The vapor barrier should be on the outside of the insulation to prevent condensation.

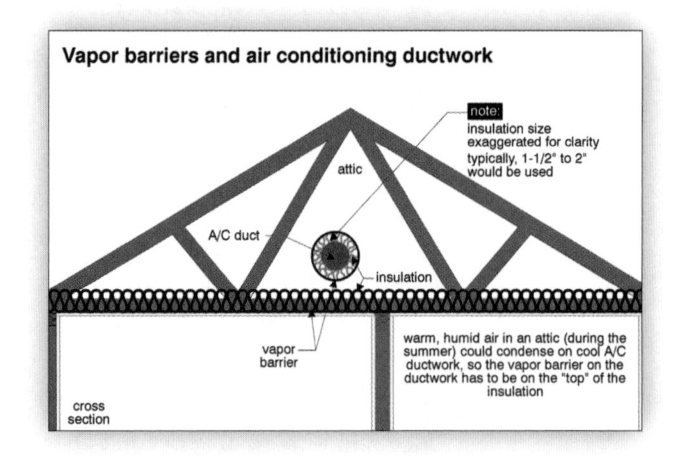

DESCRIPTION **1.1.9 Thermostat:** The thermostat allows the homeowner to adjust the house temperature. It should not be exposed to drafts, direct sunlight, heating sources or cooling sources. Homes with heating and cooling systems often have a single thermostat to control both.

SWITCHING MODES Most thermostats that are designed for heating and cooling require the operator to choose whether they want heating or cooling. We don't want a system that allows the house to try to heat and cool at the same time. Once the mode is chosen, the thermostat attempts to maintain the desired temperature. Switching back and forth repeatedly between heating and cooling modes can damage the compressor. Allow at least fifteen minutes between operation of the heating system and the cooling system.

Many thermostats also have a fan switch that allows for continuous or intermittent operation of the blower. The fan always operates when the air conditioner or furnace is working. Some people like to run the fan all the time to circulate and filter house air. Some fans can operate at a lower speed when the heating or cooling are not working.

MULTIPLE THERMOSTATS Houses with multiple heating and cooling systems or zoned heating and cooling have more than one thermostat. However, some houses with a single furnace and an air conditioner or heat pump have more than one thermostat. This is often the case with independent air conditioners or heat pumps, or systems installed on a retrofit basis. In this case, the thermostats are often interlocked to prevent simultaneous heating and cooling. If they are not, care should be exercised.

Common Problems with Thermostats

MALFUNCTIONS DAMAGE/LOOSE Thermostats can function improperly if they are dirty, not level, or improperly calibrated. They can also suffer mechanical damage. The thermostat may be poorly secured to the wall.

POOR LOCATION The thermostat should not be placed where it may get a false reading of the room temperature. It should not be close to exterior doors, in direct sunlight, or close to heat sources like ovens and heating/cooling supply registers. This will make the house uncomfortable and may increase cooling costs.

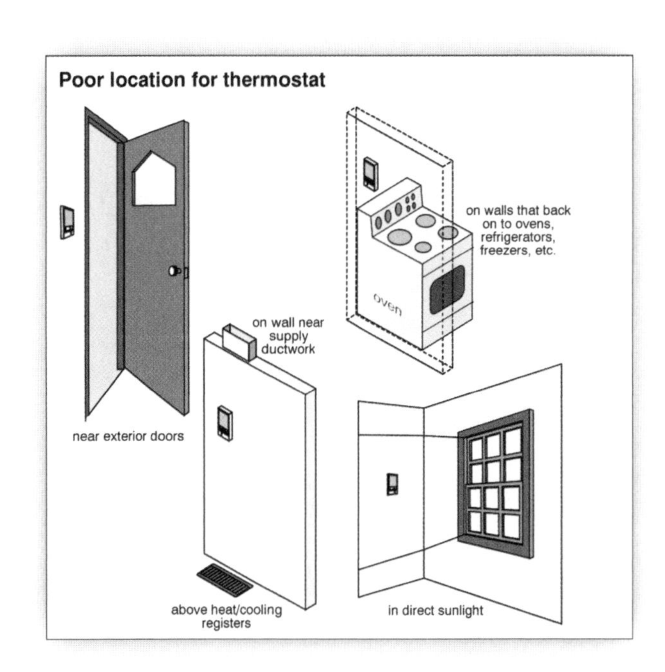

1.2 Water Cooled Air Conditioners

DESCRIPTION

1.2.1 Description and Components: Water-cooled air conditioning systems work almost the same way as air-cooled systems. They have a coil in the house ductwork that evaporates a liquid refrigerant into a gas and draws heat out of the house. The gas is then compressed to raise its temperature. Then, instead of blowing outside air across the gas to cool it, water is moved across the condenser coil. The condenser does not have to be outdoors. It can be in the home.

Once the water has cooled the gas back to a liquid, the warmed water is disposed of. It is no longer drinkable and, therefore, must go down the drain, into a swimming pool or be used to water the lawn. Water cooled air conditioners consume a lot of city water and are not permitted in all municipalities.

COMPRESSOR

On these systems, the compressor is just as critical as on an air-cooled system. It is the heart of the air conditioner. The indoor compressor is not exposed to outdoor weather conditions and often enjoys a longer life expectancy than outdoor units.

The system is simple where the discharged water goes straight down a drain. On systems where the water can go down a drain or be used to water the lawn or fill a swimming pool, there are usually several valves that determine where the water will go. At least one valve is always open to allow water to flow. Automatic valves are available.

DESCRIPTION

1.2.2 Water Coil: A water-cooled coil performs the same function as the outdoor coil on an air cooled central air conditioning system. It is a condenser that cools and condenses the refrigerant. Rather than using a finned coil with air passing across it, this coil is surrounded by a water jacket to take the heat away.

DESCRIPTION

1.2.3 Water Lines: On water-cooled air conditioning systems, water is provided from the plumbing system. The waste water must go down a drain or may be used for watering a lawn or filling a swimming pool. The water is non-potable (non-drinkable) and cannot be re-introduced to the drinking water. On systems where water can be directed to one of several locations, the supply valve and at least one discharge valve have to be open so that there is water flow through the air conditioning system. A lack of water flow can seriously damage the unit.

Common Problems with Water Cooled Air Conditioners

LEAKS/ CORROSION As with all coils, there is potential for a refrigerant leak. There is also the possibility of a water leak from the jacket. Corrosion from recycled pool water (which may contain chlorine) is also a possibility and that's why re-circulating swimming pool water is not recommended.

LACK OF WATER The water supply may be interrupted by closed valves, malfunctioning controls, a pipe leak or restricted flow. This can cause serious damage to the compressor.

1.3 System Types

SHARED DUCTWORK **1.3.1 Central:** In air-conditioned homes that also have a furnace, the indoor coil is mounted in the duct-work near the furnace and the heating ductwork is used for cooling as well. Only one set of ductwork is needed, and the house air is moved across the indoor air conditioning coil by the furnace blower.

DESCRIPTION **1.3.2 Independent – Ducted:** In houses with no ductwork, the air conditioner and ductwork must both be added and are independent of any heating system. The indoor coil is often in the attic. In some cases large ductwork is used, similar to that used with furnaces. Small diameter ducts are often used when adding air conditioning to an existing home because they take up less space, and are less disruptive to install. The small insulated ducts typically have high velocity air movement, and there may be several supply registers/diffusers/nozzles in each room.

BLOWER On a cooling system that shares ductwork with a heating system, the blower for the heating system is used for the air conditioner or heat pump. With an independent system, a separate blower is provided.

DISADVANTAGES When independent systems are installed on a retrofit basis, a few compromises have to be made. Attic-mounted units are more difficult to service because of their location. Also, a system mounted in the attic may be noisier than a system mounted in the basement. Care should be taken to avoid damage due to condensate leaking into the living space below. Please refer to 1.1.4 – Attic Drip Pan on page 247.

SPLIT SYSTEMS **1.3.3 Independent – Ductless:** There are two common types of ductless systems – split systems and single component systems. Split systems have a condenser cabinet with a compressor, condenser coil and fan on the ground or on the roof, the same as any central split system. The evaporator coil and house air fan are inside the home, in the area to be cooled. There is a condensate collection and discharge system for the interior component. There are two refrigerant lines, often in a conduit, joining the outdoor condenser unit to the evaporator inside the home. These units have no ductwork to move cooled air to different rooms.

COMPACT Split systems, also called mini-splits, are easy to install and only require a 3-inch diameter hole through the house wall. The indoor components can be wall or ceiling mounted and don't take up much space. Some have remote controls so they can be mounted out of the way, high on walls or on ceilings.

QUIET These have a remote compressor (the noisiest part of an air conditioner) so the home is quieter. Some interior fans are multi-speed to minimize noise. There are also quieter fans in some systems that operate at very low rpm (less than 900 rpm).

MULTI-ZONE SYSTEMS Split systems can be multi-zone, with one condenser unit serving up to four evaporators in four different parts of the home.

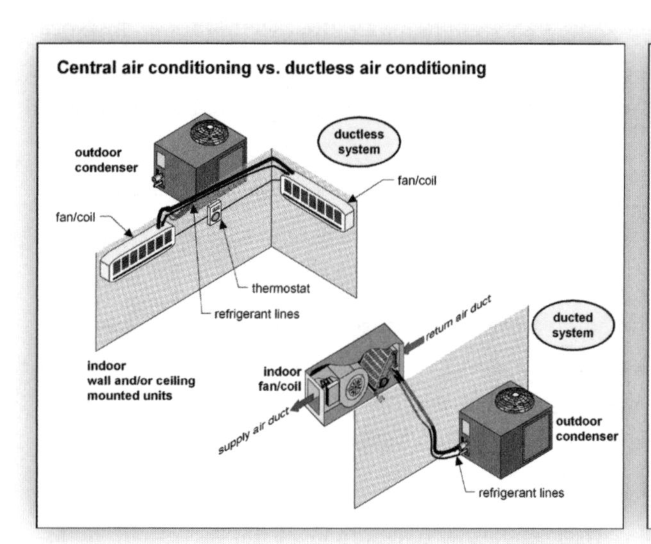

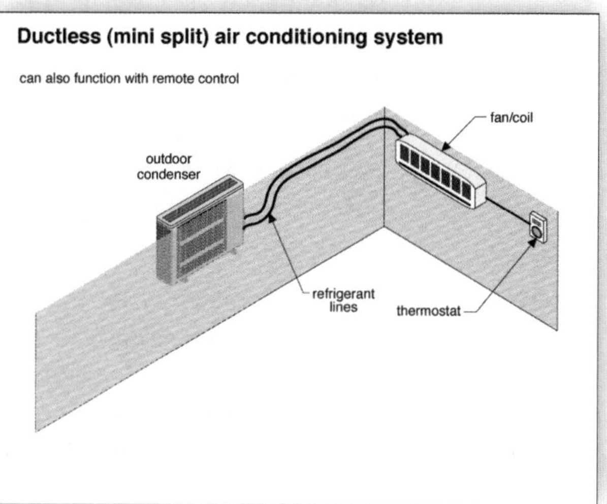

SINGLE COMPONENT SYSTEMS Single component systems are also called through-wall or package systems. These are self-contained systems with the condenser, compressor and evaporator all in the same cabinet, installed in the wall of the room or area to be cooled. These units are common in hotels and apartments. These single component systems are noisier than split systems because the compressor is in the wall-mounted unit. Some include electric elements for supplementary heating. Again, there is no ductwork to move cooled air through the home. Some people think of these as permanently installed window air conditioners.

Common Problems Specific to Ductless Units

AIRFLOW ISSUES Ductless air conditioners can blow air up to 40 feet in an open area, but since there is no distribution system, it is difficult to achieve balanced cooling in multiple rooms. In small rooms, air can bounce off walls or furnishings and create short cycling and comfort problems. These systems are often located near the top of the stairwell in a two-story home to cool as much of the home as possible.

CONDENSATE DAMAGE Condensate discharge systems are often on the building exterior, below the wall-mounted evaporator. Discoloration or wall damage may occur if the condensate runs down the wall surface.

1.4 Capacity of Air Conditioning and Heat Pump Systems

DESCRIPTION Both air conditioners and heat pumps have a rated cooling capacity. Heat pumps also have a rated heating capacity, which varies depending on outside temperature.

COOLING RATINGS Cooling ratings are expressed in tons. A ton represents 12,000 BTUs per hour. One BTU (British Thermal Unit) is the amount of heat required to raise the temperature of a pound of water by one Fahrenheit degree (or in the case of cooling, the amount of heat which must be absorbed to lower the temperature of a pound of water by one Fahrenheit degree). Typical central air-conditioning systems in homes are two to five tons.

HEAT GAIN: AIR-CONDITIONING Cooling systems are sized by calculating the heat gain for the house. The heat gain depends on several variables including climate, the size and configuration of the house, the construction, the amount of insulation, and the type, size and orientation of windows. Cooling systems are sized to keep the house roughly 15 to 20 degrees cooler than outdoors during the hottest day of the year, not necessarily at 72° F.

HEAT LOSS: HEAT PUMPS In northern climates, heat pumps are not designed to carry the entire heating load for a house. They are sized to meet the cooling demands of the house. The heat they provide varies with the outdoor temperature. As the outdoor temperature drops, the house needs more heat and the heat pump may not be able to keep up with the heat loss. Depending on the system, when the heat pump can't keep up, it may be helped with supplementary heat (electric heating elements, for example), or the heat pump may be shut off and a gas or oil furnace may take over.

CAN'T TELL WHETHER SIZE IS RIGHT Without performing heat gain calculations, it is not possible to determine the size of system needed for a house. Some systems (both heat pumps and air conditioners) are installed without matching condenser and evaporator coils. One coil might be rated for two tons while the other is rated for two-and-one-half tons. This is not determined during a home inspection. The capacity of mismatched systems is approximated by taking the outdoor coil rating and going 1,000 BTU in the direction of the plenum coil rating. For example, if the outdoor coil is 36,000 BTU and the indoor coil is 30,000 BTU, the system capacity is roughly 35,000 BTU.

Most often, inadequate air conditioning or heat pump performance is due to an inadequate ductwork system rather than undersized equipment. As a general rule, however, air-conditioning systems provide one ton of cooling for every 700 to 1000 square feet of house in moderate climates, and 450 to 600 square feet of house in warmer climates.

DON'T OVERSIZE AIR-CONDITIONING Modern, well-insulated homes may need less cooling and heating. Older, energy-inefficient homes need more. Air conditioning systems perform better and last longer if they are slightly undersized rather than oversized. Oversized units tend to short cycle and fail sooner. They also do not do as good a job dehumidifying the home. High humidity in the home makes it uncomfortable, even if the temperature is fine.

1.5 Life Expectancy of Air Conditioners and Heat Pumps

DESCRIPTION Any piece of equipment can fail at any time. We can't predict which component of our car, for example, will fail next. It could be the radio, which would be inconvenient, or it could be the engine, which would be catastrophic. A $10 fan belt or a $3 gasoline filter can make your car un-drivable. The same is true of an air conditioning system or a heat pump. When minor components fail, they can be replaced. When the compressor fails, replacement of the whole system may make sense.

10 TO 15 YEARS Air conditioning systems are often considered to have a life expectancy of 10 to 15 years. Life expectancies tend to be shorter in hotter climates where the air conditioners work harder and for more of the year.

HEAT PUMPS MAY BE LESS Heat pumps work both summer and winter, and again may have life expectancies on the shorter end of the scale. Heat pumps are also more complicated than air conditioners because of things like reversing valves and defrost systems. They may require more maintenance than air conditioning systems.

2.0 Heat Pumps

2.1 Description and Components – Air Source Heat Pumps

DESCRIPTION A heat pump is simply an air conditioner that can work in reverse to help heat the house. In the cooling season, the heat pump removes heat from the house interior and discharges it to the exterior, like an air conditioner. In the heating season, the refrigerant flow is reversed, and we remove heat from outdoors and put it into the home. The outdoor coil acts as a condenser in the summer and an evaporator in the winter. The indoor coil acts as an evaporator in the summer and a condenser in the winter. As with air conditioning, the compressor is the critical component.

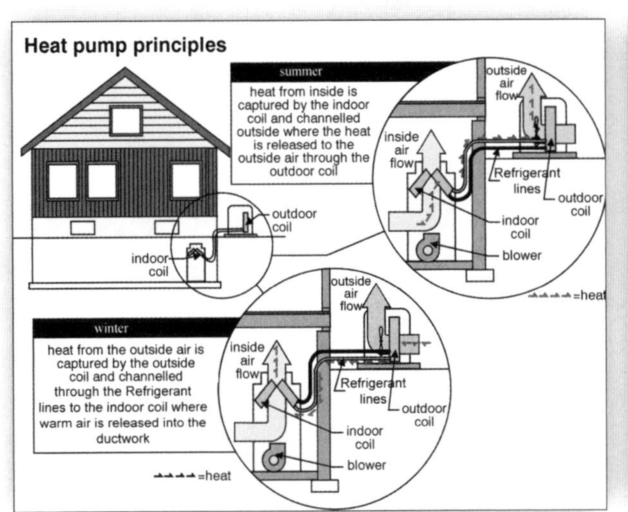

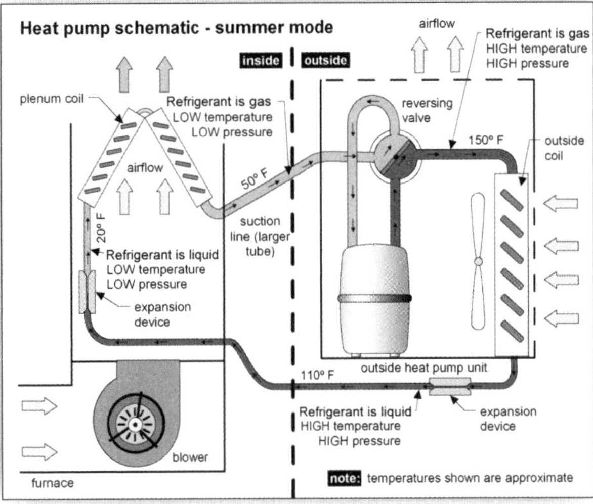

AIR SOURCE, WATER SOURCE OR GROUND SOURCE Air source heat pumps work the same as air conditioners in the summer. They use the outdoor air, water or ground to get rid of heat in the summer and they collect heat from the outdoor air , water or ground in the winter. We can also collect heat from water in wells, rivers, lakes, etc. with water source heat pumps. Ground source heat pumps collect and discharge heat into the ground through a series of buried pipes.

We will look at air source heat pumps first, since they are the most common.

COOLING/HEAT PUMPS

ECONOMICAL OPERATION In northern climates, heat pumps may not carry the entire heating load of a house. They only operate when they can add heat economically. When it costs more than a dollar's worth of electricity to add a dollar's worth of heat, the system shuts down. At this stage, the central heating system takes over. If the heating system is electric, the heat pump and electric heat can work together. If the heating system is gas or oil, the heat pump must be shut off when the furnace comes on.

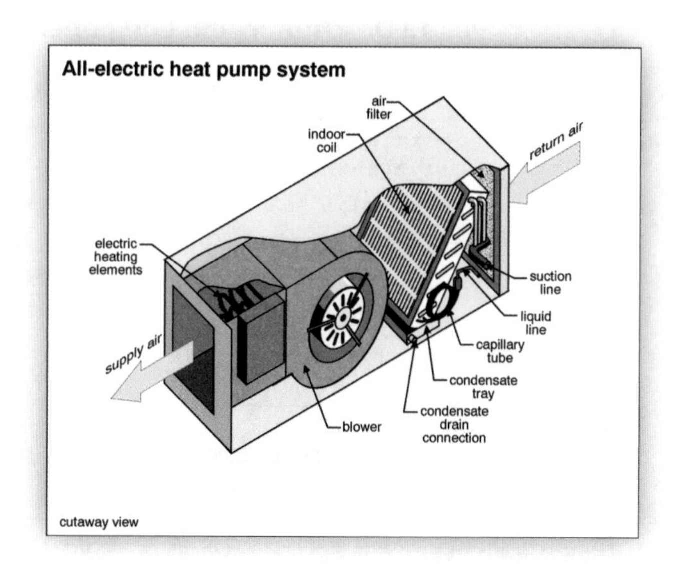

LIMITED TESTING A heat pump cannot be tested during very cold weather, when the heat pump is not working, and the heating system is gas or oil. Below a given temperature the heat pump is locked out and the only source of heat is the furnace.

Heat pumps should not be run in the cooling mode when outside temperatures are below 65°F. Above 65°F, heat pumps should not be run in the heating mode.

DRAFTY When the heat pump is operating in the heating mode, the air coming out of the registers feels drafty to some people. The air at the registers from a heat pump is not as warm as the air from a gas or oil furnace (roughly 90°F rather than 120°F). The heat provided is helpful, but the comfort may not be the same.

HEAT PUMP THERMOSTATS Thermostats for heat pumps used with gas or oil furnaces are different than air conditioning thermostats. The heat pump tries to maintain the desired temperature first. If the heat pump can't keep up, it is shut off and the furnace is activated. Most heat pump thermostats have a switch marked "Emergency Heat". This switch bypasses the heat pump and operates the furnace. This is useful because if the heat pump fails, we have a perfectly good furnace available. However if the thermostat is telling the heat pump to run, we can't get the furnace to turn on. The Emergency Heat switch allows the furnace to run.

Common Problems with Air Source Heat Pumps

Heat pumps have all the same issues as air conditioners, and some additional issues. Because heat pumps are more complicated, and because they have to operate in cold weather as well as hot weather, they are more prone to problems than air conditioners.

POOR LOCATION FOR OUTDOOR COIL (AIR SOURCE) Outdoor coils should not be exposed to ice buildup from water coming off the roof, strong winds or snowdrifts.

Poor outdoor coil location

too close to dryer vent (or water heater vent)
lint and heat
airflow obstructed by trees, decks etc.
house wall
deck
airflow
tree
heat pump
under the drip line of a roof
ice
heat pump
prevailing
wind
exposed to prevailing wind
wind
wind
heat pump
where snow drifts accumulate

ICED UP OUTDOOR COIL (AIR SOURCE) The heat pump will not work if the outdoor coil ices up. This happens because the outdoor air condenses water when it cools as it passes over the coil. The moisture falls out of the air as liquid (condensate) and quickly freezes on the coil. Heat pumps have a defrost cycle to prevent icing problems. Defrosting problems can lead to icing up.

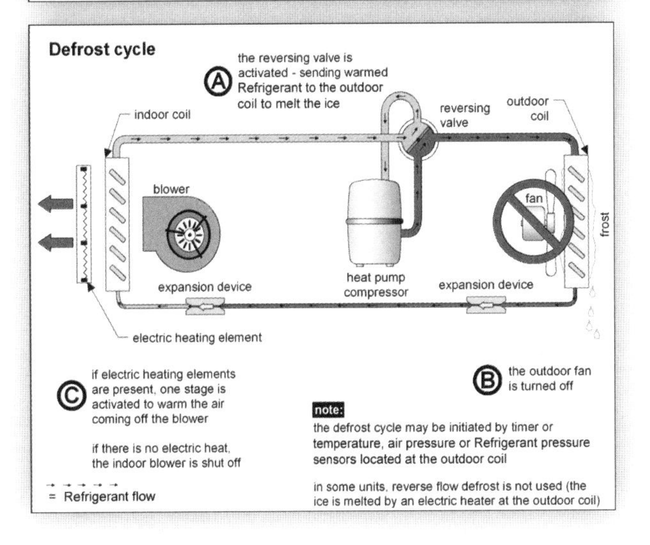

2.2 Other Types of Heat Pumps

DESCRIPTION Heat pumps can be central ducted systems, or ductless systems. They can be integrated with gas, oil or electric furnaces. They can be stand-alone systems that may have supplementary electric heating elements.

AIR SOURCE HEAT PUMP Most air source heat pumps look the same as air conditioners. There is an outside coil that is used to dissipate heat during the air conditioning season and collect heat during the heating season. The indoor section may be a coil near a furnace or a coil in an attic fan-coil cabinet where there is no furnace.

GROUND SOURCE HEAT PUMP Rather than using outside air to collect or dissipate heat, some systems use the ground or water. A ground source heat pump has piping running through the ground, with liquid that collects or dissipates the heat, depending on the season. The piping can be installed horizontally (shallow) or vertically (deep) below the ground surface.

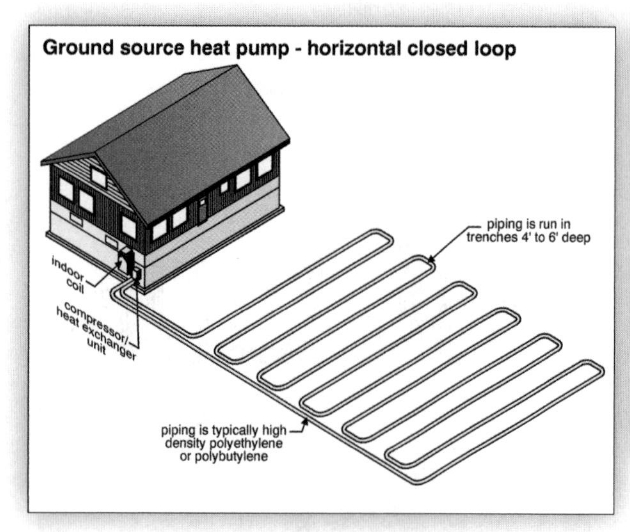

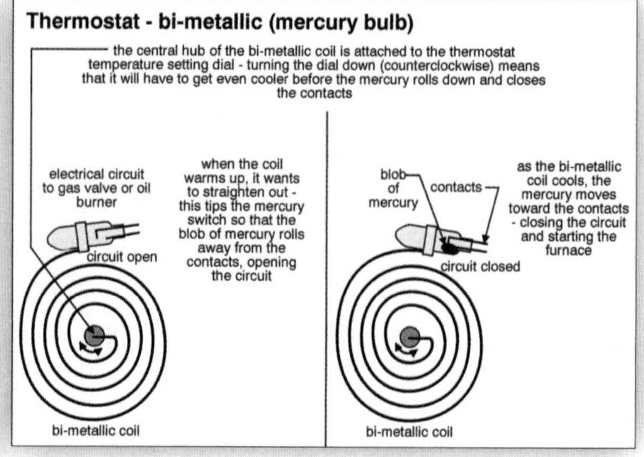

WATER SOURCE HEAT PUMP Some systems use two wells instead of piping. Ground water is pumped from one well. Heat is extracted from the water and the water is pumped back into the other well. Rivers and lakes can also be used as a source for collecting and dissipating heat. These systems are called water source heat pumps.

The advantages of ground source and water source heat pumps are that the ground and the water are warmer than the outdoor winter air. There is more heat available to collect.

These systems are expensive to install, and early units had several problems. As energy costs increase and technology improves, the systems become more cost effective. They also work well for air conditioning.

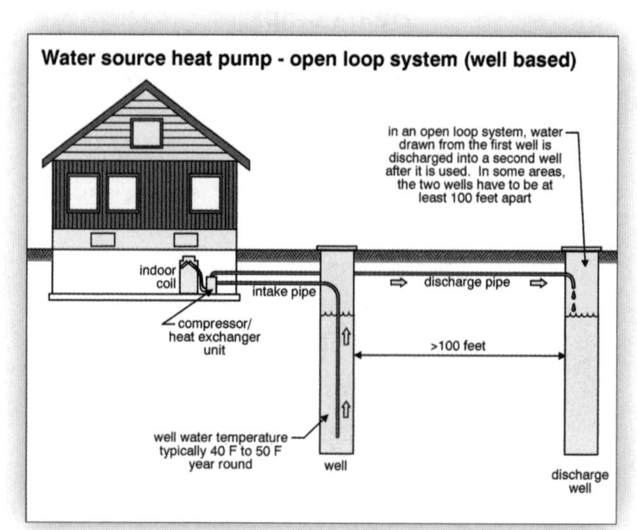

2.3 Bivalent Systems

FURNACE As mentioned earlier, heat pumps are not capable of carrying the entire heating load during the coldest parts of a northern winter. With most systems, the heat pump has to eventually shut down and let the furnace take over because the heat pump cannot collect heat economically.

BIVALENT HEAT PUMPS These systems fool the heat pump. They have a burner (usually natural gas or propane) outdoors below the coil. Just when the system is about to shut down, the outdoor burner comes on and the coil thinks that there is a heat wave. Suddenly there is enough heat in the outside air to keep going.

These systems do not require a furnace in the house to supplement the heat pump because the heat pump never experiences the coldest part of the winter – or at least it thinks it doesn't. It's getting heat from an outdoor auxiliary heater.

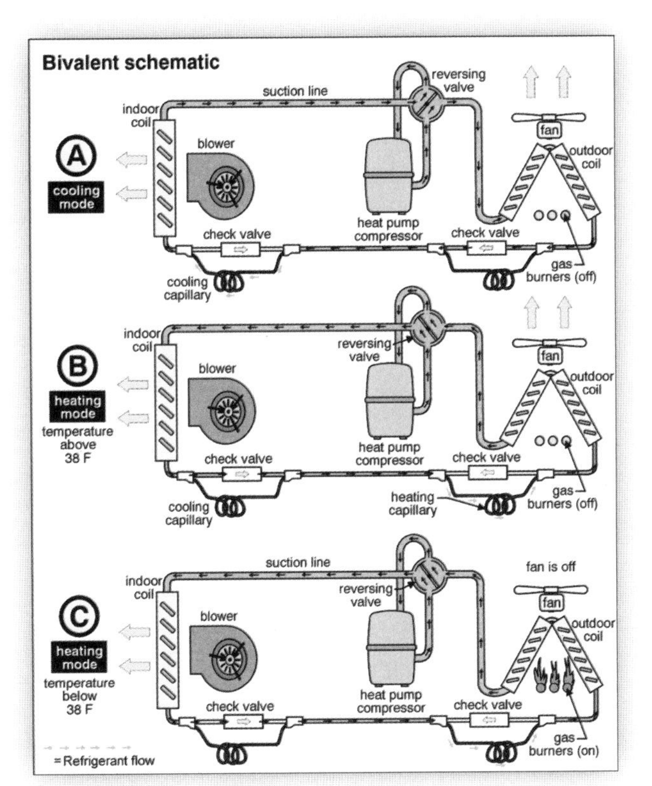

ADVANTAGES The outdoor gas burners don't need a chimney.

DISADVANTAGES These systems have a high initial cost and there have been some reliability issues. The burner and the rest of the outdoor components are in a harsh environment. Corrosion on the burner and the coil can be a problem as a result of condensation.

Common Problems with Bivalent Heat Pumps

These systems have all of the issues related to heat pumps, plus the complicating issue of an outdoor gas burner. Corrosion on the outdoor components can be a problem due to condensation from the products of combustion.

3.0 Evaporative Coolers

FUNCTION Evaporative coolers are simple air conditioners that push outdoor air into the home after adding water to the air to cool it. The unit may be mounted on an exterior wall or on the roof. There is usually a simple, supply-only duct system to distribute the cooled moist air through the home.

PRINCIPLE OF OPERATION Evaporative cooling systems are used in warm, dry climates such as those in the Southwest. Evaporative coolers use a high volume low speed blower to draw outside air into the house, typically through a moist cooling pad. As the air passes over the wet media, the water absorbs heat from the air. This evaporates some of the water and lowers the temperature of the air delivered into the house.

MOVING AIR THROUGH WATER A pump draws water out of a tray to keep the pads wet. Variations include a drip type cooler which allows water to drip down through the air flow. No pads are used with this system. The rotary type cooler has a drum made up of fine metal screening which rotates through a tank of water. The air passes over the upper part of the rotor, again evaporating some of the moisture.

WATER SUPPLY AND BLOWER The water level in the tank or tray is maintained by a connection to the supply plumbing in the house. A float valve allows water to be added as needed. An electric motor drives the blower.

Common Problems with Evaporative Coolers

INOPERATIVE An evaporative cooler may not respond to its controls because power has been shut off, the water has been shut off or the blower or motor has failed. No air-conditioning will be available if the system does not respond.

CONDENSATION/ MILDEW/ BACTERIA Evaporative coolers do not work well when the air outside is humid. Also, since the indoor air ends up being relatively humid, a drop in temperature can lead to condensation in the house and ultimately, mildew and bacteria problems. Water sitting in the tray or tank may become stagnant during idle periods. This can be a health concern. The unit should be drained seasonally. Leaking trays or tanks may cause water damage.

SEIZED MOTORS/ FAILED BLOWER BEARINGS Difficulties with electric motors and blower bearings are common failure points.

CLOGGED NOZZLES/DIRTY PADS Spray type units may have the spray nozzles clogged and water pads may be dirty, restricting air flow. Very little cooling will result.

RUST/LEAK Rusting cabinets and leakage through the enclosures are other common problems. This can damage building components.

INDEPENDENT OF HEATING DUCTWORK Evaporative coolers should not be interconnected with heating ductwork. Moist air passing over a furnace heat exchanger can rust it out, destroying the furnace.

Insulation

INTRODUCTION

THE IMPORTANCE OF INSULATION DEPENDS ON WHERE YOU LIVE. HOMES IN THE NORTH BENEFIT MORE FROM INSULATION THAN HOMES IN THE SOUTH. DIFFERENT REGIONS HAVE DIFFERENT STRATEGIES TO DEAL WITH MOISTURE MOVEMENT AND VENTILATION.

POORLY INSULATED HOMES ARE EXPENSIVE TO HEAT BUT MAY BE COMFORTABLE. ALMOST ANY HOUSE CAN BE WARM IF THE THERMOSTAT IS SET HIGH ENOUGH.

1.0 The Basics

INSULATION Insulation slows the rate of heat transfer into or out of a house. Air is a very good insulator, but only if it does not move. The problem is that air moves around and heat moves with the air. A good insulation material traps air, keeping it still.

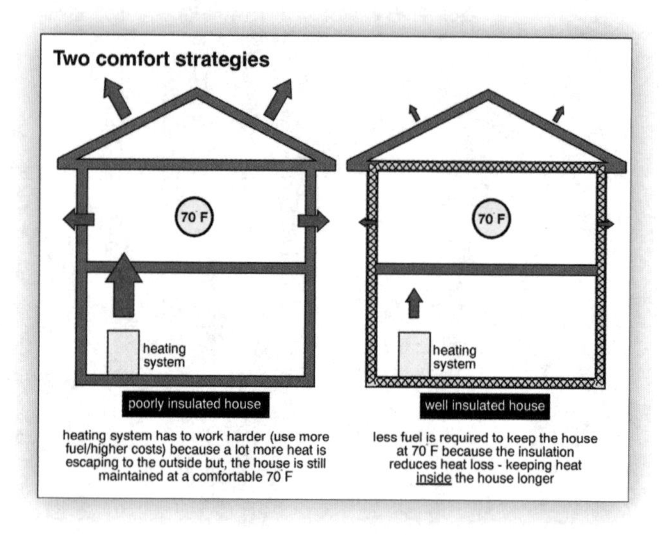

R-VALUE Insulation materials have a common measurement system. An R-value indicates resistance to heat transfer – the higher the R-value, the better. R-values are usually defined for a one-inch thickness of insulation. For example, if the insulation has an R-value of 4.0 per inch, a 4-inch thick batt of that insulation would have a value of R-16 (R-4/in. x 4in.).

Most building materials are not good thermal insulators, as you can see from the illustration.

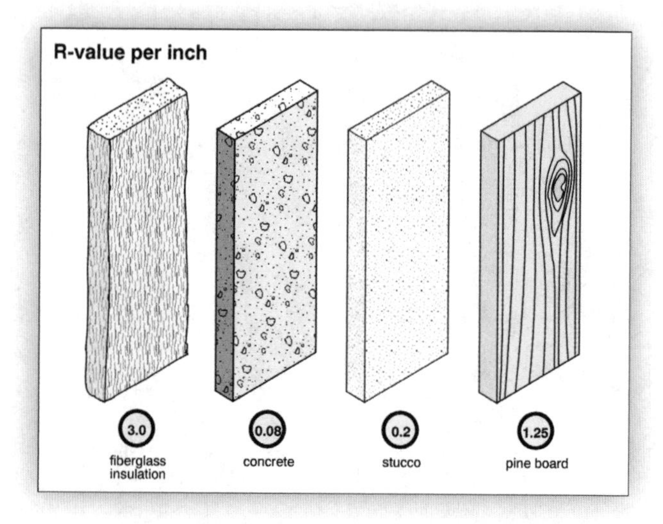

FORMS OF INSULATION Insulation can be batts, blankets, loose fill, boards, or sprayed-in-place.

INSULATION LEVELS The illustration below provides a guideline for insulation levels in heating climates.

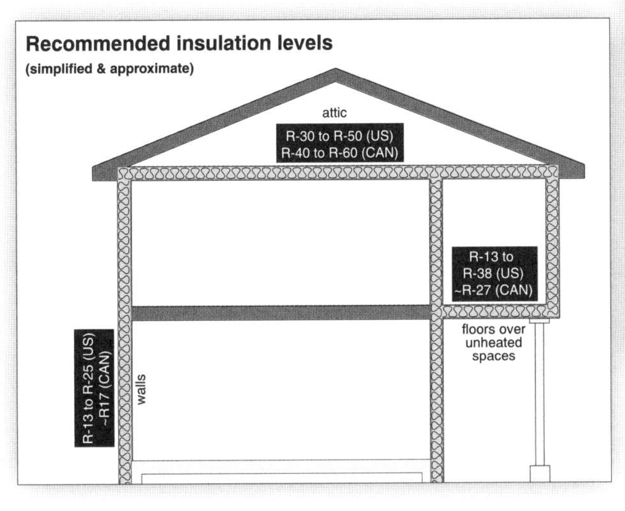

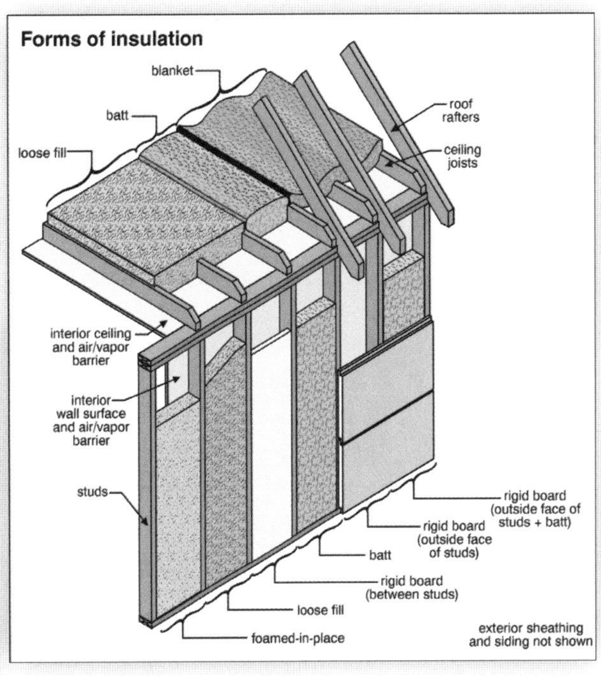

Let's look at some common insulation materials.

2.0 Common Insulation Materials

2.1 Fiberglass (R-Value 2.9-4.2 per inch)

DESCRIPTION Fiberglass insulation is one of the most common insulation materials available and is made from threads of glass glued together with phenolic resins. It is available in batt form, rigid board and loose fill. It is resistant to moisture, mildew, fungus and vermin, and some types are non-combustible. It is, however, a skin and eye irritant and inhaling small threads of fiberglass is not healthy. These irritations are only common during installation, and once the material is in place it is not considered to be a problem.

2.2 Mineral Wool (R-Value 3.0-3.2 per inch)

Mineral wool is similar to fiberglass except that mineral waste is used to form the wool-like material. It, too, is available in batt form, rigid board or as loose fill. Its insulating value is comparable to fiberglass and it has very good resistance to fire and rot. It is less irritating to work with than fiberglass.

2.3 Cellulose Fiber (R-Value 3.4-3.6 per inch)

Cellulose fiber is essentially paper, finely shredded and chemically treated to resist moisture, fire, rot and vermin. It is usually blown in or poured. It is prone to settling. Due to its relatively low cost, this material is very popular. Usually gray in color, it has a similar texture to lint. Cellulose fiber absorbs water, which reduces its effectiveness.

2.4 Plastic Board (R-Value 3.7-6.0 per inch)

Most plastic board type insulations used in homes are polystyrene or polyurethane. Both pose fire hazards if left exposed. If applied on interior walls or ceilings, they should be covered with drywall. While these materials have a good R-value per inch of thickness, they are more expensive than most other types.

2.5 Sprayed Foam (R-Value 3.5-7.0 per inch)

These insulation materials can be used in open environments or, in special cases, in closed wall cavities. They are often used in new work, before walls or ceilings are closed in. These products are plastic – typically polyurethane and polyicynene, a water-based sprayed foam. They are combustible and must be covered. Some expand aggressively and are not suitable for injecting into closed wall cavities.

2.6 Urea Formaldehyde Foam Insulation (UFFI) (R-Value 5.0 per inch)

This foamed-in-place insulation was briefly banned in the United States due to concerns about the material being a cancer-causing agent. The ban was lifted in 1983. In Canada, the ban remains in effect as of 2010. The insulation had a relatively high R-value, although some of the early installations were prone to shrinkage that resulted in a loss of insulating value.

2.7 Vermiculite (R-Value 2.1-2.5 per inch)

Vermiculite is a mineral substance made from mica. This insulation is available as loose fill and can be identified by the small rectangular shape of the individual pieces. Vermiculite is non-combustible but is relatively expensive.

ZONOLITE One brand of vermiculite insulation, Zonolite, came from ore that contained some asbestos. Although the vermiculite is not typically in living areas of the house, some consider this to be a health issue. Identification of Zonolite or asbestos cannot be done visually and is outside the scope of a home inspection. For more information on asbestos, please refer to the Supplementary section.

2.8 Wood Shavings (R-Value 2.4 per inch)

Wood shavings used as insulation today are treated with fire retardant chemicals and can be made moisture resistant. This was not the case many years ago.

2.9 Other Materials (R value less than 3.0 per inch)

Other materials were used as insulation over the years, although most of these are not commonly installed now. These include leather, gypsum slag and cork.

3.0 Location of Insulation

Insulation is found in several places in the home. Let's have a look.

3.1 Attic

DESCRIPTION The goal is for the attic temperature to be the same as the outdoor temperature. We want to keep the heat in the house. If the attic is warm, we are losing heat from where we want it.

INSULATE THE ATTIC FLOOR Insulation should be provided on the attic floor, not the underside of the roof for several reasons. The first is gravity. It is easier to lay insulation on the floor than secure it to the underside of the roof. The second is heating costs. There is no advantage to heating the attic space. The third reason is prevention of condensation. Insulation on the floor of the attic allows better ventilation of the attic space. Good air movement through the attic removes any moist air from the living space that finds its way into the attic. Refer to "Ventilation" in this section.

THE EXCEPTION/ COUNTERPOINT Homes that have the heating system and part of the ductwork system in the attic present a different situation. The ducts are usually leaky, and a significant amount of heated air escapes into the attic. This heat is lost to the home, and creates condensation problems in the attic as it cools.

INSULATE THE ATTIC ROOF? Where air leakage cannot be easily controlled, it may make sense to treat the attic as conditioned (heated) space and insulate the underside of the roof. There are many variables to consider, including not only the climate temperature, but prevailing humidity levels, the building configuration, whether insulation is impermeable to air movement or not, etc.

MORE THAN ONE APPROACH There are several design philosophies and arguments about whether attic and roof spaces should be ventilated or not. As long as building science issues are understood and addressed, there can be more than one successful approach. Professional home inspectors do not perform a design analysis but look for the results of an unsuccessful approach.

SKYLIGHT WELLS (LIGHT SHAFTS) Depending upon the configuration of the roof and the ceilings below, the light shaft (Skylight well) often passes through an unheated attic. The walls of the skylight well should be insulated where they pass through an attic. There should be an air/vapor barrier on the warm side of the insulation in cold climates.

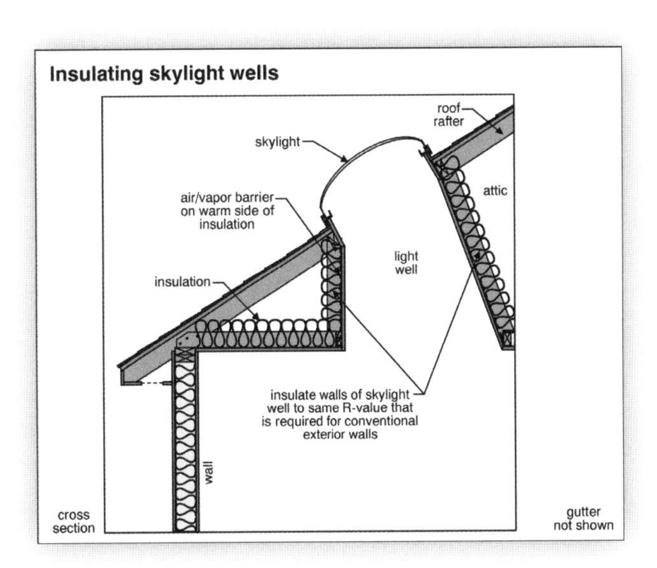

KNEE WALLS A knee wall is found in 1-1/2 or 2-1/2 story houses. The knee wall separates the upper living space from the side attic areas. Insulation is usually provided on the unfinished side of the knee wall and the floor of the attic. No insulation is needed on the end (outside) walls of side attics. A less effective alternative is to insulate the underside of the roof and the end walls of the attic. This allows heat into the unused attic area – a waste of heat.

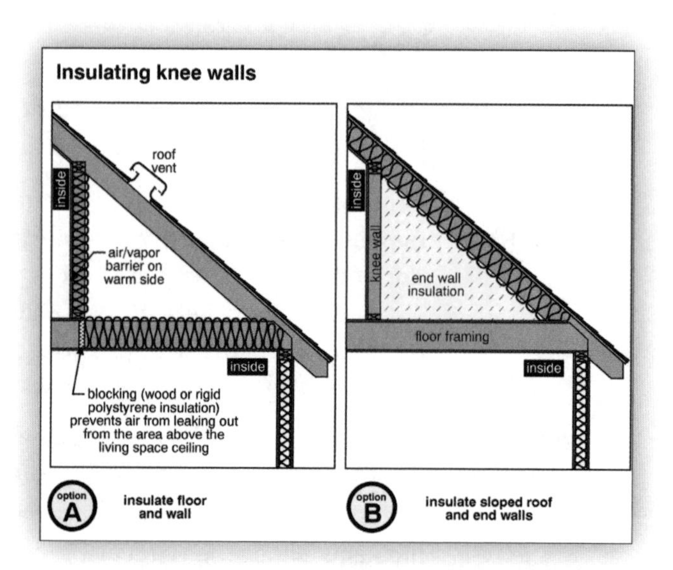

DUCTWORK Exhaust ducts from fans and ductwork for cooling and/or heating located in attics should be insulated (minimum R-7) to prevent heat gain or heat loss and to prevent condensation as the warm moist house air cools in the duct. Some ductwork comes pre-insulated. In some instances, the insulation is on the interior of the ductwork and is not visible.

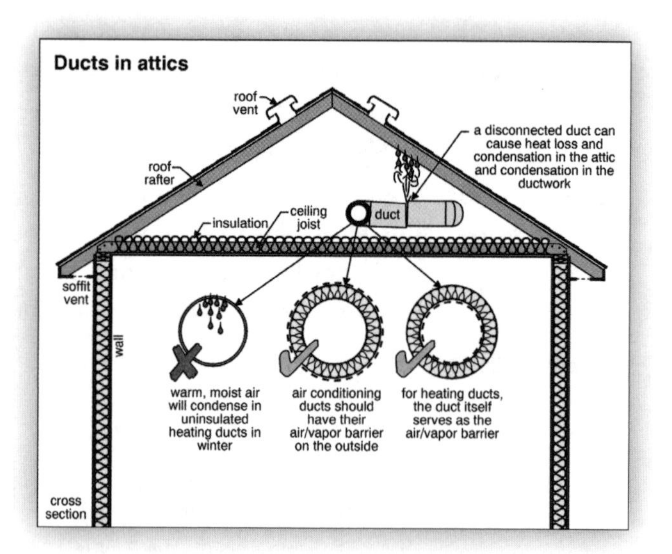

Common Problems with Attic Insulation

BELOW CURRENT STANDARDS Increasing insulation levels is an improvement rather than a repair. The right amount of insulation depends on climate, fuel costs, the cost involved in adding insulation and the length of time one is planning to stay in the house. The decision to upgrade may be different for different owners.

Adding insulation provides a quick return on investment in severe climates where existing insulation levels are low. Cellulose, mineral wool, and fiberglass insulations are most commonly used on a retrofit basis.

WET INSULATION Insulation may be wet as a result of snow blowing into the roof through vents, roof leaks or condensation. Insulation is not effective when it is wet. Some types of insulation recover their insulating properties when they dry out. Others do not.

COMPRESSED Compressed insulation loses much of its effectiveness because the air is removed. The goal of insulation is to hold pockets of air still. Adding insulation in localized areas is not a difficult improvement.

MISSING Insulation may be displaced by activities in the attic, or by wind entering through roof vents. Low spots can be filled in relatively easily, given proper access.

UN-INSULATED EXHAUST DUCTS Bathroom exhaust fans are often connected to un-insulated ducts in the attic. The warm moist air from the bathroom condenses on the inside of the ductwork. It runs back down the duct and drips out of the exhaust fan. This is dangerous as the water is dripping past the electric motor of the fan. Ductwork in the attic should be insulated.

RECESSED LIGHTS (POT LIGHTS) – RISK OF OVERHEATING Recessed lights covered with insulation can overheat and start a fire. Special barriers should be provided over recessed lights to allow for insulation above the ventilation/cooling space around recessed lights. A three-inch clearance between the fixture and insulation is often recommended. Alternatively, special lights designed for this application can be used. (IC – Insulated Ceiling or Insulation Contact) These have a double casing to keep things cool and safe, and many have a gasket to prevent air leakage past the fixture into the attic. Some recessed lights have lower bulb wattage ratings if they are installed in an insulated ceiling.

3.2 Flat Roofs and Cathedral Roofs/Sloped Ceilings

DESCRIPTION These roofs have no attics and less room for insulation and ventilation than roofs with attics. It is not usually possible to determine the amount of insulation in this type of roof.

Common Problems with Flat Roof/Cathedral Roof Insulation

NO INSULATION Insulation can be blown in from above or below; however, this requires drilling holes through the ceiling or roof membrane. In some cases, it can be blown in at the eaves. Regardless of the approach, assessing the quality of the completed job is difficult. Batt-type insulation can be installed; however, it requires the removal of the ceiling finish or roof sheathing. This is usually not cost-effective. With either approach, the amount of insulation is limited by the size of the roof cavity.

INSULATION ABOVE ROOF SHEATHING OR BELOW THE CEILING An alternative is to install insulation above the roof sheathing. This approach only makes sense when re-roofing and, even at that, the amount of rigid insulation that can be installed typically falls short of current residential standards. Without insulating at the eaves, the new insulation above the sheathing can be "short-circuited" by cold air travelling through the roof cavity and out the sides.

Insulation can be added to the underside of ceilings and a new ceiling finish provided below. This is typically done with plastic board insulation. The loss of room height is often an issue with this approach.

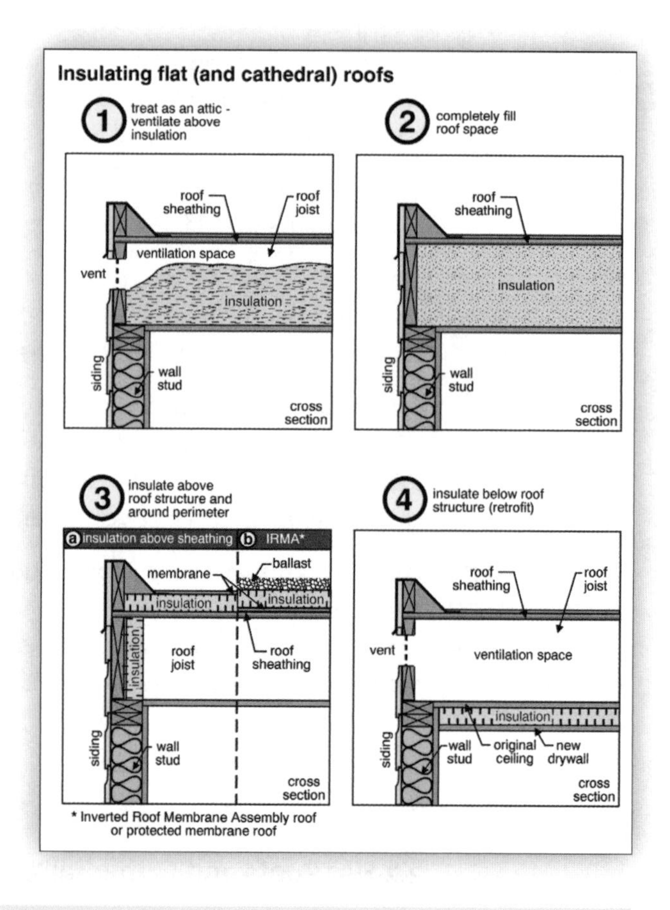

Condensation Problems in Cold Climates

Condensation can cause considerable concealed damage in flat and cathedral roofs. If warm moist air from the house gets into the roof space, it cools and condenses. This can cause mold and rot. Typical roof construction limits the space available for ventilation above the insulation, and makes it nearly impossible to retrofit an air/vapor barrier. The limited space makes it difficult to use the strategy used in attics, where warm moist air is quickly carried outdoors.

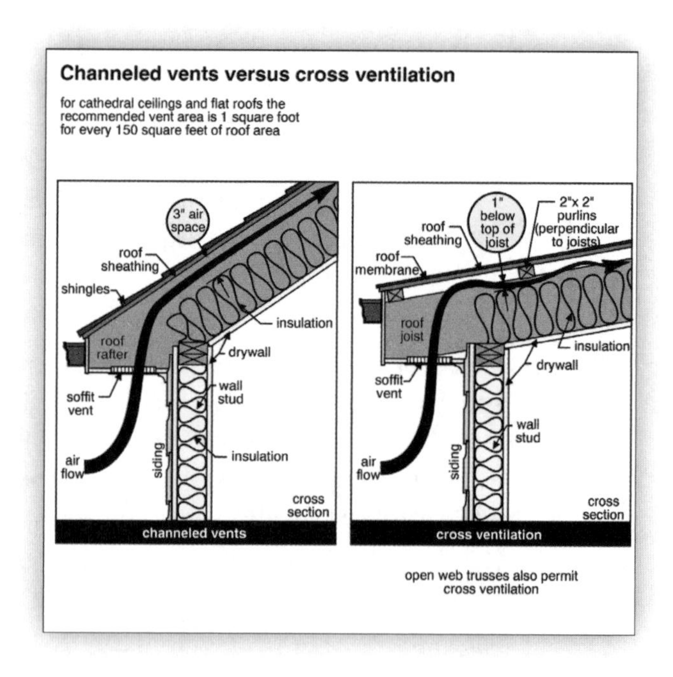

ALTERNATIVE TO VENTILATION Filling the cavity with an insulation that acts as an air and vapor barrier may be practical. The thought here is that if the roof space is sealed, warm moist air from the house can't get into the roof space and condense.

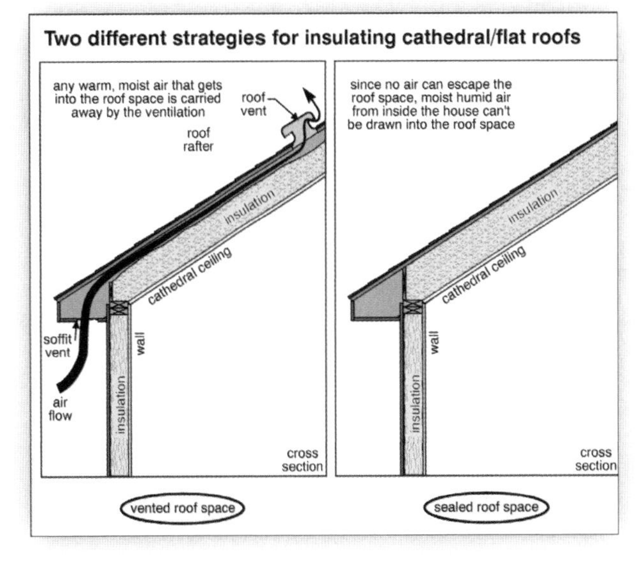

RECESSED LIGHTS (POT LIGHTS) Recessed lights in insulated ceilings should be rated IC to avoid overheating.

3.3 Walls

BATTS **3.3.1 Wood Frame Walls:** The most common method of insulating wood and steel frame walls during initial construction is with batts of insulation filling the spaces between the studs, although foamed-in-place plastic insulation is also used. Insulated sheathing is also used on the exterior of the studs, behind the siding. This adds insulation and reduces thermal bridges through the studs by covering the outer edges.

It is often difficult during a home inspection to determine whether walls are insulated, more difficult to determine the amount of insulation, and impossible to evaluate the installation and effectiveness. Upgrading wall insulation may not be cost effective except when remodelling.

POURING Existing wood frame walls can be insulated by pouring insulation into the wall cavity. Pouring insulation into wall cavities is usually only possible if the wall space is open in the attic and is continuous down to the foundation walls. Windows and doors interrupt the wall cavities, complicating the process.

BLOWING Insulation can be blown into stud spaces. Holes are typically created at the top and bottom of the cavities, with insulation blown in one hole until it comes out the other. Blown-in insulation can be installed from the inside or outside. In some cases, it is also possible to install from the basement or from the attic by drilling through the wall plates.

INTERIOR APPROACH Interior finishes can be removed and batt-type insulation can be installed in the stud cavities. An air/vapor barrier can also be installed. This may make sense during remodeling.

EXTERIOR APPROACH Insulation can be installed from the exterior if the siding is to be replaced. Installing strapping, insulation, and new siding over the old siding is not usually practical or effective because of the short circuits that are often created.

It is often not possible during a home inspection to determine whether wall insulation has been added. Many older walls have no insulation at all.

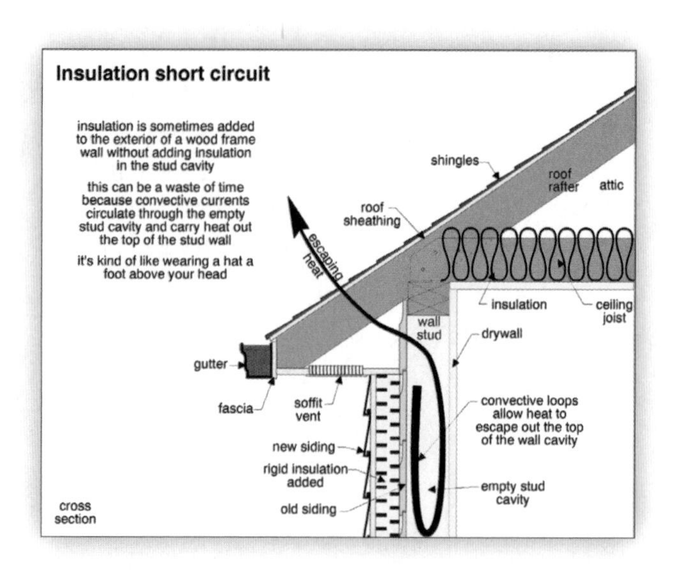

Common Problems with Wood Frame Wall Insulation

VOIDS There may be gaps between insulation and framing members. Blown or poured insulation in walls can settle leaving uninsulated spaces at the top. Foamed-in-place insulations sometimes shrink, reducing their effectiveness dramatically. Voids in insulation will not only reduce the effectiveness of the insulation, but can also result in cold wall sections that are prone to condensation and peeling paint.

Insulation voids and convective loops

LITTLE/NO INSULATION While standards change to reflect energy concerns, many older buildings' walls have little or no insulation. There is a good opportunity to improve comfort and heating costs. Insulation work is very cost effective if done with remodelling work, but is expensive on its own.

DESCRIPTION **3.3.2 Solid Walls:** There are numerous types of solid exterior walls, most of which have little insulation. Many older walls have no insulation at all, although this is difficult to determine without opening the wall.

Types of Solid Walls

MASONRY – BRICK OR STONE Masonry walls usually consist of two thicknesses of brick/stone or a layer of brick/stone and a layer of block (concrete or cinder block). There is often a one-inch space between the two layers of masonry or in the cores of the block; not enough room to insulate. There is also typically a small space between the inside layer of masonry and the interior wall finish. Again, this space is too small to insulate, usually less than an inch.

OTHER WALLS Other examples of solid walls include log or solid timber, adobe, rammed earth, straw bale and poured concrete walls. These materials have varying degrees of inherent insulation ability. Insulation can be added on the interior or the exterior of the existing walls; however, this is expensive and may change the exterior appearance of the house or reduce interior room dimensions.

ICF Insulating Concrete Form (ICF) walls are also solid, however the forms that are used in these systems are made from polystyrene, a good insulating material. These walls have a good insulating value, similar to insulated wood frame walls.

Common Problems with Solid Wall Insulation

LITTLE/NO INSULATION While standards continue to change to reflect energy concerns, many older buildings have exterior walls with little or no insulation. Solid walls can be insulated by providing a false wall on the interior or exterior of the existing wall. This not only changes the outside appearance of the house or reduces interior room dimensions; it also affects such things as baseboards, windows, doors, electrical outlets, ceiling moldings, etc. Adding wall insulation in masonry houses may not be cost-effective, except during significant remodelling.

AIR SEALING AS ALTERNATIVE A good deal of the heat loss in homes is through air leakage. Sealing air leaks is often more cost-effective than adding wall insulation.

3.4 Basement and Crawlspace

DESCRIPTION **3.4.1 Interior of Walls:** Insulating the inside of basement/crawlspace walls makes sense in cold climates, and is inexpensive if the walls are unfinished. The cost is higher if the basement walls are already finished since the finishes have to be removed.

DON'T INSULATE WET WALLS If the basement has chronic moisture problems, the interior of the walls should not be insulated. It is better to insulate on the outside, correcting the moisture problem at the same time. This is more expensive but protects the foundation walls as well as upgrading the insulation. Secondly, if the foundation walls are wet, interior insulation could result in frost damage to the foundation, since the walls will be colder after insulating. The third issue when insulating from the interior is obstructions such as electrical panels, plumbing, oil tanks, etc.

AIR/VAPOR AND MOISTURE BARRIERS

A wood stud wall is often added inside the foundation wall. The stud cavities are filled with batt-type insulation. A moisture barrier is installed against the foundation wall (before constructing the stud wall) and an air/vapor barrier is installed on the warm side of the insulation. The bottom plate of the stud wall is often kept off the floor with a sill gasket, and the plate itself may be pressure-treated wood to resist rot if the basement/crawlspace leaks.

Under some circumstances, combustible plastic insulation can be glued to existing foundation walls; however, it must be covered with drywall or some other non-combustible material to reduce the fire risk. No moisture barrier or air/vapor barrier is required.

Sprayed-on foam insulation can also be used on the interior of foundation walls, although if the insulation is combustible, it should be covered. Tests have shown polyurethane performs well if applied to dry foundation walls.

NEW CONSTRUCTION

In northern climates new houses typically have insulation on basement/crawlspace walls from the ceiling down to about eight inches above the basement/crawlspace floor. The bottom few inches of the wall are often left un-insulated to ensure the foundation wall does not freeze.

HEADER/RIM JOIST

Insulation should be added in joist spaces at the top of the foundation wall. Depending upon the direction the joists run, this space may be a series of small spaces roughly 14 inches wide (between joists) or one long space parallel to the joists. Caulking the foundation/sill, header/sill, and headed/subfloor connections helps reduce heat loss due to air leakage.

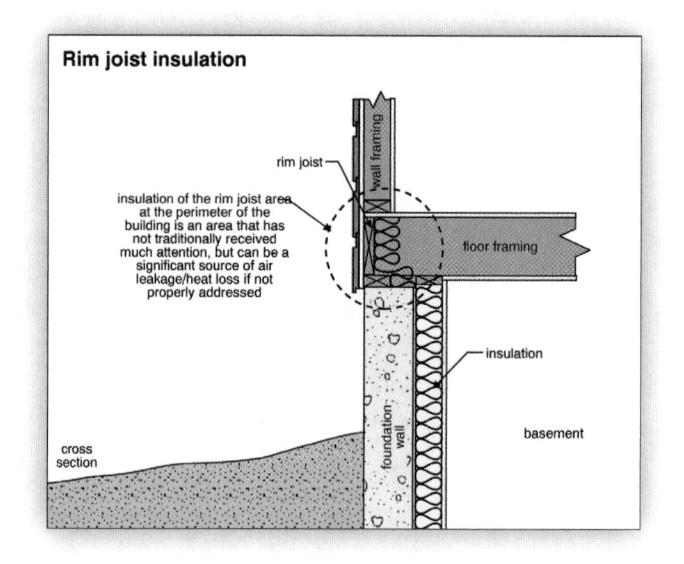

DESCRIPTION

3.4.2 Exterior of Walls: Exterior wall insulation only makes sense if exterior digging is to be done for another reason, such as damp-proofing the basement/crawlspace walls. This work often includes an egg-crate type drainage layer installed against the foundation wall. Rigid or semi-rigid insulation is added, and the upper portion of the insulation (above ground level) is covered by a protective material such as cement board.

A flashing at the top of the insulation prevents water penetration in this location.

3.5 Floors above Unheated Areas

DESCRIPTION Floors over unheated spaces (crawl spaces, garages, porches, cantilevers, etc) are often cold unless well insulated. There are several strategies and materials for insulating these areas. Insulation batts, boards or sprayed-in-place foam and other insulation materials can be used.

Common Problems with Floors above Unheated Spaces

LITTLE/NO INSULATION Inadequate insulation levels can lead to cold floors, which is primarily a comfort issue. Increasing the insulation improves comfort and reduces energy costs, but in many cases floors are still cool in extreme weather. Insulation levels can't be determined during a home inspection.

EXPOSED PLASTIC INSULATION Plastic insulation, such as polystyrene, is combustible and should be covered by drywall, with all joints properly sealed.

PIPES MAY FREEZE Plumbing and heating pipes passing through unheated areas should be insulated where freezing is a risk. In cold climates, it is often better to move the pipes to a heated area or provide electric heating cables on the pipes.

4.0 Current Insulation Standards

DESCRIPTION The numbers in the diagram are common insulation levels in new construction. The ranges reflect various climate zones. More insulation is used in colder climates. The R-value indicates resistance to heat transfer – the higher the R-value, the better.

Different insulation materials have different R-values per inch of thickness. Even the same type of insulation can have a different R-value, depending on its form. Fiberglass insulation, for example, has a higher R-value in batt form than in loose fill form.

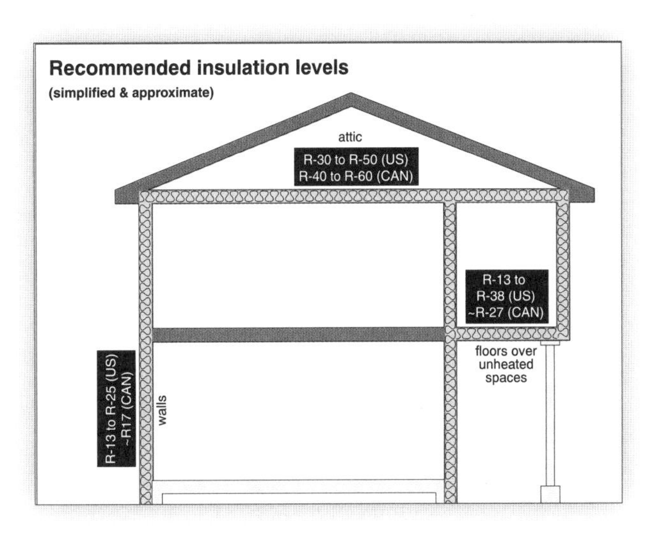

5.0 Air/Vapor Barriers (Vapor Retarders or Vapor Diffusion Retarders)

DESCRIPTION Air and vapor barriers help control the movement of heat and moisture through the walls, ceilings, and/or floors of the house. Their importance and placement depends on the climate, as well as the type of construction and insulation in the home.

AIR BARRIERS Most types of insulation let some air pass through them. Air carries heat with it, and this air can move heat into or out of the house, past the insulation. An air barrier prevents or reduces air movement. Air barriers can be installed on either side of the insulation. When installed on the exterior, air barriers help prevent wind-washing of the insulation. Wind-washing reduces the effectiveness of insulation.

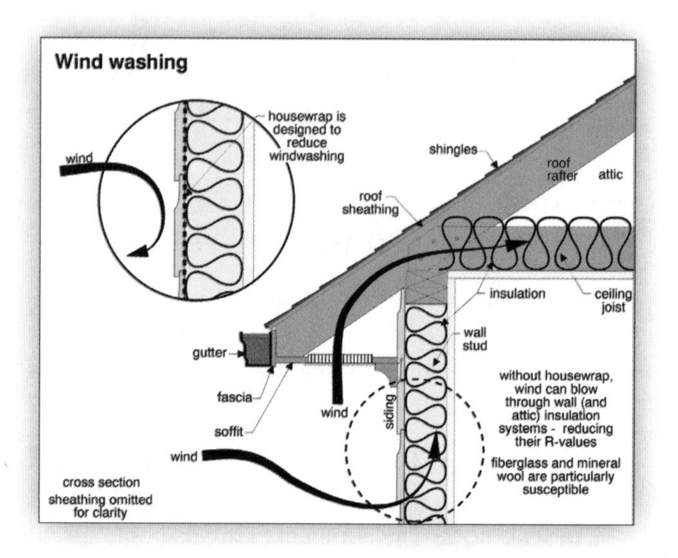

In order to be effective, air barriers must be continuous and sealed at joints and edges.

VAPOR BARRIER Vapor barriers reduce vapor movement due to vapor diffusion, which is the natural tendency of water vapor to move from areas of high relative humidity to low relative humidity. Vapor diffusion does not require air movement; in fact water vapor can move through many solid materials.

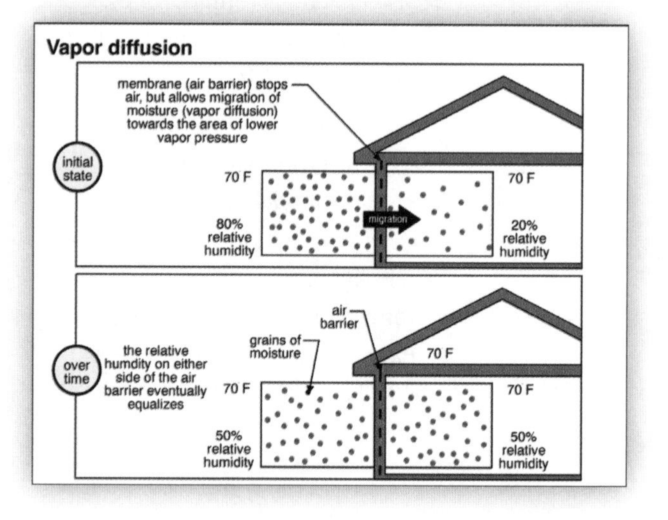

PREVENTING CONDENSATION As the air temperature drops, the relative humidity goes up. Air at 70°F and 40% relative humidity will reach 100% relative humidity as it is cooled to 45°F. When air in the insulation cools, it deposits moisture in the wall or attic insulation. This water reduces the effectiveness of the insulation, because water is a good conductor of heat. More importantly, water leads to rot, mold and peeling paint. In cold climates, a vapor barrier is required on the warm-in-winter side of insulation to stop vapor moving from the house into the insulation. The exceptions are insulations that are vapor barriers, like polystyrene and polyurethane.

In warmer climates, where air conditioning is more dominant than heating, vapor barriers are not used, because a vapor barrier in the inside of the insulation can cause problems during the cooling season. Even in cold climates, vapor barriers are not as important as air barriers.

Unlike air barriers, vapor barriers don't need to be continuous to be effective. Most vapor barriers are actually vapor retarders, or vapor diffusion retarders, since they don't stop vapor diffusion, but slow it down (the same way that thermal insulation does not stop the flow of heat, but slows it down). Let's look at some air and vapor barrier materials.

POLYETHYLENE Clear polyethylene sheets are common as both an air barrier and a vapor barrier.

HOUSEWRAP Synthetic housewraps, made of materials such as spun-bonded polyolefin or polypropylene, are often installed as air barriers. Because they allow vapor to pass through (they are not vapor barriers), they can be located on either side of the insulation and are often installed on the exterior of the home. While they allow water vapor to pass, they are water resistant and are effective as a replacement for sheathing paper.

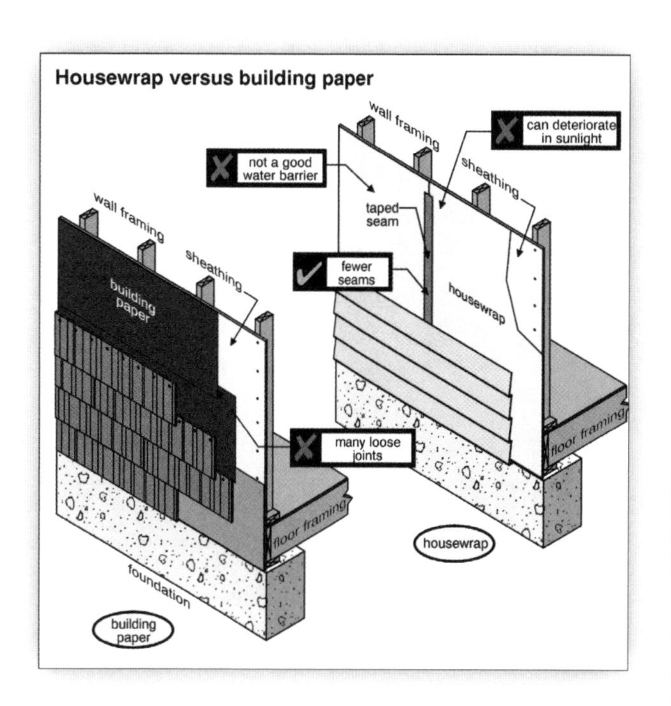

KRAFT PAPER Asphalt-coated kraft paper was used on batts of insulation in the 20th century as an air/ vapor barrier. Since adjacent sections of kraft paper were rarely sealed together, this is not a very good air barrier.

PAINT Many oil-based paints, varnishes and shellacs act as vapor barriers. Latex paints generally do not, unless they are specially formulated. Vinyl wallpapers are also vapor barriers, which can be a problem in hot, humid climates, since the wallpaper is installed on the wrong side of the insulation.

DRYWALL Drywall is a good air barrier, except that joints in walls and ceilings and holes around wires, lights and plumbing, for example, make it ineffective.

FOIL Aluminum foil is a vapor barrier, and can also be used as a radiant barrier to reflect heat. Foil may be attached to one side of a batt of insulation.

PLASTIC INSULATION Some types of plastic insulation are vapor barriers, if they are thick enough. This includes many rigid insulation boards and foamed-in-place insulations. Insulation boards can also be good air barriers if their joints are taped. Foamed in-place insulation is a very good air/vapor barrier as long as it is continuous.

SEALING THE ATTIC FLOOR Sealing holes in the floor where air may enter the attic around access hatches, lights, pipes, chimneys and wires helps keep warm moist air in the home, protecting the attic from condensation problems and reducing heat loss. Sealing openings in walls is also effective.

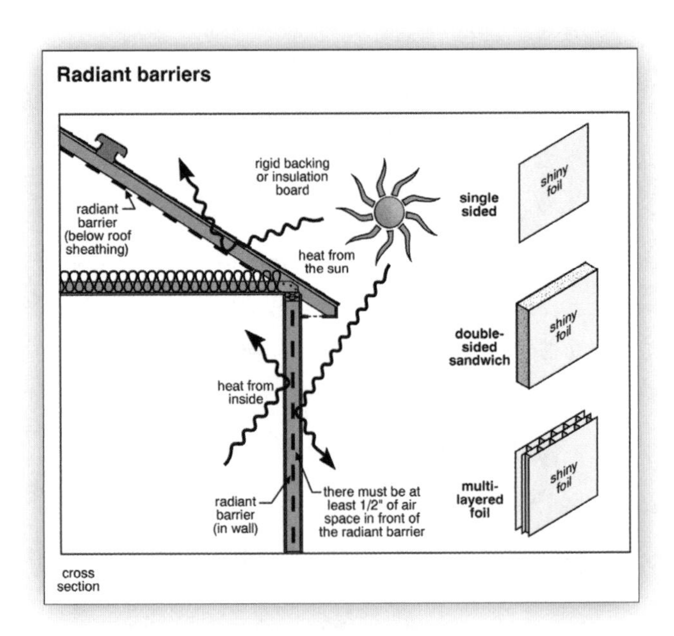

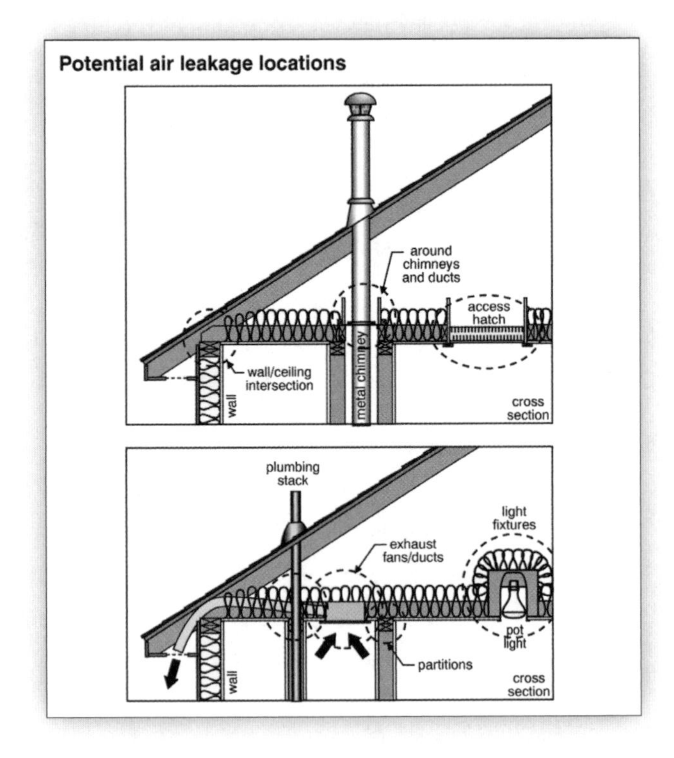

Common Problems with Air/Vapor Barriers

MISSING Many homes were built without either air or vapor barriers and perform perfectly well. While the lack of an air/vapor barrier can create problems in special circumstances, in most cases it is not practical to install one unless a house is being extensively renovated or unless there are moisture problems.

WRONG PLACE In cold climates, vapor barriers should be installed on the warm-in-winter side of the insulation, although some say they can be anywhere within the warm third of the insulation. Vapor barriers should not be on the cold side of insulation since this traps water vapor, allowing it to condense and rot building components.

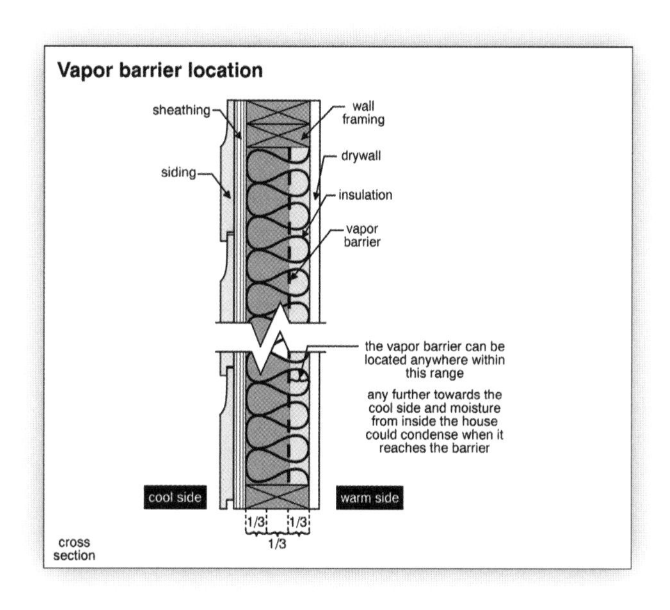

WARM CLIMATES In warm climates, it's often best not to have a vapor barrier at all, since the direction of vapor flow can go in different directions at different times of the year. Occasionally, vapor barriers are inadvertently installed on the inside of the wall (vinyl wallpaper, for example), which can lead to water vapor being trapped in the wall and causing mold or rot.

INEFFECTIVE While vapor barriers do not need to be continuous to be effective, air barriers do. It is quite common for poorly-sealed joints, edges and penetrations, and damaged materials to render the air barrier system ineffective. In most cases, it is not practical to repair an ineffective air barrier.

In most cases, the air/vapor barrier is not visible and cannot be inspected.

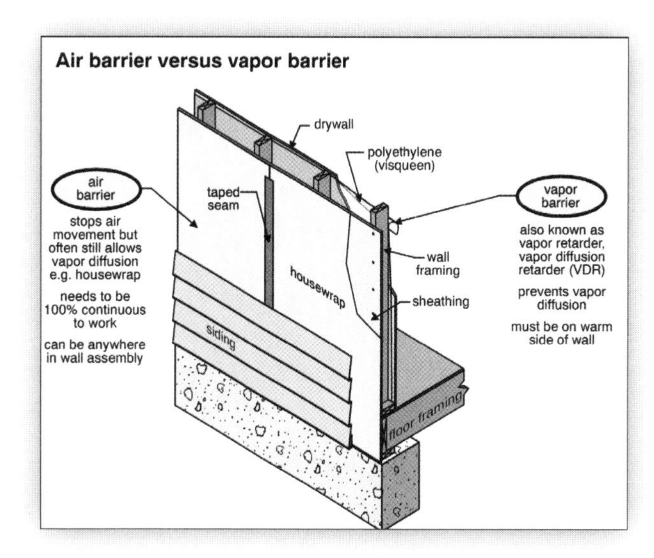

6.0 Ventilation

COLD CLIMATES An air/vapor barrier ideally prevents any moisture-laden air in a house from migrating through the insulation to cold areas. However, air/vapor barriers are rarely perfect. Therefore, we ventilate cold areas wherever possible.

Ventilation also removes warm air from the attic, keeping the house cooler in the summer and helping to prevent ice dams in the winter.

WARM CLIMATES Ventilation is important in warm climates as well. Heat build-up in the attic deteriorates some roofing materials and makes the home more difficult to cool.

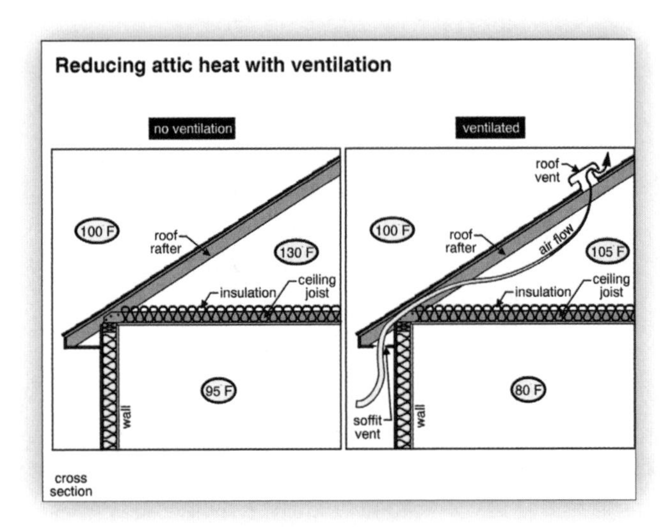

6.1 Attic Ventilation

DESCRIPTION Attics are the easiest areas to ventilate. The commonly recommended ventilation rate is one square foot of ventilation for every 300 square feet of attic floor. Ventilation should allow for good air flow from end to end of an attic space and from bottom to top. Continuous soffit vents under the eaves and a continuous ridge vent work well.

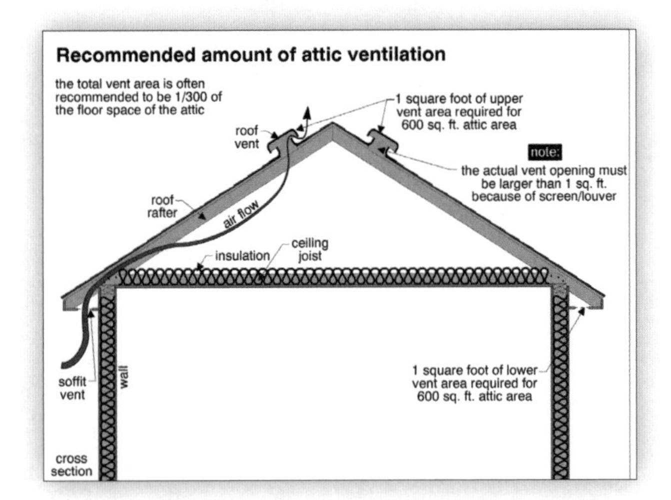

VENT LOCATION Roof vents (the common round or square metal vents) and/or gable vents should account for 50 to 80% of the total venting. They should have screens to keep insects and birds out of the attic. They are often located high on the downwind side of the house to help create a draft up through the eaves. The remaining ventilation is provided at the eaves. Baffles are used to keep soffit vents clear of insulation. On some houses, soffit venting is not practical.

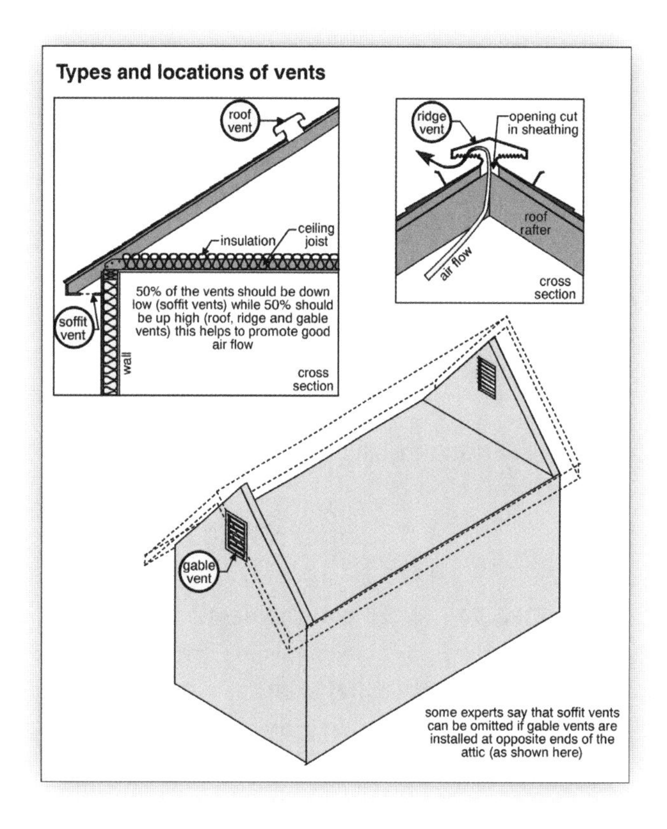

If there is no air/vapor barrier below the insulation and no soffit vents, the minimum recommended ventilation rate is increased to one square foot of ventilation for every 150 square feet of attic space.

Turbine type vents (air driven rotating vents) are not recommended as they only work on windy days, when they are not necessary. On still days, when more ventilation is required, they do no more good than a regular roof-top vent. They are also very noisy if not well balanced and lubricated.

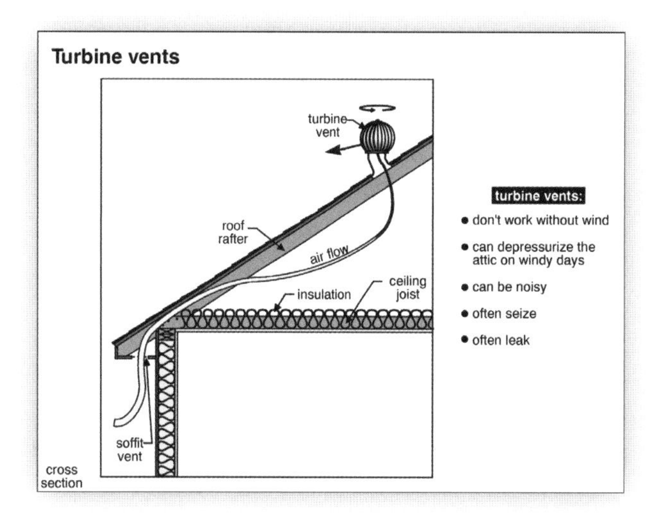

POWER VENTILATORS These fans are sometimes installed for summer use only. Removing hot attic air in the summer helps keep the house cooler.

Power ventilators are not recommended for cold weather use because they put the attic under negative pressure, drawing more warm moist air up from the house into the attic. Also, motors in attics tend to be neglected and eventually malfunction.

6.2 Crawlspace Ventilation

DESCRIPTION Conventional wisdom has held that unconditioned crawl spaces should be ventilated to the exterior to remove moisture. A common recommendation is one square foot of vent area for every 150 square feet of crawlspace area. This practice has recently been challenged in warm, humid climates, where moist air may be drawn into the cool crawlspace. In these areas, vents are usually no longer installed. There still may be a benefit to ventilation in drier climates.

MOISTURE BARRIER Where ventilation is not provided, a sealed moisture barrier should be installed over the earth floor, and the perimeter walls should be insulated. The space should either be mechanically ventilated, or be heated or cooled with the house.

VENT LOCATION Ideally, vents are located within three feet of the corners of the crawlspace.

Common Problems with Ventilation

INADEQUATE VENTILATION Many older homes do not have sufficient ventilation. To avoid problems with excessive heat or humidity, vents can be readily added to most attics or crawlspaces. While it may not be practical to install them in the ideal configuration, the situation can usually be improved. Depending on the climate, it may be best to have no crawlspace ventilation at all. Your professional home inspector can provide guidance here.

BLOCKED VENTS Soffit vents that have been blocked by insulation will not be effective. Inexpensive baffles can be installed to keep insulation back. Roof vents that have been blocked by bird's nests should be cleared out.

DAMAGED Pests such as raccoons can damage roof vents, leaving an opening in the roof vulnerable to leakage. Damaged crawlspace vents will allow pest entry and should be replaced.

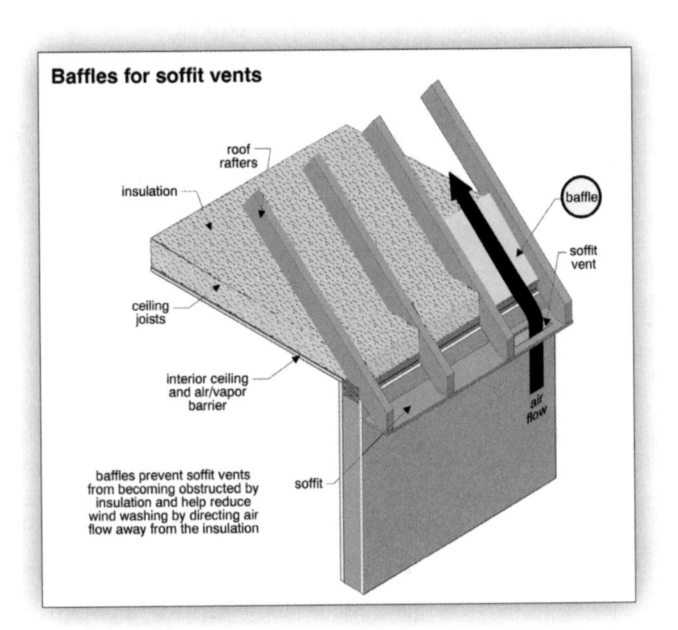

MISSING MOISTURE BARRIER Earth floors in crawlspaces should be covered with a sealed plastic sheet or equivalent to prevent moisture from the earth entering the crawlspace.

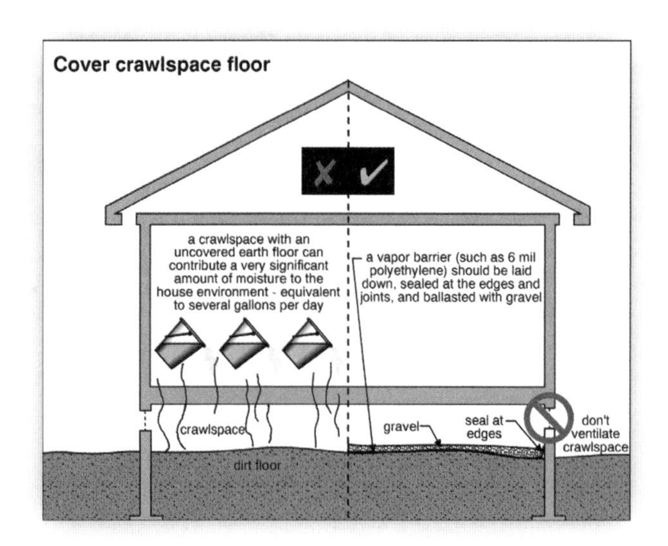

7.0 Heat Recovery Ventilators

DESCRIPTION Heat recovery ventilators, also known as air-to-air heat exchangers, are used in heating climates to maintain good house air quality. They bring fresh air into the home and exhaust stale air. This is more important in modern air-tight homes than older leaky homes. How is this different than opening a couple of windows? Heat recovery ventilators transfer some of the heat from the stale exhaust air to the incoming cold outdoor air. This reduces the amount of heat we waste getting fresh air into the home.

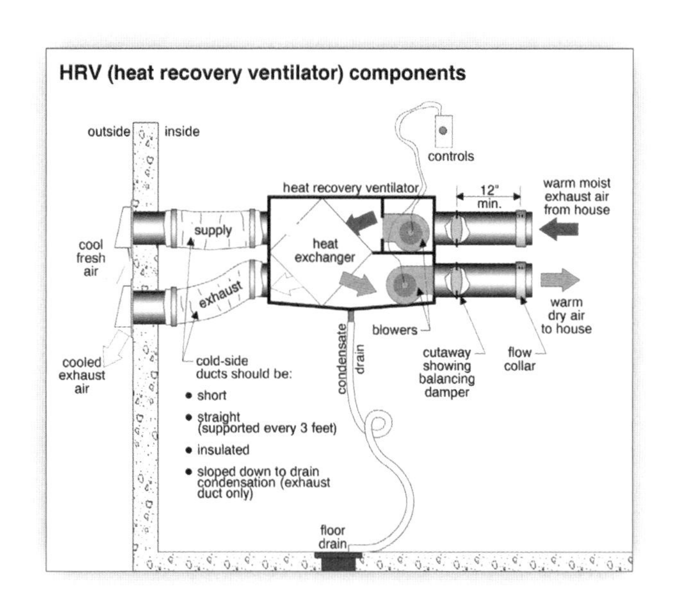

FRESH AIR DISTRIBUTION The fresh air coming into the home is filtered and then usually dumped into the return air ductwork for the furnace and mixed with the rest of the air. This distributes fresh air to all parts of the house.

EXHAUST AIR COLLECTION The exhaust air is typically taken from kitchens and bathrooms – areas where the air is likely to be stale and humid.

MOVING THE AIR One or more blowers move air across a heat exchanger transferring heat from the air being exhausted to the incoming air. The goal is to replace 1/3 to 1/2 of the house air every hour. In two or three hours, a heat recovery ventilator can change all the air in the home.

INTAKE AND EXHAUST HOODS The intake and exhaust hoods on the exterior should be at least six feet apart and three to four feet from the corner of the building. The intake hood should be at least 18 inches above grade and at least three feet away from driveways, gas meters or any exhaust vents. The exhaust hood should be at least eight inches above grade.

DEFROST CYCLE The warm moist house air may condense its moisture as it cools in the heat exchanger. The condensate is collected and drained away. Ice may accumulate in the system in cold weather, and a defrost cycle is used to melt the ice.

Common Problems with Heat Recovery Ventilators

Blowers and motors will wear out. Cold side ducts may be missing insulation. Balancing problems are common with more air drawn in than exhausted, or vice versa. Filters can be dirty or missing, resulting in clogging of the heat exchanger. A screen with openings that are approximately a quarter square inch are required on the intake located on the outside wall. This prevents vermin or debris entering the HRV system from the outside.

Defrosting systems may fail, condensate trays and lines can plug or leak. In corrosive environments (indoor swimming pools, hairdressing salons in the basement, etc.), the heat exchanger may be damaged unless it was specifically designed for that environment. There may also be problems with electric supply or controls.

Plumbing

INTRODUCTION

THE PURPOSE OF A HOUSE PLUMBING SYSTEM IS TWOFOLD. ON THE SUPPLY SIDE, THE IDEA IS TO GET WATER FOR DRINKING, WASHING AND COOKING TO THE APPROPRIATE AREAS OF THE HOUSE. THE WASTE SIDE OF THE PLUMBING SYSTEM GETS RID OF LIQUID AND SOLID WASTE.

THE SUPPLY WATER IS UNDER PRESSURE AND THE WASTE WATER FLOWS BY GRAVITY. SERVICED COMMUNITIES PROVIDE THE FRESH SUPPLY WATER AND CARRY AWAY THE WASTE. IN RURAL PROPERTIES, WELLS, RIVERS OR LAKES SUPPLY FRESH WATER AND SEPTIC SYSTEMS TYPICALLY HANDLE THE WASTE.

THE MAJORITY OF THE PIPING IN A HOME, BOTH SUPPLY AND WASTE, IS CONCEALED IN WALLS, CEILINGS AND UNDERGROUND. LEAKAGE, OBSTRUCTIONS, OR OTHER PROBLEMS MAY NOT BE IDENTIFIED DURING AN INSPECTION.

1.0 Supply

1.1 Public Water Supply Systems

Typically, the water mains in residential areas are four inches to 12 inches in diameter, and run several feet below the street level. Smaller pipes, usually 1/2 inch or 3/4 inch diameter, run from city mains into buildings. The water may typically be supplied at a pressure of 40 to 70 psi (pounds per square inch).

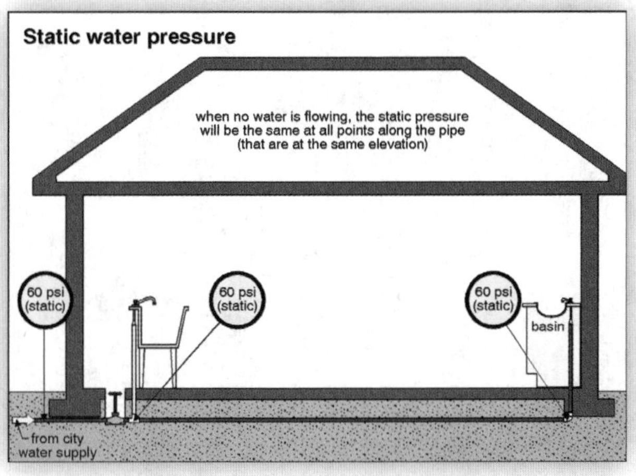

DESCRIPTION **1.1.1 Water Service Piping:** The 1/2 inch or 3/4 inch diameter service piping carries the water from the street mains to the house. Some early service pipes were 3/8 inch diameter. Most or all of this cannot be seen.

LEAD Lead piping was used between the street main and the house up until the 1950s. A good deal of lead supply line is still in use, and many health authorities recommend replacing it. Check the requirements in your area. If the water has not been run for some time, many recommend that the water be run for several minutes before using it. The life expectancy of lead piping is indefinite.

COPPER Copper piping has been used extensively since the early 1950s for supply lines from the city main to the house. From 1950 to 1970, 1/2-inch diameter piping was used commonly. After 1970, 3/4-inch diameter copper service piping has been common. The life expectancy of copper piping is dependent on water conditions. In many areas, its life expectancy is indefinite. In harsh water or soil conditions, it may fail within 20 years.

GALVANIZED STEEL Galvanized steel is not commonly used as a service pipe, although galvanized steel fittings may be found at the point of entry into the house. Where galvanized service piping is used, it is typically at least 1 1/4-inch diameter. The word **galvanized** means zinc-coated. The coating helps prevent the steel from rusting.

PLASTIC PIPING AND TUBING Plastic water service piping may be polybutylene (PB), polyethylene (PE), cross-linked polyethylene (PEX), polyvinyl chloride (PVC) or chlorinated polyvinyl chloride (CPVC). Most plastic piping is buried at least 18 inches deep. Exposed piping may be subject to mechanical damage and deterioration from sunlight.

Common Problems with Water Service Piping

LEAKS Since the supply line from the street cannot be seen, no comment is offered during a home inspection. If there is a leak, it may go undetected for some time. In some cases, water can be heard running outside the basement wall. Water accumulating in the basement or a wet spot on the lawn is often the first indication. Leaks may be caused by building settlement, excavation, poor connections, faulty valves or a flaw in the pipe itself.

The underground water service line from the property line to the house is owned by the homeowner. Beyond the property line, the pipe is the responsibility of the city. A leak in the pipe requires excavation, and it is often difficult to know whether the leak is on the city's or the homeowner's side. The city is usually contacted and they excavate their section of the pipe, correcting the problem if they discover it. If no problem is found, the homeowner is left to correct the problem on his or her own. In some cases, the homeowner must pay for the city's work if the city pipe is not at fault. Some municipalities use sophisticated leak detection equipment.

LOW PRESSURE Poor water pressure in the house may be the result of a partially closed or obstructed valve in the street. It may also be because of blockage, such as a stone or other foreign body in the pipe.

New piping may be crimped during installation or become pinched under a rock during backfilling operations. This can also cause low water pressure.

City water mains may be undersized or deteriorated in older neighborhoods. Some cities have poor pumping and/or distribution systems. In these cases, low water pressure problems are usually experienced at every home in the neighborhood. The solution is to petition the city to improve its system.

SMALL In most new housing, the supply pipe from the street to the house is 3/4-inch diameter. In older houses, the piping was as small as 3/8-inch. Modern life styles and additional plumbing fixtures usually require a larger line, capable of providing more pressure and volume. Replacing this pipe is an expensive and disruptive job. It is often deferred as long as possible.

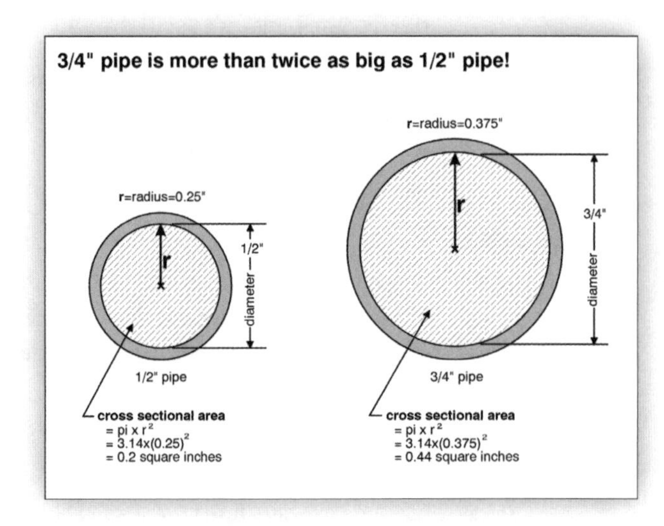

SHARED In some older semi-detached (attached) and row houses, a single supply line would run under a front lawn, and then split to feed two houses. This often yields unsatisfactory water pressure for both houses and is often replaced with two larger, separate lines.

PRESSURE REGULATOR NEEDED Where municipal water pressure is above 80 psi, a regulator should be provided to reduce the in-house pressure to prevent leaks at fixtures, stress on appliance hoses and possible broken pipe joints.

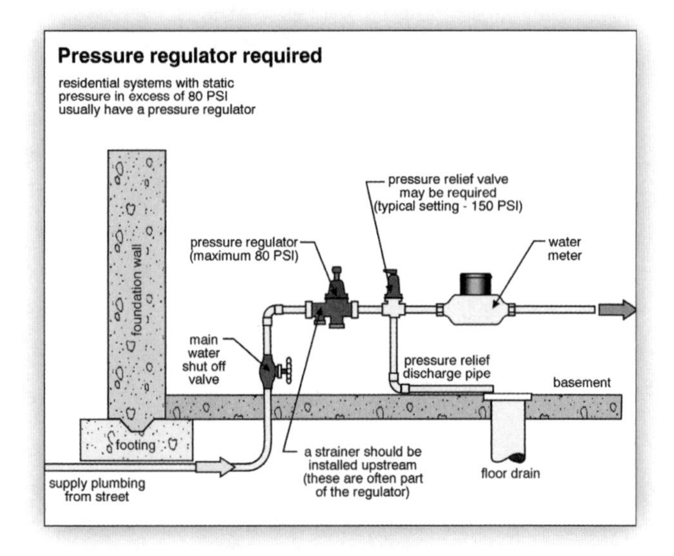

RISK OF FREEZING It is unusual, although not impossible, for the service pipe to be too close to the surface, and to freeze during very cold weather. Many service pipes extend above grade just before they enter the house. Freezing is a risk here in cold climates.

LEAD Up until World War II, most of the service pipes in built-up areas were lead. While these generally provide good service, they are small in diameter and may have to be replaced. Also, lead is relatively soft, and if building settlement occurs, there is a chance of leakage or crimping the pipe. Leaks can also occur at connections as a result of long-term deterioration.

STEEL NIPPLE NEAR END OF LIFE Many of the old lead service lines were connected to a galvanized nipple – a short piece of steel pipe that was often in contact with the soil. This pipe rusts on the outside and inside, and may be close to the end of its life. It is often wise to replace this as a precautionary measure. Galvanized steel service pipes typically last roughly 40 years.

1.2 Private Water Supply Systems

DESCRIPTION Where a city water supply is not available, water is provided from a well, river or lake. Wells may be shallow (25 feet or less) or deep (more than 25 feet). The service piping is most often plastic (commonly polyethylene).

PUMP A pump moves the water from the source into the house distribution piping system. The pump may be at the bottom or top of a well, in a pump house, in the river or lake, or in the home.

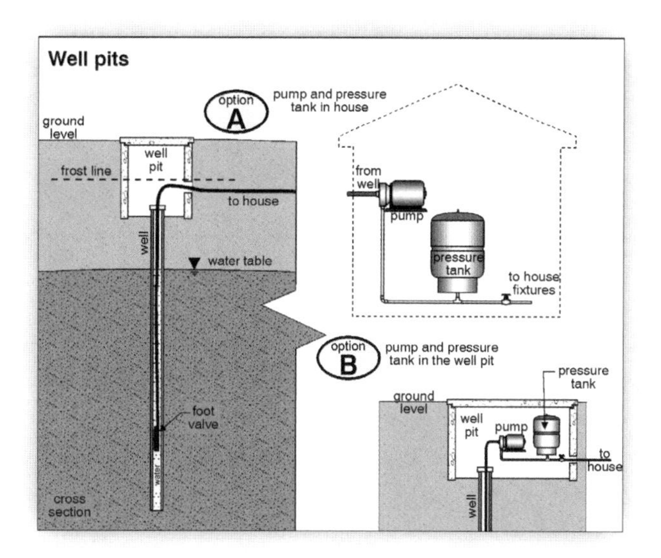

Reciprocating or piston-type lift pumps were used on older systems, while centrifugal pumps are more typical in modern installations. Shallow wells may use reciprocating or centrifugal pumps. Deep well pumps are most often centrifugal, either jet type or submersible.

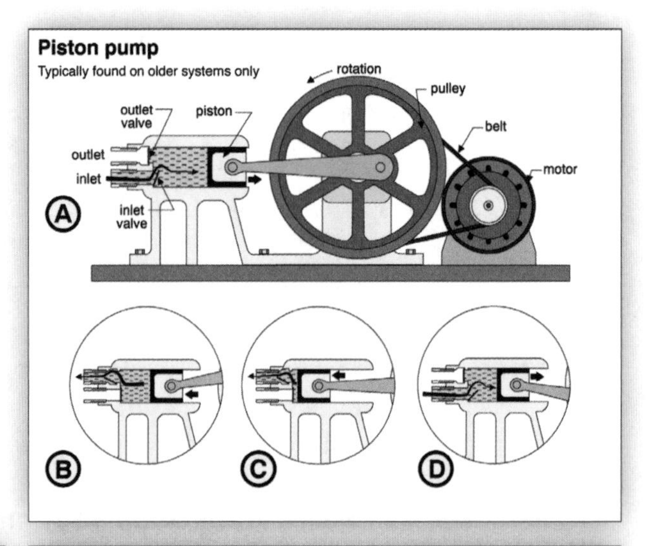

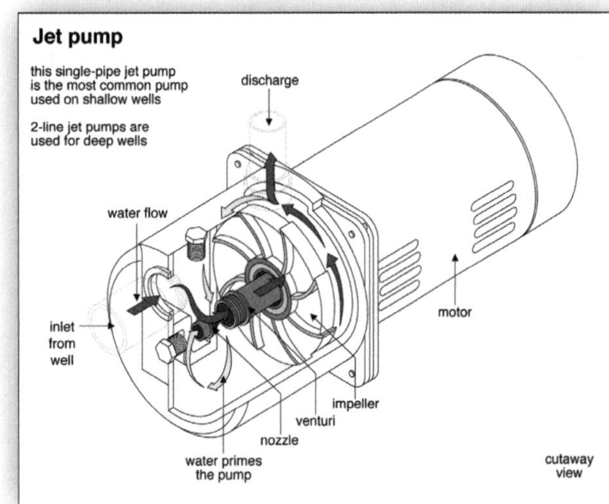

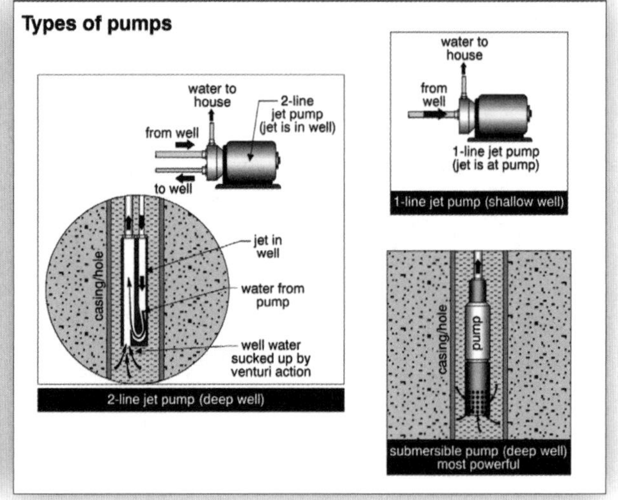

Well water should be tested on a regular basis, as recommended by the local health authorities. Typically, this involves sending a sample to the authority for testing.

The amount of water available from the well depends on the amount of water in the well and the recovery rate of the well. If water is drawn from the well faster than it is replenished, the well will eventually run dry. Many homeowners with wells manage their water demand to avoid depleting the well. The water supply may vary season-to-season and year-to-year.

PRESSURE TANK Where a pump is used, there is also a storage or pressure tank, typically located in the home. This tank provides an air cushion, so the pump does not have to come on every time a faucet is opened. This tank may be only a gallon or two, or it may be several gallons. The tank provides relatively even water pressure to the house. With no tank the water pressure in the home would vary quickly and dramatically, and the pump would cycle on and off frequently.

Since water is relatively incompressible, a portion of the tank is filled with air. The air is easily compressed, and when a valve is opened, the air pressure in the tank forces the water out. The tank pressure slowly reduces as the water leaves and the air expands. When the pressure gets low, the pump pushes more water into the tank, compressing the air. Typical low and high limit settings for a pump are 30 psi and 50 psi.

Many modern tanks have a diaphragm or bladder separating the air and water, preventing the air from being dissolved into the water.

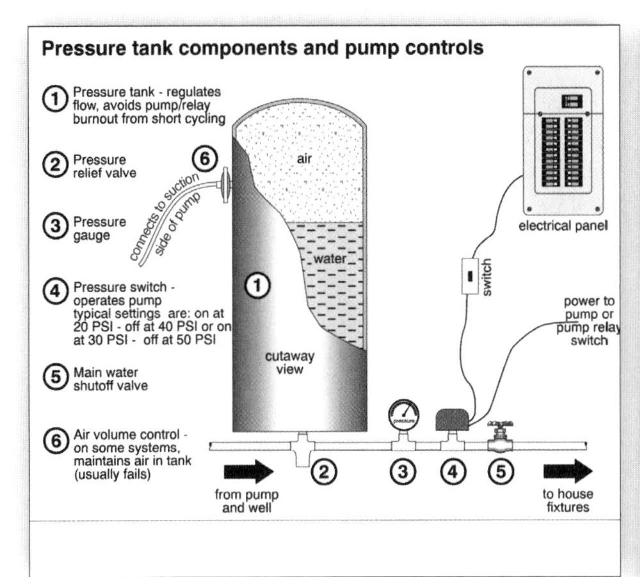

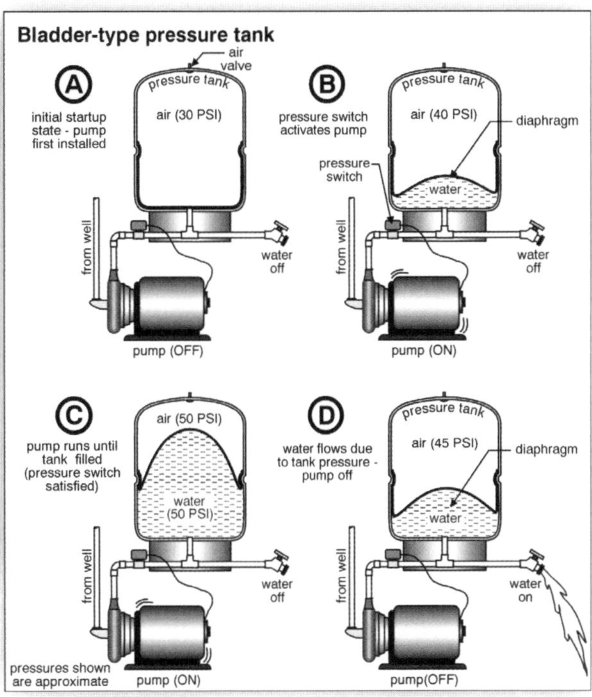

WATERLOGGED Over time, the air in the tank will be absorbed into the water and the tank will become 'waterlogged'. This means that the tank is full or nearly full of water. The pump will come on and off very quickly. This short cycling is hard on the pump, and air is added to the tank to correct the situation.

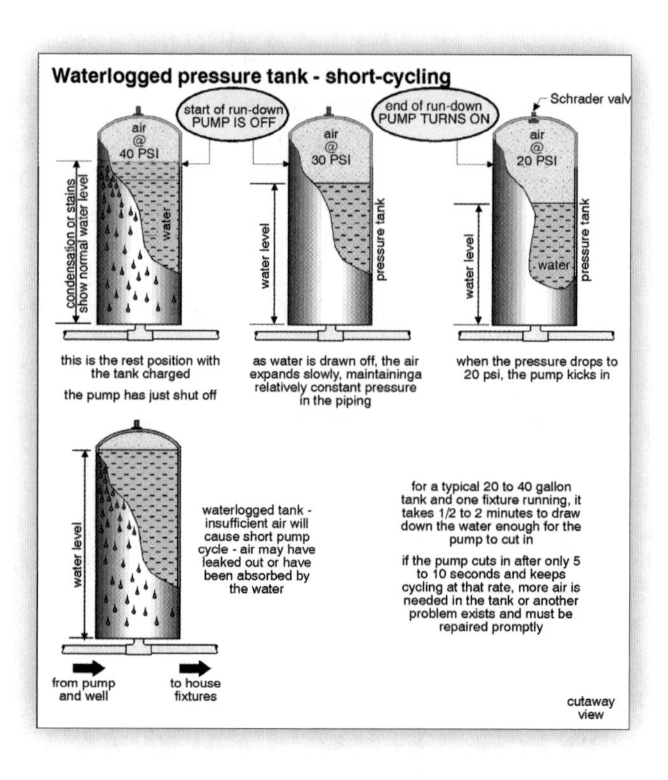

Common Problems with Private Water Supplies

PUMP PROBLEMS Inoperative supply pumps may be the result of a mechanical or electrical problem. Poor water pressure may be the result of a partially closed valve, an obstructed pipe, a leak in the system, or poor adjustment of pressure switches.

A pump may short-cycle or run continuously if the foot valve is leaking, the pressure tank is waterlogged, the pump has lost its prime, or if the pressure switch is faulty. This may also be the result of a leak in the plumbing system.

Worn pump bearings or poor alignment can result in excessive noise or vibration.

WATER SUPPLY PROBLEMS If the well is close to running dry, the water may be dirty. Alternatives are to reduce water use (stop watering the lawn, for example) or improve the water supply.

LEAKS Leaks may occur at the pump or piping.

LEAKING TANK The pressure tank is susceptible to corrosion and/or leakage. Condensation on the outside of the tank, common in hot humid weather, can rust the tank. Ideally, the tanks are insulated to minimize condensation, although very few are. A corroded tank is replaced when it begins to leak. A leak caused by a poor connection is easily repaired.

1.3 Main Shut-off Valve

DESCRIPTION The main shut-off valve controls all the house water. The valve should be readily accessible and easy to operate. Since these valves are not used regularly, it is common for them to be stiff. They often leak when operated. For this reason, they are not tested during a home inspection.

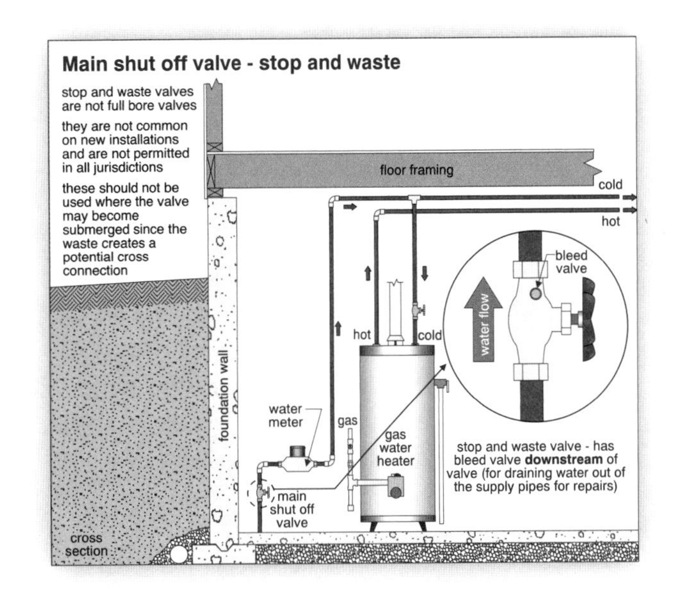

Some main shut-off valves have bleed valves to drain the system once the valve is closed. Some of these bleed valves can be shut off, although others discharge automatically, as the main valve is closed. This discharge of water can be disconcerting if one is not familiar with the bleed valve function.

Common Problems with Main Shut-off Valves

MISSING/ DAMAGED/ LEAKING/ INACCESSIBLE/ INOPERABLE These valves should be accessible and operable to shut off the water in an emergency to avoid flooding damage. Missing shutoff valves should be provided. Damaged or leaking valves should be repaired or replaced.

PARTLY CLOSED Poor water pressure may be the result of partially closed valves. This, of course, is easily corrected.

1.4 Water Distribution Piping in House

Only a small section of the distribution (supply) piping can be seen during a typical home inspection.

DESCRIPTION **1.4.1 Galvanized Steel:** Galvanized steel piping was common until roughly 1950. This piping typically lasts 40 to 60 years. Some lower-quality pipes do not last as long and there are some oversized pipes still in use after 60 years. Where it is found today in single-family homes, it is usually near the end of its life.

Galvanized steel supply pipes are typically 1/2-inch diameter. The connections are threaded. When the pipe corrodes, the rust accumulation inside the pipe chokes down the diameter of the pipe, resulting in poor water pressure. Rust also attacks the pipe walls, making the walls thinner. Eventually, the pipe will rust through, usually at the joints first, resulting in leakage.

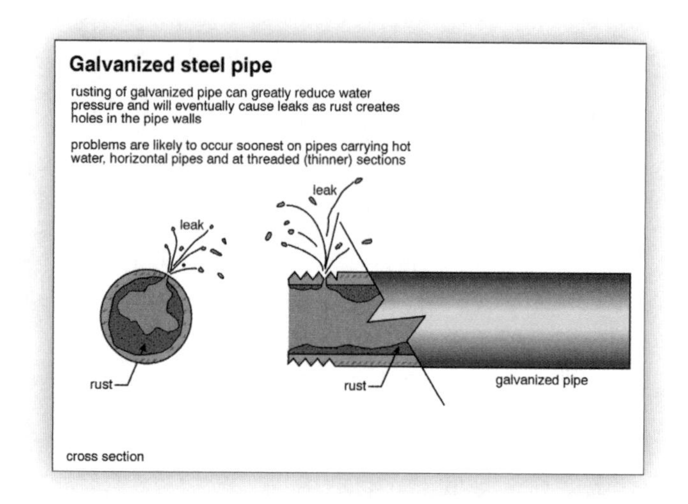

RUST As rust builds up inside the pipe, a brownish color is often noted in the water when a faucet is turned on, especially after several days of inactivity. This rust in the water usually dissipates after a few seconds.

DESCRIPTION **1.4.2 Copper Pipes and Tubing:** Copper pipes have been in use residentially since approximately 1950.

LIFE EXPECTANCY Copper piping is typically 1/2 or 3/4 inch diameter. Copper piping will last indefinitely, unless there are corrosive water conditions or manufacturing defects. Copper piping has soldered connections and the walls of the pipe are thinner than galvanized steel.

FLEXIBLE TUBING Flexible copper tubing can be bent around corners using special tools. This is not common since it is more expensive and can be awkward to work with in close quarters.

DESCRIPTION **1.4.3 Plastic Pipes and Tubing:** Plastic supply piping is popular because it is less expensive and easier to work with than copper. Connections can be made without soldering, and the pipe is easy to work with. There are many types available including cross-linked polyethylene (PEX), polybutylene (PB), and chlorinated polyvinyl chloride (CPVC).

CROSS-LINKED POLYETHYLENE (PEX) AND POLYBUTYLENE (PB) PEX and PB pipe use mechanical fittings (crimp and compression type). Care must be taken that the pipe does not contact heating ducts. If the pipe freezes, it is less likely to burst than copper piping. The pipe tends to sag and should be well supported by hangers. PEX should not be installed outdoors or exposed to sunlight for long periods. Polybutylene piping has been the source of considerable controversy due to failed fittings, especially first generation plastic fittings.

CPVC Chlorinated polyvinyl chloride (CPVC) pipe is not as flexible as PB or PEX and the fittings are solvent welded (glued) rather than press-on. This pipe is likely to split if freezing occurs. CPVC pipe is suitable for use on both hot and cold water lines.

Many plumbers prefer to work with copper and, although plastic pipe is less expensive than copper, the fittings are expensive. Some areas do not allow plastic pipes based on environmental concerns. Some questions have been raised about the chemicals used in the adhesives used to join sections of piping, and the toxic gases given off from plastic piping during a fire.

Polyethylene (PE) and polyvinyl chloride (PVC) are only suitable for waste, underground water service pipes or cold water piping systems.

Common Problems with Distribution Piping

FLOW (PRESSURE) People like to have lots of water flow and pressure at faucets. Water flow (in gallons per minute) is a function of several things, including the size and shape of the faucet opening, and the pressure at the faucet. The pressure at the faucet is a function of the pressure available from the source, and the pressure lost moving the water through the pipe to the faucet. Typically, city water supplies are at 40 to 70 psi (static pressure). **Psi** means **Pounds per square inch,** and is a common way of measuring water pressure. Pressure loss in the home is due to elevation (we lose pressure when we push water up from one story to the next) and friction as water flows through piping. Larger pipes lose less pressure due to friction.

PRESSURE VS. FLOW Static pressure is exerted by the water against the pipe walls with no water flowing. Here's a simplified (and not 100% accurate) way to look at it. A 100-foot long horizontal pipe connected to a 60 psi supply will have a pressure of 60 psi anywhere along the pipe, with no flow. As water begins to flow, the pressure drops. This is a result of friction loss along the pipe walls. If gauges were put on the pipe every ten feet, the gauge at the source would still read 60 psi, and (depending on the pipe diameter and the amount of water flowing), the gauge ten feet from the source might read 58 psi; the gauge twenty feet down would read 56 psi, the next gauge 54 psi, etc. At the faucet, the pressure might be 40 psi.

As the flow increases, the pressure drops more at each point along the pipe. The water pressure at the source (city water main) will remain at 60 psi. The amount of pressure lost due to friction as water flows depends on the pipe diameter and the amount of water flowing. With several faucets open, the flow at each faucet may be weak and there may not be enough pressure for a shower, for example.

IMPROVEMENT APPROACH As more plumbing fixtures flow, the pressure and flow drops more at each fixture. If we replace any ten-foot section of pipe with a larger pipe, the pressure drop across that section will be reduced. Replacing any section of pipe improves pressure (and flow) throughout the system.

GRAVITY PROBLEM Gravity is another source of pressure loss. Energy is required to push the water uphill. For every one foot we push water up, we lose 0.434 psi. Another way of saying this is that it takes one psi to move water up 2.31 feet. A system will typically lose eight psi in a two-story house, getting the water from the basement up to the second floor bathroom. With no water flowing, the static pressure at the street main may be 60 psi, but the static pressure at the second floor basin might be 51 psi. Houses that are above the street or have third story plumbing fixtures, have a pressure disadvantage.

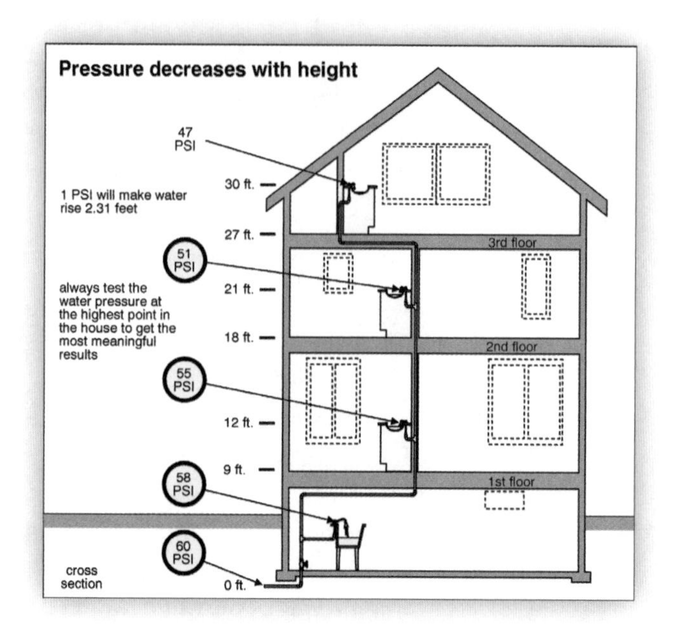

GALVANIZED STEEL FAILURE Galvanized steel piping will often leak first at the joints. Steel pipe has threads cut into it where it joins a fitting. The pipe wall is thinner at the threaded connections. As the piping rusts from the inside, the pipe rusts through first at the threaded connections, where the pipe wall is thinner. We saw this in the illustration on Page 298.

As steel piping corrodes, it may rust through at one spot and begin to leak; however, the rust may form a scab over the leak and the leak may be intermittent as the rust progresses. This scabbing means the pipe is close to the end of its life, even though it may not be actively leaking.

Poor pressure and flow may be noted before the pipe leaks. The rust inside reduces the diameter, restricting flow.

OTHER REASONS FOR POOR PRESSURE OR FLOW The main shut-off valve or isolating valves may be partially closed or obstructed. The city valve near the property line may restrict flow. The supply line from the street to the house may be undersized, damaged or leaking. Long runs of relatively small (1/2-inch diameter) pipe result in considerable pressure drop, especially with more than one fixture flowing. Solutions include replacement with larger pipe or shortening the runs.

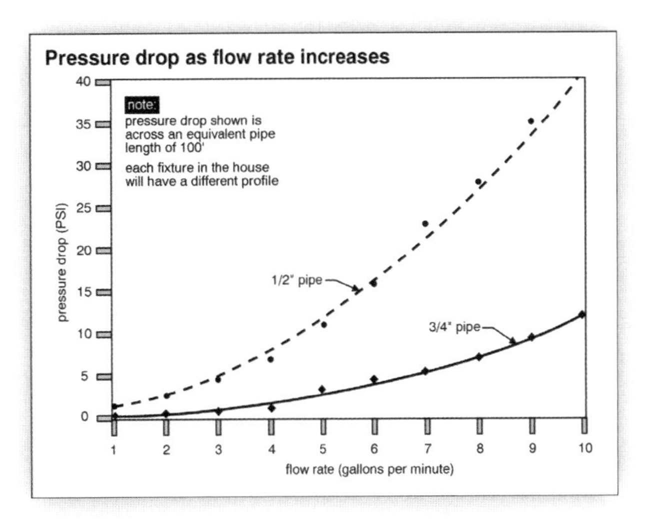

Sludge build-up in a water heater can lead to poor hot water pressure. The tank should be flushed every year or so. A water softener, especially if not well maintained, can adversely affect water pressure.

Adding plumbing fixtures (a new bathroom, for example) without enlarging or adding pipes often leads to pressure complaints.

A crimped, damaged or clogged pipe within the house will adversely affect pressure. This is common with amateurish work. On a private system, a defective, undersized or poorly adjusted pump will result in poor pressure. Individual faucets may also be defective.

LEAKS Leaking supply pipes can range from an annoying drip to a major flood. In most cases, however, leakage appears first as a drip. This can usually be picked up before serious flooding occurs.

CONNECTIONS Leakage as a result of a poor connection is impossible to anticipate, and may be caused by vibration over a period of time. If a connection lets go suddenly, there will be a flood.

DAMAGE Mechanical damage will sometimes result in a leak immediately, although in other cases a joint is simply weakened and subsequent vibration will cause the leak sometime later. Concealed piping may be damaged by drilling or nailing into walls.

FREEZING Leakage can be a result of pipes freezing. A one-time freeze may not result in leakage. In some cases, copper piping may develop a bulge, although the piping may not split on the first freeze. Frozen pipes, of course, do not leak until there is a thaw. Some types of plastic supply pipe have better resistance to freezing damage than copper.

It is easy to see how pipes can freeze if they are installed in an unheated area such as a garage or crawl space. Pipes inside the house that have been in place for 50 years may freeze if they are cut off from their heat source when adding insulation to walls, for example. Supply piping on exterior walls is always vulnerable to freezing.

In an old house, pipes running up to a kitchen sink may not have frozen in the past simply because the air under the sink circulated freely and kept the pipes warm. If the kitchen is remodeled, and a closed cabinet is provided under the sink, the same pipes may now freeze since they are cut off from the warm circulating air.

SWEATING (CONDENSATION) In some homes, the cold water piping is insulated to avoid sweating of pipes. On a warm humid day, cold water running through a pipe will cool the adjacent air, causing condensation on the pipes. This 'sweating' can be annoying, and if allowed to continue, can damage ceilings, floors, furniture or storage below. If a basement is to be finished, the cold water piping above the ceiling should be insulated.

NOISE Noisy piping is usually the result of inadequately secured pipes. When pipes are not well secured where they run through floors walls and ceilings, they may be noisy.

As valves are opened and closed, vibration can be set up in the piping making it rattle. Sometimes this can be corrected by pushing newspapers into the wall cavity to keep the pipes from contacting the walls or each other. Foam insulation can also help in some cases. Where a pipe passes through the floor system or wood studs, it may rub on the wood and squeak as the pipe expands and contracts with heat.

WATER HAMMER Water hammer (or hydrostatic shock) is a noisy pipe problem that occurs when valves are shut off quickly. Water hammer can damage pipe connections and result in leakage.

Water hammer works like this: water passing through a pipe has momentum. When the valve is shut quickly, the momentum of the water carries it into the valve with considerable force. Since water is essentially incompressible, a large pressure is built up against the valve, and there is low pressure upstream in the pipe. The high-pressure water wants to flow to the low-pressure area. This happens so quickly that a small vacuum is created against the valve as the water moves away from it. This can result in cavitation as the water is pulled back against the valve a second time. This continues back and forth in slowly diminishing shock waves. Pressures up to 600 psi can result from water travelling up to 3,000 miles per hour, for very short periods.

Water hammer can result in loud noises in supply plumbing pipes. Water hammer only occurs as valves are closed. If a valve is closed slowly, and the noise does not occur, one can be sure that water hammer is the problem. Water hammer is common with quick-closing electrically operated valves on appliances such as washing machines and dishwashers.

Air chambers can be installed to control water hammer.

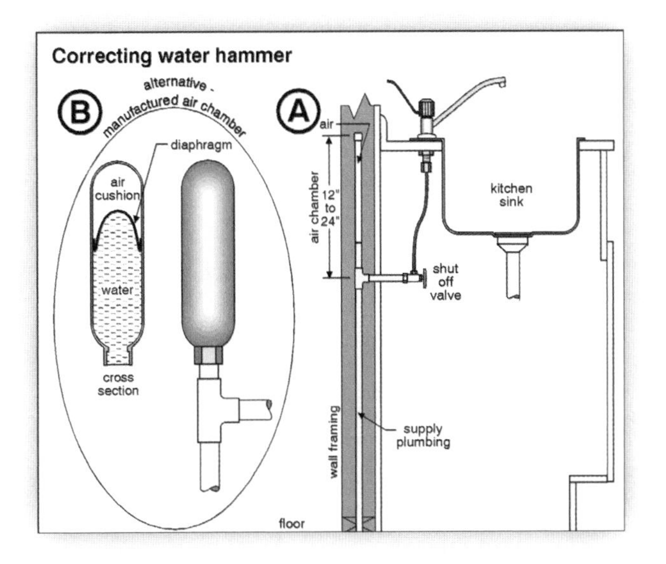

EXPOSED TO DAMAGE Pipes or tubing that are exposed below a basement ceiling or surface mounted on walls are easily damaged. Pipes should never be located so that they can be struck by a door, or be pushed out of position by storage. Wood blocks can be run beside pipes to protect them from damage.

INADEQUATE HANGERS All piping and tubing should be adequately supported with hangers. Copper piping should not be supported with steel hangers because of the corrosion that will take place. Copper pipes should not contact heating ducts for similar reasons. Plastic piping and tubing should be well supported and be kept away from heat ducts.

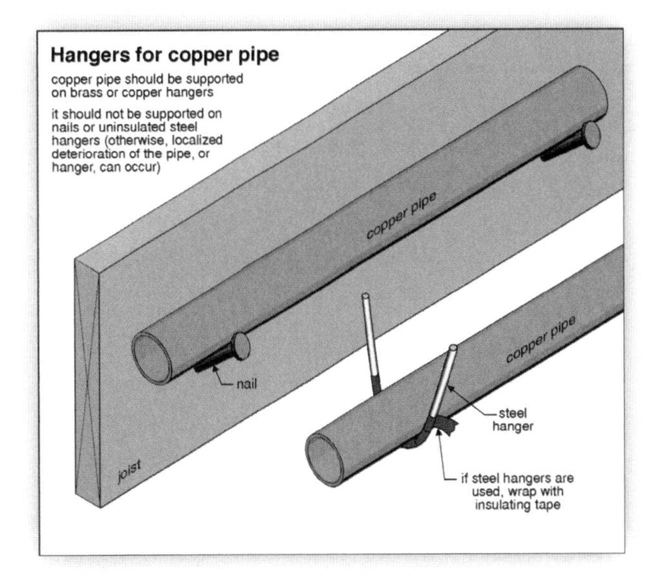

POLYBUTYLENE LEAKAGE ISSUES There has been a great deal of publicity in various parts of North America regarding leakage problems with polybutylene plumbing supply lines, including class action lawsuits.

PLASTIC FITTING FAILURES The majority of leak problems with polybutylene supply lines involve failure of plastic (acetal) fittings. Fitting failure may lead to the need for system replacement. This type of fitting was commonly used from the late 1970s until the late 1980s. Copper fittings were used in most installations from the late 1980s until the late 1990s. Failure of copper fittings is rare. Failure of the actual polybutylene piping also seems relatively uncommon.

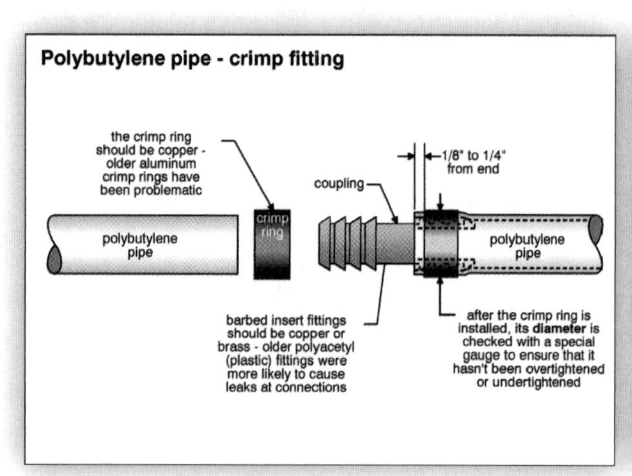

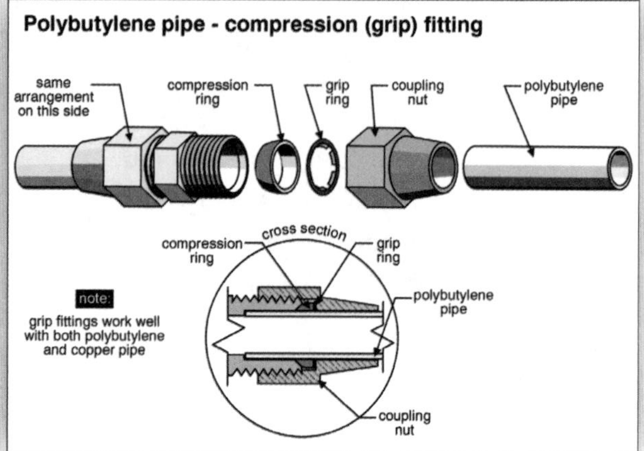

CROSS CONNECTIONS A cross connection is a dangerous situation where waste water may enter and contaminate the supply water. A cross connection can occur in many places. One example is where a laundry tub has a faucet below the top of the laundry tub. If the faucet enters the tub through the wall, it is possible that when the tub is filled, the faucet will be submerged. If this happens, the waste water in the tub may back up into the drinking water through the faucet if the supply piping is being drained.

The solution is to raise the faucets above the top of a tub or basin, creating an air gap between the faucet and water in the tub. Cross connections are avoided through the use of an overflow. In bathtubs, for example, where the faucets may enter through the wall of the tub below the top, an overflow provided below the faucets will prevent a cross connection.

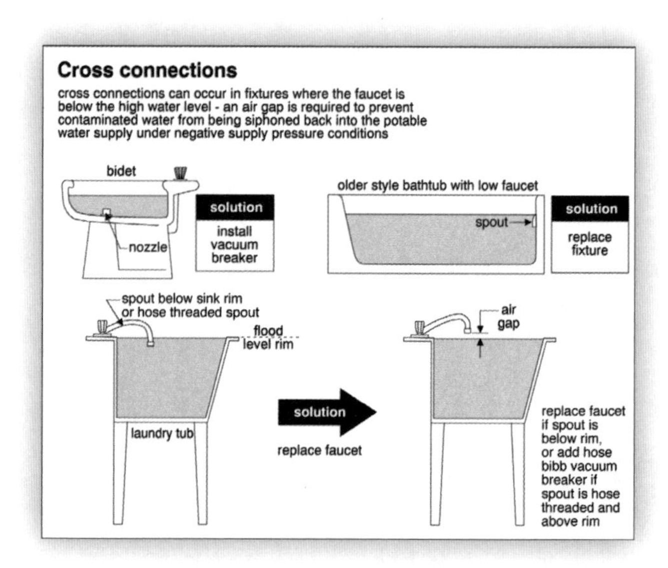

BIDET IS ACCEPTABLE

Some plumbing fixtures necessarily create a situation which could lead to a cross connection. A bidet is a good example of this. A bidet has a water supply at the bottom of the bowl. This allows water to be directed up in a spray from the bottom center of the bowl. There is, of course, the potential for waste water in the bowl to get into this supply water. A special device (vacuum breaker) prevents water from flowing back into the supply plumbing.

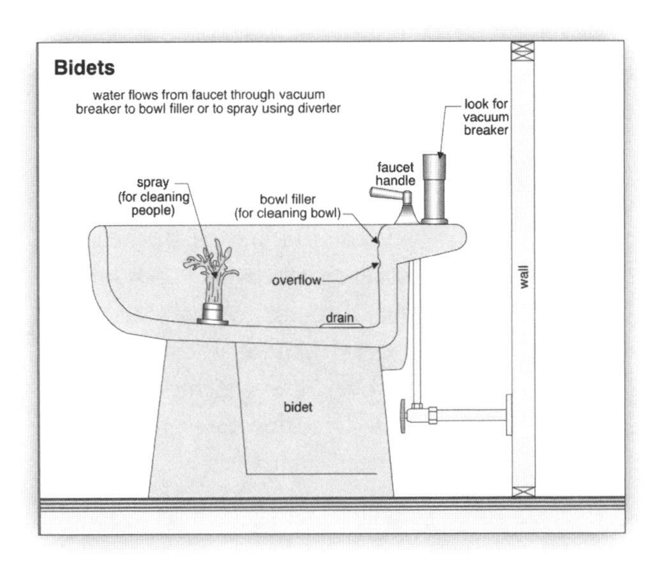

GARDEN HOSE – CROSS CONNECTION

While cross connections are normally avoided during original plumbing work, home handy man changes can create them. Careless use of the house plumbing system can also create a cross connection. Care should be taken, for example, to avoid placing a garden hose in a position to allow waste water to flow back into the supply plumbing system. For example, if the hose is left in a pail of water, it is possible for the contaminated water to flow back through the hose into the drinking water. This may happen if the house water supply is shut off and partially drained for some reason, while the hose is in the pail. Back-flow preventers (like the atmospheric vacuum breaker in the illustration) on the hose bib can prevent this.

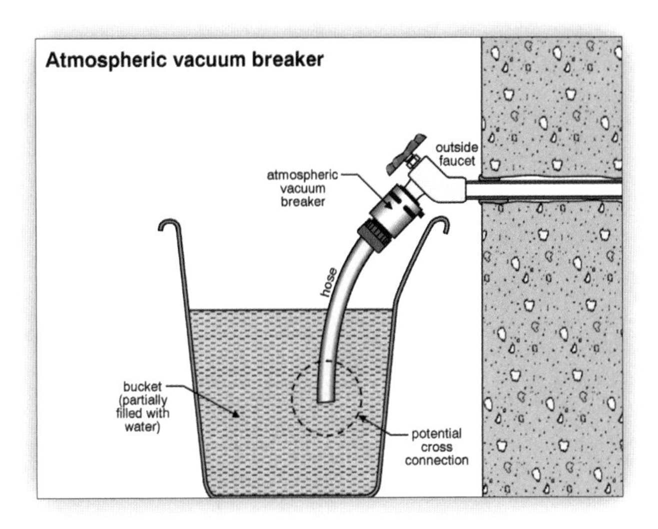

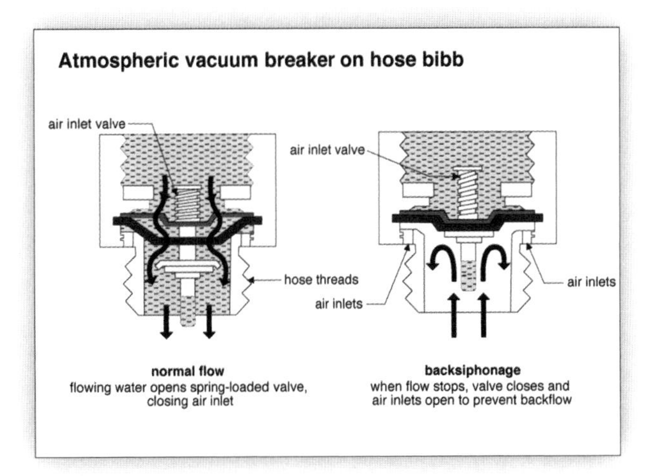

PLUMBING

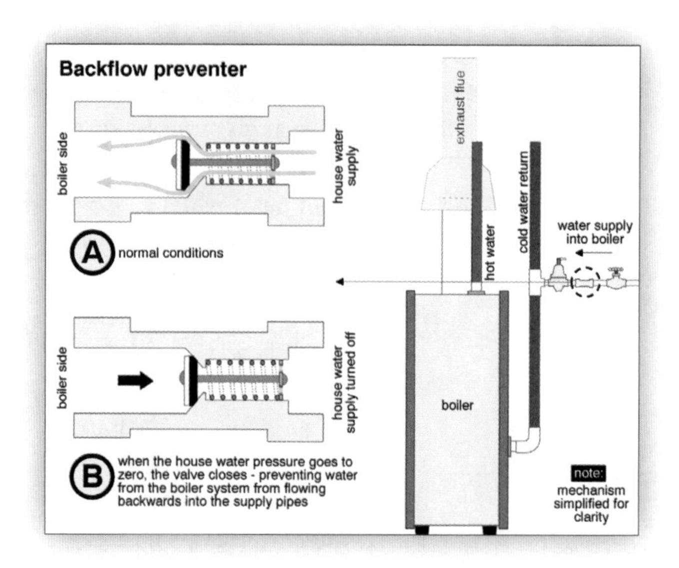

BOILER CROSS CONNECTION On hot water heating systems, the plumbing is connected to the boiler so that water can be added to the boiler. Modern installations have a back-flow preventer to prevent the boiler water from coming back into the drinking water. This is another potential cross connection. Older systems may not have back-flow preventers to protect against this.

INAPPROPRIATE/ LOW QUALITY MATERIALS Many materials used for supply plumbing were not intended for this use, and may be expected to have a short and troublesome life. These materials include rubber hoses, garden hoses, and non-certified plastic piping. Polyvinyl chloride (PVC) and polyethylene (PE), for example, should not be used as hot water piping. Connections made with the wrong materials or wrong devices cannot be expected to perform properly. Special connectors are provided for special types of piping.

1.5 Isolating Valves

DESCRIPTION Isolating valves allow someone to work on a part of the plumbing system without shutting off the entire house water supply. Almost every toilet has an isolating valve, and there should always be an isolating valve on the cold water supply to the water heater. High quality installations have isolating valves on every set of risers running up from the basement and isolating valves under each sink and basin.

Common Problems with Isolating Valves

LEAK The most common problem experienced with isolating valves is leakage through the valve connection, packing or washer.

INOPERATIVE Inoperative valves are often not noted until there is an emergency. Many toilet isolating valves become stuck, and are therefore useless. Replacing the isolating valve is not a large expense. If an isolating valve does not turn with normal effort by hand pressure, a wrench should not be used unless one is prepared to shut off the main supply valve very quickly if the valve is damaged. Sometimes forcing a valve will result in leaking when the valve is re-opened.

Isolating valves are not operated by home inspectors due to the risk of leakage.

1.6 Water Heaters

DESCRIPTION Domestic water heaters provide hot water to the faucets and appliances. Most water heaters are conventional storage-type heaters, where heated water is stored in a large tank. There are also tankless systems, where water is heated on demand, either by a boiler, or a dedicated water heater. Indirect water heaters are a third type. They typically have a large tank, with the heat being provided by the boiler that heats the house.

Water may be heated by gas, propane, oil or electricity. Solar water heaters are also available.

Water heaters may be used to heat all, or part of a house, through the use of fan-coil units, or radiant heating. This is called a combination heating system because the water heater provides domestic hot water and it heats the home.

OPERATION **1.6.1 Conventional Water Heaters:** Whether heated by gas, propane, oil or electricity, all conventional water heaters work the same way. Cold water enters the tank, and heated water leaves the tank. The heated water temperature is typically 120 to 140° F. When a fixture runs

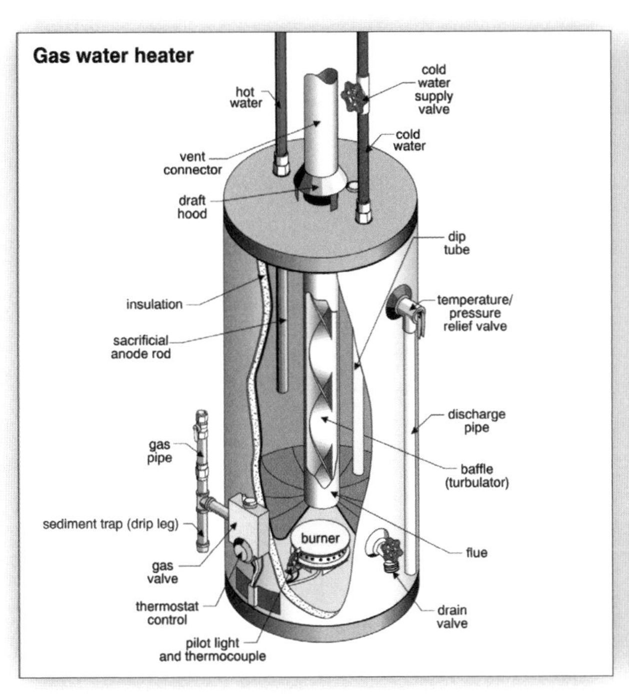

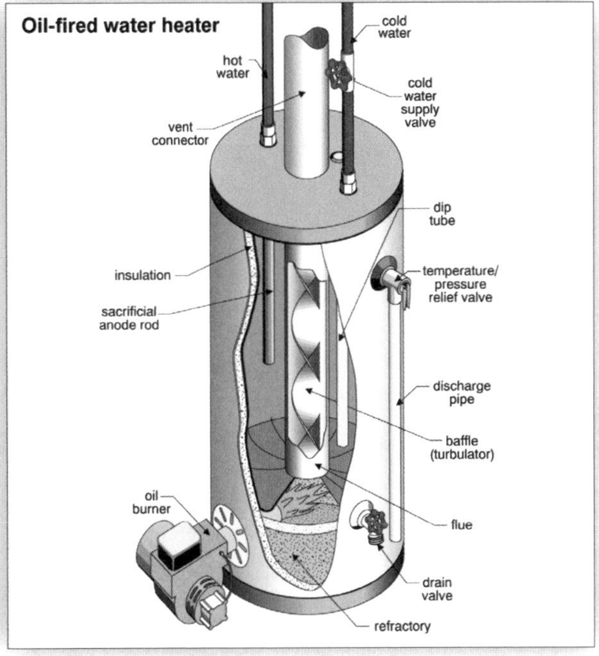

hot water, the heated water leaves the tank and cold water enters, triggering the thermostat and turning on the burner or element. If heated water flows out faster than the incoming cool water can be heated, we will run out of hot water. The larger the tank, the longer it takes to run out of hot water.

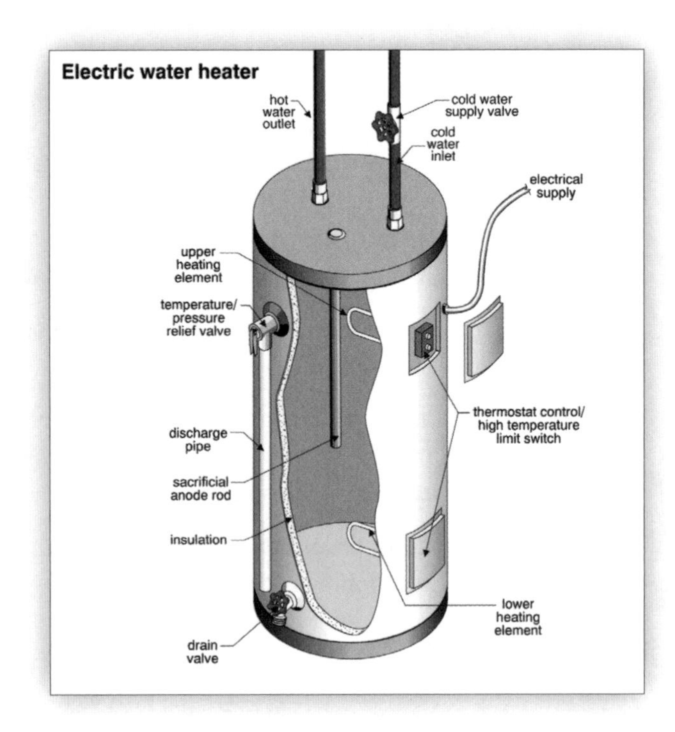

SIZE Water heaters should be big enough to satisfy the needs of the house. A family of four will often find a 30-gallon gas or oil system or a 40-gallon electric system satisfactory.

RECOVERY RATE When the hot water is depleted, the recovery rate becomes important. Generally speaking, oil has the fastest rate of recovery, with gas second and electricity third. If water is drawn off slowly, the recovery rate may be such that the tank can be kept filled with hot water. Faster recovery rates allow more water to be drawn off without running out of hot water.

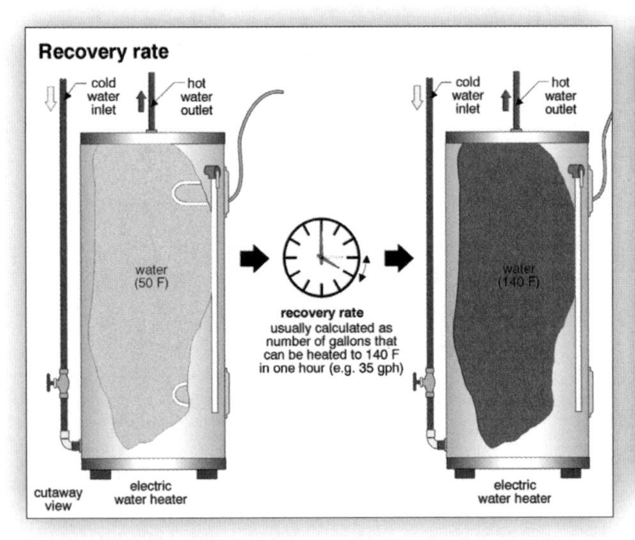

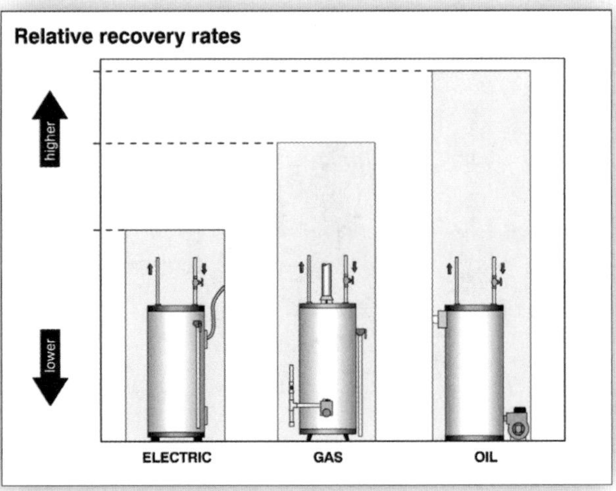

INSULATION The tanks are insulated to slow the heat loss from the tank. Energy-efficient tanks have better insulation. Some people also insulate their hot water piping.

TEMPERATURE SETTINGS Thermostats control the water temperature. There are some conflicting issues around appropriate water temperature. We don't want the water so hot that it scalds people, but we want it hot enough to prevent bacteria like Legionnaires disease from growing in the water heater. Also, dishwasher manufacturers often recommend that the water be 140° F, since some dishwashing detergents will not dissolve completely at lower temperatures. Many dishwashers have internal heaters to bring cooler water up to appropriate temperatures for washing dishes.

MIXING VALVES (TEMPERING VALVES) Some jurisdictions require tempering valves on water heaters, so water in the tank is at 140°, but as it leaves the tank, cold water is mixed in to deliver 115° to 120° water. These tempering valves may be installed at the water heater, or at individual fixtures.

Common Problems with Conventional Water Heaters

FUEL PROBLEMS Malfunctioning burners, electric elements, sensors or controls will cause poor operation or may result in the system not working at all, meaning no hot water. Please see the Heating chapter for more information about fuel systems, burners and electric elements.

EXHAUST VENTING ISSUES Most gas and oil water heaters have to be vented into a chimney with adequate draft. Poorly arranged or disconnected vents are safety hazards, which should be corrected promptly. Aluminum vents are not permitted. Vent sections should be as short as possible, screwed together, and should slope up 1/4 inch per foot, minimum. Vents should extend two feet above the roof and should be two feet above anything within ten feet horizontally. Vents should extend at least five feet above the draft hood. Exhaust gases spilling out at the draft hood or burner may present a life-threatening situation. This problem requires immediate action. Some modern gas water heaters employ induced draft fans and high-temperature plastic venting that discharges out through the house wall. The vent materials were originally PVC, CPVC or ABS. In some areas these are replaced with special plastic vent pipes rated for the high exhaust gas temperatures.

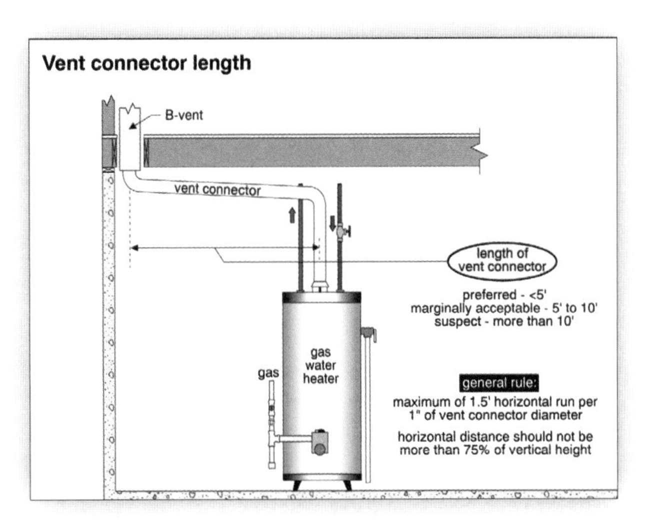

POOR LOCATION Gas or oil water heaters should not be in sleeping areas. This is a safety issue. Gas-fired heaters in garages should be 18 inches above floor level to reduce the risk of the heater igniting gasoline fumes, and should be protected from mechanical damage. Some jurisdictions call for electric heaters in garages to be similarly elevated.

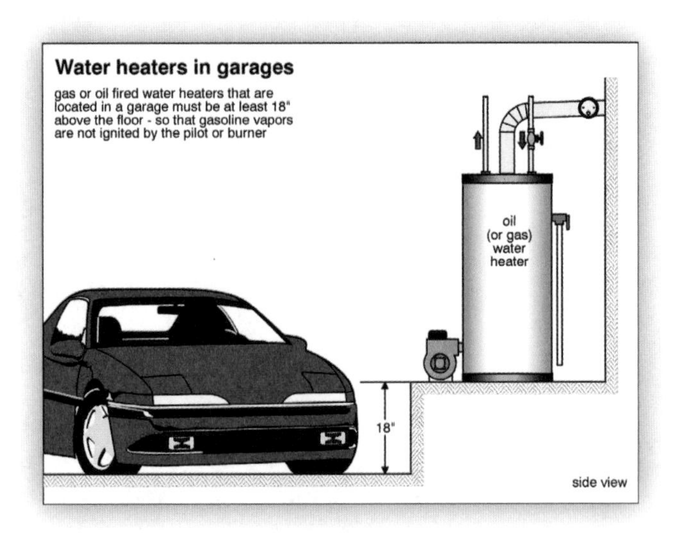

FAILED ELECTRIC ELEMENTS It is not unusual to find one of the two elements in electric water heaters burned out. Replacing an element is not expensive. Most heaters are arranged so that both elements cannot be on at the same time – the elements operate in a sequence. Depending on which element fails, there may be some hot water, or none.

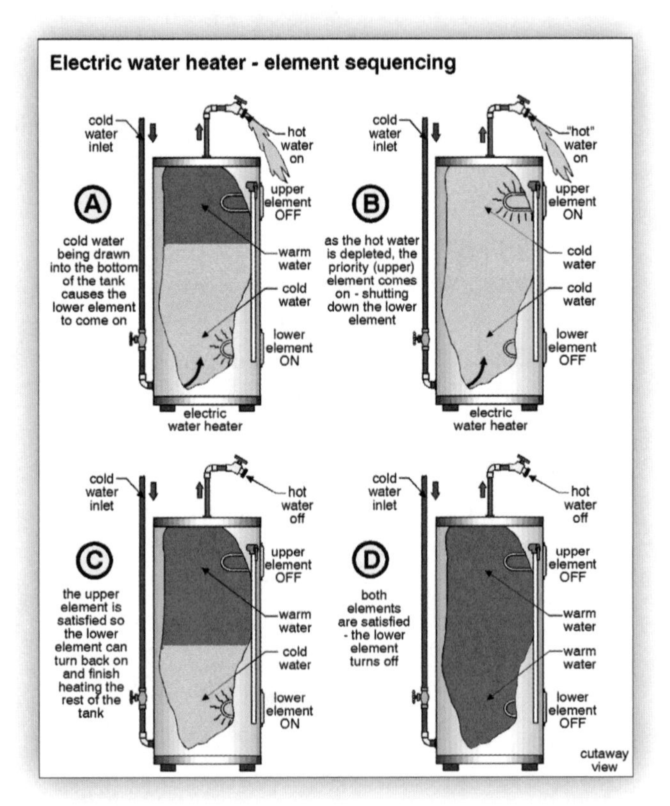

LEAK/ DAMAGE Water heaters can, of course, leak, and the tanks can be mechanically damaged.

SLUDGE Where sludge has accumulated in the bottom of the tank, water pressure from the hot water system may be limited. When water pressure problems are experienced on the hot water system only, it makes sense to drain the water heater to ensure that sludge accumulation is not the problem. Some experts recommend draining one or two gallons out of the bottom of the tank monthly to prevent sludge build-up.

RELIEF VALVE UNSAFE The temperature/pressure relief (TP or TPR) valve lets water escape if the temperature or pressure is too high. This valve should be connected to a tube that discharges no more than six inches above floor level so hot water is not sprayed on to anyone nearby. Some areas require that the tube discharge outside the building. The tube should be as large as the tank fitting and the tube end should never be threaded, capped or plugged. The tube diameter should be at least as large as the TPR valve fitting. The tube should be able to withstand 250°F temperatures, should have no shut-off valve, and should be as short and as straight as possible.

An alternative to the high temperature function of the relief valve is a high temperature shut-off in the tank.

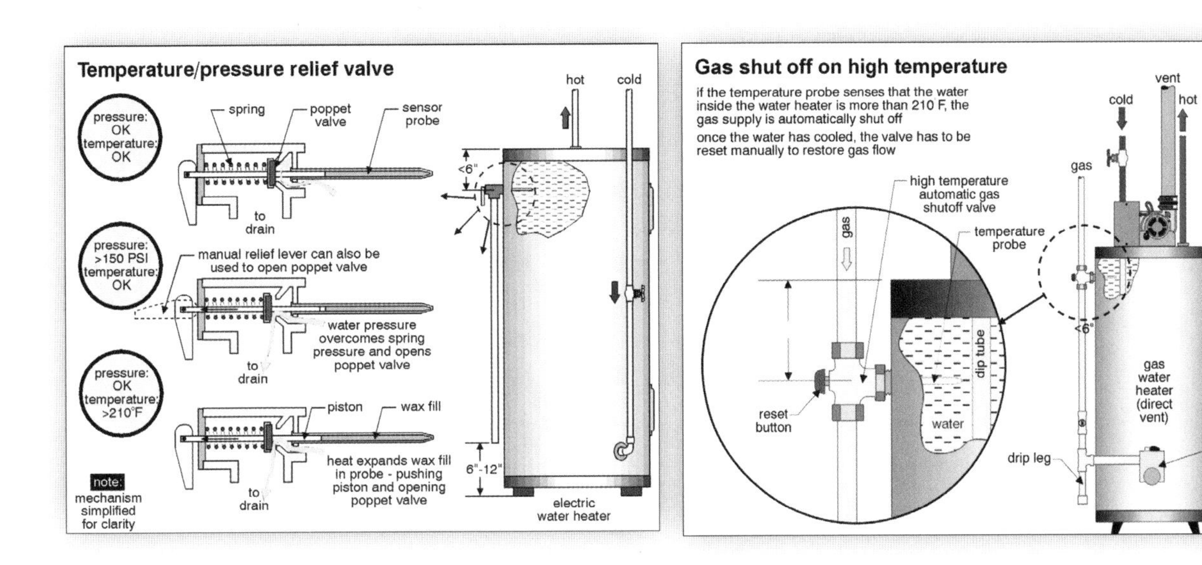

AGE – NEAR END OF LIFE The life expectancy of a water heater is typically eight to 12 years, although there are exceptions on both sides.

1.6.2 Tankless Water Heaters (Instantaneous or On-Demand Heaters)

OPERATION As the name suggests, tankless water heaters have no storage capacity. Tankless heaters are typically gas or propane fired and have a burner, heat exchanger, venting system, and controls. When the faucets and fixtures in the home are idle, the water heater is dormant. When there is a call for hot water, the heater detects the water flow and ignites the burners. These powerful burners quickly heat the water inside the small heat exchanger. As hot water leaves, fresh cold water is drawn in and heated as it passes through. An advantage of this system is that you can't empty all of the hot water out of the tank because there is no tank – just continuous hot water.

NO STORED WATER The other major advantage over conventional water heaters is energy savings. Tankless water heaters have no reservoir of hot water sitting idle. It takes energy to keep the tank of water hot all the time for when it's needed.

SMALL SIZE Tankless water heaters are much smaller than conventional heaters with storage tanks, and are usually wall-mounted. They do not take up much space.

FUEL AND VENTING Most tankless water heaters are fuelled by natural gas or propane and are vented through a side wall of the house or through roof venting, with specialized kits. In moderate climates the entire heater may be mounted on the exterior of the house. The vent system is built into the face of the appliance. When mounted outside in areas where freezing is a risk, some tankless water heaters fire briefly on a regular basis to prevent freezing. The pipes connected to the heater are also protected from freezing, typically by insulation and/or heat tapes.

EFFICIENCY Tankless water heaters are often more efficient than conventional water heaters, using modulating burners, direct venting and/or condensing combustion systems.

MIXING VALVE Most systems include a mixing (tempering) valve and a means of setting a maximum water temperature to avoid scalding. This tempering valve mixes some cold water with the hot water leaving the unit to reduce the temperature.

REMOTE CONTROL Some tankless systems include a remote control, which can be used to monitor the performance of the system, display error codes or change the desired water temperature.

OTHER USES Tankless water heaters may also be used to heat the home, either as part of a forced air combination system, or a radiant hot water system.

Common Problems with Tankless Water Heaters

FUEL SUPPLY PROBLEMS The water heater must have a continuous fuel supply. Malfunctioning burners, sensors or controls will cause poor operation or may result in the system not working at all, meaning no hot water. These units typically require much more gas than a tank type heater. Unless connected to a higher pressure (2 psi or greater) gas system, a direct switch from a storage tank heater to a tankless water heater is unlikely to work. Failure to provide an adequately sized gas supply can cause the system to periodically fail or not function at all.

SCALE BUILD-UP The small diameter of the heat exchangers means that these units are susceptible to clogging with scale, especially in areas with hard water. In hard water areas, annual de-scaling is recommended.

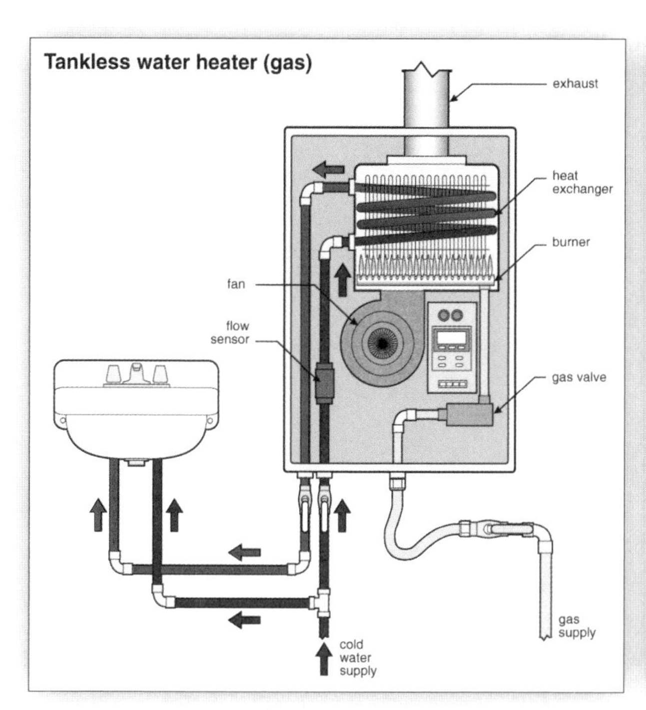

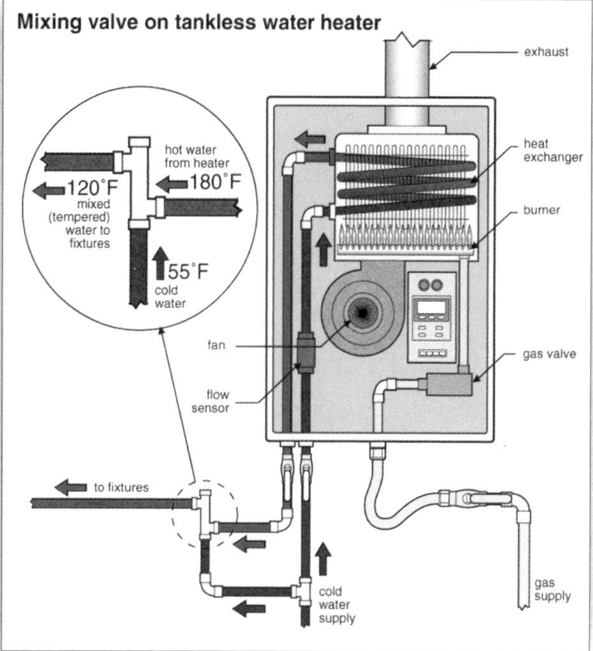

LONGER WAIT When a hot water faucet is turned on, it may take longer to get hot water with a tankless heater than a conventional system.

The delay between opening the faucet and getting hot water can be longer with tankless heaters than conventional tank heaters. Better tank locations and multiple tanks can help with issue. Some recent system designs allow for circulating loops to be used with tankless water heaters to get hot water to remote fixtures faster.

MAXIMUM FLOW RATE LIMITED The hot water flow rate is not only dependent on the heating capacity of the water heater and the output water temperature, but also on the inlet water temperature. Homes in northern climates draw water from colder sources, and since it takes longer to heat up colder water, tankless water heaters installed in these homes have lower hot water flow rates.

MINIMUM FLOW RATE PROBLEM The burners are triggered by sensors that detect the flow of water. If the flow rate is less than 1/2 gallon per minute, the burners may not turn on and no hot water will be delivered. Water-saving shower heads, for example, may not have enough flow to turn the water heater on, especially if the water heater needs a high flow rate before it will come on.

RELIEF VALVE PROBLEMS The temperature/pressure relief (TPR) valve lets water escape if the temperature or pressure is too high. This valve should be connected to a tube that discharges no more than six inches above floor level so hot water won't scald anyone nearby. Some codes require that the tube discharge outside the building. The tube should be as large as the tank fitting, arranged so water flows downward, and the tube end should never be threaded, capped or plugged. The tube should be able to wit stand 250°F temperatures, should have no shut-off valve, and should be as short and as straight as possible. The tube should not be connected directly to another plumbing system, such as a plumbing vent or condensate drain, and the tube should supply relief venting for only one relief valve.

HIGH COST Tankless water heaters are considerably more expensive than conventional tank-type heaters, and although tankless units are more energy efficient, it may take a long time to recover the extra investment.

HIGH MAINTENANCE Conventional water heaters are relatively inexpensive due to their simplicity. Tankless water heaters are more expensive and more complex. Their complexity also means that maintenance and repairs can be more expensive. Isolating valves help simplify draining and other regular maintenance.

DIRTY FILTER If the heater is equipped with a water filter, this should be checked and cleaned monthly, or performance will suffer.

2.0 Waste Systems

BLACK WATER, GRAY WATER AND STORM WATER Plumbing waste is divided into two types. Black water is from toilets and contains human waste. Gray water is from bathing, clothes washing, dish washing or cooking, and does not contain human waste. Most municipalities require both types be treated as sewage. Storm water is from rain or melting snow. It is not typically treated as sewage.

Only a small percentage of the waste piping system is visible in a home.

2.1 Public Waste Systems

DESCRIPTION Most houses in built-up areas are connected to a municipal sewer system. This is a system in the street that allows waste from a house to flow by gravity into sewer piping. The waste is carried to a treatment facility where it is cleaned prior to being released.

COMBINATION SEWERS Older neighborhoods have a combination storm/sanitary sewer system. Storm water and sewage go through the treatment facility. Modern developments have a sanitary sewer to carry house waste and a separate storm sewer for rain and snow run-off. The storm water does not have to be treated, reducing the load on the treatment plant.

RISK OF BACK-UP Where homes have basements, flooding as a result of storm sewer back-up is less likely in a house with separate sewers. With combination sewers, a sewer back-up through basement floor drains will contain storm water and raw sewage. This is a health concern. In some areas, homeowners install one-way valves in their floor drain to

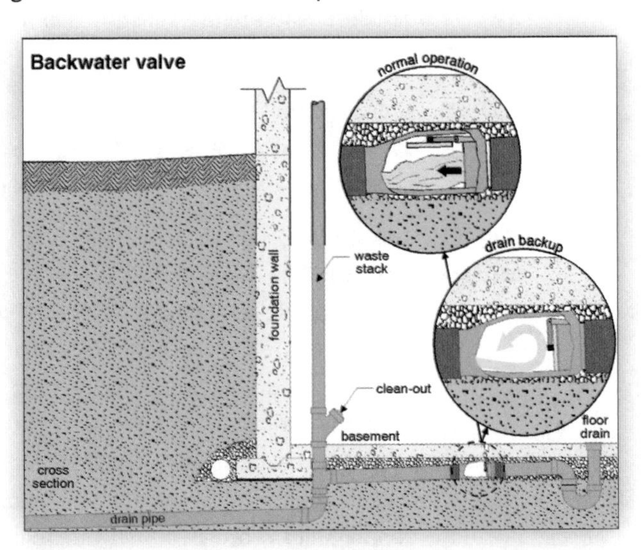

allow water down into the drain, but prevent water from coming back up. If pressures are high enough, sewage may back up through basement plumbing fixtures. In some cases, a check valve is put into the main drain line itself. These are short-term solutions and the municipality is often petitioned to improve the sewer system.

FLOOR DRAINS AND DOWNSPOUTS Where there are separate sewers, the floor drains should go into the sanitary sewer and gutters and downspouts should go into the storm sewer, or onto the ground several feet away from the building.

SEWER LINE FROM HOUSE TO STREET These lines are often clay in older homes and are vulnerable to collapse and obstruction by tree roots or soil.

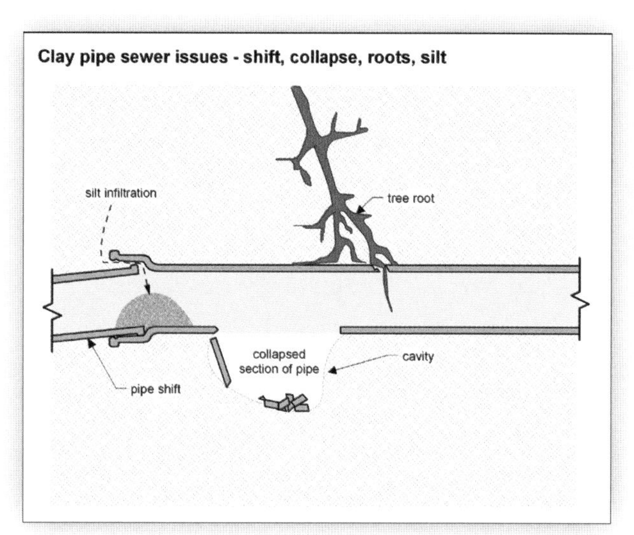

OVERLOADED DRAIN There are a limited number of fixtures that can discharge into any given size of drain pipe. This can be a stumbling block during a house expansion or renovation. Although it is rare, it is possible that a house with a city sewer system is refused permission to add more plumbing fixtures.

2.2 Private Waste Systems

DESCRIPTION The traditional private sewer system is typically a septic tank and weeping tile bed. This system is used where city sewers are not available. There are many variations of this. The septic tank is a watertight container usually made of concrete, steel or fiberglass. It serves as a holding tank, allowing heavy solids to settle to the bottom of the tank. Lighter materials that float, are also in the tank. The heavy solids are known as **sludge** and the lighter, floating materials are known as **scum.**

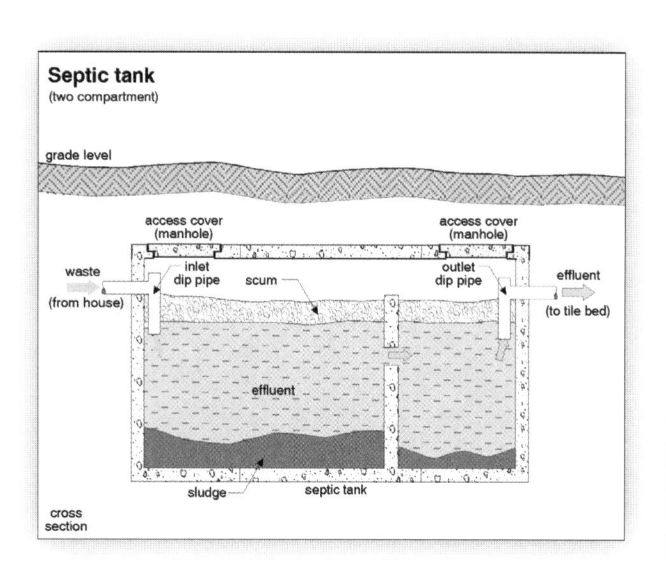

Most of the material entering the tank is in a liquid state. Within the tank, the majority of the solids are broken down to gases and/or liquids. The breakdown takes place as a result of bacterial action, both aerobic and anaerobic. The liquids are discharged from the tank into the tile bed. The gases escape through the plumbing vents in the home.

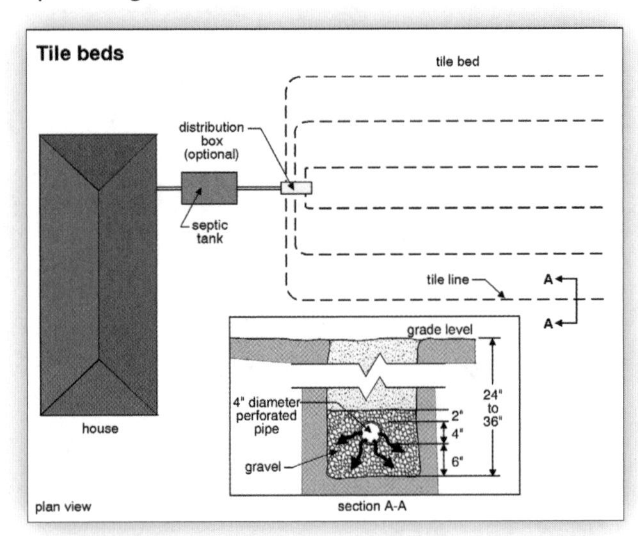

The tile bed is also known as a leaching bed, disposal field, soil absorption field or drain field. It consists of a network of perforated or open jointed pipes in trenches below the ground surface that allow the liquid waste (effluent) to percolate into the soil. The leaching bed is sized for the soil's ability to absorb effluent, and the amount of waste the system receives.

There are many variations on the conventional septic system, including closed holding tanks that are pumped out on a regular basis. There are also sophisticated systems with agitators and aerators that accelerate the chemical decomposition of the solids in the tank. These systems allow for smaller tile beds and are useful on smaller properties. While there is an advantage to this, the complexity of electrical and mechanical parts creates the potential for higher maintenance.

There are several types of tile beds as well. Special sand can be used, allowing for small tile beds. This is expensive, since the sand has to be brought onto the site, but it may be important to keep the tile bed small. These special tile beds may be used with conventional or specialized systems.

Septic systems should be kept away from supply wells and other sources of drinking water, for obvious reasons. Generally speaking, a well and a tile bed should be at least 100 feet apart. A well and septic tank should be at least 50 feet from each other.

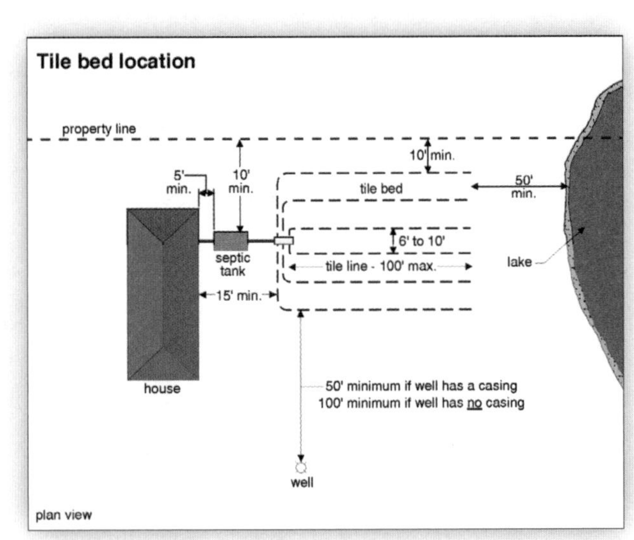

It is helpful to know the location of the tank and tile bed, the age of the system, and the installation and service history. Where building expansion is planned, the tank and tile bed can get in the way. The tile bed location can often be identified by greener, healthier grass growing above the bed. The homeowner or health authorities may have a record of the tank and tile bed location.

MAINTENANCE Septic systems require regular maintenance. The system should be inspected annually and the tank should be pumped out every two to four years, as required. Tile beds do have a fixed life expectancy (often roughly 25 to 30 years). This depends on many factors and is difficult to predict. Bleaches and strong detergents should be avoided where possible, since they may kill the bacteria in the tank. The amount of water entering the system should be minimized. Water saving toilets and showerheads reduce the load on a septic system.

CITY SEWERS There are several areas where houses with septic systems can now connect to street sewers. The connection to a municipal system can be expensive, but is typically less expensive than replacing a private waste disposal system.

BUILDING ADDITION Local authorities may refuse to allow an addition to a home, depending on septic system capabilities. A new septic system adds significantly to the cost of an addition.

Common Problems with Private Waste Systems

ODOR/ POOLING A septic system that is not performing properly can pose a health hazard and should be treated as high priority. The condition of a septic system and tile bed cannot be determined during a home inspection. The homeowner should watch for water pooling above the tile bed, or an odor coming from the bed. Homes that have been vacant for several months may show problems when the system is back into service.

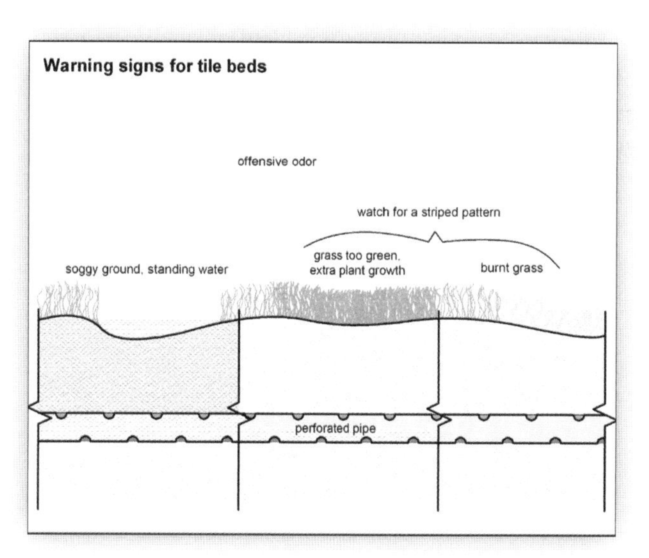

SYSTEM FAILURE Problems leading to failure of septic systems include overloading of the tile bed, soil breakdown around the tiles, high water tables, clogging of the tiles, and broken or cracked tanks and tiles.

2.3 Waste Piping in House

DESCRIPTION Drain, waste and vent piping (referred to by plumbers as DWV) carry solid, liquid and gas waste products out of the building. Solids and liquids flow through the main drain, and gases escape through vent piping that extends through the roof. Several materials are commonly used in these systems.

2.3.1 Galvanized Steel: Galvanized steel venting was used in some areas. Vents carry air but do not carry water, so the pipe doesn't rust. Its life expectancy is very long, easily more than 50 years.

Galvanized steel drain and waste pipes were used in some cases. These have a relatively short life expectancy since the steel corrodes and the rough inner surface created by the corrosion can cause blockages as solids get hung up.

2.3.2 Copper: Copper waste plumbing was used commonly after World War II, up until the mid 1960s. Copper piping works well for branch drain lines, main stacks, and vent piping. It has become rare in homes, since plastic waste plumbing is less expensive. In multi-family construction, copper waste plumbing may be used where authorities will not allow combustible plastic piping due to fire spread concerns.

The joints in copper piping are soldered and an indefinite life expectancy is expected.

2.3.3 Plastic: Since the 1960s, plastic piping has become almost the exclusive waste plumbing material. Plastic piping may be ABS or PVC. It is used for drains, wastes and vents and connections are made with plastic cement (solvent). The piping is inexpensive, light, easy to work with and durable. Its only disadvantage is that it is somewhat noisy when water is running through it. Efforts to control the noise include wrapping it with fiber glass insulation.

2.3.4 Cast Iron: Cast iron piping was used for the main plumbing stack in houses up until the 1950s. Its life expectancy is 50 years and up. It employs a bell-and-spigot connection traditionally, with oakum packed into the joint and caulked with lead to seal it. There is also hubless cast iron pipe joined with neoprene sleeves clamped over the joint.

Cast iron is expensive and difficult to work with because it is very heavy. Cast iron waste piping generally fails in two ways. The pipe can rust through, often in a pinhole pattern. It is also prone to splitting along a seam, particularly on horizontal runs. When cast iron waste piping fails, it is typically replaced with plastic.

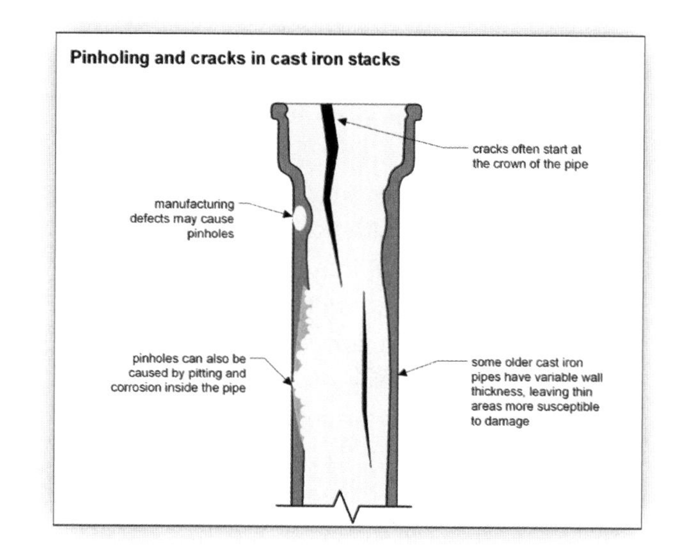

2.3.5 Lead: Lead waste plumbing was used until the 1950s to connect plumbing fixtures to a main cast iron or copper drain. Lead was used because of its resistance to corrosion, and its workability. A piece of lead pipe can be bent fairly easily.

Lead piping is prone to leakage, usually at the connections. It is soft and susceptible to mechanical damage. It is typically replaced with plastic pipe. Lead waste lines are usually replaced during any major plumbing work, whether problems are being experienced or not.

LEAD SUSPECTED Since the sections of lead piping used are relatively small, they are often not visible. In houses built before the 1960s that have not been remodeled, we assume there is concealed lead waste plumbing that will eventually leak. We suggest replacing lead waste piping during any work that provides access to this piping.

Common Problems with Waste Piping

LEAKS – CRACKS/ HOLES/JOINTS/ DAMAGE Waste plumbing leaks pose a health hazard and should be corrected immediately. Leakage may be from failed connections, damage, or pipe deterioration (holes or splits). Leaks may go undetected for some time, particularly if the fixtures are only used occasionally.

IMPROPER SLOPE Waste plumbing pipes may run almost horizontally, with a minimum slope of 1/4 inch per foot. Pipes that are at least three-inches in diameter are often permitted to have slopes as low as 1/8 inch per foot. Too little slope results in blockage and too much slope can cause siphoning at traps and poor drain performance. A maximum slope of roughly 1/2 inch per foot is often recommended. Where the slope would be greater, vertical sections of pipe are preferred. With house settlement or pipe sag, the minimum slope can be lost. Low spots in waste plumbing may lead to a blockage.

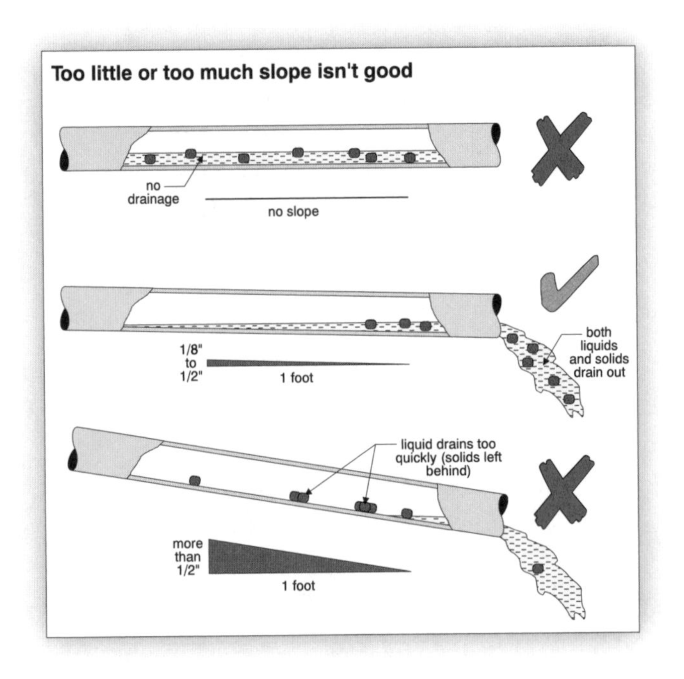

POOR SUPPORT Waste pipes should be well supported and protected from damage. Poor support may result in the slope problems described above.

INAPPROPRIATE MATERIALS Many materials used for waste plumbing were not intended for this use, and may be expected to have a short and troublesome life. These materials include rubber hoses, garden hoses, and non-approved plastic piping. Connections made with the wrong materials or wrong devices cannot be expected to perform properly. Special connectors are provided for special types of piping. Inappropriate materials raise questions about workmanship throughout the system. Traps and vents are commonly omitted on amateurish installations.

2.4 Traps

DESCRIPTION Traps are provided below house plumbing fixtures and are designed to hold some water in the waste piping system. The main purpose of a trap is to prevent sewer odors from coming back into the home through the fixture drain. There are several different styles of traps (P traps, S traps, and drum traps, for example). The P traps are considered the best for homes, as they are least vulnerable to siphoning or obstruction problems.

Traps are typically installed so they can be removed easily to clear obstructions or retrieve items that go down the drain.

Most fixtures require traps, although a toilet does not, since the water in the toilet bowl creates a natural trap.

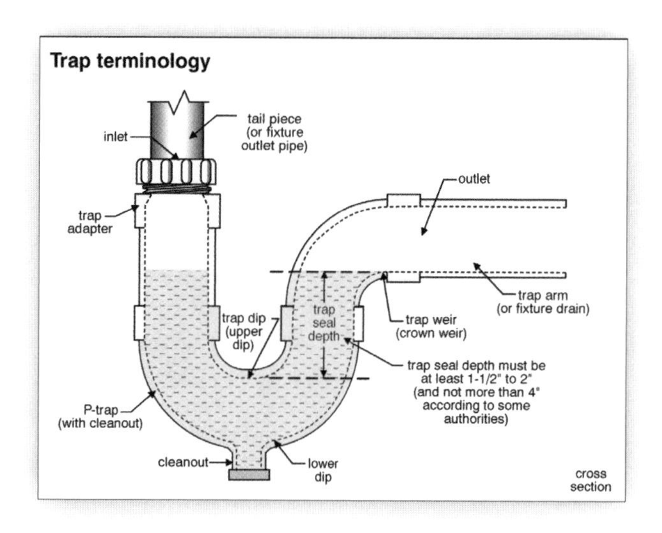

TRAP SEAL PRIMER If water evaporates from floor drain traps that rarely see water, odors may get into the home. Since the 1960s, primers have been used for traps in many floor drains. This is typically a 1/4-inch clear plastic tube connected to a laundry tub faucet or toilet, for example. Water flows through the plastic tube into the floor drain whenever the fixture is used. Water is added to the trap to replace any water lost through evaporation. The same thing can be accomplished by pouring a bucket of water down the drain every month or so. Another solution is to fill the floor drain trap with mineral oil. It will not evaporate and is environmentally safe.

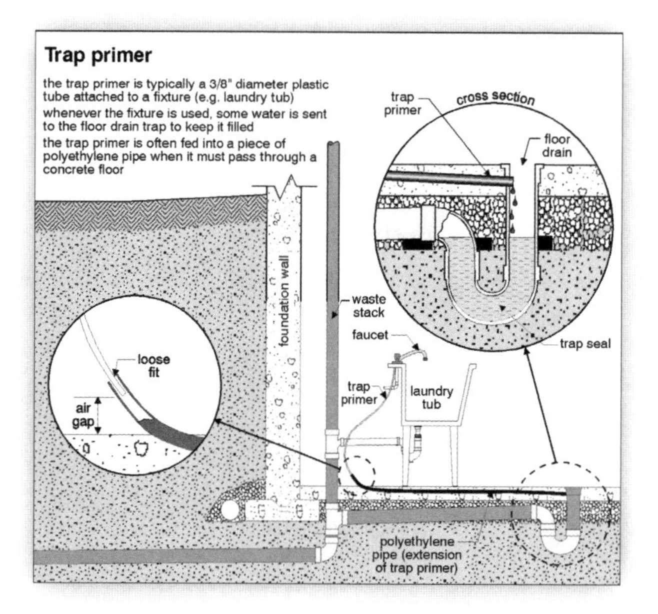

Common Problems with Traps

MISSING/ LEAKING Amateur installations may omit traps, and leaking traps are ineffective. Leaks in traps under sinks can be seen when water is flowing, but leaking traps under concealed fixtures such as bathtubs and shower stalls may not be discovered until damage is visible below.

Leaking basement floor drain traps are often not detected for some time. A sewer odor or air movement up through the floor drain may indicate a problem. (Air movement may be the result of downspouts discharging into the floor drain above the trap. This may not be a problem. It is also possible that the water has evaporated out of the trap, or the trap may be leaking.)

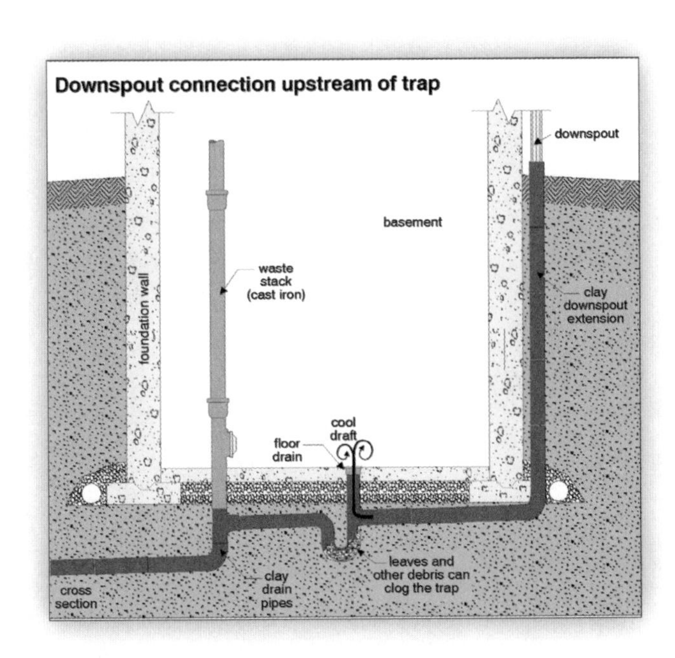

S TRAP – SIPHON RISK S traps often lead to siphoning problems and most plumbers recommend replacement with P traps. Bell traps, drum traps and crown vented traps are not recommended for plumbing fixtures in homes.

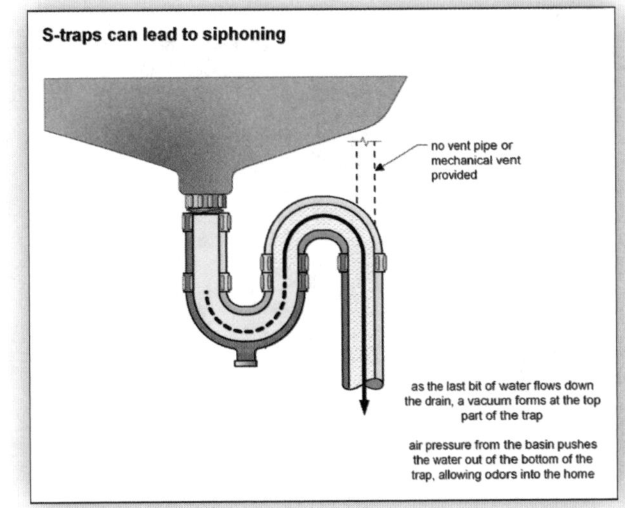

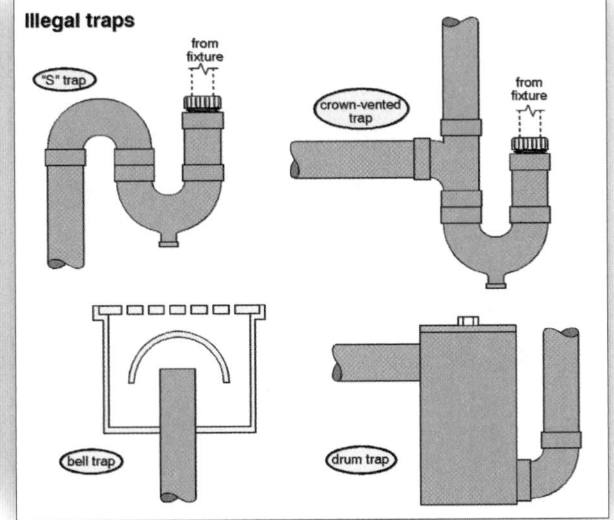

OBSTRUCTIONS Clogs develop at traps because the tight corners catch debris. Traps should be easy to remove in order to clear obstructions. Modern traps often include a drain plug at the trap bottom. This is useful for removing objects that are dropped down drains, but may not be large enough to allow clearing of an obstruction. Obstructions are sometimes cleared with plungers or plumber's snakes. In some cases, the piping has to be dismantled. This work can create a health hazard, and care should be taken when dealing with any waste water problems.

Older homes connected to city sewer systems often have traps in the front yard on the main waste system. These are common spots for obstructions, including tree roots. The waste line outside the house is also vulnerable to tree roots. Where the pipe has not been seriously damaged, a plumber's snake may clear a blockage. If the pipe is broken, digging and replacing are necessary. Video cameras are sometimes used to scan waste lines to find problems.

FREEZING IN COLD CLIMATES When a house is winterized, the supply pipes are drained. The waste pipes contain no water and are not susceptible to freezing. The traps, however, will freeze. The traps cannot simply be drained, since sewer odors will enter the house. Anti-freeze is provided for the traps. Since this anti-freeze will ultimately be flushed into the waste system (either city or septic), the anti-freeze should be a type that will not harm the environment.

DOUBLE TRAPS – MAY CLOG Two traps are not a good thing on any plumbing fixture. This arrangement may produce chronic blockages.

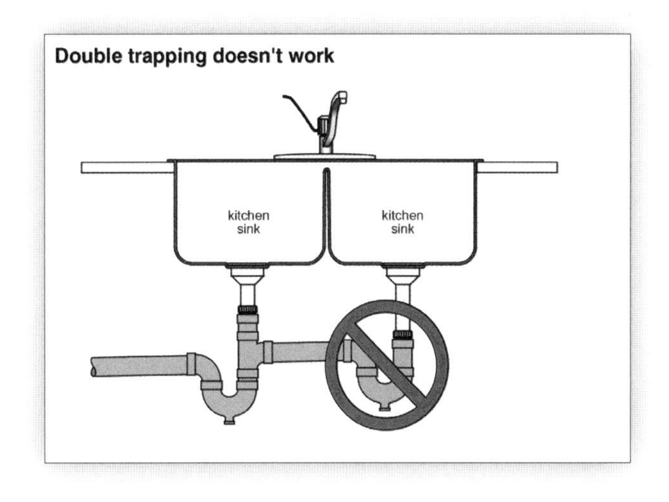

2.5 Floor Drains

DESCRIPTION Floor drains should be provided at the lowest living level of any house with a basement. Floor drains can be inadvertently covered if the basement floor is resurfaced. If the basement floor is lowered, the floor drain may be unwisely deleted. Where an addition is provided, there may be no floor drain for this section of the basement. If this is lower than the original basement, this is a very risky situation.

The floor drain should be at the low point in the floor. This is always a compromise to some degree, since people do not like their basement floors to slope dramatically. Floor drains are often located close to the boiler, water heater or laundry area, where leakage is most likely. There should be a grate over the floor drain to prevent things falling in. The grate should be kept clear.

Common Problems with Floor Drains

MISSING The most common problem is the absence of the floor drain. These are expensive to add, but do provide great protection in the event of a flood.

POOR LOCATION Floor drains are not always at the low point. The implication is that some water will remain on the floor if there is a flood. It is rarely cost effective to correct this.

TRAP DRY There should always be water in the floor drain trap. Sewer odors at floor drains are a result of leaking traps or trap water evaporating. Repairs are expensive but a good investment.

GRATE The grate should cover the top, but allow water into the drain.

2.6 Venting

DESCRIPTION Venting allows waste and water to flow properly. The venting performs three functions. It allows air in front of the water flowing through the waste pipe to be pushed out of the way. It allows air back into the waste piping after the water has gone by. Lastly, it allows sewer gases to escape outside through a vent stack.

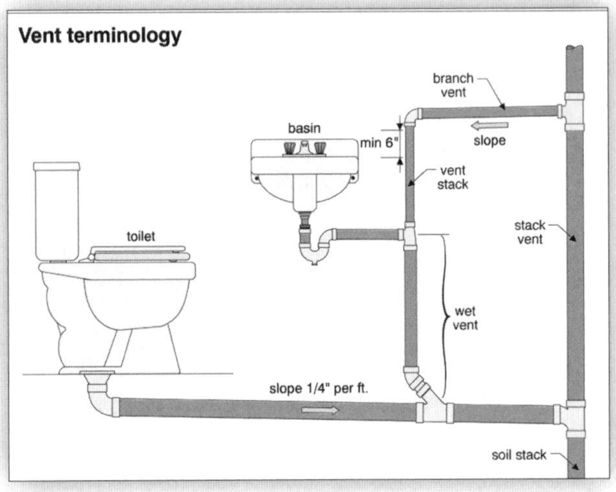

SIPHON The second function is the most important. The trap at each fixture provides a water seal to prevent sewer odors from backing up into the house. After a fixture is used, some water should stay in the trap to provide the seal. If a system is not properly vented, water will siphon out of the trap. Let's look at how venting works.

As water runs through a drain pipe, we want to leave the last bit of water in the trap to seal off the waste piping system from the house air. It is difficult to separate that water into two pieces (leaving the last part in the trap) because the space in the middle forms a vacuum. The water in the trap can be siphoned out and down the drain.

A vent just downstream of the trap allows air into the pipe, preventing a vacuum and allowing the last bit of water to remain in the trap. With the exception of some floor drains, all fixtures should be vented.

As a rough rule, any fixture within five feet of the main stack does not need a separate vent, because the main stack acts as a vent. Where fixtures are more than five feet from the main stack a vent should be provided that extends out through the roof. Vents may connect to a main stack above all the fixtures in the house.

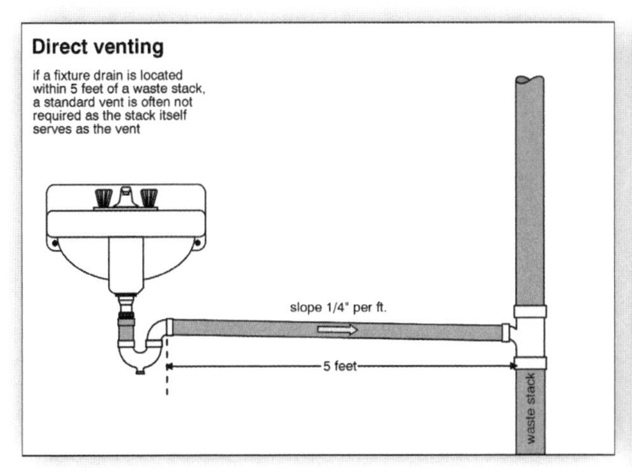

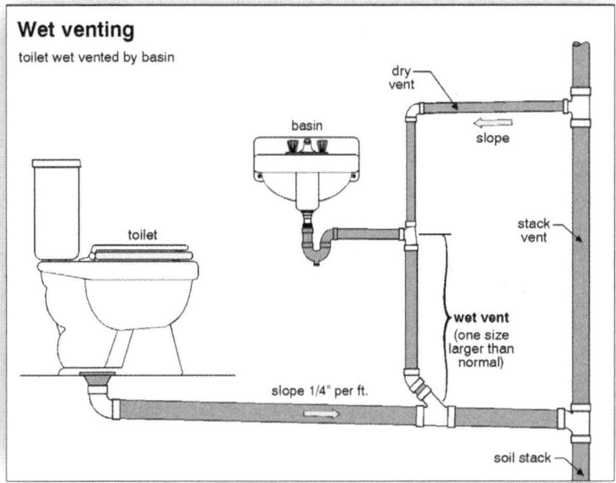

MATERIALS Vent piping may be cast iron, copper, galvanized steel or plastic. Because vent piping only carries air (no water) it tends to last a long time no matter what material is used.

Common Problems with Venting

The implication of venting problems is unhealthy sewer gases getting into the home.

MISSING/ INCOMPLETE/ INEFFECTIVE The venting system is almost always concealed from view, except in a few small areas. A siphoning or gurgling noise when water is drained out of a plumbing fixture suggests venting problems. This indicates the trap is siphoning and losing its water. A sewer odor at a fixture indicates a trap or venting problem.

AIR ADMITTANCE VALVES Unvented fixtures may siphon. Traps with no water allow unhealthy sewer odors into the home. Air admittance valves are mechanical devices that simulate vents. They allow air to be drawn into the waste plumbing system under negative pressure to prevent siphoning, but prevent any air escaping from the plumbing system under positive pressure. Air admittance valves should be installed in an accessible, ventilated area. These devices are a low cost alternative to venting, although they are not as good as conventional venting. Some plumbing authorities will not allow these.

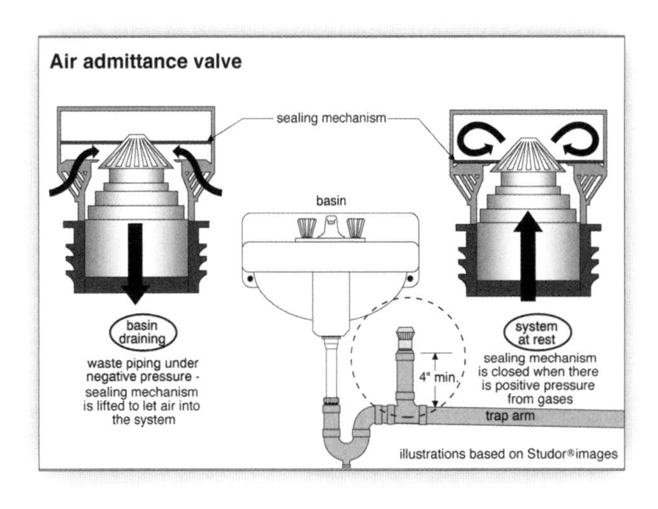

AUTOMATIC AIR VENTS While air admittance valves are approved in some areas, older style automatic air vents (see illustration), which rely on metal or rubber components, are not approved and should be replaced.

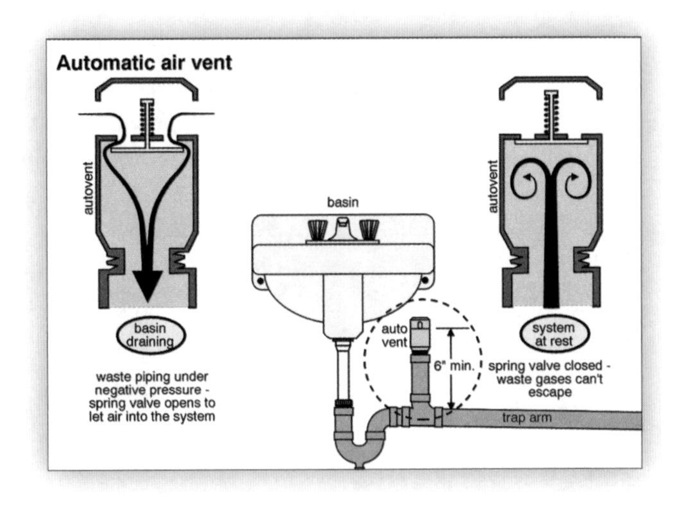

HEIGHT/ LOCATION PROBLEMS The vent pipe should extend at least six inches up through the roof of the house. When the vent extends through a roof that is used as a deck, the vent should be at least seven feet above the deck (taller than most people). Vents should not terminate in the attic, since this may allow odors into the house. In cold climates, this adds very moist warm air into a cold attic, leading to condensation and frost damage.

Vents should terminate at least three feet above any door or window openings within 10 feet horizontally. Vents should be at least 12 inches from a wall.

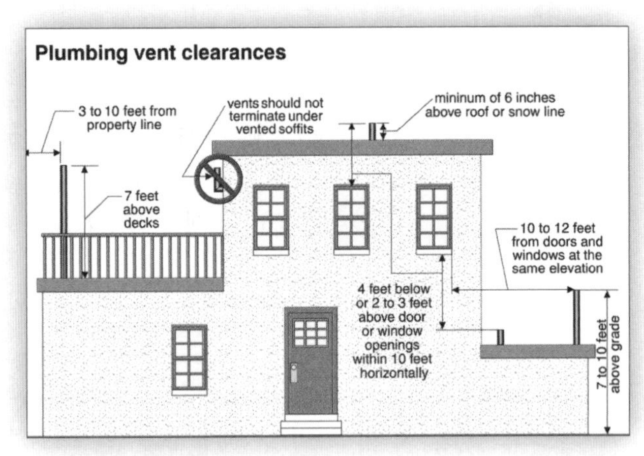

FROST CLOSURE IN COLD CLIMATES In cold climates, some recommend that the vent extend only about 12 inches above the roof line. Very long vents may be subject to frost closure in the winter. The warm moist air inside the vent cools as it contacts the cold outdoor section of the pipe. The moisture condenses and freezes on the inner pipe walls. In a prolonged spell of cold weather, this frost can build up and block the vent. This may lead to sewer odors inside the home. Vents should be at least three inches in diameter where they penetrate the roof system to reduce the risk of frost closure. Increasing the pipe size just before the vent passes up through the roof also helps prevent closure.

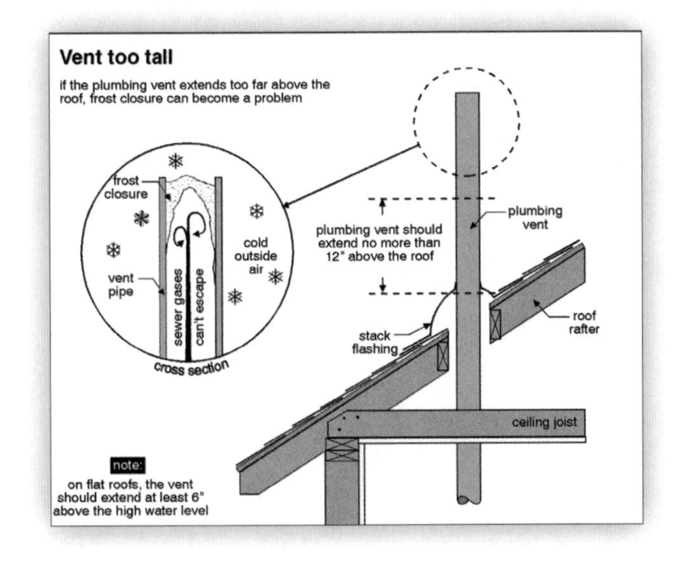

CONNECTION/ PIPE SUPPORT Since the venting system only carries air, leakage is usually not a big problem. Deterioration of the piping is also very unusual, although poor connection or poor pipe support is a possibility.

WET VENTS Wet vents (vents that also serve as drains) can become clogged or deteriorate as a result of the waste flowing through them.

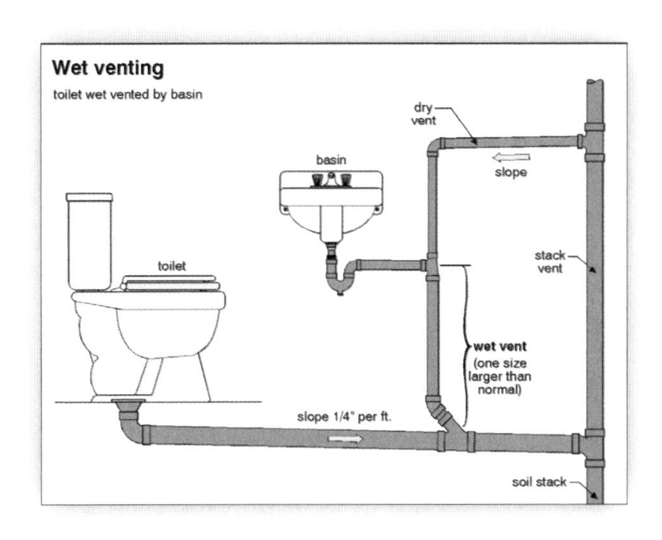

OUTSIDE VENTS When a basement bathroom is added to a home, it is difficult to run a vent pipe up through the house and roof. A vent is often run out through the wall and up the outside of the building. This is acceptable although not attractive, and frost closure problems in cold climates both are more likely with this arrangement.

2.7 Sewage Ejector (Solid Waste) Pumps

DESCRIPTION Solid waste pumps are used where gravity cannot carry toilet waste away. Basement fixtures in a house with a septic system usually need a solid waste pump to carry the waste up to the main sewer line, which typically leaves the house halfway up the basement wall. These systems are expensive and relatively complex.

Solid waste pumps are installed in a tank with a sealed top. The plumbing fixtures drain into the tank, and as the tank fills, the pump comes on, discharging the waste to a city sewer or a septic system. The specially designed pump handles both solids and liquids. The incoming line is typically three-inch diameter and the discharge line is usually two inches. A vent pipe is typically connected to the top of the tank. Some have high level alarms to notify the homeowner of a malfunction.

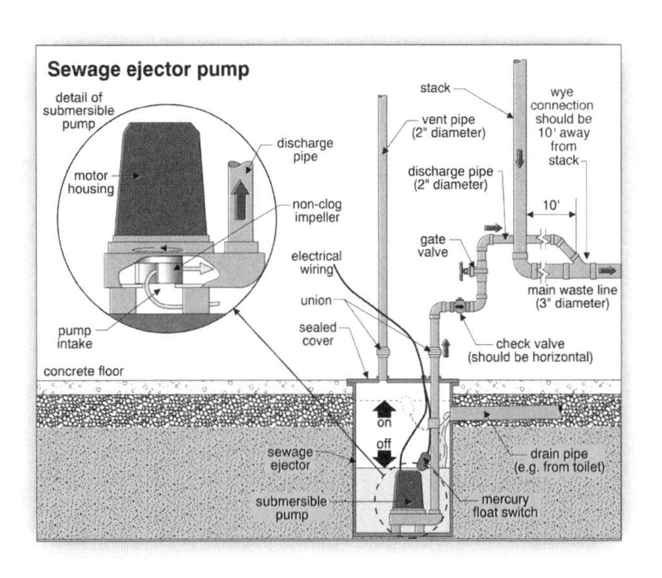

The discharge line should be equipped with a union (a connection fitting), a check valve (to prevent sewage moving backwards), and a shut-off valve, in that order.

Common Problems with Sewage Ejector Pumps

ELECTRIC SUPPLY/ MOTOR/PUMP PROBLEMS Problems can develop with the electrical supply or the electric motor. The pump can become obstructed or damaged.

LEAKS/CLOGS Leaks can develop in the holding tank, piping, or the connections. Clogs can develop in the piping systems draining into or out of the tank. Care must be taken with these systems, since raw sewage is a health hazard.

2.8 Sump Pumps

DESCRIPTION A sump pump is used to lift storm water from a low spot into a storm sewer or other discharge point, well away from the house. This electric pump is located in a sump (pit) below the basement floor level. Sumps are typically plastic or concrete tubs. Foundation drainage tiles and/or downspouts may discharge into the sump. A float switch activates the pump as the water level in the sump rises.

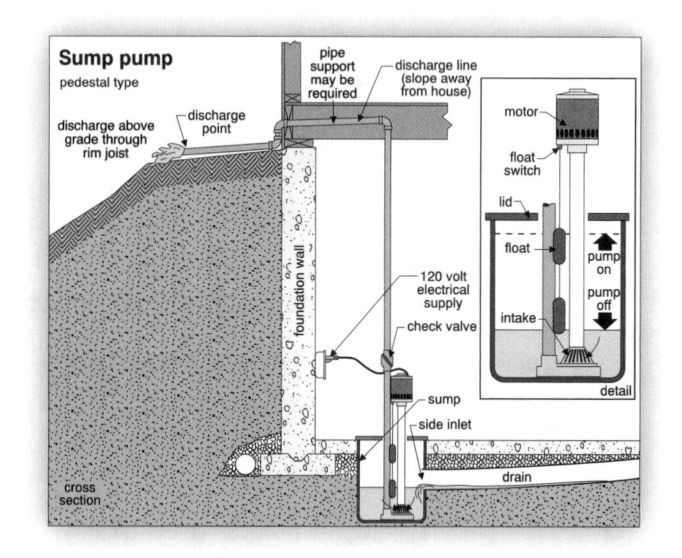

Pedestal type sump pumps are more common, less expensive and less reliable than submersible pumps.

Common Problems with Sump Pumps

SUMP DETERIORATION Problems occur if the sump deteriorates and allows debris or earth to enter the pump mechanism.

PUMP FAILURES A sump pump failure can lead to considerable damage due to flooding. There are several reasons for failures. A back-up pump in the sump, a high-water alarm and back-up power are all options.

ELECTRICAL PROBLEMS If the electric supply to the pump is interrupted, during a power failure for example, the sump may flood. Since power failures often occur with heavy rains and storms, this can be a problem.

PUMP AND MOTOR ISSUES The pump mechanism or electric motor may become defective. Since the pumps are relatively inexpensive and easy to install, many people keep a spare pump on hand in case of failure. This, of course, will be a function of how critical the sump operation is. In many cases the sump operates only a few days per year; in other situations the pump may operate almost continuously.

FAILED FLOATS Problems with the float system that controls the pump are very common. These are inexpensive to replace and adjust, but regular maintenance and inspection should include testing to verify that they are not damaged, disconnected or entangled with the pump, the sump wall, or any foreign objects.

DISCHARGE PIPE PROBLEMS The discharge piping for the pump is often a source of leakage. The plastic piping can easily be crimped or damaged. It is often difficult to find the discharge point of the piping. It may discharge into a city sewer system, a storm ditch at the front of the property, a French drain (a buried gravel pit designed to allow water to accumulate quickly and dissipate slowly by soaking into the soil), or simply onto the ground, several feet from the house. Water in the discharge pipe may freeze in cold climates if the pipe slope is poor.

2.9 Laundry Tub Pumps

DESCRIPTION Where a laundry tub cannot drain by gravity into a waste system, an electric pump is usually provided below the tubs to carry water into a municipal sewer, a septic system or a dry well. Most municipalities now require gray water (waste water which does not contain human waste) to discharge into a sewer disposal system.

Some pumps have an automatic control (typically a float system within the tub), although many are manually operated by wall switches.

COMMON PROBLEMS WITH LAUNDRY TUB PUMPS The issues with laundry tub pumps are similar to sump pump problems. See above.

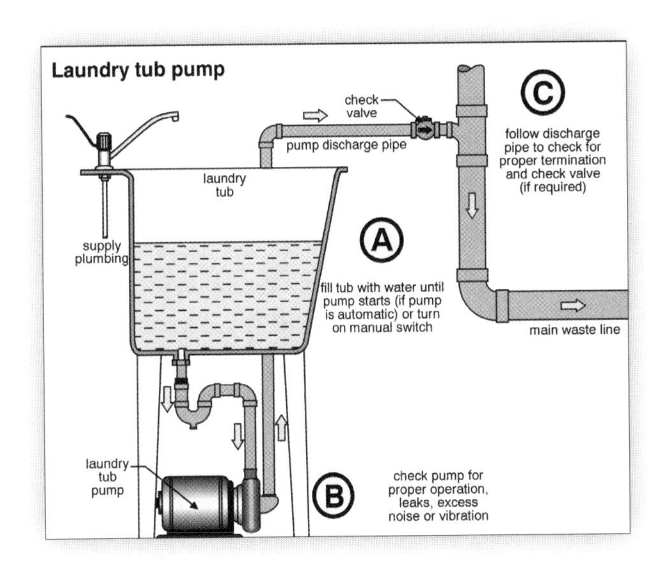

3.0 Plumbing Fixtures

3.1 Sinks

DESCRIPTION A sink is a fixture used for cleaning things, rather than people. A basin, on the other hand, is used for personal washing. We refer to a kitchen **sink,** but to a bathroom **basin.** Basins are also called **lavatories.**

Sinks may be made of stainless steel, enameled steel, enameled cast iron, copper, porcelain, and plastic, for example. Each material has its advantages and disadvantages. We don't want sinks to absorb things and support bacteria growth. Some areas do not permit sinks made of wood, concrete or tile.

A sink with an integral platform at the back for the faucets is generally better than a sink without such a platform. Since faucets often leak, we want the water to run off the platform into the sink, rather than onto the counter top. This is only an issue if the counter can be damaged by water. Particleboard counters are more vulnerable than granite counters, for example.

Sinks should have a crossbar, strainer or stopper to prevent large objects getting into the waste piping. Sinks typically do not have an overflow because we don't want bits of food collecting in an overflow pipe.

Common Problems with Sinks

LEAKAGE/ OVERFLOW Leakage may be the result of a cracked or rusted sink, or a poor drain connection. Sinks should not have overflows, though multiple sinks may have dividers that allow overflowing water from one sink to go into the next sink rather than onto the counter.

Poorly-secured sinks are prone to leakage. Sinks may rust or crack over time.

CROSS CONNECTION Cross connections with sinks are possible. A vegetable sprayer or extendable faucet can end up in a sink full of dirty water. Please refer to the discussion of Cross Connections on pages 304 and 305.

AIR GAP FITTINGS FOR DISHWASHERS In some areas, air gap fittings are required on the discharge from a dishwasher. This is typically a chrome fitting that projects roughly three inches above the counter top adjacent to the kitchen sink. Waste water from the dishwasher travels up to the air gap fitting and back down through another line into a food waste disposal or drainage piping. The flood level of the fitting must be above the rim of the kitchen sink and the kitchen counter top. This fitting prevents water or other waste from flowing back into a dishwasher. If water discharges from the air gap fitting during dishwasher use, service is required.

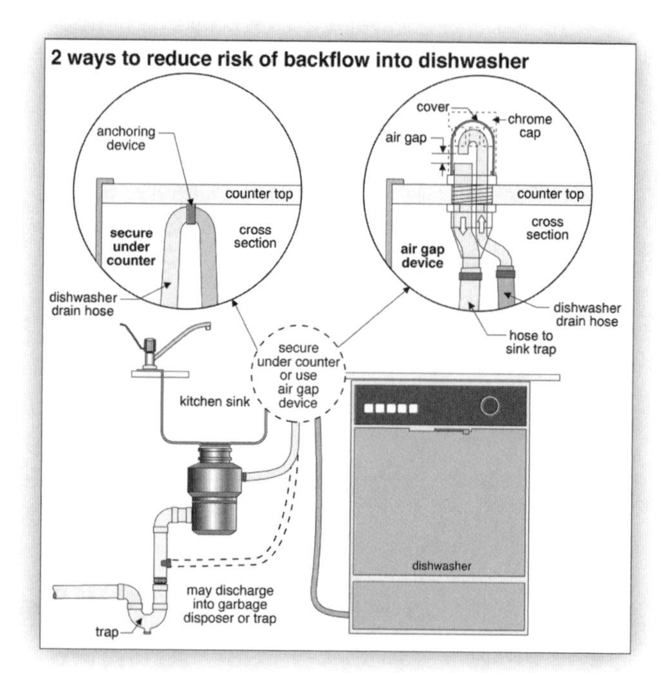

Air gap fittings are not required if the dishwasher has an integral backflow preventer.

SECURE A HIGH LOOP UNDER COUNTER When an air gap device is not required, the dishwasher's drain hose should be secured to the underside of the countertop creating a high loop to help prevent backflow.

3.2 Basins

DESCRIPTION Basins, typically located in washrooms or bathrooms, may be made of several materials including stainless steel, enameled steel, enameled cast iron, copper, vitreous china, plastic, marble simulated marble, etc. None of these materials will last forever, and all have their strengths and weaknesses.

Basins should have a crossbar, strainer or stopper to prevent large objects getting into the waste piping. Basins typically have overflows.

Common Problems with Basins

LEAKAGE/ OVERFLOW Common problems include leakage and overflowing. Most bathroom basins, but not all, contain overflows. Where there is no overflow, the basin should not be left unattended while filling.

RUST Many enameled steel basins have a welded steel overflow, which is a common spot for rusting to occur. This rusting, visible from the underside, will eventually result in leakage and can appear just a few years into the life of the fixture. Some basins rely on a siliconed joint rather than a welded seam.

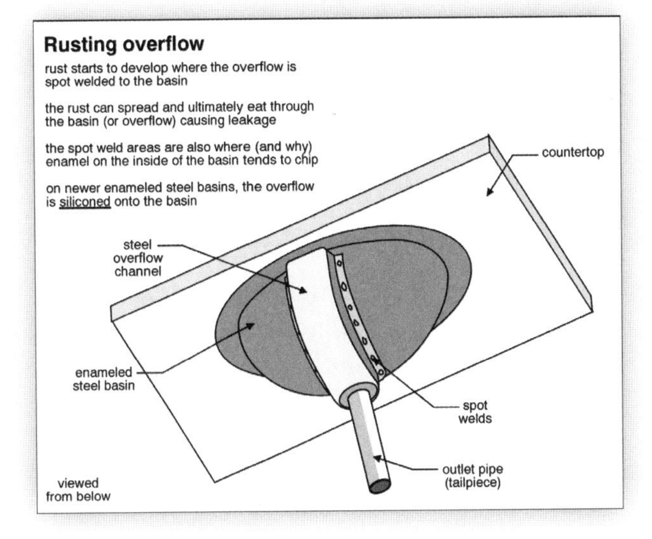

CRACKS Cracking of cultured marble sinks around the drain connection is common. This does not normally lead to leakage in the short term, but is unsightly. Ultimately the basin has to be replaced.

Cross connections with basins are possible, although not common. Please refer to the discussion of cross connections on pages 304 and 305.

PLUMBING

3.3 Laundry Tubs

Traditional concrete laundry tubs have been replaced, for the most part, by steel and plastic tubs.

Common Problems with Laundry Tubs

CRACKS/LEAK The concrete tubs, although durable, are heavy and ultimately are prone to cracking. Replacing the tubs is not expensive. Lead waste plumbing common with older tubs is usually replaced with plastic pipe when the tubs are replaced.

CROSS CONNECTIONS Older laundry tubs may be subject to cross connections. It should be ensured that the faucet set is above the laundry tub, so there is no possibility of the faucet becoming submerged when the tub is full. Refer to the discussion of cross connections on pages 304 and 305.

3.4 Faucets

DESCRIPTION There are many types and styles of faucets with a wide range of qualities available. The traditional compression faucet employs a stem washer to shut off the water when the washer is turned down against a seat. Leakage through the faucet usually means a deteriorated washer. Leakage around the handle of a faucet usually indicates deteriorated packing. Both problems require minor repairs, and leaking packing is considered to be a greater threat than a leaking stem washer. A leaking washer will only allow water to drip into the fixture, while leaking packing will allow water to run onto a counter top, where it may cause damage.

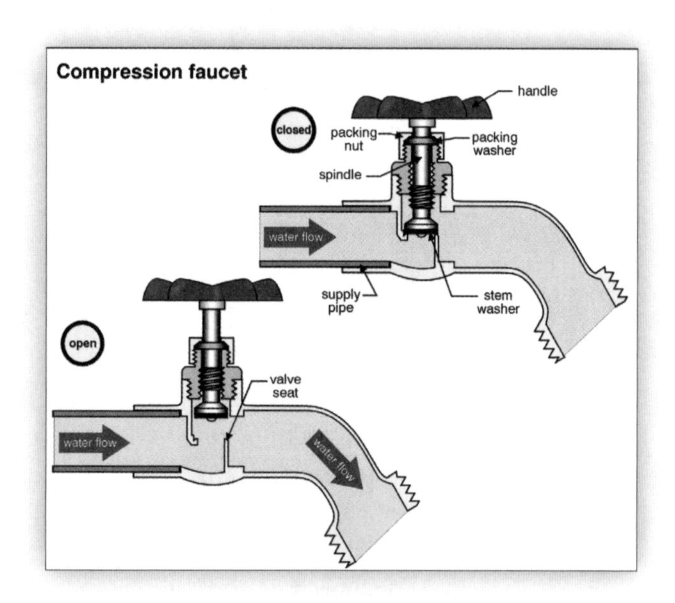

Many modern faucets use a cartridge, ceramic disc, or ball valve to control water flow. Single-lever and twin handle faucets are both common for sink, basin and bathtub use.

There are sophisticated faucets available for showers, which will maintain the temperature selected, irrespective of pressure changes in the system. For example, if someone is having a shower, and two other cold water fixtures in the house are turned on, the cold water pressure to the shower will decrease. This can lead to scalding, since there is now much more hot water being delivered than cold.

A temperature- or pressure-sensitive mixing valve will adjust to this automatically, maintaining the desired temperature.

Common Problems with Faucets

LEAKS/DAMAGE Leakage and difficulty in operating the valve are the two most common problems. Damaged faucet handles may be dangerous if there are jagged edges.

LOOSE It is common for a faucet to be poorly secured to the wall, counter top or fixture. This is a minor problem, although it can be difficult to access. If not corrected, it may result in leakage.

3.5 Outdoor Faucets (Hose Bibs)

DESCRIPTION Outdoor faucets are conventional cold water supply valves, typically. The water is shut off by another valve in the building interior during the winter months in cold climates. The outside valve is typically left open to allow any water in the pipe to escape. The inside winter shut off valve may be provided with an auxiliary bleed valve to allow any water between the two valves to escape.

Backflow preventers are now required in many jurisdictions on outdoor faucets to protect against cross connections. See cross connections on pages 304 and 305 .

FROST-PROOF Frost-proof valves for hose bibs do not have to be shut off in the winter in cold climates. These valves have a long stem that penetrates through the building wall and shuts off the water supply inside the building. These valves should be sloped to drain any water in the stem to the outdoors.

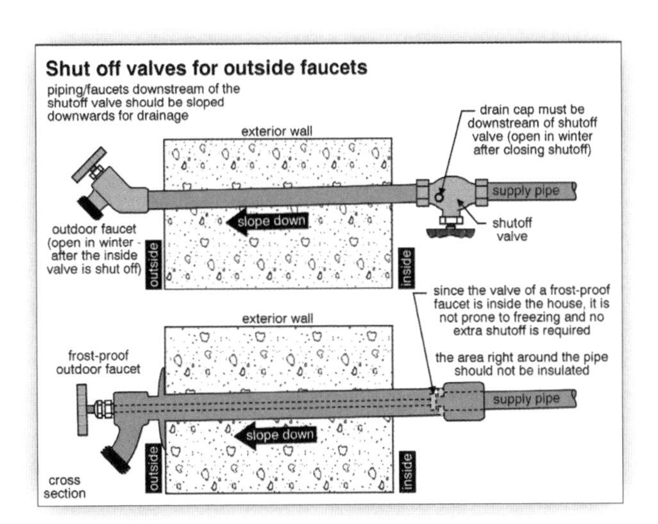

Common Problems with Outdoor Faucets

LEAKAGE/ DAMAGE Outdoor faucets are susceptible to washer and packing failure and resultant leakage. They are also more vulnerable to mechanical damage than inside valves. Because of their exposure to extremes of weather, it is possible for the valves to become inoperative. Replacement of these is not a major expense.

BACKFLOW PREVENTERS Missing backflow preventers can be added easily and inexpensively.

FREEZING Conventional hose bibs can be damaged by freezing, if they are not turned off in cold weather.

3.6 Toilets

DESCRIPTION Most toilets are made of vitreous china, although other materials are occasionally used. There are several different styles of toilets and several different flush mechanisms. Some of the older toilets have relatively weak flush mechanisms and are more prone to clogging. Many modern toilets are low-flush, designed to conserve water. Some of these do not handle solid waste as well as traditional toilets. Dual-flush toilets use different amounts of water for liquid and solid waste. Toilets are the only common plumbing fixture that does not need a trap – because there is one built in.

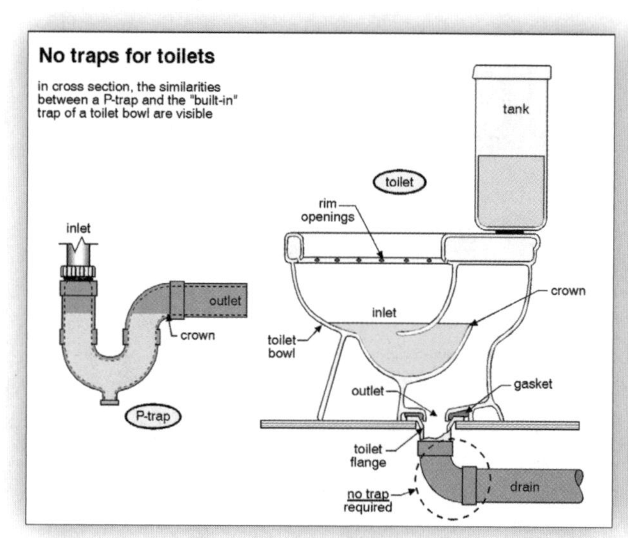

No traps for toilets

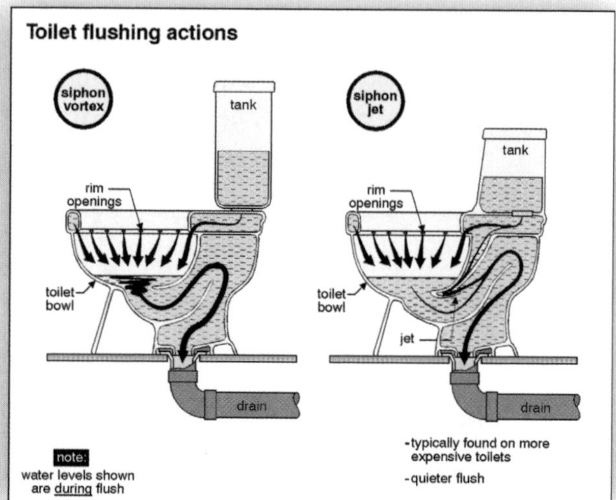

Toilet flushing actions

Common Problems with Toilets

LEAKAGE Problems can occur with leakage at the toilet supply line, at the storage tank, at the connection between the tank and the bowl, at the bowl itself (e.g. if the bowl is cracked), or at the connection between the toilet bottom and the drain pipe. Damage to the floor finishes and floor structural components around toilets is a common problem.

LOOSE Toilets are often poorly secured to the floor system. This can result in leakage at the base of the toilet over the long term. It is usually easy to secure a loose toilet, unless the floor has rotted.

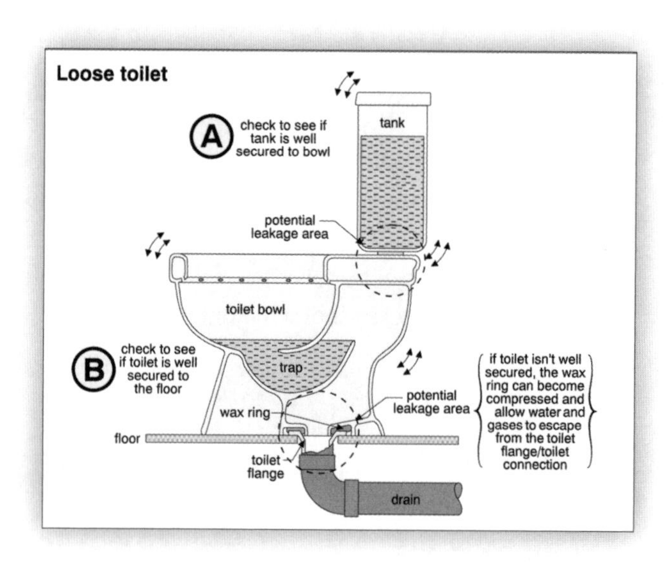

Loose toilet

INOPERATIVE / RUNNING CONTINUOUSLY If a toilet does not flush at all, there is usually no water in the tank due to a supply problem. If the toilet runs continuously, this means there is leakage from the tank into the bowl. While this will not cause any direct water damage, a continuously running cold water pipe and a continuously running drain may lead to condensation problems on the outside of these pipes, particularly during warm humid weather. The resulting water damage can be significant. A continuously running toilet also wastes a good deal of water. Repairs to the flush mechanism are needed. The flush mechanism is a relatively complicated mechanical device and problems may develop with the float, rod, plunger, ball cock, filler tube, refill tube, trip lever, tank ball, etc. These are typically inexpensive repairs.

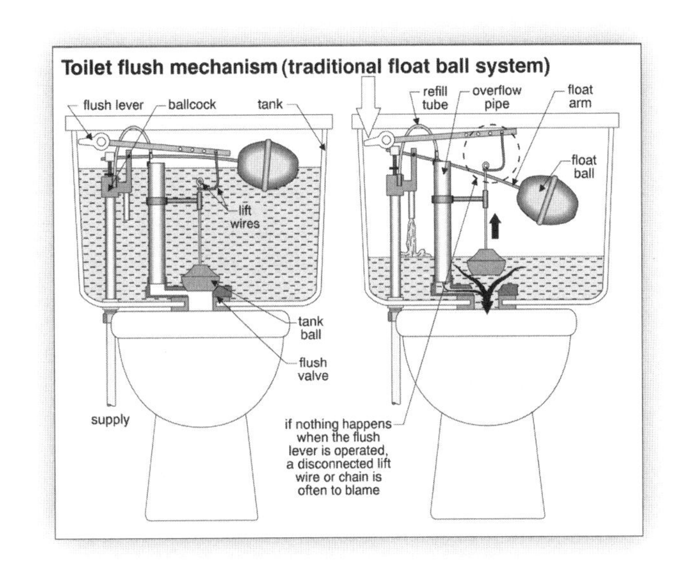

SLOW FLUSH Slow flushing toilets are usually partially obstructed. In some cases, a plunger will clear the obstruction; in others, a plumber's snake is necessary. Occasionally, the toilet has to be temporarily removed to get at the problem.

SEAT ISSUES Problems with the toilet seat are not functional from a plumbing standpoint. Seats can usually be replaced readily.

3.7 Bathtubs

DESCRIPTION Bathtubs may be free-standing or built-in, and may be enameled cast iron, enameled steel, fiber glass, plastic, etc. Custom bathtubs can be made of tile, marble or copper, for example.

SLOPE The bathtub should be installed so water in the tub will flow naturally to the drain, and so water on the shelf around the perimeter of the tub will run into, not out of the tub.

Cast iron bathtubs are credited with keeping the water hotter than the modern tubs, although this is not a big issue for most people. Some builders add insulation around modern steel and acrylic tubs, to keep the water hot and reduce the noise of water hitting the tub. Sprayed-on insulation also makes the tub feel more rigid and substantial.

Common Problems with Bathtubs

DAMAGE/ LEAKAGE Bathtubs are susceptible to chipped enamel, rusting, and leakage through supply or drain connections.

LEAK AT OVERFLOW Bathtub overflows are a common source of leaks. Since they are not used on a regular basis, they are often installed poorly with the potential for leakage. When the bathtub does overflow in an emergency, water may escape around the overflow connection. A home inspection does not include testing overflows, since they often leak, causing concealed damage.

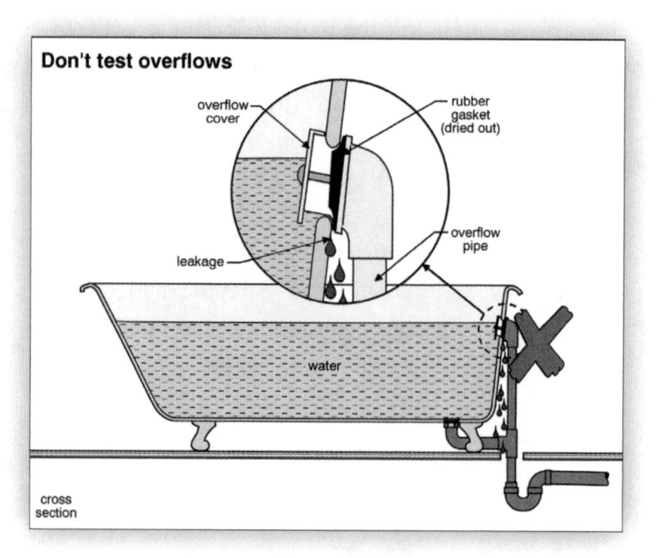

LEAK AT TUB/TILE INTERSECTION When leakage is noted on a ceiling below a bathroom, the source is usually the bathtub area. In many cases, the leakage is not from the bathtub, but from the connection between the tub and tile enclosure. Conventional bathtubs have a one-inch lip around the top of the tub on the side and ends against the wall. When the wall is finished, the lip cannot be seen, since it goes up behind the ceramic tile. This lip is intended to minimize leakage at the tub/tile intersection. This lip is often not effective in preventing leaks. Early signs of a problem may be loose ceramic tiles.

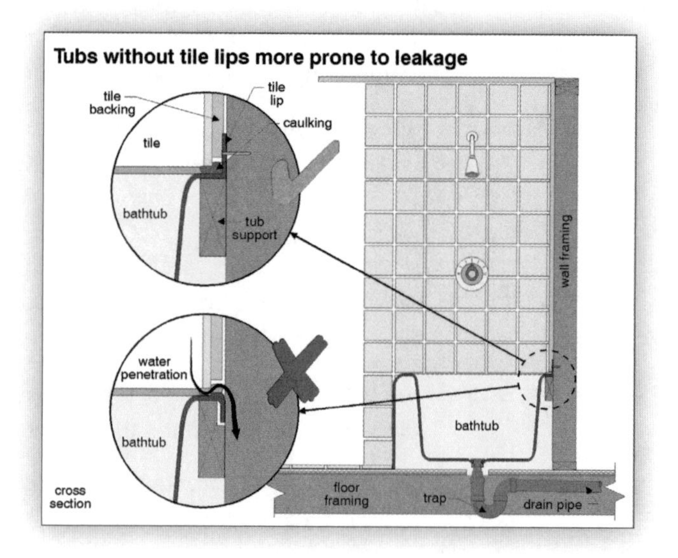

3.8 Bathtub Enclosures

DESCRIPTION Bathtub enclosures may be ceramic tile, plastic, marble or other stone, simulated marble tile, glass tile, plastic tile or plastic laminates. All of these materials, if properly installed, are considered acceptable. Modern one-piece acrylic or fiber glass enclosures are also considered effective if properly installed. Porous materials including wood enclosures and hardboard materials with a simulated tile finish are not considered good long-term materials where a shower is to be used.

TILES IN CONCRETE In older houses, it is common to find ceramic tiles set in concrete. This is a good installation method and the life of the tile system can be 50 years or more. This system, however, is expensive to remove during remodeling.

TILES GLUED ON Modern tile application typically uses an adhesive, that bonds the tile to plaster, drywall, plywood or a lightweight concrete board. This method of securing tiles is less desirable since the adhesive can be weakened as water gets in behind the tile. Perhaps more importantly, concealed wall surfaces such as plaster, drywall or wood can be damaged by the water.

BEHIND THE TILES Where drywall is used in a bathtub or shower stall enclosure behind the tile, water-resistant type (green drywall) is better than ordinary drywall. This is not waterproof drywall, but does afford some protection against moisture. Cement board (a lightweight concrete panel) is better still.

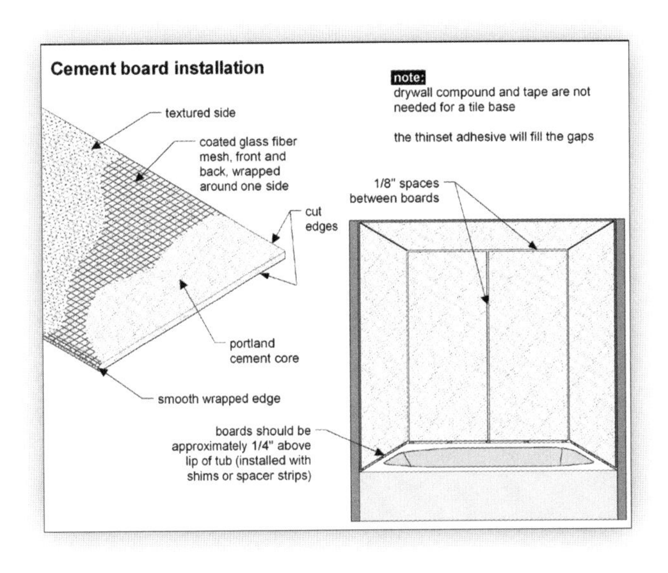

GROUT AND CAULK Water penetrates a tile enclosure two ways, typically. Openings in grout joints or poor grout mixes will allow water to pass through during showers. Secondly, the connection between the tile and the tub is a weak spot. No matter what quality caulking is used, over a period of time, an opening will develop between the tub and tile. Although there is often a lip on the tub going up about one inch behind the tile, this does not always prevent water damage. Since bathtubs will flex to some degree, when filled with water and a person, this movement contributes to deterioration of the caulking.

Common Problems with Bathtub Enclosures

LEAKS AROUND TILE OPENINGS Leakage can occur in the bathtub enclosure through openings created for faucets, spouts and soap dishes, for example.

LOOSE TILE When the tile is loose or buckling, the tile must be removed, and in many cases the support material (plaster, drywall or plywood) must also be replaced. Low-density concrete boards are better than drywall or plywood in terms of rigidity and resistance to moisture.

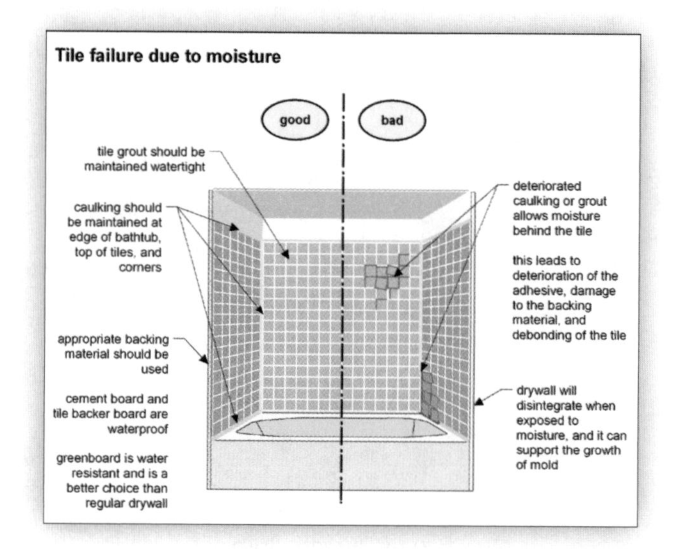

RISK OF DAMAGE CONCEALED There is often considerable concealed damage around and below bathtubs and showers that cannot be identified until things are pulled apart.

DAMAGE AROUND WINDOWS Windows can be damaged by water in bathtubs with a shower. Interior window sills should be avoided as much as possible, as should any other horizontal ledges that allow water to collect.

3.9 Shower Stalls

DESCRIPTION Traditionally, shower stalls were often lined with ceramic tile, glass or marble tile. Modern one-, two- or three-piece shower stalls in fiberglass or acrylic are popular. Some of these are quite good quality. One of the problems with fiberglass and acrylic is that abrasive cleansers will scratch the surface, making it almost impossible to clean.

Metal shower stalls are typically low quality and are prone to rusting around the bottom within the first few years.

Common Problems with Shower Stalls

TILE LEAKAGE Shower stalls are notorious for leakage through the tile work. Since there is lots of tile work in traditional shower stalls (all walls and the floor typically), any small openings in the grout or caulking may cause problems. Because shower stalls are often poorly lit, small tile flaws often go unnoticed until damage appears below. Leakage through the faucet and soap dish joints is common.

BOTTOM PAN LEAK The construction of the tile shower stall includes a lead (traditional) or neoprene (modern) pan around the bottom of the stall. This one-piece pan below the tile typically extends up about six inches above the bottom of the shower floor on all four sides. This pan will catch minor leakage, although if it is not well secured around the drain, leakage will develop here. In the event of a serious leak, this pan will not be effective. Tile shower stalls are very expensive to rebuild, and are sometimes replaced with fiberglass or acrylic shower stalls. One-piece china shower bases are also available. New shower enclosure approaches include a continuous membrane in the pan and up the sides of the stall behind the tile.

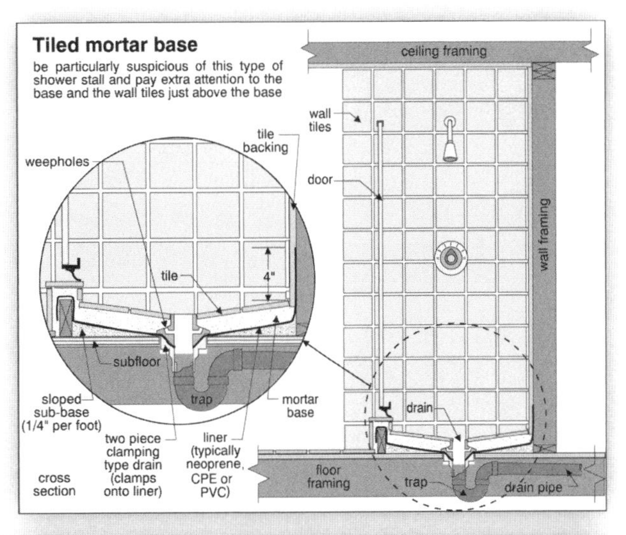

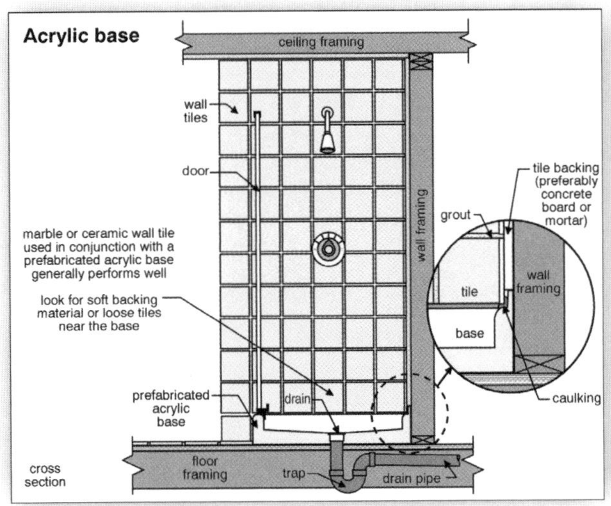

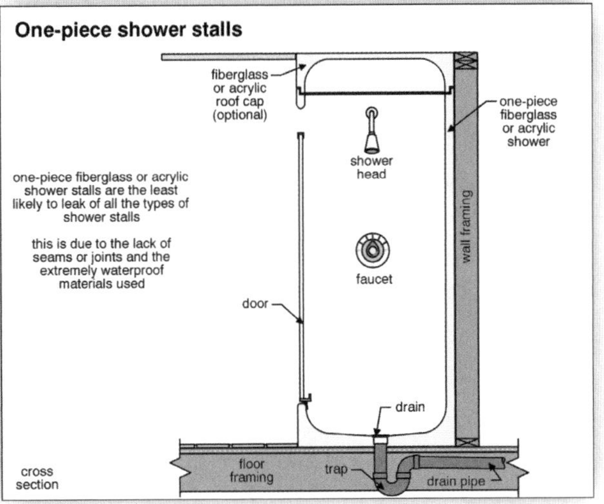

RISK OF CONCEALED DAMAGE There is often considerable concealed damage around and below bathtubs and showers that cannot be identified until things are pulled apart.

RUSTED METAL SHOWER STALL These low-quality shower stalls are often deteriorated by rust. This can result in leakage and water damage to adjacent house components.

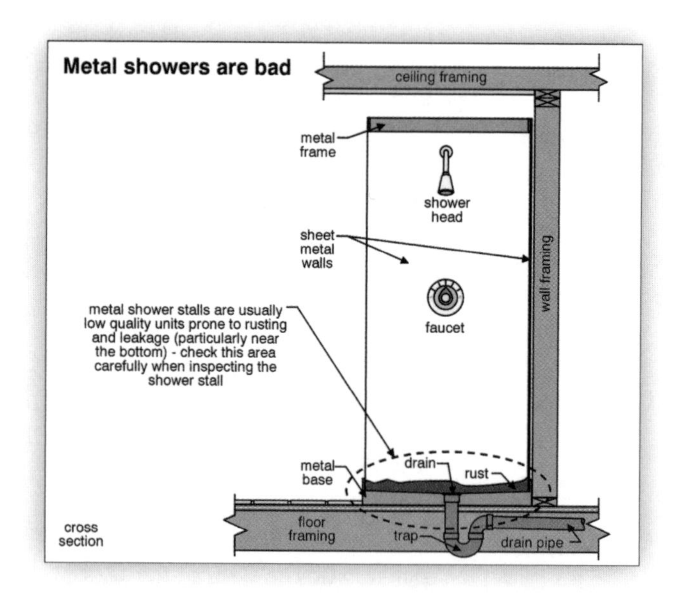

3.10 Whirlpool Baths

DESCRIPTION A whirlpool bath is essentially a conventional bathtub with a circulating pump, supply jets and a return intake. Whirlpool baths can be very large, and contain a great deal of water when filled. In some cases, the floor structure below has to be strengthened to carry the load.

GFCI The electric supply to the whirlpool should be protected by a ground fault circuit interrupter. This is a special, highly sensitive device that will shut off the electricity in the event of a very small electrical fault. This additional safety is important where water and electricity come together.

SERVICE ACCESS A readily accessible service door to work on the pump and motor should be provided. Where this is not available, repairs will be more expensive.

LARGER WATER HEATER Larger whirlpools may require larger water heaters to ensure the tub can be filled with hot water. Some manufacturers recommend water temperatures not exceed 104°F, to avoid discoloration of the acrylic surface.

CIRCULATION SYSTEM The circulation pipes and pump should be arranged to drain after use. We don't want water to accumulate and promote concealed growth of bacteria, etc.

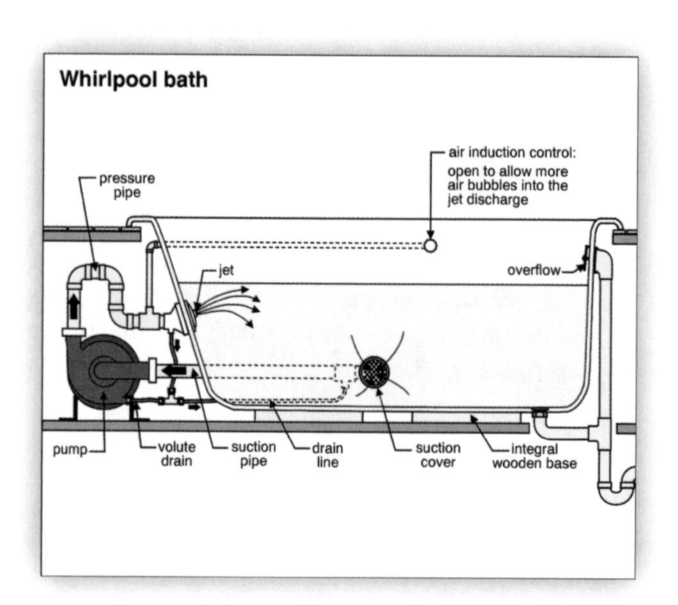

Common Problems with Whirlpool Tubs

PUMP AND MOTOR PROBLEMS Problems may develop with the electric motor or the pump mechanism. If the system does not respond to the operating controls, a service technician may be needed. While it cannot be determined during an home inspection, standing water should not remain in the pump or piping system to avoid bacteria growth and health issues.

LEAK/ACCESS ISSUES Leaks or obstructions in the piping lines around the tub can appear, and may be difficult to access and repair. Connection points of the piping to the tub may be potential leakage areas as well.

ELECTRICAL SUPPLY – NO GFCI Ground fault circuit interrupters should be installed where missing.

3.11 Bidets

DESCRIPTION Bidets are complex plumbing fixtures that are susceptible to cross connections. As a result, a vacuum breaker is provided at the supply piping connection to a bidet. This prevents waste water from flowing back into the supply water.

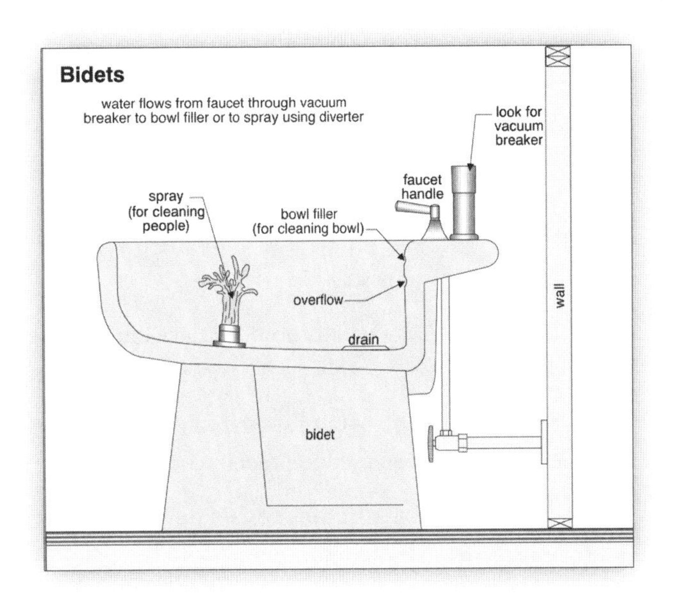

Common Problems with Bidets

CRACKS/LEAKS/ CLOGS/VALVE ISSUES Most bidets are china, and are subject to cracking or leakage. In areas of hard water, the small jets of a bidet can become clogged. Control valves and diverters may leak or break.

3.12 Bathroom Fans

DESCRIPTION Exhaust fans are recommended in all bathrooms, and are more important where a bathroom does not have an operable window.

DISCHARGE OUTSIDE The fan should discharge directly to the building exterior. In many cases, the fan terminates inside the house or roof space. This can add considerable moisture to a house, leading to condensation and rot problems.

CAPACITY The exhaust fan should provide at least 12 air changes per hour. That means it should replace all the air in the room every 5 minutes. For example, in a bathroom that is 320 cubic feet (five feet by eight feet by eight feet high) the exhaust fan should have a capability of more than 64 cfm (cubic feet per minute).

Common Problems with Bathroom Fans

MISSING The concentration of moisture in a bathroom where showers are used can lead to premature failure of interior finishes such as paint and wallpaper, and result in mildew and rot in concealed areas.

NOISY Lower quality bathroom fans are noisier than better quality fans. The fan may be operated by a separate switch, or by the room light switch. Timers on bathroom fans are useful, so the fan can run for a few minutes after a person leaves the bathroom to get rid of the accumulated moisture.

INOPERATIVE Many bathroom fans are inoperative because the motor or fan mechanism has failed. Some occupants disconnect the fan, irritated by the noise.

NO DUCT INSULATION Where the exhaust fan ductwork passes through unheated spaces such as attics, it should be insulated to prevent condensation.

POOR TERMINATION POINTS Exhaust fans should never discharge into attics, roof spaces or chimneys. Ductwork running through the attic should be insulated to prevent condensation inside the duct.

3.13 Kitchen Fans

DESCRIPTION The kitchen fan may discharge outside, or may simply re-circulate the air into the kitchen after passing it through a charcoal filter. Most fans that discharge outside have some sort of filter. In either case, the filters should be cleaned and/or replaced, following the manufacturer's recommendations.

DOWN-DRAFT Some cooktops have built-in fans with down draft that exhaust air from the cooktop area. On some appliances, these fans are of modest capacity, and the fan performance may be weak where the exhaust ductwork to the exterior is lengthy or contains several bends.

Common Problems with Kitchen Fans

NO DUCT INSULATION Exhaust fan ductwork passing through unheated areas such as attics should be insulated to prevent condensation.

DISCHARGE INTO CHIMNEY Kitchen fans should never discharge into chimneys.

INOPERATIVE An inoperative kitchen fan is usually the result of an interruption in the electrical supply, or failure of the electric motor. The fan itself can be jammed or the bearings may have failed.

OVERSIZED FANS Kitchen fans may be so powerful that they cause furnaces and water heaters to backdraft, drawing dangerous combustion products into the home.

Interior

INTRODUCTION

THE INTERIOR OF A HOME PROVIDES CLUES TO STRUCTURAL ISSUES AND IS OFTEN THE AREA WHERE WATER LEAKAGE IS FIRST NOTED. THE INTERIOR FINISHES THEMSELVES REFLECT THE OVERALL BUILDING QUALITY, AND THEIR CONDITION INDICATES THE LEVEL OF MAINTENANCE.

EACH ROOM SHOULD HAVE AN ADEQUATE HEAT SUPPLY AND SUFFICIENT ELECTRICAL OUTLETS. DOORS AND WINDOWS SHOULD OPERATE PROPERLY. HOME INSPECTORS FOCUS ON FUNCTION RATHER THAN APPEARANCE, AND EMPHASIS IS PLACED ON WHETHER THE ROOM WILL WORK AS IT WAS INTENDED. THE HOME INSPECTOR DOES NOT COMMENT ON COSMETICS.

1.0 Major Floor Finishes

DESCRIPTION Floors provide a durable surface for foot traffic and furniture. Good floors are level, have an even surface, and are low maintenance. Floors can be an architectural feature of the home. Some floors are water resistant; some are soft to walk on; some require no sealing or waxing; some are quiet; some are particularly long lasting.

1.1 Concrete

DESCRIPTION Concrete floor finishes are typically only used in basements and garages. The floor should slope down to a floor drain in basements and other areas where water may accumulate.

In modern construction, a four to six inch gravel base below the 3-inch thick floor slab allows water below the slab to drain away. Moisture barriers (plastic sheets) may also be provided under the slab, and in energy efficient construction or slab-on-grade construction, rigid insulation may be used below the floor.

In older construction, concrete floor slabs were as thin as 1/2 inch. These are prone to impact damage, heaving and break-up. This is a cosmetic issue and may be a trip hazard.

Most concrete floors are not part of the structure. Basement floors are typically installed after the home is completed, and their main function is to keep our feet out of the mud.

Concrete basement floors can be overlaid with finished flooring. Since almost every house with a basement has water on the basement floor at some point, water-resistant floors make sense.

In slab-on-grade construction, the concrete floors provide a substrate for floor finishes.

1.2 Hardwood

DESCRIPTION Hardwood floors are traditionally oak, although other woods such as cherry, walnut, birch, beech, mahogany, elm and maple, are also used. Bamboo is not technically wood, but is also used as flooring. Hardwood flooring may be in the form of strips or parquet, which often consist of six inch squares with each square made up of six one-inch strips. The squares are laid with the grain in adjoining squares at right angles, giving a checkerboard effect. Parquet flooring may be nailed or glued down. There are several different types and installation techniques. Parquet flooring can also be made up of a combination of rectangles, triangles and lozenges and can be very decorative and very expensive.

Strip flooring is typically tongue and groove, secured with nails driven diagonally through the tongues into the subfloor. Hardwood flooring in modern construction is typically 3/8 inch to 3/4 inch thick and may be pre-finished or finished on site.

Hardwood flooring is a high quality and durable floor system. It can be mechanically damaged, attacked by termites, rot and fire, or damaged by water. Wood flooring is not ideally suited to kitchen and bathroom areas, since it is susceptible to water damage. Nonetheless, hardwood flooring is regularly found in kitchens. Individual boards can be replaced, but matching can be tricky.

Worn 3/8 inch thick hardwood flooring can be sanded once to provide a new wood surface. 3/4 inch hardwood flooring can be sanded several times before the tongues are exposed. Wood flooring can be covered with carpeting or other flooring materials.

1.3 Laminate and Engineered Wood

LAMINATE In recent years, laminate flooring has become very popular, especially among do-it-yourselfers. Laminate floor planks (or tiles) have several layers. The top layer is generally a clear laminate that is bonded to a decorative layer below, often creating the look of a wood floor. These layers are bonded to a wood- or fiber-based core. The bottom layer may be a paper or melamine backing. The product is similar to resilient countertops. A complete floor is created by either snapping planks together with specially-designed fasteners along the edges, or by gluing planks together along traditional tongue and groove edges.

Laminate flooring is not secured to the subfloor beneath it. Instead, it is installed as a floating floor, allowing it to expand and contract. A sheet of cushioning foam is installed between the laminate flooring and the subfloor. There may also be a sheet of plastic below the foam to act as a moisture barrier and to allow the floor to slide as it expands. A gap is required between the flooring and the walls to allow for expansion. This gap is covered by trim.

Laminate flooring cannot be sanded, stained, or otherwise refinished, although damaged planks can be replaced. Laminate flooring is resistant to small amounts of water, such as quickly wiped-up spills, but precautions should be taken in kitchens or bathrooms including applying a sealant around the perimeter. This is not visible during a home inspection. Laminate flooring should not be installed in damp basement areas.

ENGINEERED WOOD Engineered wood is similar to laminate flooring, except the thin top layer is actually hardwood that is bonded to a base that may be hardwood, plywood, or high-density fiberboard. The hardwood layer is usually pre-finished. The floor may be sanded and refinished, depending on the thickness of the hardwood layer.

Engineered wood flooring may be installed as a floating floor, or it may be glued, stapled, or nailed in place.

1.4 Softwood

DESCRIPTION Pine is the most common softwood flooring. Fir and cedar are also used. Pine floors were typically used as a subfloor or as finish flooring in a 1x4 tongue-and-groove configuration. When used as a subfloor below hardwood, the softwood was typically laid in 1x4 or 1x6 planks, perpendicular or diagonal to the floor joists. The boards were typically separated slightly to allow for expansion.

Softwood subflooring used under linoleum or other thin kitchen floor coverings was usually tongue-and-groove and tightly fit to provide a smooth, continuous surface to support the flexible flooring system. Modern construction often includes 1/4 inch plywood underlayment between the subfloor and finish flooring to provide a smooth surface for the finishing material.

1.5 Carpet

DESCRIPTION Carpet may be synthetic or natural fibers like wool. Synthetic carpeting is the most common and is a good choice in areas where the carpeting may become wet. Common materials include polypropylene, nylon and acrylic. Where the backing material is not moisture resistant, synthetic carpet will be quickly damaged if wet. Jute-backed carpets, for example, should be kept dry. Many types of synthetic carpet can be cleaned more easily than wool carpets. Synthetic carpeting is available in a wide variety of colors, weights and weaves.

Wool is an expensive material favored for its look, feel and durability. As synthetic products have improved and remain less expensive, wool is becoming rare. It is sometimes blended with a synthetic material. Wool is a natural product and is less resistant to water damage than synthetics. It also has less resistance to stains than some synthetics.

The quality of a carpeted floor depends upon the type, weight and construction of carpeting, the type of underpad, and the installation work.

1.6 Resilient

DESCRIPTION Resilient floor coverings include vinyl-asbestos, solid vinyl, vinyl faced, rubber, cork, asphalt and linoleum. It is installed in sheets or tiles. More expensive products include a cushioned backing material and a no-wax surface.

In modern construction, these materials are typically applied over a 1/4 inch plywood underlayment. These thin, flexible materials will show through any irregularities in the floor surface.

1.7 Ceramic/Quarry Tile

DESCRIPTION Generally considered high quality, ceramic or quarry tiles are hard, fired-clay products that may be glazed or unglazed. These materials stand up well to heat, water and normal wear and tear, and have good resistance to stains and cuts. These brittle floor systems will crack if not well supported. A conventional wood flooring system often has too much flex to support ceramic or quarry tile. Better installations include a concrete base for the tile, typically one to five inches thick. Tiles may be pressed into the concrete while it is setting. Joints are then grouted. Tiles are typically 1/16-inch to 1-inch thick and are commonly from 1 inch by 1 inch to 24 inches by 24 inches. Many shapes, colors, patterns and finishes are available.

In modern construction, a thin mortar base or adhesive is used over a thick subfloor. If well installed, this can be satisfactory. Again, joints have to be appropriately grouted. It is common for ceramic or quarry tile floors to be cracked where floor joists deflect, or in heavy traffic patterns. Tiles can be damaged by dropping tools, pots, pans or other heavy objects.

Traditionally, ceramic tile floors were used in bathrooms and vestibules, because of their natural resistance to moisture. Ceramic or quarry tile floors are used in kitchens, for the same reason, although they are unforgiving if one drops glass on them, and they are also more tiring to stand on because of their hard surface. Wet floors can be slippery.

1.8 Stone Floors – Slate, Granite, Limestone and Marble

DESCRIPTION These are natural materials cut into flooring tiles. Terrazzo is made of marble chips set in concrete, usually laid in squares defined by lead beading. The surface is polished to give a smooth floor. Terrazzo is more common in commercial buildings, hospitals and schools than in homes.

Stone and terrazzo are good flooring materials because of their strength, appearance and durability. Installation considerations are similar to ceramic and quarry tile, in that the weight of the material itself may deflect conventional flooring systems. Joints on stone floors are grouted.

Common Problems with Floor Finishes

WATER DAMAGE/ STAINS Common sources of water damage include leaks from roofs, windows, doors and skylights, plumbing leaks (especially toilets and showers), leaks from hot water heating systems, and condensation. Aquariums, room humidifiers or dehumidifiers, over-watering of plants, melting snow and ice from boots, etc. can all cause water damage.

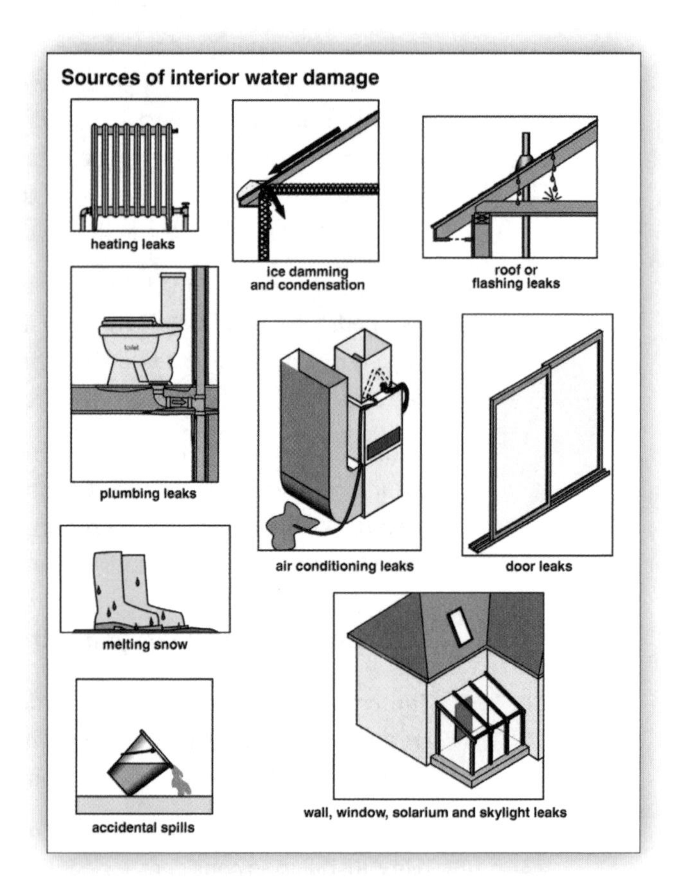

Wood-based floors may discolor, cup, buckle, warp or rot as a result of exposure to water. Carpet may develop mold. Flooring may be stained by water, food spills, improper cleaning, dirt, sunlight, or other factors.

MECHANICAL DAMAGE AND WEAR When softwoods such as pine, fir or cedar are used as finish floorings, they can be damaged by high heeled shoes, for example. Furniture marking and denting is another common problem with softwood and resilient floors.

Softer materials, such as resilient flooring and carpet, will eventually wear out in high traffic areas. Sharp objects and furniture dropped or dragged across flooring may also damage the surface.

CRACKED OR BROKEN The most common problem with brittle floor tiles is cracking. This is usually the result of a floor system that is not stiff enough to support the tile. Tiles can also be cracked by impact damage. Heavy items dropped on the tiles will sometimes crack or break them. Replacing individual tiles is not difficult, although color, style and grout matching may be a problem.

A cracked and broken concrete floor may only be a problem if it is not safe to walk across, or if there is moisture coming up through the floor. Since it is not a structural component, replacement of this floor is rarely a priority item.

LOOSE, TRIP HAZARD Loose or missing sections of flooring should be replaced. These areas may present a trip hazard. Carpet with ridges and buckles can be pulled tight to lie flat again by a carpet installer.

IMPROPER APPLICATION Some ceramic tiles are intended for wall use only. When used on floors, they will wear quickly. Carpet may not be laid flat. Wood flooring may not be well secured. Tile and stone may not be set properly. Grout may be poor quality or an incorrect type.

SQUEAKY FLOORS Squeaky wood floors are a nuisance, not a structural problem. A floor usually squeaks when walked on because the flooring finish or subfloor is not tightly secured. The subfloor may not be well-secured to the joists, or the finished flooring material (e.g. hardwood) may not be tightly fastened to the subfloor.

Flooring that is not tightly secured sits just above the support in some spots. When someone steps on the flooring in this area, it is pushed down onto its support. When the foot is taken off the floor, it springs back up. The squeaking is usually the result of the nails sliding in and out of the nail holes, or adjacent wood surfaces rubbing.

POOR SLOPE A concrete basement or crawl space floor that does not slope down to a floor drain can lead to water accumulation on the floor and resulting damage. Adding more concrete to an existing slab to improve the drainage slope is difficult, since new concrete does not usually bond well to old concrete. A better solution may be to add another floor drain. This is expensive, because it requires breaking up some of the concrete floor. Replacing a deteriorated floor may be more cost effective than trying to repair or re-slope the floor.

BURNS Most types of flooring are susceptible to burns, with the exception of stone, terrazzo, ceramic and quarry tile.

2.0 Major Wall Finishes

DESCRIPTION Wall finishes provide a decorative skin to conceal building components including structural members, insulation, ductwork, pipes, and wires. Good wall finishes are plumb and straight. Surfaces may be smooth or textured and better wall finishes are durable. Some wall finishes are versatile, taking decorative finishes such as stain, paint or wallpaper readily. Walls may make a decorating statement, or may be simply background. In some cases, the combustibility of wall finishes may be an issue. In kitchens and bathrooms, resistance to water damage is an asset.

2.1 Plaster/Drywall

DESCRIPTION Plaster and drywall are essentially the same material. Drywall is manufactured while plaster is mixed and applied by trowel on site. Plaster and drywall are made largely of gypsum, a common mineral (calcium sulphate hydrate).

These interior finishes are very common because they are inexpensive, relatively easy to apply, stable and afford good fire resistance.

WOOD LATH Older plaster systems employ a wood lath, comprised of boards roughly 1 inch wide by 1/4 inch thick. These "yardstick" type boards were nailed to the studs or strapping horizontally, with roughly 1/4 inch spaces between each board. The plaster was then troweled on in two or three coats. The first coat of plaster would ooze through the spaces between the wood lath, sag, and harden to form a "key" which held the plaster onto the lath. This first layer is called a "scratch" coat. Where a three-step process is used, the second coat is called the "brown" coat and the third is a "finish or putty" coat. In a two-step process, there is still a scratch coat and a brown coat, but they are applied one immediately after the other. The finish coat is applied after the brown coat has set.

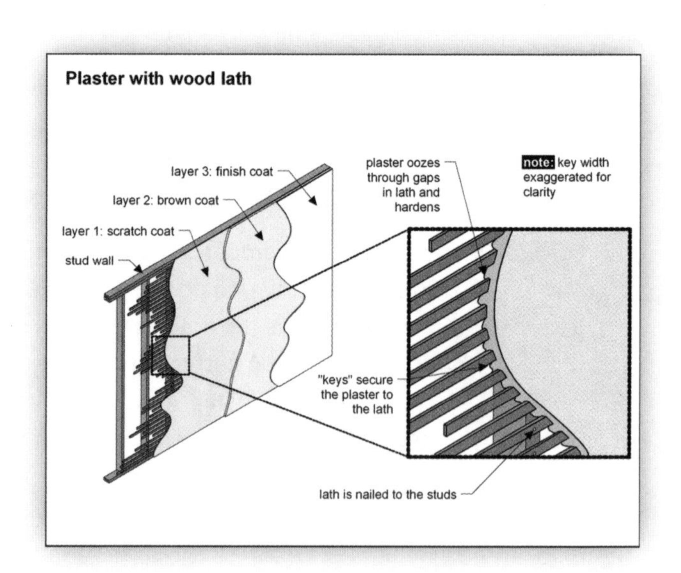

GYPSUM LATH In the 1930s, gypsum lath became popular. These manufactured plaster sheets replaced wood lath because they were quicker and less expensive to install. The gypsum lath was paper covered, similar to drywall. It came in various sizes, but was typically 16 inches by 48 inches. The gypsum lath was covered with one or two coats of plaster and the total thickness of the system was 1/2 to 5/8 inch. The lath itself is typically 3/8 inch thick.

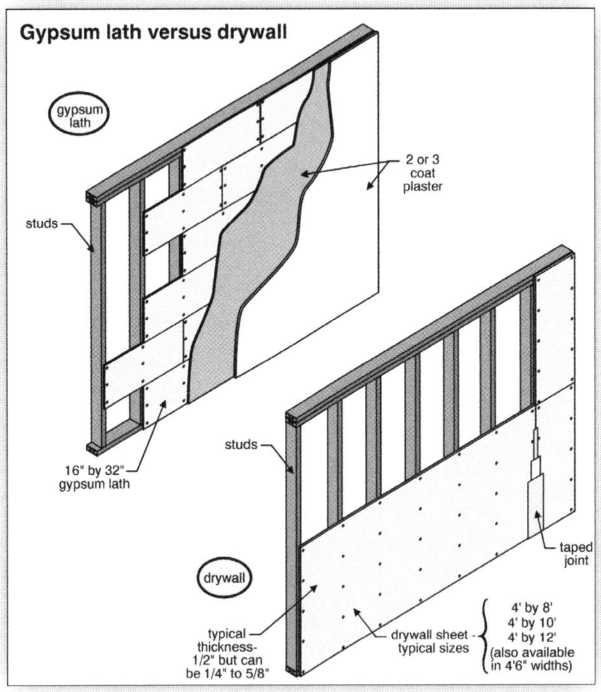

Gypsum lath versus drywall

WIRE LATH Wire mesh lath was sometimes used where reinforcing was necessary, for example, on door frames and corners. Wire lath was also used in some bathroom areas where ceramic tile was to be provided.

DRYWALL Drywall became popular in the early 1960s, and is used almost exclusively today. There is very little difference between properly executed drywall and plaster jobs. Poor drywall work is usually identified at the seams. Sections of drywall are typically 4 feet by 8, 10, 12, or 14 feet sheets. Drywall is typically available in 3/8 inch, 1/2 inch and 5/8 inch thicknesses. Special drywalls, more resistant to water or fire, are available.

Drywall is typically nailed or screwed onto framing members. The seams between boards are taped and filled with drywall compound (also called joint compound, drywall mud and taping compound). The joints are sanded when they dry to create a homogeneous wall surface. If the taping and finishing work is poor, the seams are noticeable.

Drywall is also called wallboard, sheetrock, plasterboard and gyprock.

2.2 Paneling

DESCRIPTION Paneling may be veneered plywood, asbestos-cement board, veneered particle board, fiberboard or solid wood. It is available in many forms and appearances, from a simple and inexpensive 1/8 inch sheet of 4x8 plywood, to an intricate, highly finished hardwood system, found in dining rooms and libraries of high quality homes.

Paneling is often more durable than a plaster or drywall finish, although wood materials move more than drywall as a result of expansion and contraction. These finishes can be considerably more expensive than drywall. In some applications, the combustibility of this material may be an issue. Most paneling does not take paint or wallpaper as readily as drywall or plaster. Redecorating paneling can be difficult without removing it. Some paneling is difficult to patch without leaving any evidence.

2.3 Brick/Stone

DESCRIPTION These are not common interior wall finishes in homes. Some work on old homes includes removal of original plaster to expose brick on walls. This brickwork was usually not intended to be viewed, and may show a large number of small, damaged or off-colored bricks. Mortar joints may be quite irregular.

Removing plaster from the inner face of an exterior brick wall reduces the insulating value of the wall slightly, and can make the room less comfortable in cold climates. Removing plaster from an interior brick wall does not pose the same problem, although it does reduce the acoustic insulating properties of the wall. This may be an issue, for example, on attached homes with a common brick wall. Sealing exposed brick walls helps control the dust from the bricks and mortar.

Thin slices of brick or stone roughly 1/2- inch thick, or imitation brick can be applied to a wall using an adhesive or embedding the brick in mortar. They may be individual pieces or larger panels. Slices are sometimes used around fireplace openings to create the effect of solid masonry. Full bricks are not used because their weight would require strengthening the floor below.

2.4 Concrete/Concrete Block

DESCRIPTION These materials are associated with unfinished walls, typically in a basement. They can be painted to provide a more finished appearance. Concrete is strong and these walls are unlikely to be damaged as a result of normal usage.

2.5 Stucco/Textured

DESCRIPTION Interior stucco is essentially plaster, and is typically installed in a two or three coat process. The finish is often sculpted or worked to provide a decorative appearance. The texturing is done with trowels, sponges, brushes, or other tools to give the desired effect.

Common Problems with Wall Finishes

WATER DAMAGE/ STAINS Water damage is one of the most common problems on interior finishes. It is helpful to know a) the source of the water, b) whether the problem is still active, c) whether there is any concealed damage, d) the cost to correct the water problem if needed, e) and the cost to repair the damaged building materials.

Common water sources include roof leaks, flashing leaks, ice damming, window and skylight leaks, plumbing leaks, leaks from hot water heating systems, and condensation. Water damage may also result from such things as aquariums, room humidifiers or dehumidifiers, over-watering of plants, spills, melting snow and ice from boots during wintertime, etc.

Water damage often looks more serious than it is. Short term exposure to water will not harm most building materials. Plaster and drywall however, are easily damaged by water. Stains appear quickly and persist after the problem is solved. The material that can be easily seen is the first material to deteriorate. Mold can develop on the front or back surface of plaster or drywall if it is chronically wet. Mold will not disappear but will go dormant if the moisture source is removed.

CRACKS Most cracks on interior surfaces are cosmetic. They usually suggest incidental movement of the structure. In a few cases they suggest ongoing significant structural movement. If there is concern about structural movement, it is a good idea to take photographs of cracks with a reference point such as a ruler indicating crack size. This is a great way to monitor cracks to determine whether there is enough structural movement to worry about. A series of dated photographs can be very useful to a specialist.

DAMAGE Both plaster and drywall can be readily patched where small damaged areas are noted. Drywalling over old plaster or drywall is sometimes done where large areas are damaged.

Localized repairs to any textured surface are usually noticeable because the texturing is difficult to match. Cleaning and painting textured surfaces is more difficult than flat surfaces, and wallpapering over textured finishes is usually not possible. The strength and durability of textured surfaces is similar to plaster or drywall, although small projections are easily worn off the surfaces, if people or animals brush against the wall.

LOOSE Large sections of walls or ceilings may become loose where plaster has lost many of its keys due to vibration and wear and tear. Where there is danger of plaster falling, this should be corrected promptly so people won't be hurt by falling plaster.

NAIL POPPING IN DRYWALL This minor cosmetic issue is common in new construction. As wood studs shrink, nail heads 'pop' out from the drywall surface, causing a bump or blemish on the wall or ceiling. This usually happens only on new work, and only one time. Repairs are straightforward.

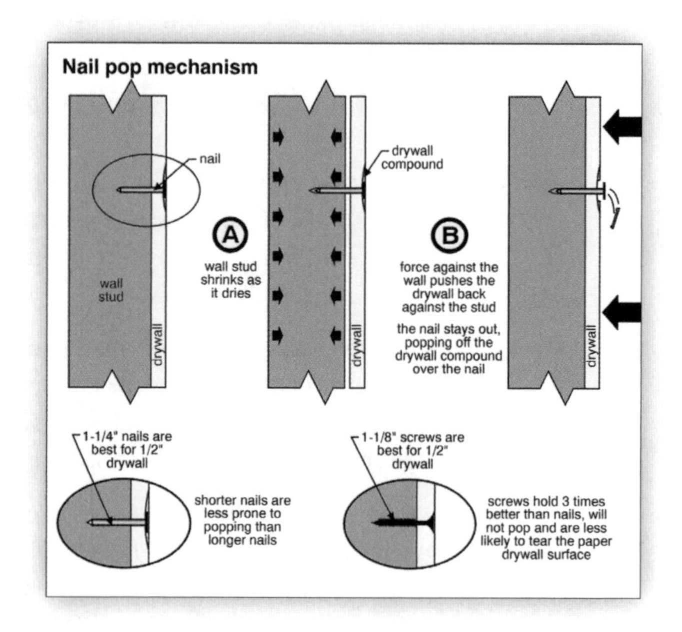

3.0 Major Ceiling Finishes

DESCRIPTION Ceiling finishes provide a decorative skin to conceal building components. Ceiling finishes hide structural members, insulation, ductwork, pipes, and wires. Most good ceiling finishes are flat and straight. Surfaces may be smooth or textured and better ceiling finishes are durable. Some ceiling finishes are versatile, taking decorative finishes such as stain, paint or wallpaper readily. Ceilings may make a decorating statement, or may be simply background. In some cases, the combustibility of ceiling finishes may be of interest. Below roofs, kitchens and bathrooms, resistance to water damage is an asset.

3.1 Plaster/Drywall

See Section 2.1 for a description of plaster and drywall.

3.2 Acoustic Tile

DESCRIPTION These tiles, typically made of fiber board and perforated to improve their acoustic performance, have been popular since the 1950s. Typically, they are 12 inches by 12 inches and are stapled or nailed to strapping. This type of ceiling tile was often installed when finishing a basement, or was installed over a damaged plaster ceiling.

The tiles have better acoustic properties than plaster and drywall, although they are subject to mechanical damage and water damage, similar to drywall or plaster. Repairs are easy if matching tiles can be found. The tiles can be painted, with some loss of acoustic performance.

3.3 Suspended Tile

DESCRIPTION Suspended tile became popular in the 1960s, and can be made of fiber board or fiberglass, for example. Some have a plastic coating. Combustible plastics, such as polystyrene, should not be used as ceiling tiles. This system utilizes a metal T-bar grid supported by wires from above. Advantages include relatively good acoustic properties, ease of removal to access things above the ceiling, and individual tiles can be replaced readily. On the downside, suspended tiles lower the ceiling at least two to three inches.

3.4 Metal

DESCRIPTION Metal ceilings were typically tin and most often in kitchens, during the late 1800s and early 1900s. Their design was often a decorative square pattern intended to simulate ornate plaster ceilings. This was a fairly durable ceiling system and in some areas has become fashionable again. The metal is normally painted.

3.5 Stucco/Textured/Stipple

DESCRIPTION Interior stucco is essentially plaster, and is typically installed in a two- or three-coat process. The finish is sculpted or worked to provide a decorative appearance. The texturing is done with trowels, sponges, brushes, or other tools to give the desired effect.

In modern construction, a sprayed on one-coat stipple finish is often used over drywall. This textured finish is inexpensive and quick to apply. It does not, however, cover poor drywall work, as flaws will show through. It is not used in kitchen or bathroom areas since the irregular surface is difficult to clean. Localized repairs are usually noticeable because the texture is difficult to match. Painting is more difficult than a flat surface, and wallpapering is usually not possible. The strength and durability is similar to plaster or drywall.

Common Problems with Ceiling Finishes

WATER DAMAGE/ STAINS Water damage is one of the most common problems on interior finishes. It is helpful to know a) the source of the water, b) whether the problem is still active, c) whether there is any concealed damage, d) the cost to correct the water problem if needed, e) and the cost to repair the damaged building materials.

Common water sources include roof leaks, flashing leaks, ice damming, window and skylight leaks, plumbing leaks, leaks from hot water heating systems, and condensation. Water damage may also result from such things as aquariums, room humidifiers or dehumidifiers, over-watering of plants, melting snow and ice from boots, etc.

Water damage often looks more serious than it is. Short term exposure to water will not harm most building materials. Plaster and drywall however, are easily damaged by water. Stains appear quickly and persist after the problem is solved. The material that can be easily seen is the first material to deteriorate. Mold can develop on the front or back surface of plaster or drywall if it is chronically wet. Mold will not disappear but will go dormant if the moisture source is removed.

DAMAGE Both plaster and drywall can be readily patched where small damaged areas are noted. Drywalling over old plaster or drywall is sometimes done where large areas are damaged.

LOOSE/SAG Large sections of ceilings may become loose where plaster has lost many of its keys due to vibration and wear and tear. Where there is danger of plaster falling, this should be corrected promptly. People can be seriously hurt by plaster falling, especially from a ceiling. A sagging ceiling might indicate that the plaster or drywall is about to fall.

CRACKS Most cracks are cosmetic. Patching and monitoring makes sense. Where cracks are accompanied by sagging, at least partial ceiling replacement may be necessary.

TRUSS UPLIFT This cosmetic problem in homes in cold climates with roof trusses may result in significant cracks between interior walls and ceilings, or between interior walls and floors. The cause is upward bowing of the roof trusses to which the ceilings are attached. The cracks typically open in the winter and close in the summer. They can be very alarming, but are not a structural issue.

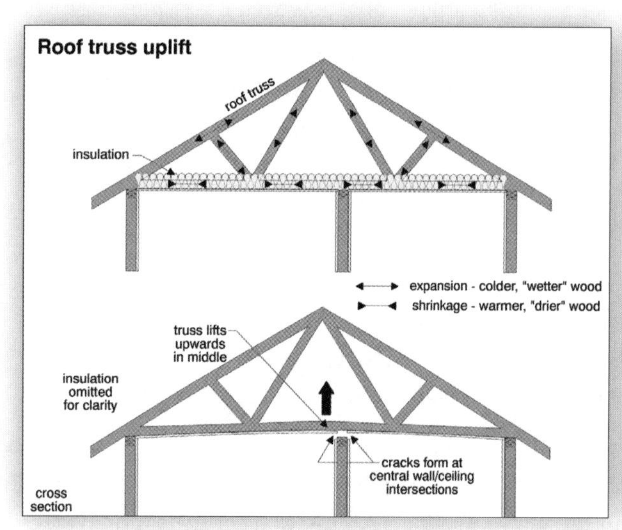

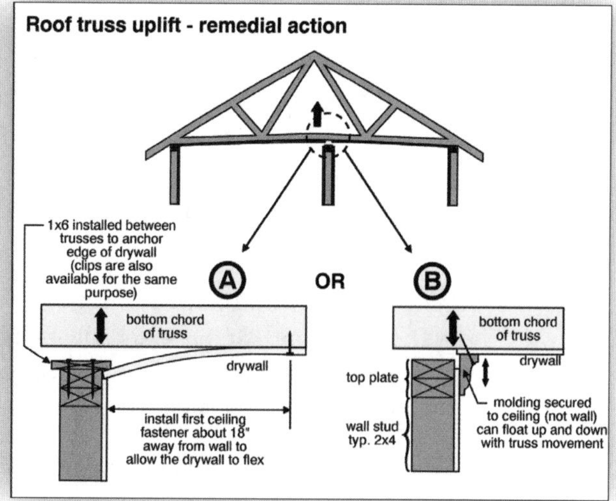

4.0 Trim

FUNCTION Most houses have interior trim including baseboard, quarter round and door and window casings. These trim details protect and conceal joints, corners and changes in material. They add architectural appeal to a home, and better quality moldings and trim may indicate better quality construction.

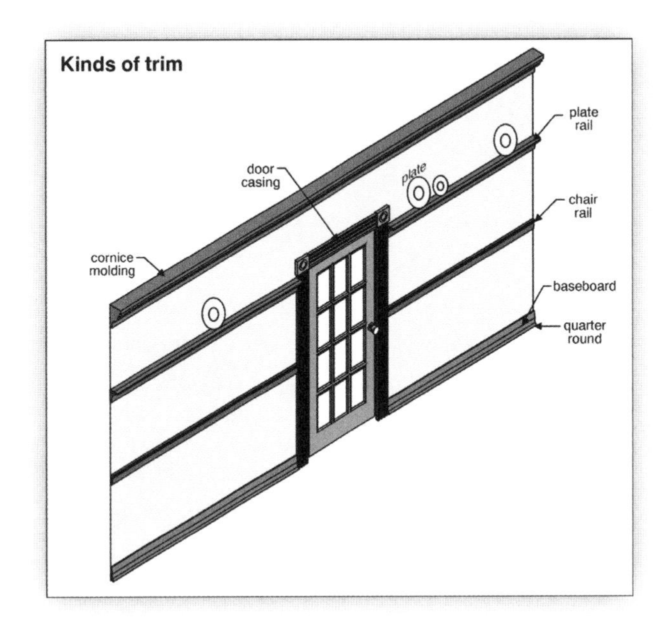

4.1 Baseboard and Quarter Round

DESCRIPTION Baseboard and quarter round are usually wood (or wood fiber) components installed at wall/floor intersections. Baseboard protects the bottom of the walls from things like feet, brooms and vacuum cleaners, and provides a clean joint at walls and floors. Baseboard can be anything from a two-inch high piece of plain lumber to an intricate two or three piece architectural molding, 10 or 12 inches high. Quarter round is usually relatively small (approximately 3/4 inch radius) and covers the joint between the floor and the baseboard. It may be the same material as the baseboard. Some architectural treatments omit quarter round, and occasionally baseboard is omitted as well.

WOOD ALTERNATIVES Tile or marble may be used for baseboard. This is an expensive treatment, of course. Other materials include vinyl and rubber. A commercial treatment occasionally found in homes is broadloom flooring turned up the wall a few inches to form a carpet baseboard.

4.2 Casings

DESCRIPTION Door and window casings provide a finished look to the junction of a wall and door or window opening. Casings are most often wood.

4.3 Moldings

CORNICE MOLDINGS Moldings at wall/ceiling intersections are referred to as cornice moldings. They may be made of wood, plaster or foamed plastic.

MEDALLIONS OR ROSETTES Ceiling medallions or rosettes are decorative wood, plaster or foamed plastic details on ceilings around light fixtures. These details were common in principal rooms such as living rooms or dining rooms. They can be fabricated on site although most are pre-manufactured.

Common Problems with Trim

MISSING/LOOSE/ DAMAGED Trim can be missing, damaged or loose. Replacement of decorative trim with a matching system may not be practical. Custom millwork is expensive. Also, some of the woods used in the past are not available today. It may be more cost effective to replace the entire trim in a room.

Quarter round is often removed and not replaced when wall-to-wall broadloom is installed. New quarter round is often provided when broadloom is removed.

Plaster trim such as cornice moldings and ceiling medallions are difficult to repair. Rebuilding or repairing a damaged molding is time consuming and expensive. Replacement with a manufactured system is often practical.

WATER DAMAGE/ STAINS/ROT Water damage from leaks can stain or damage trim. Wood rots and plaster deteriorates quickly with exposure to water.

5.0 Cabinets and Countertops

CABINET DESCRIPTION Cabinets may be installed anywhere but are most common in kitchens and bathrooms. Cabinets may be built of wood, although many today are veneer-covered fiberboard. Shelves and doors are commonly solid wood, veneered fiberboard or glass. The quality of cabinets is a function of the materials, assembly techniques and hardware used on doors and drawers.

COUNTERTOP DESCRIPTION Countertops can be made of many materials. Laminated plastic surfaces applied to fiberboard are common because they are inexpensive, water resistant, available in a huge selection of colors and patterns, and are easy to clean. They are difficult to repair if cut by knives, chipped or burned. These are referred to as laminate countertops.

Other materials include granite, marble, stainless steel, ceramic tile, concrete, hardwood (butcher block), soapstone and a number of manufactured products including engineered stone and other solid surface materials. The ideal countertop won't burn, crack, chip or break, is easy to clean, non-porous, and is resistant to rot, water damage, stains and knives.

Problems with Cabinets and Countertops

DRAWER AND DOOR OPERATION Cabinet problems may include improper operation of doors and drawers. Sticky drawers and doors that will not stay closed are common. Hardware may be missing, worn or inoperative.

UPPER CABINETS NOT WELL SECURED/ DAMAGE More serious problems include poor attachment to walls. Loose cabinets may fall and injure people. Joints may be separating and shelves may be poorly supported. Cabinets may be damaged or deteriorated due to wear and tear. Cabinets, doors and drawers may be mechanically damaged or worn. Knobs may be loose, missing or broken. Many of these are cosmetic or nuisance issues. The decision to replace cabinets and countertops is subjective.

COUNTERTOP DAMAGE Countertops may suffer cosmetic damage, and fiberboard countertops often rot, especially around sinks and faucets. Burns and mechanical damage are common on laminate countertops. Cracked tiles and missing grout are common on ceramic tile countertops.

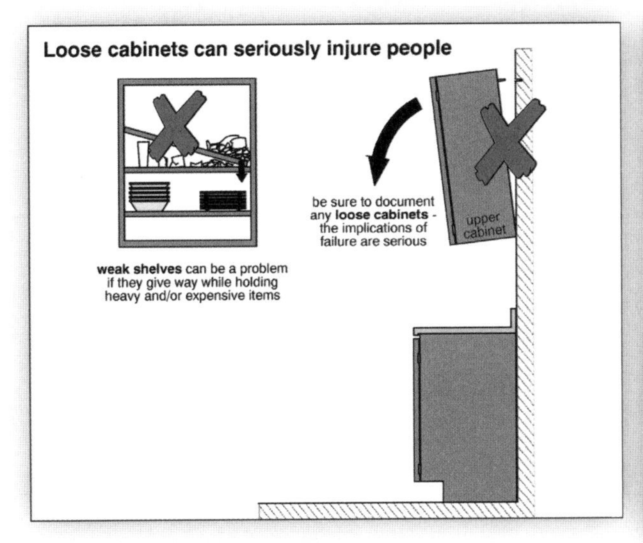

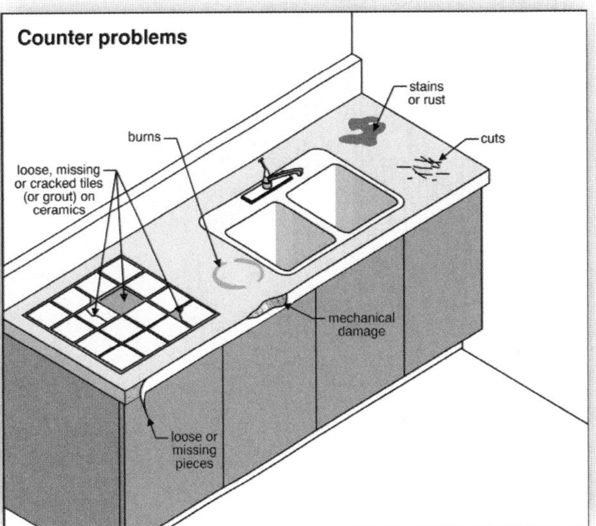

6.0 Windows

DESCRIPTION Windows provide light and ventilation for homes, at a cost in heating climates – windows let more heat escape than walls. Windows are an interruption in the weather tight skin of the building created by the siding. Windows allow air leakage, and may allow water through or into the walls if poorly installed or maintained. Well-designed windows add to the aesthetic appeal of a home. Windows increase cooling load in air conditioning climates.

Windows may be fixed or operable. Operable windows may slide up and down, slide side to side, or swing in or swing out. Swinging windows may be hinged at the side, top, or bottom. There are many different styles and shapes of windows, as can be seen in the illustration.

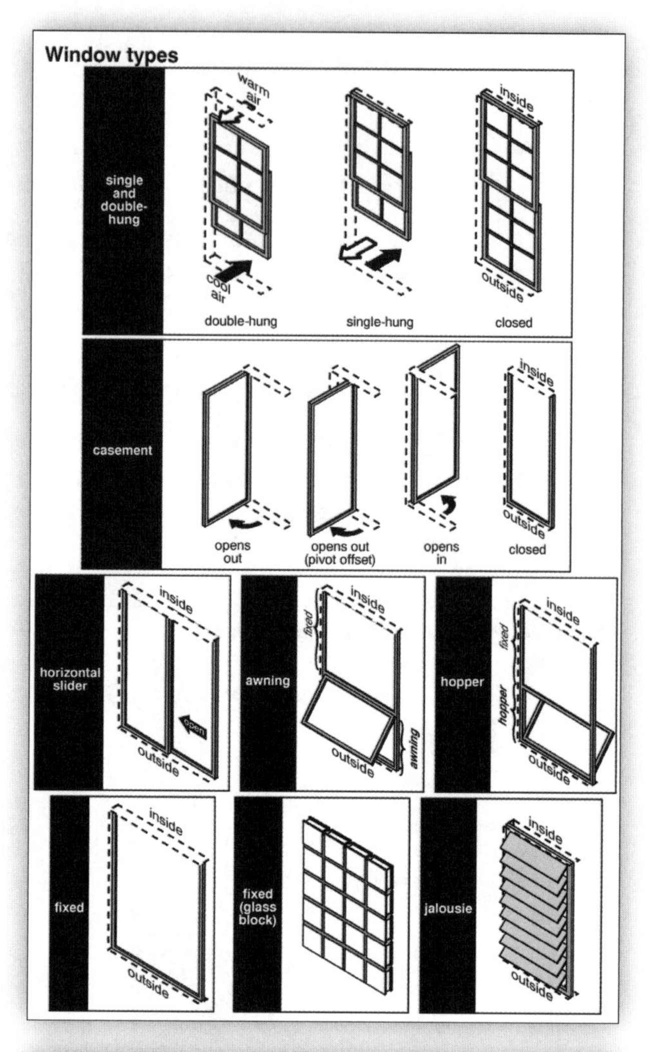

6.1 Anatomy

DESCRIPTION The pieces of glass in a window are called panes, glazing or lites. The panes are held in a sash, which may move as the window is opened. When the window within the sash is divided up into several small panes, the dividing pieces are muntins.

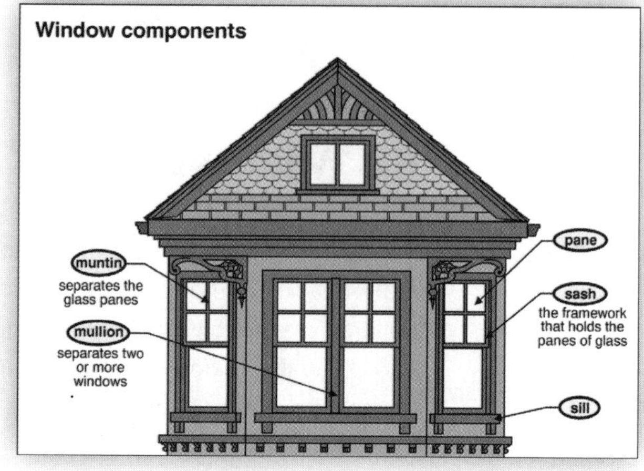

GLAZING Single-pane windows have a single sheet of glass. Windows with two or three panes of glass (double glazed or triple glazed) have improved energy efficiency and reduced sound transmission. These are common in colder climates. Further improvements in energy efficiency can be gained by filling the space between the glass panes with an inert gas (e.g. argon), or the addition of a low-e coating on the glass.

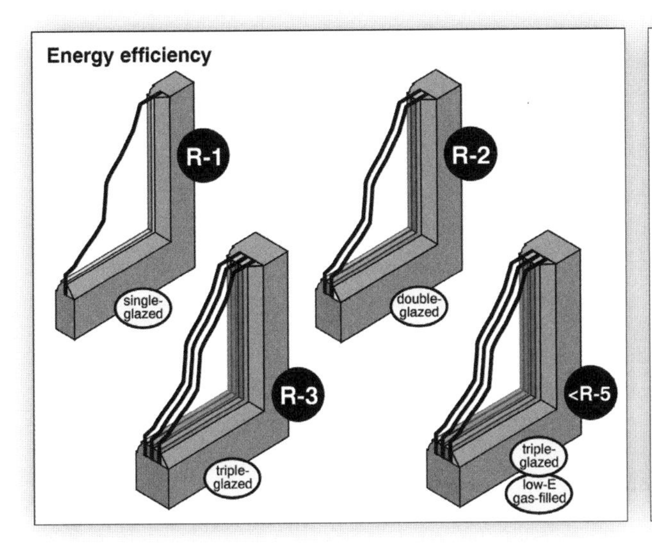

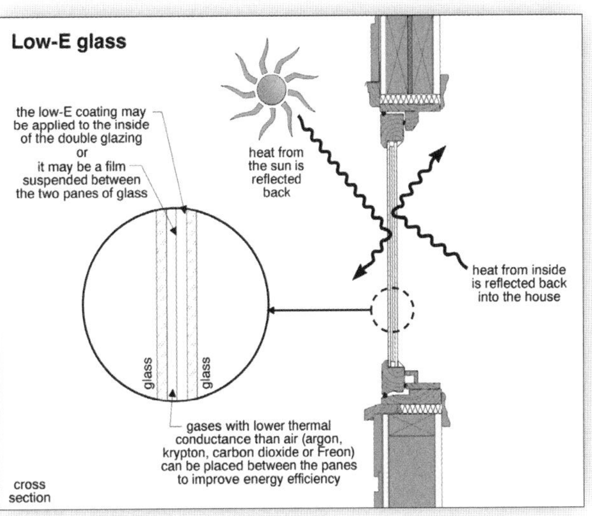

STORM WINDOWS The efficiency of single-pane windows can be enhanced with storm windows. These may be self-storing storms, or they may require removal in the spring and installation in the fall.

SAFETY GLASS/ TEMPERED GLASS Glass may be strengthened by tempering. Fully tempered glass is made three to five times stronger than ordinary glass by heating it and then cooling it very quickly. Tempered glass is also safer than ordinary glass because it breaks into small rectangular pieces, less likely to cut people. Tempered glass is used in sliding doors, bathtub and shower doors and skylights, for example. Laminated glass or plastic is also used where more strength and safety are needed.

REPLACEMENT WINDOWS Windows are complex and can suffer several problems. Where difficulties are experienced with several windows, it may make sense to replace all the windows. However, this is rarely cost-effective. Replacement windows are expensive and rarely pay for themselves in reduced heating costs over several years. Replacement windows may provide benefits of improved appearance, reduced maintenance and ease of operation. Some improvement in room comfort and energy consumption may also be enjoyed, although these items rarely justify the cost of new windows.

Common Problems with Windows

DIFFICULT TO OPERATE/ INOPERABLE Inoperable windows are very common and may be the result of paint or dirt in the operating mechanisms or tracks. Building settlement or swelling of wood components may also result in inoperative windows. Jammed, broken or missing hardware may also prevent easy operation.

HARDWARE Window hardware may be missing, broken or inoperative, making it difficult to open, close or lock the windows. In many cases, it is cheaper to replace hardware rather than repair or clean heavily painted hardware.

SASH CORDS Sash cords or chains on single or double hung windows are often broken or missing. The pulleys at the top of the jamb are often inoperable because they have been painted. Sash cords, incidentally, should not be painted; nor should the window guides in the frame. While cotton sash cords can last for many years, some people prefer to replace them with nylon or metal sash cords. The chain sash cords are somewhat noisier, of course.

SPRINGS The spiral spring hardware used to hold up some single and double hung windows is prone to jamming, particularly if the hardware is painted. It is also common for the springs to break or become detached from either the window or the jamb.

ROT Rot attacks wood windows, usually due to water leaks or trapped water due to poor drainage. Rotted wood windows may have to be replaced, an expensive problem. Metal or vinyl-clad wood windows may have concealed rot that goes undetected for some time.

GLASS ISSUES Panes of glass may be missing, broken or cracked. Glass may be heavily covered with several layers of paint on older houses. Removing this paint often scratches the glass, impairing visibility. Older glass has more bubbles and distortions, although this may not be considered a defect. Manufacturers' flaws include discoloration, clouding and rust streaking of the windows. In some cases, distortion may also be a problem.

SAFETY GLASS Safety glass is used on skylights, sliding doors and in shower and bathtub doors for example, where there is a risk of people falling into or through the glass. People may fall out windows that extend down within 18 inches of the floor and safety glass is often used here. Windows along stairs and at stair landings are often safety glass.

LOST SEAL Double or triple glazed windows are typically sealed with dry air or gas between the panes. These windows may lose their seal, resulting in intermittent or permanent condensation or clouding between the panes of glass. It may not be possible to identify a failed seal during a home inspection. The corrective action for these problems is replacement of the glass. Unless the glass is missing or broken, replacement of the glass is not a priority item.

GASKET MOVEMENT The gaskets on double or triple glazed windows sometimes pull away from the sash, reducing energy efficiency and moving into the field of the glass. The glass and gasket unit has to be replaced.

PUTTY The putty or glazing compound holding a window in place may be deteriorated, loose or missing. This is normally improved when repainting.

MUNTINS Muntins between panes of glass may be rotted, broken or cracked. Rotted wood usually has to be replaced. Loose muntins should be re-secured. Where the muntins are decorative lead (typical of homes built in the first half of the 20th century), the panes may bulge inward or outward. This is thought to be a result of impact or the thermal expansion of the lead, and may be related to the addition of storm windows. Depending on severity, this can sometimes be repaired by a glass specialist, although the window may have to be replaced. Specialty shops can reproduce leaded glass windows, at significant costs.

SASH DAMAGE/ ROT Wood sashes may be deteriorated as a result of mechanical damage, rot, or failed joints. It is not unusual to find the stiles and rails of wood double hung windows coming apart. This is often a result of people opening the window by lifting up on the top rail. Hardware attached to the bottom rail should be used for opening and closing double hung windows. Where this hardware is missing, it should be replaced. Metal and vinyl sashes may also fail, but this is less common than on wood.

On some horizontal sliding windows, it is common for the vinyl sashes to be pulled away from the glass. This is often because the sash is used to pull a window closed. It is better practice to push a horizontal slider closed than to pull on it, even though manufacturers may provide pulling hardware.

Rot often starts on the exterior, although it may appear on the interior, especially if there is chronic condensation.

CONDENSATION – WATER DAMAGE/ ROT Sashes and frames on older metal windows are susceptible to condensation problems. Because metal is a good thermal conductor, the inside face of the metal can be very cold, promoting condensation on the inside surface. Warm moist house air contacting cold metal cools quickly, losing its ability to hold moisture. This causes the condensation. Modern systems have a thermal break, which keeps the inside metal surface warmer. Vinyl frames can suffer similar problems.

All windows can suffer condensation. Condensation is more likely to occur with extremely cold outdoor temperatures, high indoor humidity levels and leaky, low-quality or single glazed windows. Double or triple glazed windows or windows with storms are less likely to have condensation problems.

SILL PROBLEMS Sill assemblies can be loose, rotted or improperly sloped. All these lead to water damage at the windows and walls.

DRAIN HOLE ISSUES Window systems with a primary and a storm window typically have drain holes below the outer pane so that any water between the inner and outer panes can escape. In some cases, these windows are installed backwards, with the drain holes on the inside and the sill sloping into the house. This results in damage to the walls below the sills on the inside of the house. Blocked drain holes are a related problem, but these are easily cured by removing the obstructions.

LEAK AT SILL/ JAMB A common problem with manufactured window systems is a poor connection at the sill/jamb intersection. Rain or condensation accumulates on a window sill. Although the sills should be sloped to drain water, and there should be drain holes, imperfections in this system (or a sudden build up of water) will pond water on the window sill. If the corners of the sill are not tightly sealed to the bottom of the windows, water will leak through. It is common to see water staining or wall damage below the corners of windows inside the home. Sometimes caulking this joint is adequate, although, in severe cases, the window has to be taken out and replaced or reassembled. Concealed wall damage around and below leaky windows is a common problem.

LEAK AT TOP Windows and wood frame walls tend to be installed close to the outer surface of the wall. Flashings at the top of the window help prevent water getting into the window assembly. Windows may leak at the top if the flashings are missing, poorly installed, or deteriorated.

CASING ISSUES Interior window casings or trim may be loose, missing or damaged. While this is largely a cosmetic problem, some additional air leakage and resulting heat loss may occur where the trim fit is poor.

CAULKING MISSING/ DETERIORATED Caulking of windows is done for two different reasons. Caulking on the outside helps prevent water penetration. Caulking on the inside helps prevent air leakage into or out of the house. There are several types of caulking suitable for each application, and the manufacturers' recommendations or the recommendation of a specialist should be followed when choosing a caulking. Caulking is not a lifetime material and modest quality caulkings have to be replaced every year or two.

SCREEN PROBLEMS Window screens may be aluminum, steel, bronze, fiber glass or nylon, for example. Metal screens may be rusted and all screens can be torn or loose. Missing screens should be replaced.

6.2 Skylights

DESCRIPTION Skylights or roof windows typically use tempered glass or acrylic panes and may have flat or curved glazing. Acrylic is very sensitive to scratching damage from abrasive cleaners or tree branches, but is more impact resistant than glass. Single, double and even triple glazed skylights are available. Older units or special-use skylights may have wired glass to increase strength. Some skylights are operable for ventilation. Some skylights have an integral curb to help with installation. Others are designed with no curb and are installed flush with the roof surface.

Skylights installed on at least 4 inch high curbs perform better than lower skylights. It is easier to make a good roof/skylight connection with flashings where there is a curb.

A HOLE IN THE ROOF Skylights are often installed after original construction, and installation can be tricky. In addition to cutting a hole in the roof, (and the structural considerations involved) leakage must be prevented around the skylight. The skylight should have a flashing detail that makes a good watertight connection between the roof and the skylight. Poor installations are common.

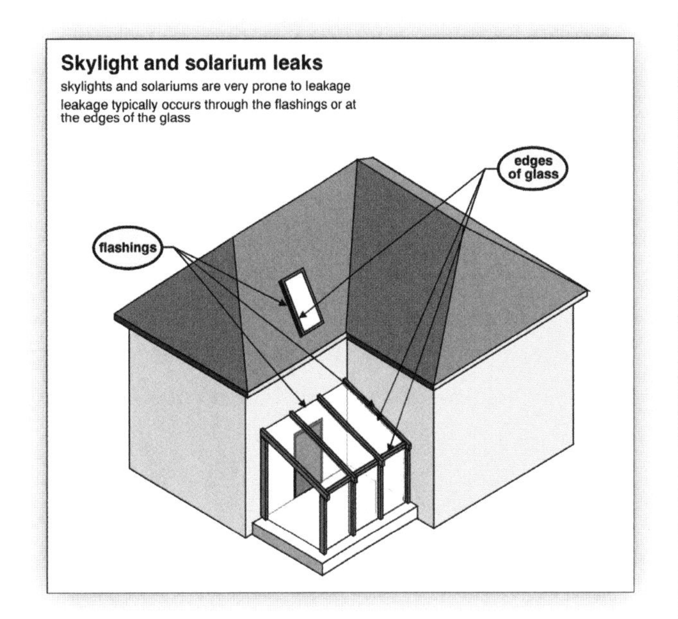

Common Problems with Skylights

LEAKS Leakage is a common problem, often a result of poor installation rather than a poor quality fixture. It may be difficult to identify the leakage source without dismantling the system. Low quality and poorly installed skylights are very common and most skylights leak at some point.

OTHER PROBLEMS Skylights have the same issues as windows with respect to cracked panes, lost seals, condensation, rot and mechanical damage.

6.3 Solariums

DESCRIPTION Solariums have walls and a roof made mostly of glass. They are also called sun rooms, Florida rooms, plant rooms and greenhouse rooms. The framing for the solarium may be wood, metal, vinyl, or a combination, and the glazing may be glass or plastic. Glass used in anything other than a vertical plane should be strengthened by tempering or laminating. Glass used in roofs may have to withstand a falling tree branch or hailstones, for example.

Solariums are inherently difficult to heat and cool, due to the large glass area and absence of insulation. Comfort issues are common in solariums.

Common Problems with Solariums

LEAKS Solariums are complicated sets of interconnected windows. Water leakage problems are very common. Even high quality solariums will leak around the roof and windows if not perfectly installed. Leakage is most common at the bottom of the glass roof areas, where good flashing details are difficult to achieve, and where water may collect.

OTHER PROBLEMS Skylights have the same issues as windows with respect to cracked panes, lost seals, condensation, rot and mechanical damage. Rotted wood framing members in solariums is common, often caused by leaks or condensation.

7.0 Doors

DESCRIPTION Doors provide a way to get into and out of the house, and can add to the architectural appeal of homes. Many doors have windows associated with them. Doors may have panes of glass in the door. Sidelights are fixed windows on either side of the door. Transom lights or fanlights are fixed windows above the door. Some doors add natural light and ventilation (e.g. sliding glass doors) to a home.

Doors are typically a security weak spot in most houses, especially if they have glass in the door or in the sidelights beside the door. Wood doors are a source of heat loss in cold climates, since they are not typically as well insulated as walls. Doors and windows are holes in walls and inherently susceptible to leakage. Air and water leakage around door openings is common.

Doors may be hinged, opening into the house typically. They may be single, or arranged in pairs (French doors). Doors may also be sliding (patio doors). These are typically all-glass doors.

SAFETY GLASS See Section 6.1 in this chapter for a brief description of safety glass.

7.1 Types

SOLID WOOD Traditional exterior doors are solid wood. These doors can be made of many wood species including oak, mahogany, walnut, hemlock, pine, cherry and alder. Wood has some modest insulating properties, although the heaviest wood door does not provide as much insulation as a poorly insulated wall.

From a security standpoint, a solid wood door is relatively good, depending on the amount of glass area and, of course, the hardware quality and condition.

METAL (INSULATED CORE) Insulated core steel or aluminum doors are common in modern construction. They are cost effective, durable and low maintenance. With a metal exterior skin and insulating material (polystyrene or polyurethane) inside, this makes a good insulating door. Some metal doors have concealed wood stiles around the perimeter, to provide rigidity and support for hinges and handles. These also allow for trimming and fitting the door in the opening. Steel doors use magnetic weather stripping to create a good air seal around the perimeter. Metal doors are susceptible to denting.

FIBERGLASS DOORS Fiberglass doors have an insulated core, much like metal doors. They are relatively low maintenance, again, much like metal doors. Fiberglass doors can be much more energy-efficient than wood doors. Fiberglass doors do expand and contract with changes in temperature more than wood or steel doors. Many feel that fiberglass doors are more durable than wood or steel doors. Fiberglass doors do not dent as easily as steel doors.

ALUMINUM-CLAD AND VINYL-CLAD DOORS These doors are generally considered high-quality. They combine the low maintenance exterior of metal or vinyl with the strength of wood. These are common on patio doors, both French style and sliding.

SLIDING GLASS DOORS (PATIO DOORS) Sliding glass doors have been popular since the 1950s. They provide a large glass area with good visibility. Sliding glass door frames are available in wood, metal and vinyl or a combination thereof. Metal-clad wood and vinyl-clad wood frames for sliding doors and windows are common.

A common problem with the early sliding doors in cool climates was condensation and ice on the inside of the metal frame. The condensation can damage interior floor surfaces and building components below. Modern doors include a thermal break between the inner and outer halves of the metal frame. This keeps the inside metal part of the frame warmer, and reduces condensation and icing problems.

Sliding doors typically have a fixed sash and a movable sash as well as a screen. The glass may be single, double or triple glazed.

Better quality sliding glass doors are distinguished by more expensive operating and adjusting hardware. The locking system on early generation and inexpensive sliding glass doors can be easy to defeat. Better quality doors have more secure locking systems.

FRENCH DOORS (PATIO DOORS) French doors are a double door system with the hinges on the outside edges. They close together in the middle. French doors are typically mostly glass, often broken up into several small panes by muntins. These doors can be wood, metal, fiberglass, or aluminum- or vinyl-clad wood.

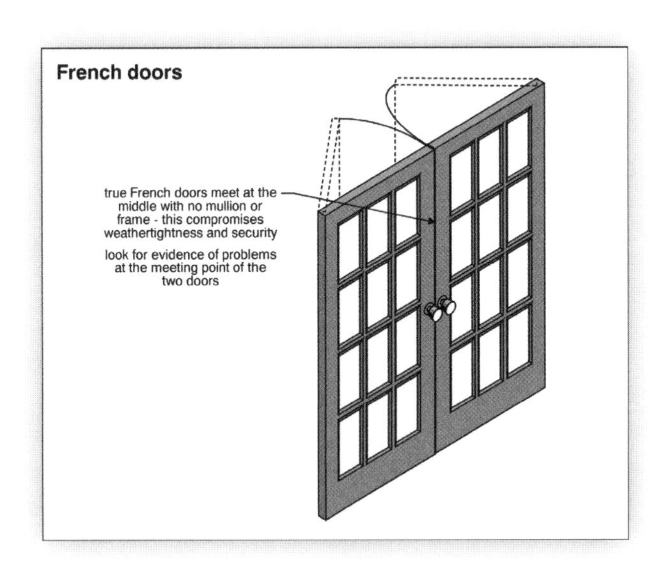

STORM DOORS Storm doors in cold climates are popular where the main door is solid wood. Most storm doors are metal, although wood storms are also available. Many include a removable glass pane that can be replaced with a screen. Others have a self storing storm and screen system, similar to conventional storm windows. No matter how weather tight a single exterior door is, a storm door usually improves the situation. The second door, if properly fit, will reduce air leakage around the single door. Most storm doors are equipped with a self closer that should be adjusted to close the door tightly, for a snug fit.

Common Problems with Doors

DAMAGE, HARDWARE, OPERATING PROBLEMS Functional problems with doors include damage to the door material (rotted wood, buckled metal, etc.). Damaged or poorly installed hinges make doors difficult to open and close and, if not corrected, will lead to damage of the door and the frame. Warped doors may be difficult to operate and may be very leaky when closed. Defective latching and locking mechanisms impair security.

SLIDING DOOR DAMAGE Damage to the frame is common on sliding doors. This is often caused by excessive force used in opening and closing the door, resulting from damaged or poorly adjusted hardware, or a dirty track. Where the guides or rollers have been mechanically damaged, the door will not ride freely.

WEATHER-STRIPPING INEFFECTIVE If the door is not properly weatherstripped, excess heat loss is experienced. Where the door frames are damaged or out of square, the doors may be difficult to operate and there may be considerable heat loss around the doors. Weatherstripping on early sliding doors was often low quality.

DOOR THRESHOLD PROBLEMS Loose or damaged door thresholds are unsafe and should be repaired or replaced as necessary. Thresholds that are not sloped properly to drain or are not well sealed may lead to water damage to the home.

STORM DOOR Storm doors that do not close properly are ineffective from an energy efficiency standpoint, and may be damaged in strong winds. Many storm doors have inexpensive hardware resulting in operating problems over the long term. Auto-closers are often ineffective.

In some cases, the door frame has to be straightened or the door re-hung. Damaged glass should be repaired for safety, security, and heat loss reasons. Damaged screens and storm doors can also be safety concerns and should be repaired or replaced promptly.

SLIDING DOOR – HARDWARE Sliding doors may not operate easily because the track is damaged or dirty, or because the rolling hardware is defective. Sometimes cleaning and adjustment can solve the problem. In other cases, replacement parts are needed. Problems with latching and locking mechanisms are common.

SLIDING DOOR – WATER DAMAGE On older sliding doors in cold climates, the damage to the building interior can be significant as a result of condensation and ice build-up. The absence of a thermal break in the metal frame leads to a very cold interior metal surface. The cold metal cools the warm moist house air and condensation develops as droplets on the metal frame. The water runs onto the floor, or forms ice temporarily and as it thaws, melts and runs onto the floor. This damages the door sill, floor boards, subfloor and, in severe cases, the joists and header below. The preferred solution is, of course, to replace the sliding door system.

SAGGING HEADER (LINTEL) When sliding glass doors are installed in a new wall opening, a substantial header is required above the opening to carry the load of the wall above around the opening. If this is not done well, the header may sag, interfering with door operation.

THRESHOLD TOO CLOSE TO GRADE All doors in cold climates should have at least a six inch step up to the door sill from outside. Where this step is not done, snow accumulation may result in leakage through the bottom of the door. Where no six inch step-up is noted, good maintenance (including snow clearing) is needed to prevent water damage.

LOST SEAL CLOSE TO GRADE The loss of a seal between double glazed panes on doors is common. This results in a clouding of the glass that may be permanent. The condition is primarily cosmetic, and only a small reduction in energy efficiency occurs. Many people replace the panes because of the unsightly appearance of the clouded glass, although this is a discretionary improvement.

SAFETY GLASS Safety glass (tempered or laminated) or plastic is used on sliding doors and at shower and bathtub doors for example, where there is a risk of people falling into or through the glass. People may fall out windows that extend down within 18 inches of the floor and safety glass is often used here.

ROT AND INSECT DAMAGE Wood doors are susceptible to all of the things that attack wood-based products including rot and insect damage. Wood doors are not maintenance free, requiring regular painting or staining.

INAPPROPRIATE DOOR Hollow wood doors are generally not for exterior use. They don't stand up well to weather and do not provide great security.

DOORS INTO GARAGES They should protect the house from a fire in the garage and exhaust fumes entering the house. Good weatherstripping and automatic closers are needed. There are several types of vehicle doors. They should operate freely and auto-reverse if they meet an obstacle.

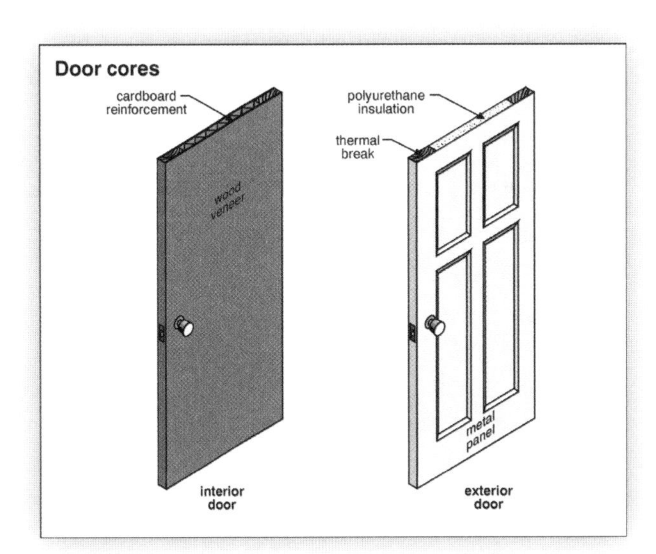

DENTED METAL DOORS Some metal doors are easily dented. This is not a functional problem, although many people object to the appearance.

PLASTIC MOLDINGS DEFORM Metal doors often have decorative plastic moldings on the surface. Problems have been experienced when a storm door is added to an insulated metal door. The space between the doors can become overheated, and the plastic moldings may deform. In the worst cases, the metal door panel may even buckle. Many manufacturers recommend against the use of storm doors with insulated core metal doors.

8.0 Stairs

Stairs and stairwells are an integral part of most homes. Structural issues related to stairwell openings are addressed in the Structure chapter.

8.1 Components

DESCRIPTION Stairs are made of stringers, treads and risers. The stringers are the long diagonal supports for the stairs that rest on the floor of the lower story and are usually secured to the side of a floor joist on the upper story. The stringers are commonly wood (e.g. 2x10s), although they can be metal. There are usually two stringers, although there can be one stringer or three. The treads are what people step on and the risers are the vertical members at the back of each tread. Again, treads and risers are most often wood. Open staircases have no risers.

8.2 Rise and Run

RISE AND RUN Stairwell terminology is not consistent but includes "rise and run". For our discussion, the tread depth or run is the horizontal distance from the leading edge of one tread to the next. The rise is the vertical distance from the top of one tread to the top of the next. The rise and run for each step should be the same in any staircase to minimize the risk of tripping on the stairs.

NOSING The front of the tread typically extends roughly 1 inch beyond the riser below. This extension is called a nosing.

MINIMUMS AND MAXIMUMS Well-designed stairs are easy to climb. They have a maximum rise of about eight inches, and a minimum run or tread depth of 10 inches (US) or 8 1/4 inches (Canada). Generally speaking, the lower the rise and the wider the tread, the easier the staircase is to use. Dimension rules are often broken on basement and loft stairwells. It is difficult and expensive to rearrange a poorly built staircase and, in most cases, the occupants simply live with it.

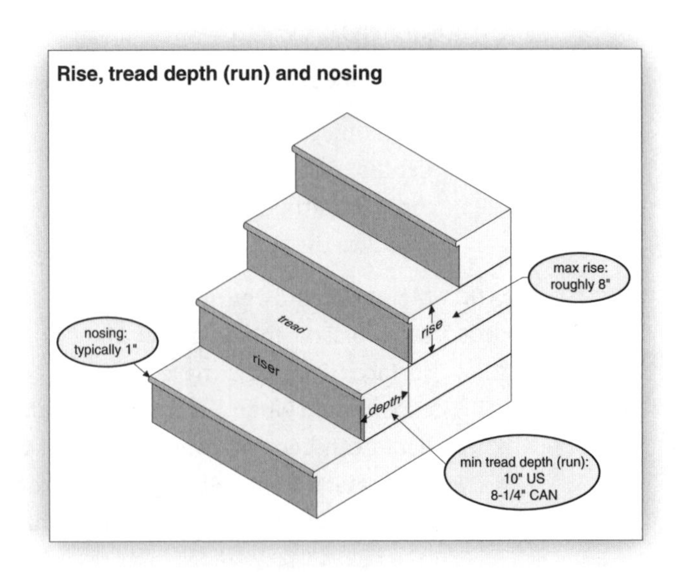

8.3 Width and Headroom

DESCRIPTION A stairwell should be at least 36 inches wide. Wider stairs are more pleasant and make it easier to move furniture. The headroom above each tread should be about 6 1/2 feet. More is better, but less is common on basement stairs. Again, it is difficult and expensive to change the stairwell head room.

8.4 Doors and Landings

DESCRIPTION Where there is a door at the top of the set of stairs, it should open away from the stairs unless there is a landing so that someone coming up the stairs won't be knocked down by another person opening the door.

We often find the situation where a storm door has been added. The original front steps come up to a door that opened into the house. The storm door opens outward, creating a slightly unsafe situation. Ideally, the stairs should be rebuilt with a landing. Many people live with this condition.

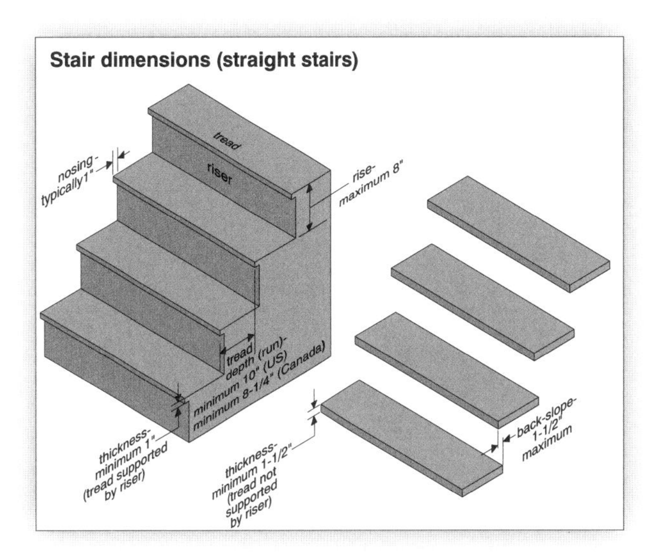

8.5 Curved Stairs/Winders

DESCRIPTION Curved stairs or stairs with winders are not as safe as straight stairs. The treads get narrow on one side. Tread runs on curved stairs can be as narrow as six inches in some cases. Winders are pie-shaped treads that shrink to a point at the inside edge. Spiral staircases are built entirely of winders and, in many areas, are not permitted as the only way to get from one floor to another. These staircases are dangerous in a fire situation because they are difficult to get down quickly.

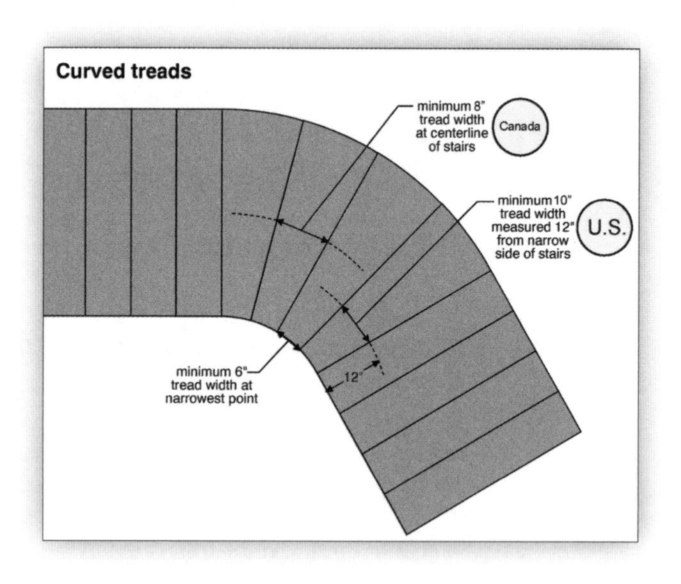

8.6 Railings

HEIGHT Railings are usually provided on at least one side of any staircase with more than two risers. Railings on stairs in new construction are usually 34 to 38 inches high, depending on the area. Railings around the top of open stairwells are typically 36 to 42 inches high. On older homes, railings are often lower and, rather than rebuilding an elegant railing, most people live with the lower one. Where child safety is an issue, a higher temporary railing is sometimes added.

OPENINGS AND CLIMB-ABILITY Openings in railings are ideally no larger than four inches in diameter, so small children will not fall through them. Good railing design avoids horizontal members that allow children to climb the railing and fall over.

Handrails should be easy to grab. They should be set out from the wall, and small enough to get one's hand around easily. A 2x4, for example, does not make a good handrail. Handrails should end at a post or wall so clothing does not get caught on the end of the rail, creating a fall hazard.

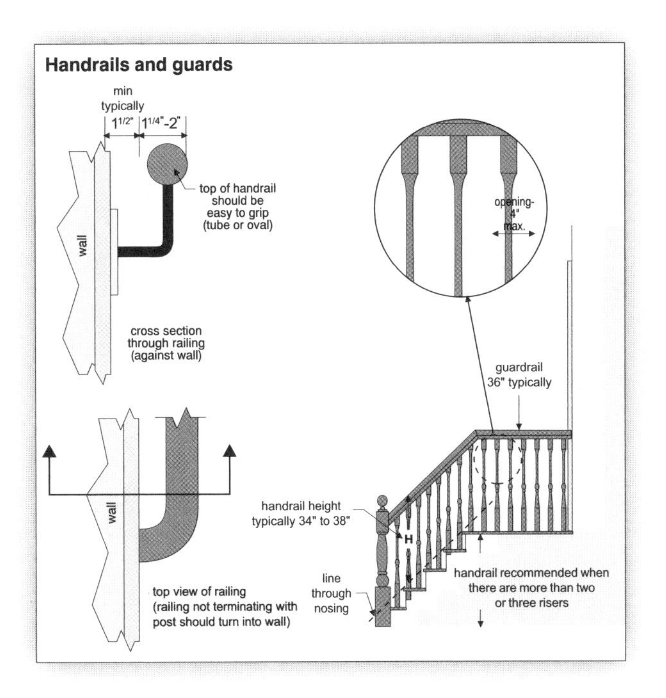

Common Problems with Stairs

DAMAGE AND ROT Stairs may be damaged by mechanical impact or wear and tear. Damaged, loose or poorly supported treads are dangerous. Rot is common at the bottom of stringers, particularly on basement and exterior stairs. This may lead to instability of the staircase.

POOR SUPPORT Stairs may be poorly supported if the floor system is weak or if the stringers are poorly designed, fastened, damaged or have shifted. Where a stringer has pulled away from the treads, the treads may lose their support and fall out.

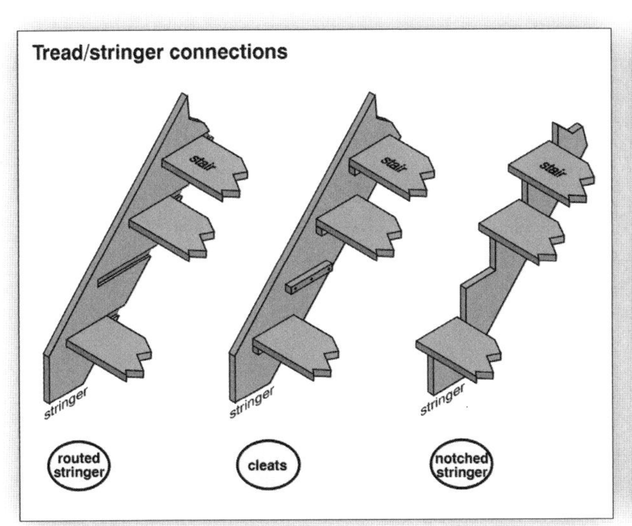

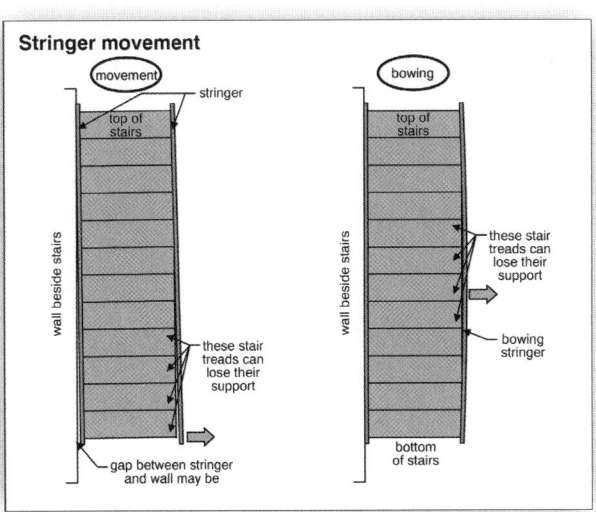

UNEVEN STAIRS – SAFETY PROBLEMS The rise on every step should be the same, and the treads should all be the same width. Stairwells that do not follow size or uniformity guidelines are more difficult to use and may lead to an accident. Imperfect staircases are common in older homes and may not be cost-effective to rearrange.

RAILING ISSUES Missing, weak, loose, damaged, rotted or poorly arranged railings are a safety concern. Railings with large openings or horizontal members that make it easy to climb are safety issues.

WIDTH AND HEADROOM Narrow stairwells make moving furniture difficult. Stairwells with inadequate headroom are a safety concern. The low headroom should be marked if the stairs cannot be rearranged.

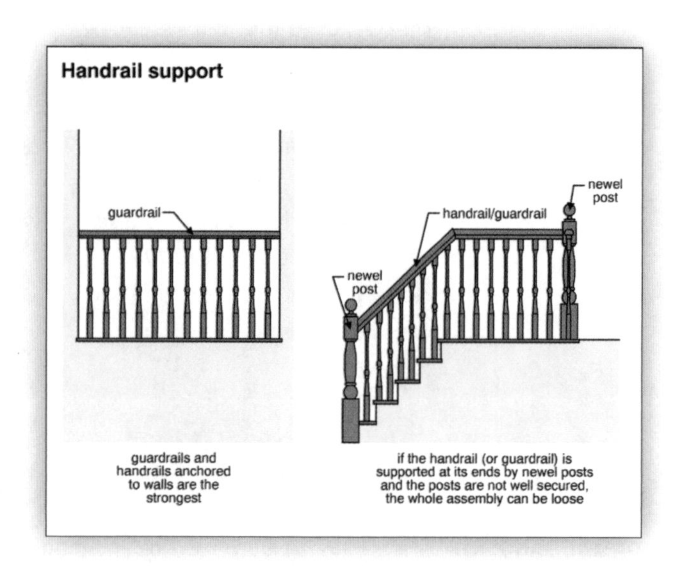

9.0 Fireplaces and Wood Stoves

DESCRIPTION Fireplaces were used historically for heating homes and preparing food. Today, fireplaces are primarily recreational. Most fireplaces use more heat than they provide and in this sense, are a luxury item. How can this be? Fireplaces provide radiant heat into a room, but consume warmed house air for combustion and draft. The warmed house air that goes up the chimney typically represents more heat loss than the radiant heat gain from the flames. A roaring fire can draw 300 to 400 cubic feet of air out of a house every minute. Warm air circulators, glass doors and outside combustion air intakes help reduce the heat loss.

Wood stoves are enclosed units and are somewhat more energy efficient than fireplaces. Although they may be used recreationally, they are often important sources of heat for the home.

INSPECT BEFORE USING! All fireplaces and wood stoves should be inspected by a specialist before the first use, and at least annually thereafter.

CHIMNEY DRAW There are many types of fireplaces, each with their own advantages. It is tough to know which fireplaces will draw well and which will be problems during the home inspection. Some draw well most of the time, but are troublesome under certain wind conditions. Chimneys that are exposed to cold outdoor weather sometimes have trouble establishing a good draft. Interior chimneys tend to be warmer and often draw better. Home inspectors do not light fires in fireplaces and do not evaluate draw.

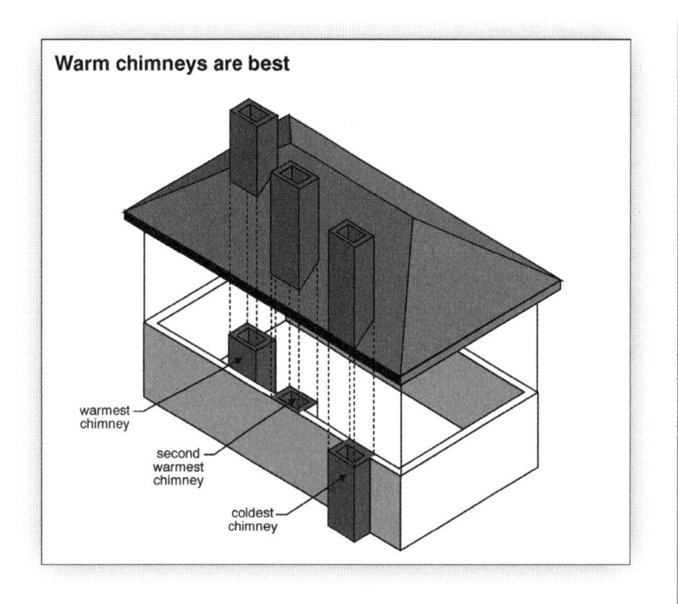

SAFETY Fire safety is a much greater concern than the quality of draw. Fireplace, stove and chimney systems may be unsafe because of poor construction or installation, building settlement, improper usage or poor maintenance. Many safety-related items are not visible. Where there is reason for doubt, it is best to engage a fireplace specialist. In any case, fireplace and chimney systems should be inspected (and cleaned if necessary) before use when taking possession of a house, and at least annually.

Combustible clearances are a big issue with wood-burning fireplaces and stoves. If these are not maintained, there is a fire hazard. Creosote (a tar-like substance) buildup in chimneys is also a significant fire hazard. This product of incomplete combustion has tremendous energy content, and a fire in a chimney with heavy creosote deposits can create very high temperatures and cause a lot of damage.

9.1 Fuel

DESCRIPTION **9.1.1 Wood:** Wood is the traditional fuel for fireplaces and stoves. Wood fires can be roaring blazes or slow smoldering burns. There are several variables, including the design and shape of the fireplace or stove and chimney, the amount of air available, the type, size and moisture content of wood used, the amount of wood in the firebox, and how the wood is arranged in the firebox.

DESCRIPTION **9.1.2 Gas:** Many fireplaces installed in the late 19th and early 20th century were designed for use with natural gas or manufactured gas. These systems typically employ a very small firebox and often have decorative marble, cast iron or ceramic borders around the fireplace opening. These are generally not suitable for conversion to wood-burning fireplaces without major improvements.

Modern natural gas fireplaces are also available, some of which do not even require a chimney. Natural gas fireplaces or logs are often inserted into a masonry fireplace. In some cases, a chimney liner is necessary.

DESCRIPTION **9.1.3 Coal:** Coal-burning fireplaces were common in the 1800s and early 1900s. They typically employed cast iron grates with a pull-out drawer in the bottom to remove the ashes. Most units had two dampers and the firebox was both narrow and shallow. Some units had slotted, heavy, cast iron covers available to put over the entire opening. These fireplaces are often used for burning wood, although most specialists recommend that this not be done without a careful examination of the fireplace and chimney system. These fireplaces are invariably old and should always be inspected by a specialist prior to using them, even for burning coal.

9.2 Fireplace Type

MASONRY FIREBOXES

9.2.1 Masonry (Wood Burning): There are three types of wood burning fireplaces – masonry firebox, metal firebox and zero clearance (all metal). We'll start with masonry fireplaces.

The firebox walls are usually brick, stone or concrete block with a firebrick liner. The mortar joints in the firebrick should be a special refractory mortar and should be as thin as possible. No mortar is required in the firebrick on the hearth, since the bricks are not likely to move out of position.

Some early masonry fireplaces did not include a special firebrick liner. Ordinary brick eventually breaks down and has to be replaced.

METAL FIREBOXES

Some masonry fireplaces have a manufactured metal firebox. In these cases, the walls of the firebox are steel plate, surrounded by masonry. These can be satisfactory, although some fail by bowing or buckling. This is usually a result of inadequate clearance between the metal and the masonry. (A metal firebox, incidentally, should not be confused with a zero-clearance fireplace or a fireplace insert. These are discussed later in this section.)

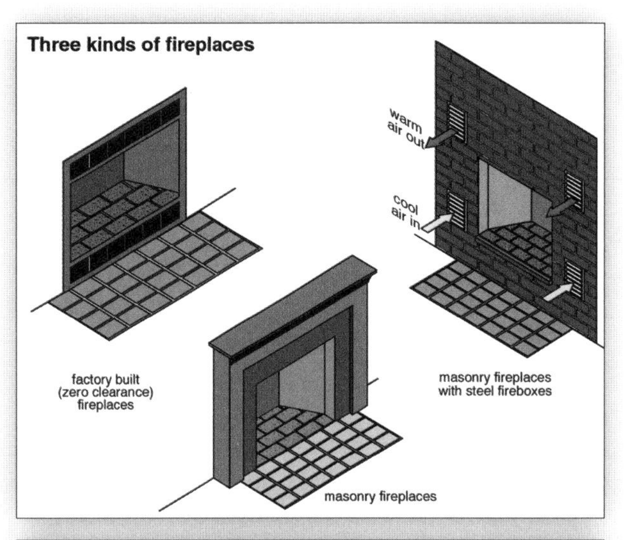

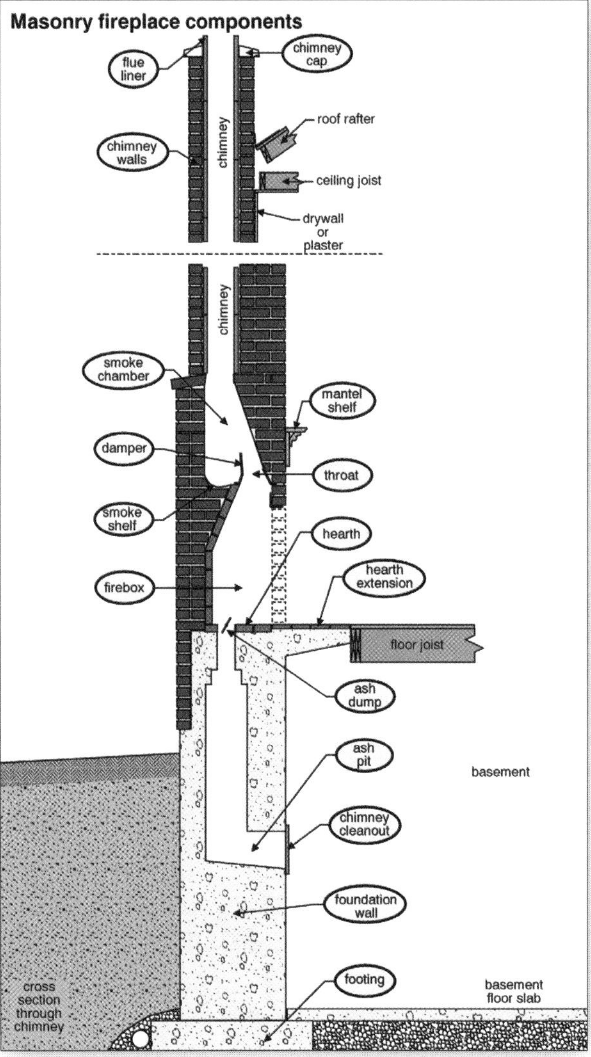

DAMPERS Masonry fireplaces have a metal damper that is usually just above the firebox. The damper may be operated from a handle on the mantle face, or a lever located inside the firebox. Dampers are closed when the fireplace is not in use to minimize heat loss. Dampers must be open for fireplaces to operate.

CHIMNEY The chimney itself is usually made of the same masonry unit as the fireplace and, since approximately 1950, 5/8 inch thick clay tile liners have been provided on the inside of the chimney. Liner sections are usually two to three feet long and the joints are mortared together.

MANTLES Mantles for wood burning fireplaces should not have combustible materials within six inches of the fireplace opening. As a guideline, where there is combustible material around the fireplace opening, and it projects 1-1/2 inches or more out from the surface of the mantle, it should be at least 12 inches above the opening. Many wood mantle shelves break this rule and may be subject to overheating.

ASH PIT (ASH DUMP) An ash pit is a covered opening in the fireplace floor for disposing of ashes. There is typically a clean out at the bottom of the chimney in the basement below. Ash pit covers prevent hot embers accumulating in the ash pit and igniting nearby combustible materials.

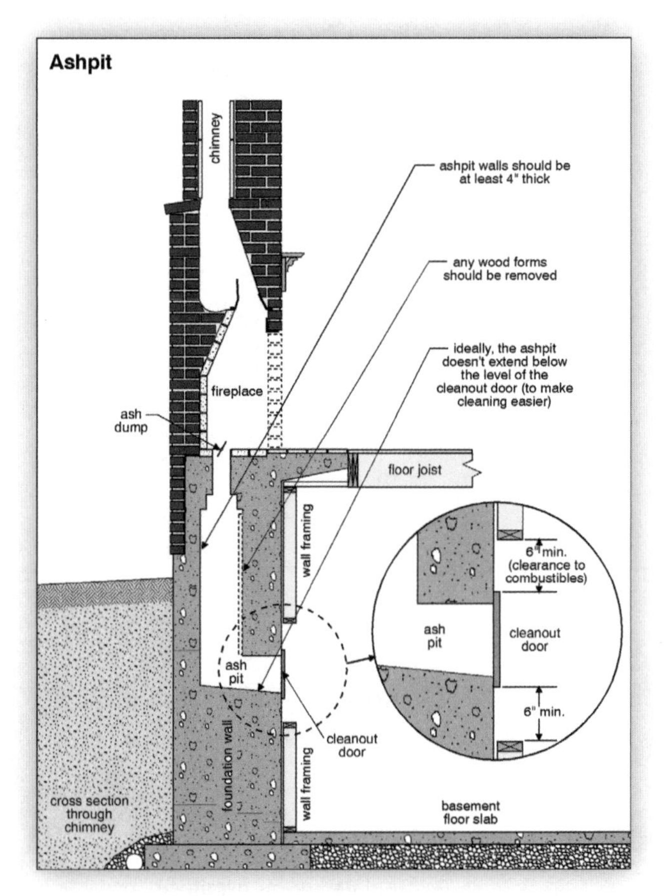

OUTSIDE COMBUSTION AIR Some fireplaces bring combustion air from outside, so that warm house air will not be wasted. Glass doors are often used to prevent house air from being drawn into the fireplace.

HEAT CIRCULATING SYSTEMS Some fireplaces allow house air to be drawn in to pick up some heat from the outside of the firebox to help heat the home. These systems may operate by natural convection or with a fan to help move the air.

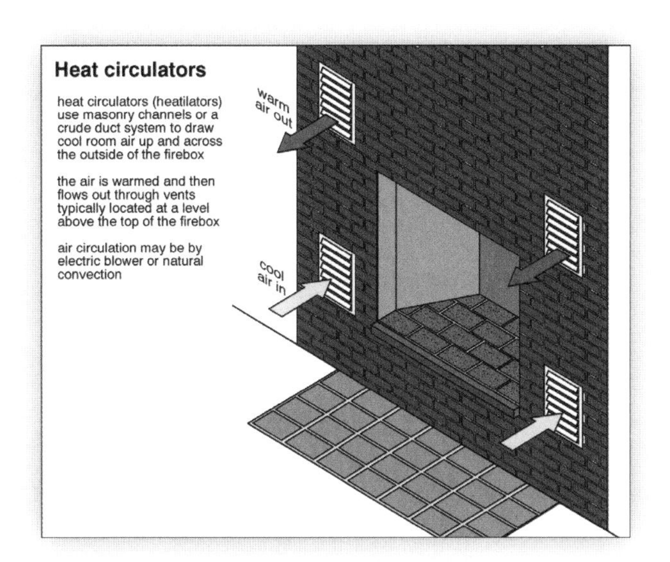

GAS IGNITERS Some wood burning fireplaces have gas igniters. These are typically controlled by manual valve just outside the firebox. They are turned on when lighting the fire and then turned off. These are not permitted in all areas.

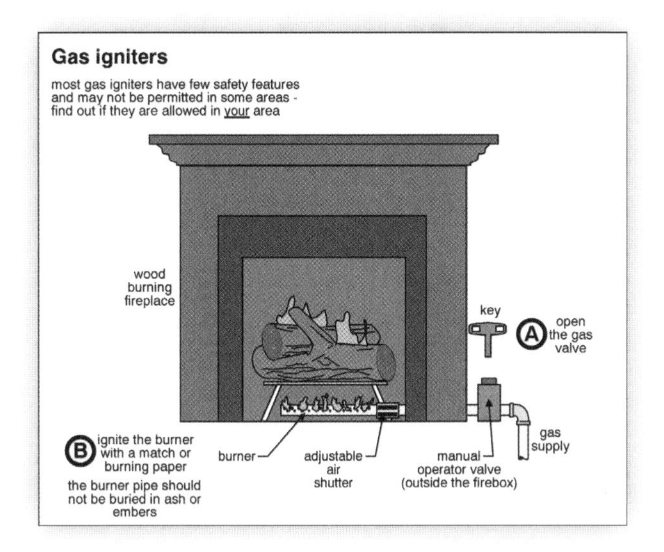

Common Problems with Masonry Fireplaces

UNSAFE Fireplaces may be unsafe for a number of reasons. Common problems include cracked hearths (often a result of building or fireplace settlement), deteriorated firebrick, inadequate clearance from combustibles (walls, mantles, lintels, etc.), openings in the fireplace or chimney (as a result of building settlement, poor construction technique or deterioration of materials) and dirty chimneys coated with creosote. Wherever safety related problems are suspected, a specialist should be engaged.

UNDERSIZED HEARTHS Many wood burning fireplace hearths are undersized. They should project 16 to 20 inches out in front of the firebox and 8 to 12 inches beyond either side. Improvements may or may not be cost-effective, although with small hearths, close attention should be paid to sparks and embers.

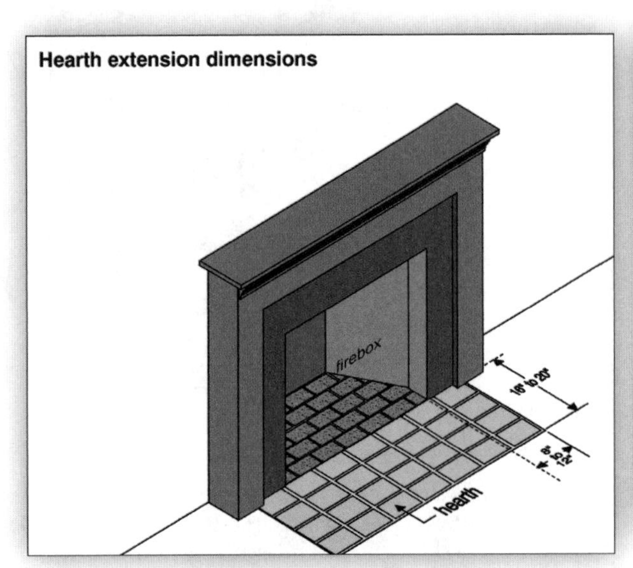

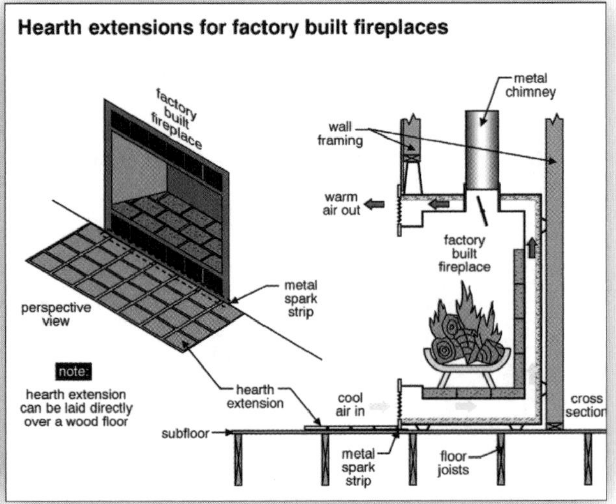

POOR DRAW (THE FIREPLACE SMOKES) Poor draw on a wood-burning fireplace may be the result of a chimney that is too short, a flue that is too small, a fireplace opening that is too large, a poorly shaped firebox, a damper that is too small, too low or too far back, a rough surfaced or poorly shaped smoke chamber, an excessive offset in the chimney flue, the absence of a smoke shelf, or inadequate combustion air. As you can see, analyzing chimney draw is complex.

Another simple cause for a smoking fireplace is the fire being too close to the front of the fireplace. Moving the fire back sometimes solves a smoking problem. If the fireplace is too shallow to permit this, the fireplace may have to be rebuilt.

A dirty chimney can result in a smoking fireplace because it is difficult to fully open the damper, or the accumulation of debris on the smoke shelf will change the direction of air movement in the chimney.

Most fireplaces break at least some guidelines of good design. The trick is not to create the perfect fireplace, but to correct the most serious flaws as economically as possible. Generally speaking, simple solutions should be tried first and more substantial work only undertaken if the inexpensive approaches are unsuccessful.

Straightforward solutions include reducing the fireplace opening size (for example, by adding more firebrick on the hearth), extending the chimney height, or adding glass doors. In some cases, adding a rain cap on the chimney top prevents down-drafts and cures the problem. Adding combustion air may solve a smoking problem while reducing heat loss. Where these do not work, a specialist should be engaged and more extensive work may required.

DAMAGED/ DETERIORATED BRICK Deteriorated brick or mortar in the firebox may be a safety concern. This should be checked and corrected as necessary promptly.

BUCKLED/ DAMAGED/ RUSTED METAL FIREBOXES Metal fireboxes should be kept 1/2 inch to one inch away from masonry. The gap should be filled with noncombustible insulation. Where this gap is not provided, the metal firebox may buckle as it expands during a fire. In some cases, the masonry will crack. The metal and/or masonry may have to be replaced, depending on the advice of a specialist.

Rusted fireboxes may be caused by chimney or roof leaks. Rust can weaken the metal and make the fireplace unsafe. Where rust is noted, a specialist should be engaged to investigate further.

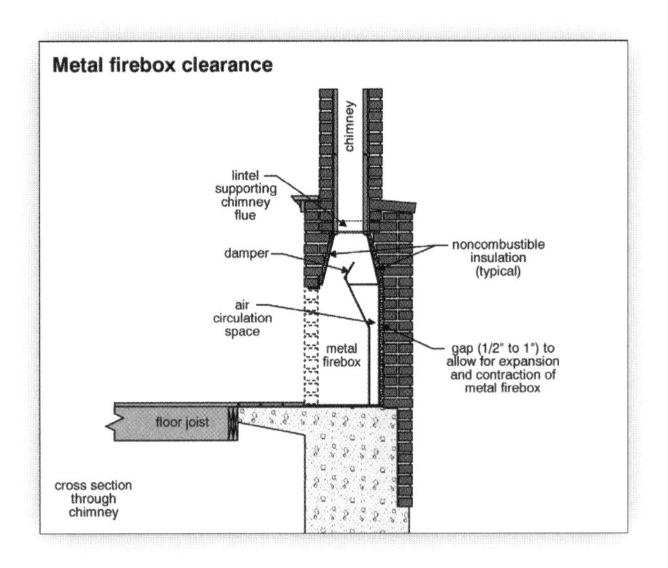

DAMPER PROBLEMS Dampers may be rusted, damaged, jammed or misaligned. Perhaps the most serious problem is a missing damper. It is fairly expensive to install a damper where none was allowed for on original construction. Glass doors may be an acceptable alternative. Dampers installed too low may lead to a smoking fireplace.

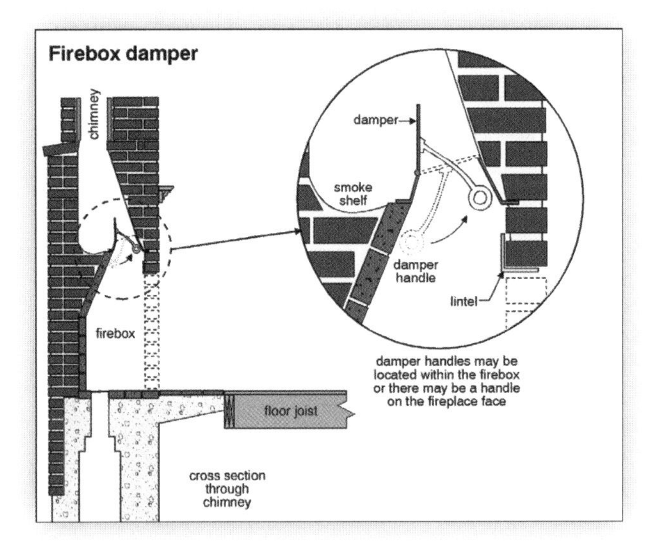

SHARED FLUES A wood burning fireplace should not share a chimney flue with any other appliance, including another fireplace. There is a danger that products of combustion will enter the house through the idle appliance flue. Some older houses were built with shared flues, and in these cases, one of the two appliances should be abandoned. Specialists may be able to provide alternative solutions.

Shared chimneys are found in many attached houses, where back-to-back fireplaces in adjacent homes share a chimney flue. This can be an awkward arrangement to detect initially, and to resolve amicably.

A furnace in the basement may share a flue with a fireplace in the living room above, and a second floor parlor fireplace directly above the living room. Often the chimney will have two flues for the three appliances. These situations require assistance from a specialist.

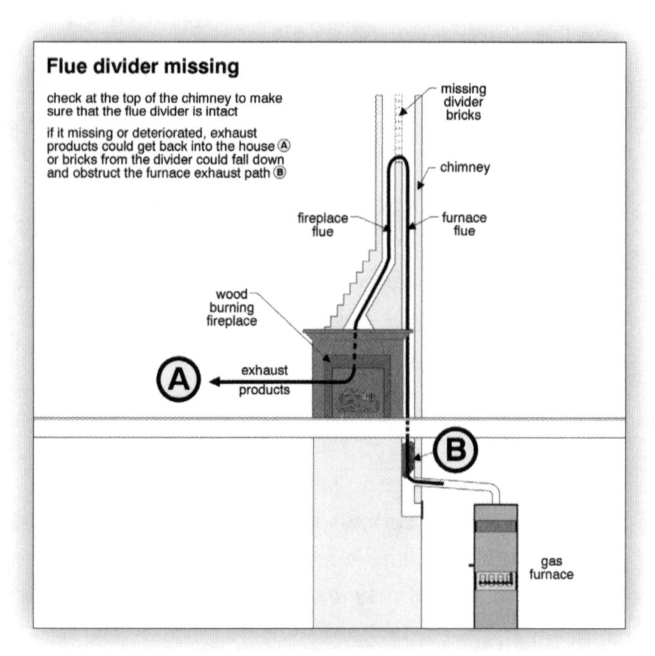

FACADE/ MANTLE MOVEMENT A common problem on modern fireplaces is a masonry facade pulling away from the wall with the mantle leaning out into the room. There may be a gap visible between the top of the facade and the wall. The cause is usually a floor system sagging under the weight of the concentrated masonry load. In most cases, the problem is not serious, but where the tightness of the firebox is compromised, repairs are necessary. If the masonry is at risk of falling, there is a safety concern. Repairs may include re-supporting from below.

COMBUSTIBLE CLEARANCES Combustibles should be at least six inches away from the sides of the fireplace and six inches above. Where combustibles project out more than 1-1/2 inches from the wall, they should be at least 12 inches above the opening. There may be evidence of overheating on the underside of mantle shelves.

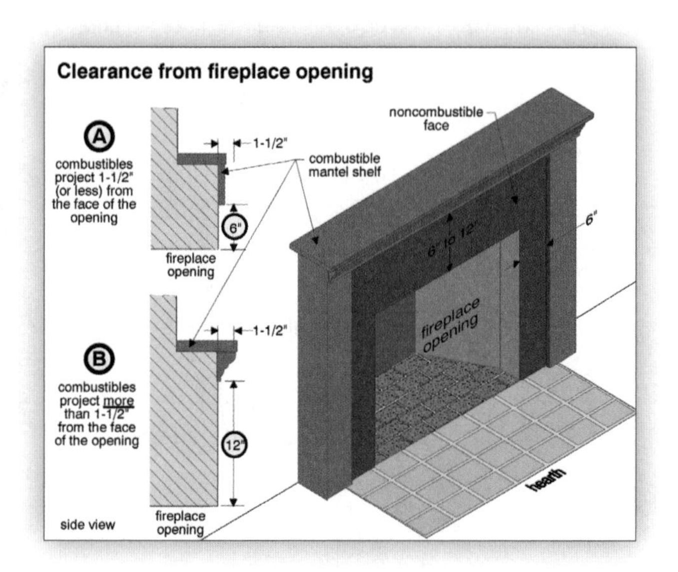

DESCRIPTION **9.2.2 Zero Clearance, Prefabricated or Factory Built Fireplaces (Wood Burning):** Zero clearance fireplaces have been popular since the 1970s. These are insulated metal units that weigh much less than masonry fireplaces. They can be located almost anywhere in a house, since no foundation is required. Despite the name, care must be taken during installation to ensure appropriate clearances from combustibles, as recommended by the manufacturer. These clearances cannot be verified once construction is complete.

CHIMNEYS These fireplaces are typically connected to metal chimneys specially designed for this use. Chimneys typically include a rain cap and a spark arrestor screen. A safe installation depends on a good connection between the fireplace and chimney, good connection of the chimney sections, and proper extension of the chimney above the roof. The system should be well secured and combustible clearances for the chimney should be maintained.

DAMPERS AND GLASS DOORS Zero clearance fireplaces have a damper, but usually have no smoke shelf. Many include a built-in warm air circulator system and some are approved for use with glass doors. Only the glass doors specified by the manufacturer may be used. In some cases, glass doors are required.

DESCRIPTION **9.2.3 Fireplace Inserts (Wood Burning):** Many conventional masonry fireplaces have a metal insert added to increase energy efficiency. These usually include a door and operate much like a wood stove. The units are more energy efficient than open fireplaces.

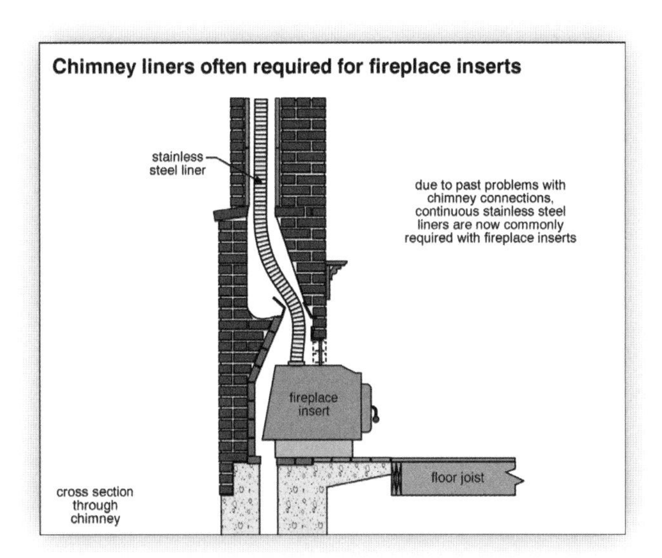

A Problem Unique to Fireplace Inserts

POOR CONNECTION TO CHIMNEY Many difficulties have been experienced with poor connections between the insert and the original chimney. This cannot be checked without pulling out the insert , which is not done during a home inspection. This should be done by a specialist when the system is serviced annually. A continuous chimney liner connected to the top of the insert is a good solution.

Problems Specific to Zero Clearance Fireplaces

These fireplaces have most of the same issues as masonry fireplaces. Problems with the firebox, damper and hearth are common. Combustible clearances can be an issue.

SAFETY CONCERNS Unsafe zero clearance fireplaces are common due to poor connections, missing insulation, provision of insulation where none is allowed, dirty chimneys coated with creosote and inadequate clearance from combustibles. (Even zero clearance fireplaces need some clearance.)

MISSING/ UNDERSIZED HEARTH The absence of a hearth in front of the fireplace is a common problem with these systems. Other hearth problems include undersized or poorly installed hearth systems. It is often difficult to see these problems once the system has been installed.

DESCRIPTION **9.2.4 Gas Fireplaces and Gas Logs:** Although these are primarily decorative appliances, some gas fireplaces provide heat for rooms. Some contain a heat exchanger to help transfer heat into the house air.

Gas fireplaces and gas logs may be standalone or installed in existing wood burning fireplaces. Gas fireplaces designed to fit into masonry fireplaces are often referred to as fireplace inserts.

GLASS DOORS Some systems have glass doors which cannot be opened. Others have operable glass doors. Some glass door systems have been problematic and there have been recalls. Identification of product recalls is not within the scope of a home inspection.

COMBUSTION AIR Combustion air for these devices may be taken from house air or from outside.

REMOTE CONTROLS Remote controls are available to turn the fireplace on and off and to control circulating fans. Fans may be manual or thermostatically controlled.

Problems Specific to Gas Fireplaces

INOPERATIVE Inoperative gas fireplaces may be the result of a defective gas valve, thermocouple or igniter, an electrical problem, or the gas may be shut off. Diagnosing fireplace problems is not within the scope of home inspection.

BEDROOM OR BATHROOM In many areas, gas fireplaces must be approved for use in bedrooms or bathrooms, or must meet certain requirements to reduce the potential for exhaust gases entering the home. A common requirement is that the fireplace be direct-vented.

DAMPER CLOSED Where gas logs are installed in an existing fireplace, the fireplace damper must be permanently opened or removed so that the exhaust can go up the chimney. If the damper is accidentally closed, the combustion gases cannot leave the home, creating a health hazard.

GLASS DOORS Some glass door systems have overheated and may present a safety concern. We recommend checking with a specialist during regular servicing to ensure there has been no recall or problem with the glass doors on the gas fireplace.

9.3 Wood Stoves

DESCRIPTION A well-manufactured and properly installed wood burning stove can be a safe and energy efficient system. Poorly installed or maintained stoves have caused some fires, and some insurance companies will not provide insurance for homes with wood stoves.

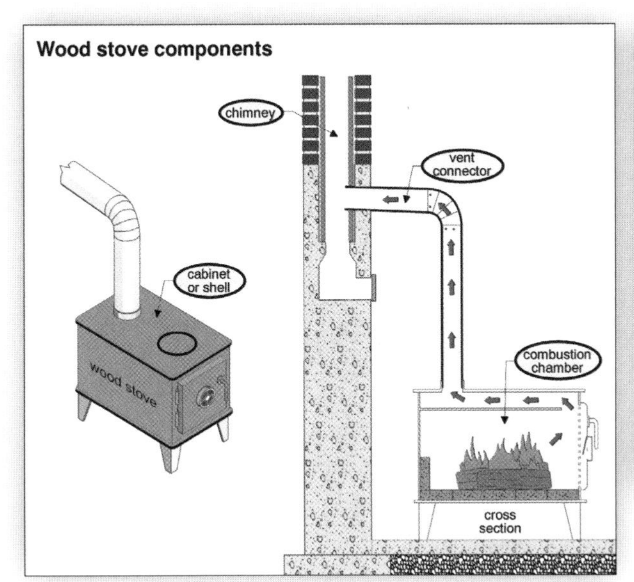

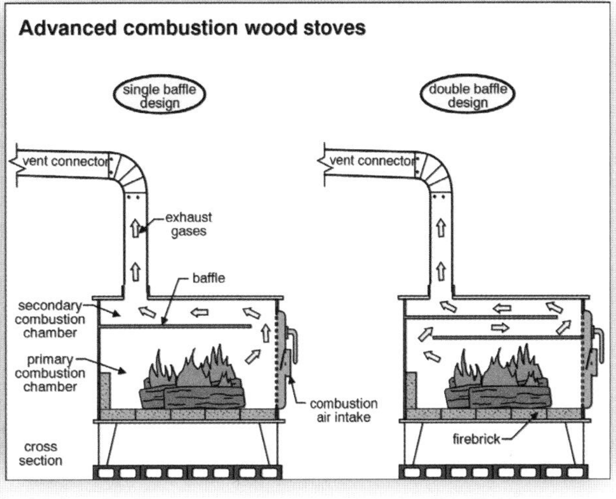

LISTING Wood stoves may be listed by several agencies. Installation clearances are set out in the listings for individual stoves. Where a listing cannot be found on a unit, the following guidelines are typically used.

FLOOR PROTECTION Wood stoves typically sit on a concrete floor or a protected wood floor. The wood floor should be protected with a noncombustible pad (sheet metal, for example), extending 18 inches beyond the stove door and eight inches beyond the other sides. On top of this should be eight inches of hollow masonry. Usually, two courses of four-inch units are used, arranged to allow air circulation. Stoves that sit off the floor can rest on special metal plates with spacers and the masonry units can be omitted.

COMBUSTIBLE CLEARANCES Unlisted stoves should be 48 inches from combustibles (including walls, even if covered by plaster or drywall) on all sides and 60 inches above. Clearances can be reduced if special protection is provided, or if the unit is designed for reduced clearances. Side clearances can be as small as 18 inches.

Side and rear clearances can be reduced by two-thirds if the wall is protected by metal sheets spaced out one inch from the wall. A reduction of one-half is acceptable if brick or ceramic is spaced out from the wall one inch.

Many installations will not meet the clearances indicated above. The original installation instructions may have called for less clearance. Standards have become more strict in recent years.

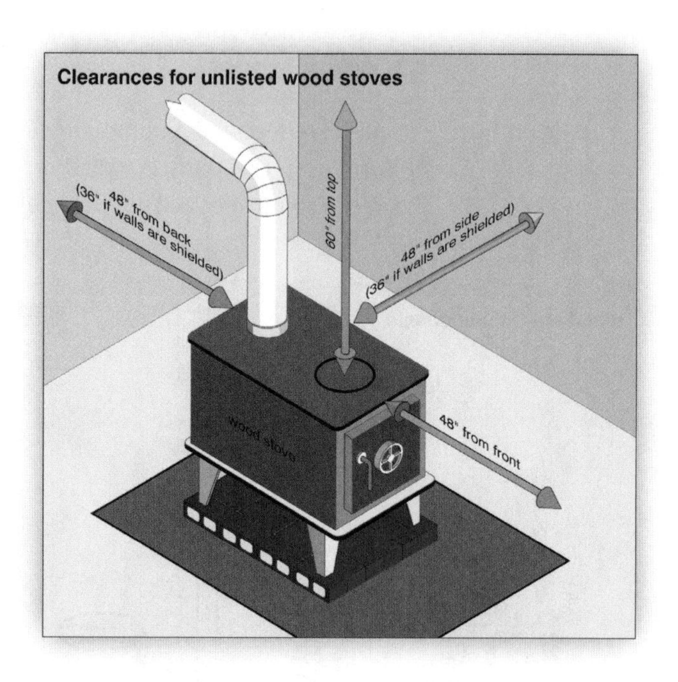

FLUE PIPE Single wall flue pipes should be kept at least 18 inches from combustibles, including wood-frame ceilings and walls, even if covered with plaster or drywall. Flue sections should be fit together so that condensing creosote running down the chimney will not leak out at seams. Adjacent sections should overlap by at least one to two inches and should be secured with three screws.

Flue pipes should be black steel, stainless steel or enameled steel; not galvanized steel.

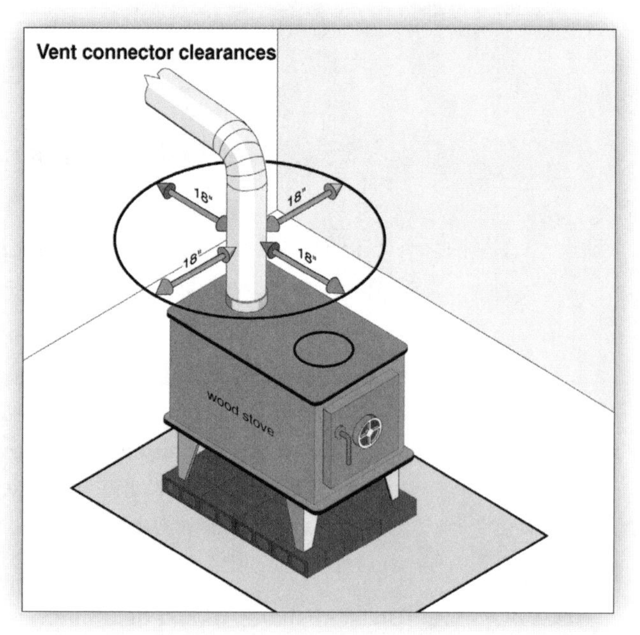

CHIMNEY A masonry chimney or a metal chimney specially designed for solid fuels should be used. Under normal circumstances the stove should not share a flue with any other appliance. Under no circumstances should a stove share a flue with an appliance on a different story.

Common Problems with Wood Stoves

COMBUSTIBLE CLEARANCES Proper clearances from combustible materials are described above, although individual units may have been tested and approved for installation with lesser clearances. This information is usually found on the stove itself. Inadequate clearances are a significant fire safety issue, since long-term exposure to high temperatures will reduce the auto-ignition temperature of combustibles. Eventually, the combustible materials may spontaneously ignite.

Many stoves are installed properly, but homeowners store their firewood, kindling and newspaper adjacent to the stove, defeating the combustible clearance requirements.

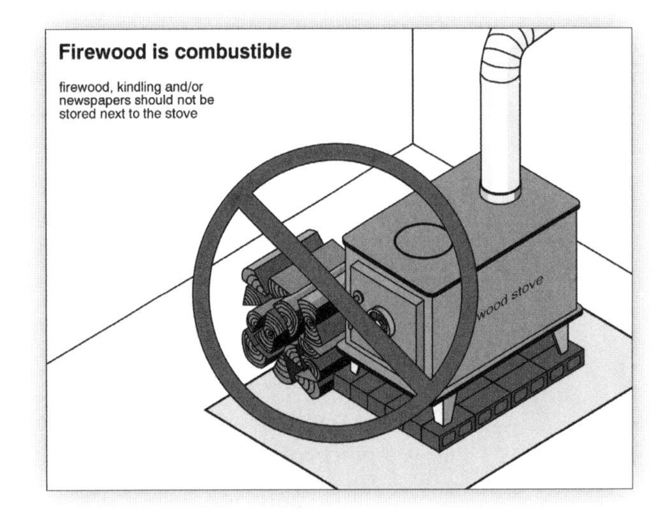

PELLET STOVE Some stoves burn compressed wood or biomass pellets rather than wood.

FLOOR PROTECTION Inadequate floor protection is a fire hazard, especially when sparks or embers drop out of the open door.

FLUE PIPE PROBLEMS Flue pipes or breechings (the pipes that join the stove to the chimney) should have no more than ten feet of horizontal run, no more than two 90-degree elbows, supports every three feet, and should have joints that allow condensate to drain into the stove. Joints have one sleeve that fits inside another, with the lower sleeve outside the upper sleeve. The minimum flue slope up from the stove to the chimney is 1/4 inch per foot. The flue/chimney connection should be tightly made with a thimble or flue ring. The exhaust flue pipe should not extend into the chimney flue opening.

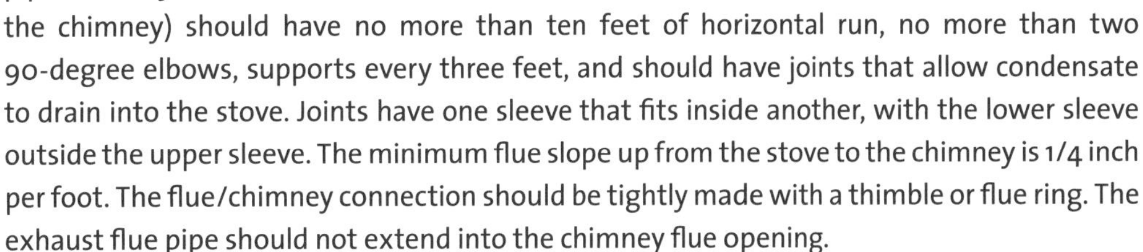

Rust is a significant problem with metal flue pipes and chimneys.

SAFETY INSPECTIONS Many insurance organizations are concerned with wood stove safety, and may insist that a specialist inspect a wood stove installation. Others may refuse to offer insurance if the home has a wood stove. Because of the controlled and relatively slow burn of a wood stove, creosote deposits in chimneys can be a problem. All chimneys should be cleaned regularly, but special attention should be paid to wood stove chimneys.

10.0 Basement Leakage (Including Crawlspaces)

DESCRIPTION Basement leakage is one of the most common problems found in houses; almost all basements will leak at some point during their life. (We use the word basement in this section to include basements and crawlspaces.) While structural damage caused by leakage is very rare, water in the basement can be a major inconvenience and often causes damage to interior finishes and storage. In addition, mold has become a significant health concern.

Unfortunately, we cannot determine how often a basement may leak and how serious the problem might be during a one-time home inspection. There may or may not be clues that indicate a history of basement dampness. These clues usually do not give an indication of the severity or frequency.

Section 10.1 lists some of the clues that suggest basement dampness. They can be misleading. For example, efflorescence (white salt crystals) forms on basement walls as water migrates through and evaporates, leaving minerals behind. Most people assume that the greater the efflorescence, the more severe the problem. In reality, more deposits come from drier air in the basement, greater rates of evaporation and hence, more mineral deposits. Strangely, a de-humidifier in the basement can increase the amount of efflorescence.

Rust, mold and mildew can be caused by moisture penetration into the basement, but can also be caused by condensation forming on foundation walls as hot, humid summer air comes in contact with the cool walls.

Moisture problems are intermittent. In some houses, water penetration will occur after virtually every rain. In other houses, it will occur only after periods of prolonged rain, and in still others, it will only happen with wind driven rain from a certain direction or during a spring thaw. In most cases however, the resultant damage gives no indication of frequency.

10.1 Identification of Problems

WALL REPAIRS Repairs noted on the exterior that may suggest wet basement problems include patching with tar-like materials, cement parging, or any one of a myriad of waterproofing products. Freshly excavated areas may also indicate recent repairs. New sod along the edge of a house also suggests recent exterior work.

On the interior of poured concrete walls, plugged holes may indicate that cracks have been filled with epoxy or polyurethane for example. Patching or a trench around the perimeter of the floor may indicate an interior drainage system has been added.

EFFLORESCENCE Efflorescence is a whitish mineral deposit often seen on the interior of foundation walls. Efflorescence indicates moisture penetration, although it does not indicate the severity or whether the problem is active. As water passes through a wall, salts in the masonry, concrete or mortar are dissolved, so that when the water arrives at the wall surface, it contains salts in solution. As water evaporates from the wall surface, a crystalline salt deposit, known as efflorescence, is left. This may be the result of outside water passing through the wall, condensation, or water wicking up through the wall by capillary action.

RUST Rusty nails in baseboards or paneling, rusted electrical outlet boxes or rusted metal feet on appliances may indicate wet basement problems.

MOLD/STAIN/ DAMAGED STORAGE/ETC. Other indicators include mold; water stains; odors; sagging cardboard boxes stored on the floor; crumbling plaster or drywall; lifting floor tiles; rotted or discolored wood at or near floor level; storage on skids or boards raised off the floor; dehumidifiers; peeling paint; and crumbling concrete.

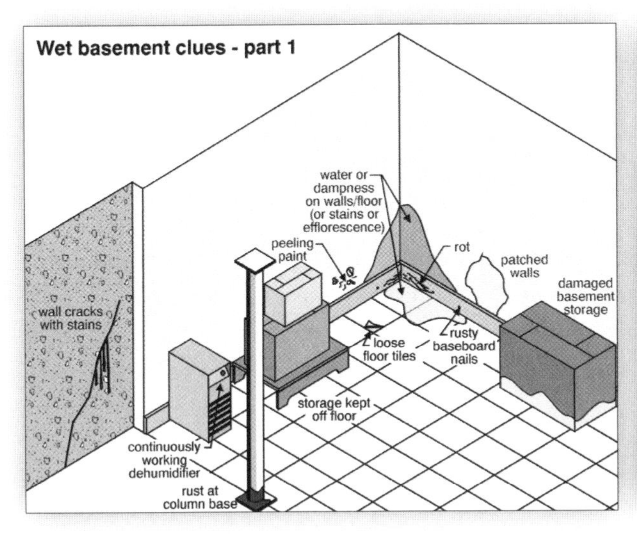

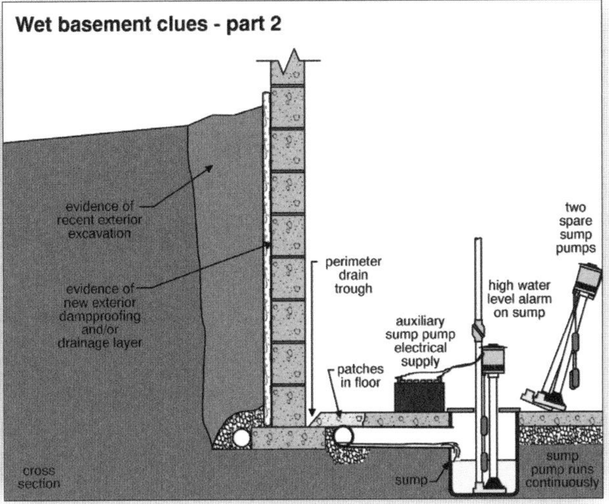

LOWERED BASEMENT FLOORS When basements are lowered, the exterior drainage tile around the perimeter of the home becomes largely ineffective, because it ends up above the floor level. Houses with lowered basements are much more prone to leaking basement problems. This is anticipated in some cases, and interior drainage tile may be provided below the new basement floor.

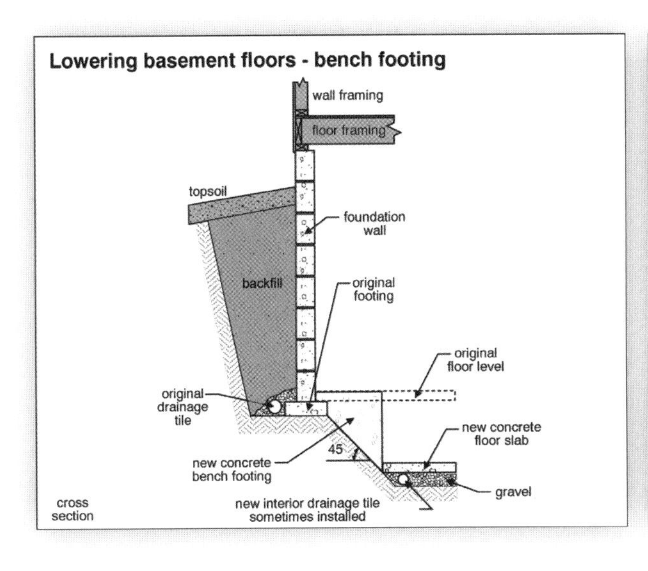

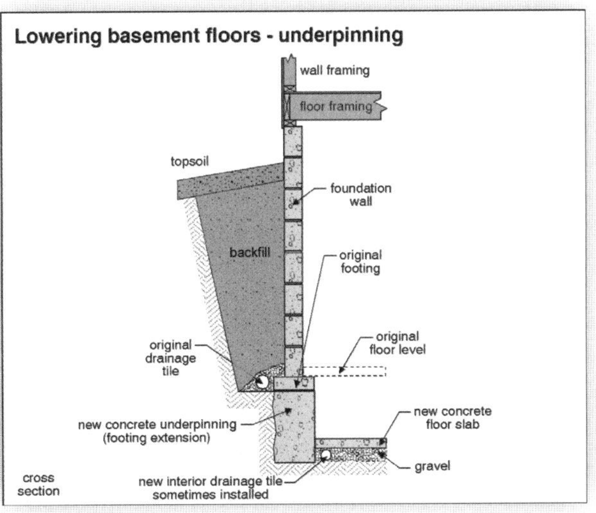

WATER SOURCE

When a wet basement problem is identified, the first step is to make sure the source is not from within the house. A leaking plumbing system, water heater, washing machine, or hot water heating system, may all be confused with basement leakage. Sewers may back up through floor drains, causing basement flooding. During the summer months, condensation on cold water piping can make a localized section of a basement surprisingly wet. Condensation on cool foundation walls can also be mistaken for leakage. This often results in a damp basement odor. These issues require specific action.

10.2 Approach

DESCRIPTION

Basement leakage clues do not indicate the severity or frequency of leakage. Since virtually all basements leak at some point, the question is not, "Will the basement leak?" but, "When?" With a few exceptions, wet basement problems can be cured or significantly reduced inexpensively.

Most contractors asked to solve wet basement problems are not prepared to bear this responsibility. They do not want to suggest solutions that usually work, but not always, even if those suggestions save the homeowner a lot of money. Many contractors offer solutions that minimize the risk of future problems and complaints. These solutions tend to be the more disruptive and expensive.

If one cannot afford to experiment (because, for example, the basement is going to be rented out, or is about to be finished), the higher cost but lower risk approach makes sense. However, a less radical and more systematic approach will usually yield a far less expensive solution.

90% OF PROBLEMS ARE FROM SURFACE WATER

Less than 10% of basement leakage problems are caused by ground water (underground streams and high water tables). Since more than 90% of wet basement problems are caused by surface water (rain or snow) collecting around the building, the surface water issues should be addressed first.

Two things have to happen for a basement to leak:

1. There is water outside the basement.
2. There are flaws in the basement wall that allow water through.

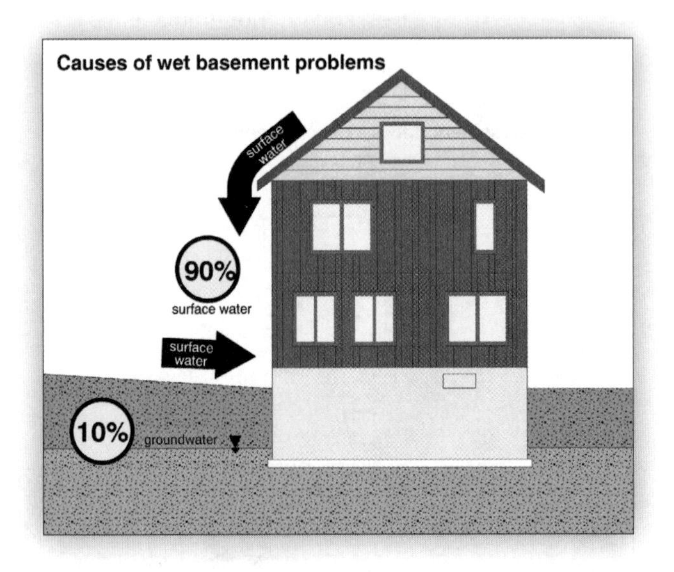

SOLVE PROBLEM AT THE SOURCE Rather than trying to make a basement or crawl space into a perfectly watertight vessel, it makes sense to keep water away from the building. It's difficult and expensive to turn a house basement into a boat. Even houses with leaky foundation walls will be dry if the water from rain and melting snow flows away from the house and does not accumulate in the soil around the building.

KEEP WATER AWAY FROM FOUNDATION Rain water and water from melting snow accumulates in the soil outside the building from two sources – the roof and the ground around the building. We can keep the soil around the building dry if we drain the roof water into gutters and downspouts, and slope the ground around the building so water naturally drains away.

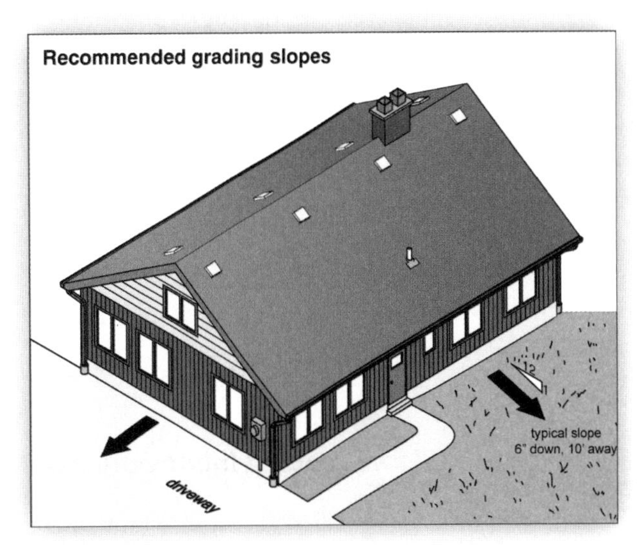

Once the source of the water has been eliminated, that is usually the end of the problem. As a precaution, obvious cracks and holes in foundation walls can be addressed, if needed. Large scale digging, dampproofing, drainage membranes and drainage tiles are a last resort after improving gutters and downspouts to control roof water, improving grading to drain surface water away, and correcting obvious points of water penetration.

The following step-by-step process solves most basement dampness problems relatively inexpensively.

10.3 Gutters and Downspouts

DESCRIPTION The key to keeping any basement/crawlspace dry is eliminating or minimizing the source of outside water. The gutters and downspouts have to do their job, collecting all the water from the roof. The downspouts should either discharge into a drainage system below ground, or preferably, above grade at least six feet away from the building, depending on land slope, soil porosity, etc.

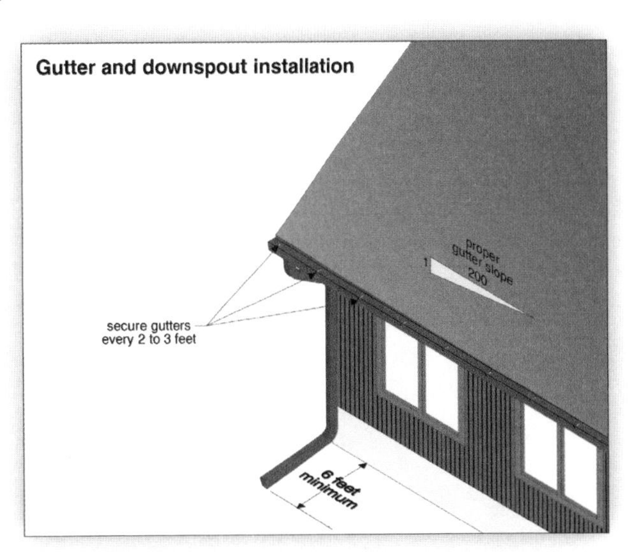

ABANDON UNDERGROUND DOWNSPOUTS It is common for downspouts that discharge into an under ground waste plumbing system to become obstructed or broken below grade level. This collects water outside the foundation wall, resulting in leakage. Excavating and repairing this pipe is expensive. It's much easier to cap the downspout where it goes below grade, and add an elbow and downspout extension to discharge water onto the ground several feet from the building.

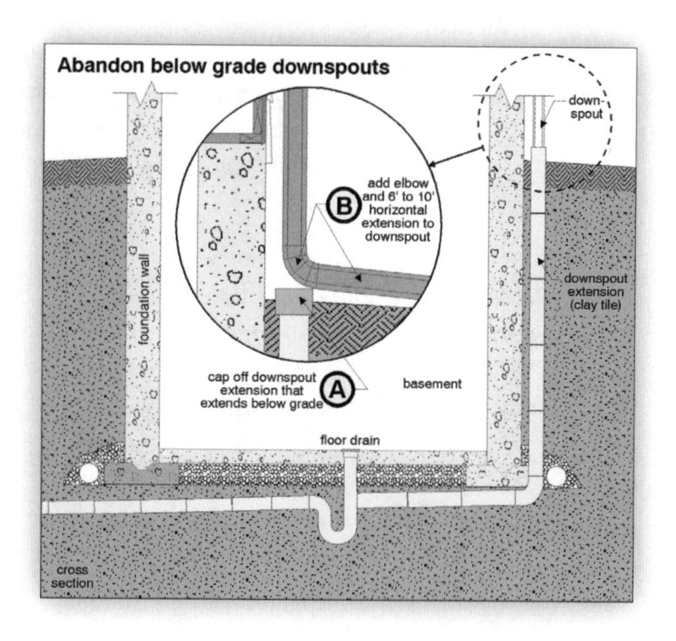

10.4 Grading Improvements

DESCRIPTION Re-grading the exterior to drain water away from the building is one of the most effective solutions to wet basement problems. The ground should slope down away from the house at a minimum rate of one inch per foot for at least the first six feet out from the building. Hard surfaces like asphalt driveways can slope less, with almost any positive slope being effective. In some cases, the yard is re-sloped creating gentle valleys or swales to direct water away.

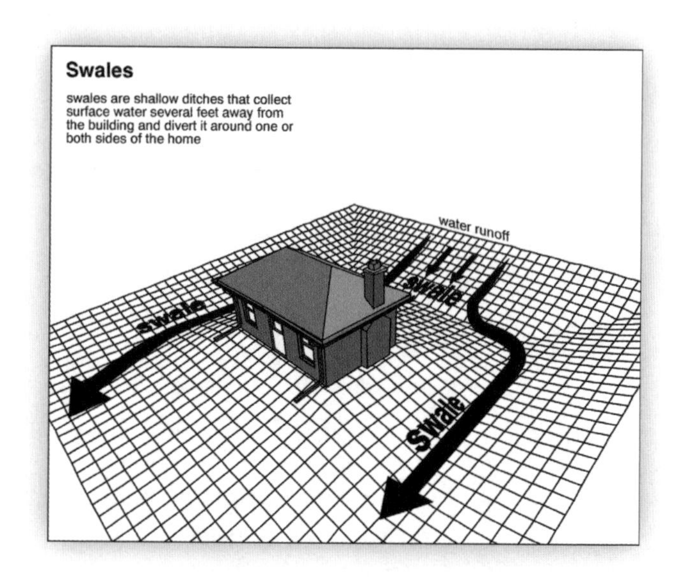

This work can be expensive where driveways, patios or sidewalks have to be lifted, although in lawn and garden areas, adding some inexpensive topsoil works fine. Sand and gravel are not effective materials, since water will flow through these easily. Well compacted soils that force most of the water to run across the surface are better.

BASEMENT STAIRWELLS AND WINDOW WELLS Localized low areas that collect water, including open basement stairwells and window wells, should have drains to remove the water. There are usually no traps in these drains in freezing climates. If necessary, these openings can be covered to prevent water accumulation. There are clear plastic dome covers, for example, available for basement window wells. These do allow light into the basement, although, of course, ventilation is cut off. Grading should be well sloped to direct surface water away from these openings.

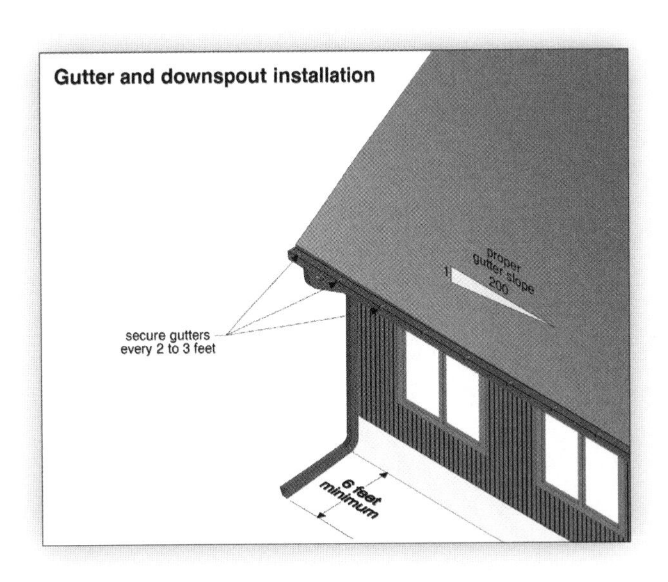

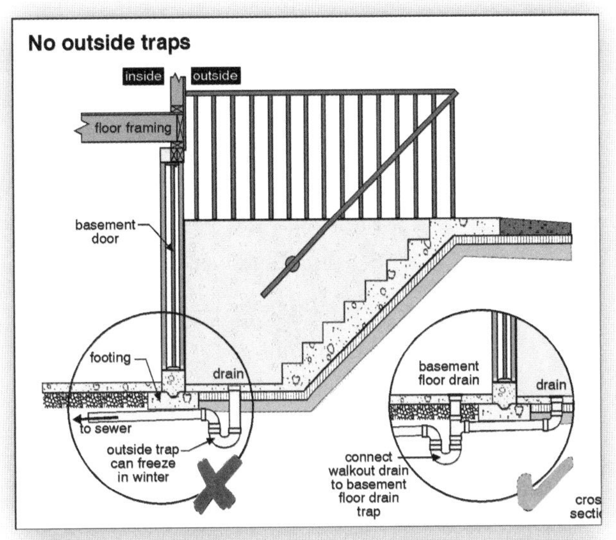

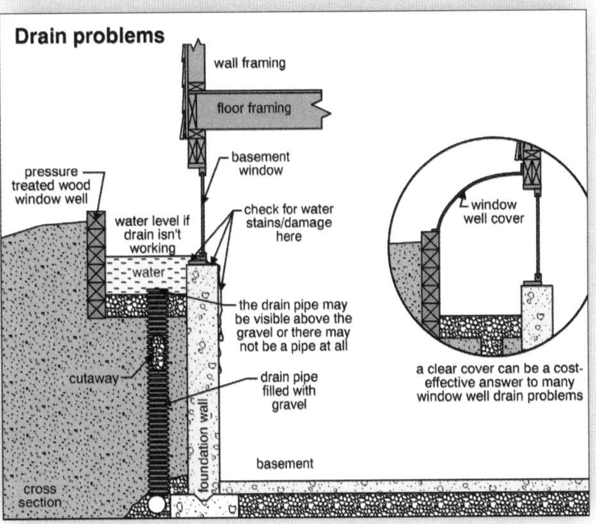

CATCH BASINS Even if there is no evidence of leakage, good drainage should be ensured during any landscaping or driveway work. Where good grading cannot be achieved, catch basins are used. Water is directed into basins that carry water to a drainage system. Catch basins are prone to clogging and frost heaving. Good maintenance is necessary to ensure a dry basement.

Where the grading problem is from an adjacent property, the local building authorities can help if neighbors are not cooperative. City building departments are generally aware of the importance of good grading.

Catch basins - drain pipe should face down

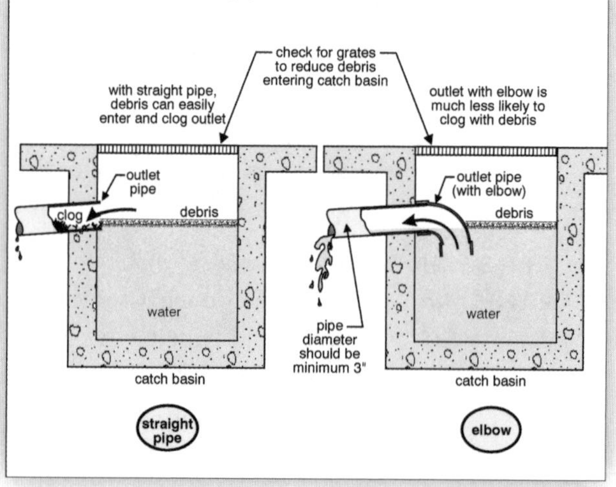

Where drainage cannot be away from the building for six feet or so (because of a neighbor's house, for example) the best compromise is a low area between two buildings that directs water along a trough to a point away from both buildings. If this is not possible, a catch basin may be the answer.

BACKFILL SETTLING AROUND NEW HOMES Poor grading is a common problem on newer houses. The backfill around new houses is often not well compacted (for fear of damaging new foundation walls). Over the first few years, the soil settles, and the ground around the building slopes toward the foundation. The solution is to add material to re-slope the grade.

Settled backfill

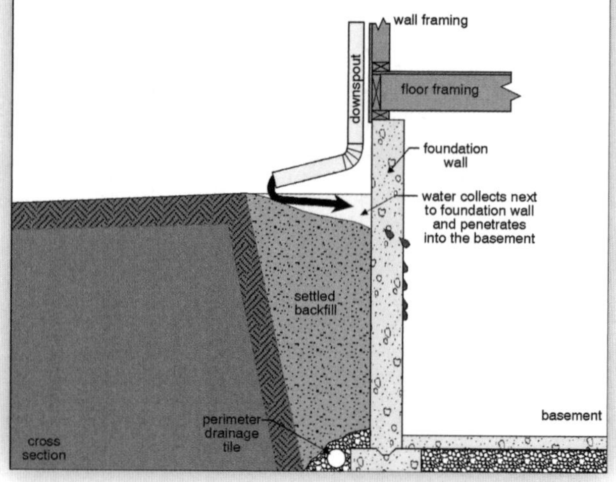

10.5 Patching Cracks

FROM INSIDE Cracks in poured concrete basement walls can sometimes be successfully repaired from the inside. There are several products available in building supply stores. We suggest only accomplished technicians perform this work.

EPOXY AND POLYURETHANE Epoxy and polyurethane can be injected into the crack until the crack is filled. Epoxy is usually installed by a contractor and is considered by some to be the best patch material for poured concrete walls. It is, however, only as good as the person who mixes and installs it. Epoxy is different than most patching materials in that it does have structural integrity. A properly installed epoxy patch will never crack again. The wall will fail elsewhere first. If the forces that caused the crack are still present, a new crack may develop. For this reason, some contractors prefer polyurethane injection, as it stays flexible.

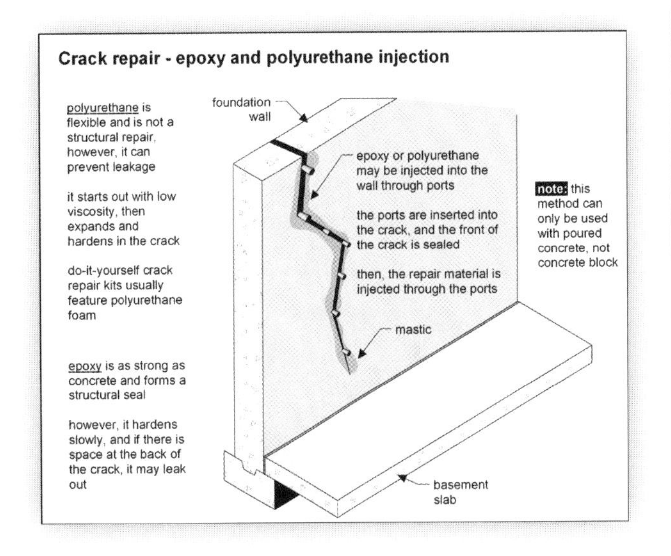

FOR MINOR PROBLEMS ONLY Patching cracks on poured concrete walls does not remove the water problem; it only traps it outside the basement. Patching cracks is usually only successful for minor, occasional problems. In many cases, the water will simply find another way in. It is better to prevent water accumulating outside the basement, than to try to turn the basement wall into a dam, holding the water back. The big appeal of patching cracks inside the basement is that it is inexpensive. Interior patching is not effective for hollow block walls since the water has too many paths it can follow.

OUTSIDE PATCHING BETTER Patching from the outside is more expensive, but may be more successful. Covering a patch with a good draining material, (there are several drainage membranes designed for below grade use) will protect the patch and keep water away. If the basement is only wet where there are cracks, patching may be a practical approach.

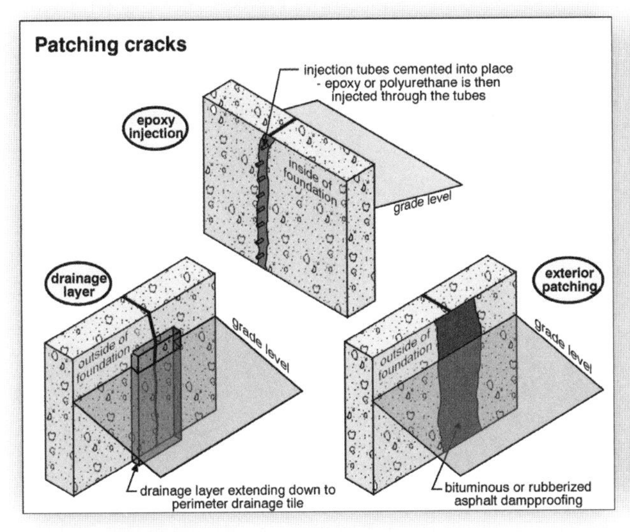

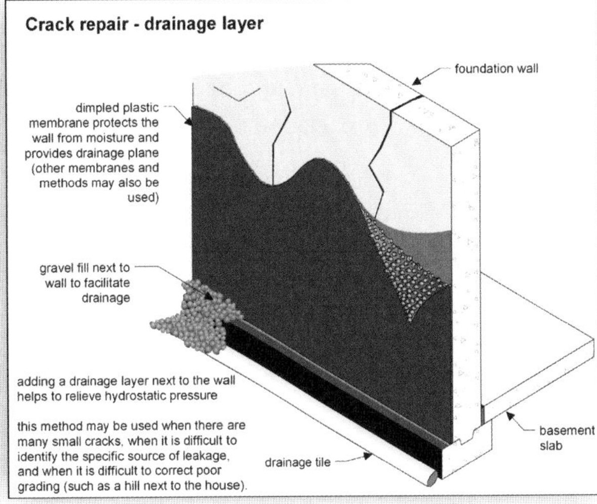

10.6 Excavation, Dampproofing and Foundation Drainage

DESCRIPTION When basement leakage cannot be controlled by managing roof water and surface water or by patching, there may be a need to excavate on the building exterior, dampproof the outside walls, provide a drainage membrane against the wall and add or replace the perimeter drainage tile system.

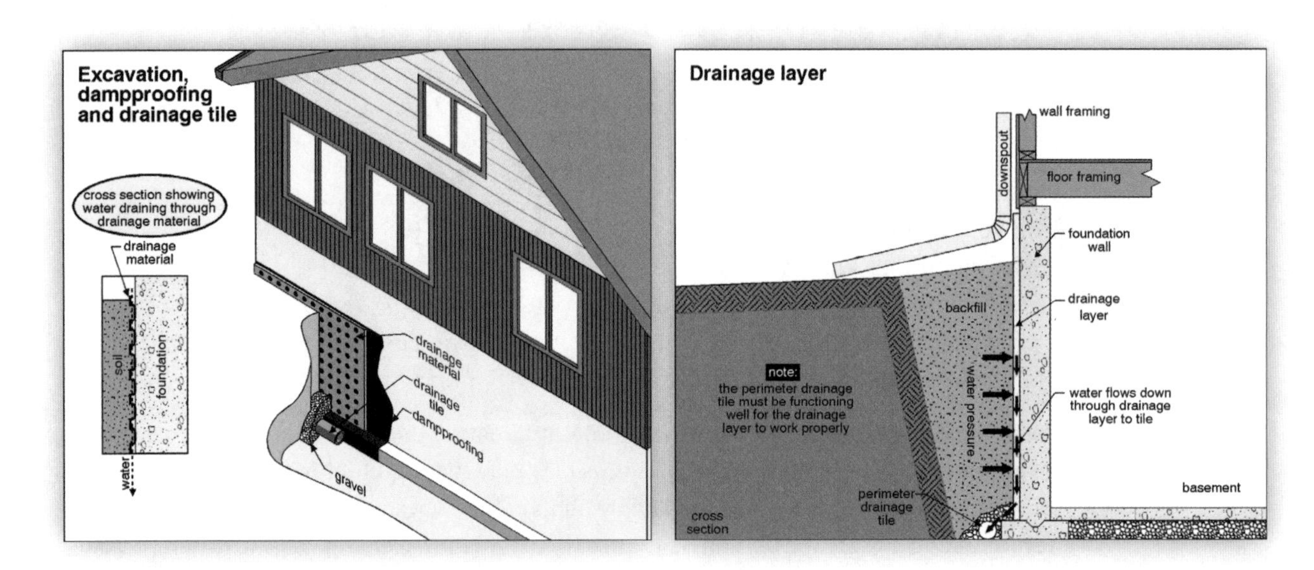

DRAINAGE TILE Perimeter drainage tile systems for basements were introduced to residential construction in the early 1900s. They did not become popular until some time after this. On an older house, even if they are present, they are often obstructed or collapsed. This drainage tile system was traditionally a four-inch clay tile pipe. The piping was laid outside the footing around the perimeter of the house, below the basement floor level with roughly a 1/4-inch space left between each section of pipe. This allowed water to run into the piping if the soil was saturated. The joints were covered at the top with building paper to prevent soil and other debris from getting into the piping system.

The pipes were surrounded and covered with gravel to allow water to penetrate quickly to the pipes and be carried away. In older homes, the piping system would discharge into the combination sewer.

This approach was somewhat effective, although over the long term tree roots and debris inevitably found their way into the pipe.

MODERN PERIMETER DRAINAGE TILE

In modern construction, the piping used is perforated plastic, and it is arranged to discharge straight into a storm sewer. The perforated plastic piping that has replaced the clay tile piping is corrugated and very flexible. The perforations are in half of the diameter of the pipe only. The piping is laid with the holes down.

The top of the drainage pipe is below the bottom of the floor slab. The pipe is covered on the top and sides with at least six inches of gravel or crushed stone. Geotextile fabric wrapped around the pipe will hold back soil, but allow water to pass, helping to prevent clogging.

The work is expensive and disruptive. If the basement is only wet along one or two walls, it makes sense to address just those walls, rather than the entire foundation perimeter.

WHERE DOES THE WATER GO?

The drainage system ideally discharges into a storm sewer. Where no sewer is available, the discharge point can be above grade well away from the house. Where permitted, the foundation drain can discharge into a dry well. This is a gravel pit, typically located below the foundation drainage system, at least 15 feet from the building. This is also called a French drain, and is only suitable with good draining soils. The water table, of course, must be below the bottom of a dry well.

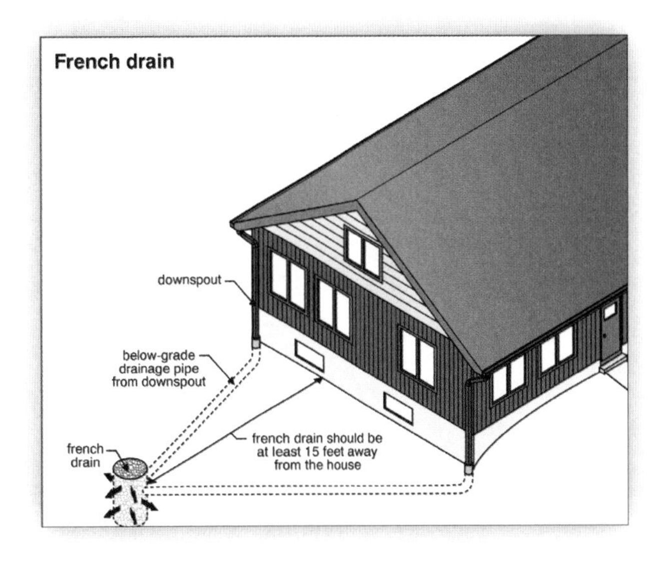

Where none of these approaches is practical, the water can be collected in a sump and pumped onto the ground a good distance away from the house.

DAMPPROOFING

The dampproofing on the exterior typically involves parging concrete block walls with a 1/4 inch layer of mortar extending down to the footing. (Parging is not required on poured concrete.) The foundation/footing joint is coved (sloped) to seal this joint and direct the water into the drainage tile. Next, a dampproofing layer, which may be an asphalt or plastic material, is applied to the wall.

DRAINAGE LAYER/ MEMBRANE A drainage layer can be placed against the exterior walls below grade. This often takes the form of a dimpled plastic membrane that holds the soil away from the foundation, creating an air gap to allow water to flow freely into the drainage tile.

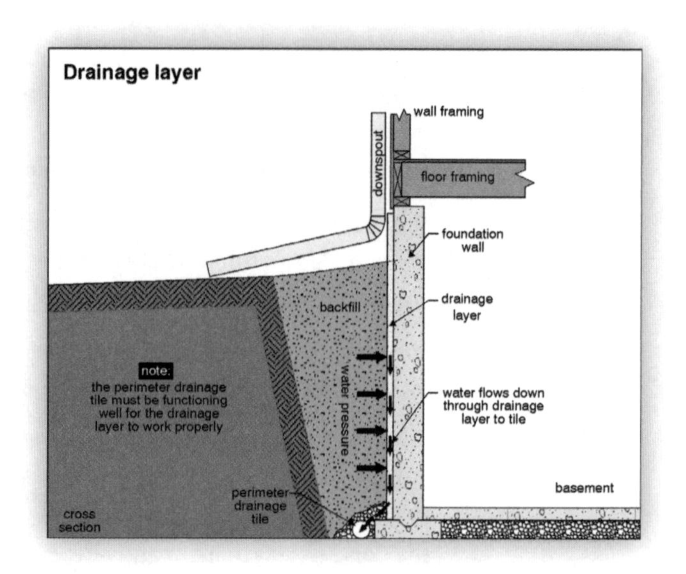

EXTERIOR BASEMENT INSULATION Another approach is the use of exterior basement insulation. Rigid fiberglass insulation board designed for use below grade provides good insulation and helps keep the basement dry. Water entering the insulation flows quickly down through it to the drainage tile.

INTERIOR BASEMENT INSULATION Sprayed foam is sometimes used on the interior of foundation walls to control basement leakage and to reduce basement heat loss.

10.7 Interior Drainage Systems

DESCRIPTION Because excavating on the exterior is expensive and disruptive, an interior drainage system sometimes makes sense. A strip of the concrete floor is broken up around the perimeter of the foundation wall. A drainage system is installed below the basement floor inside the footings. The water can then flow into a waste sewer system, if gravity permits, or a sump with a pump. This approach is more practical and less disruptive if the basement is unfinished.

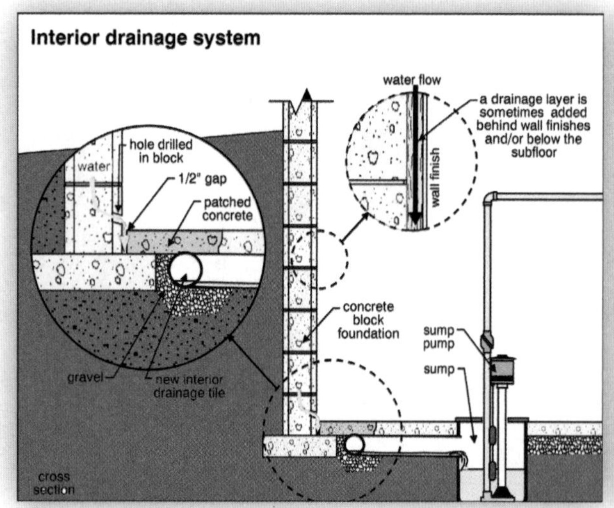

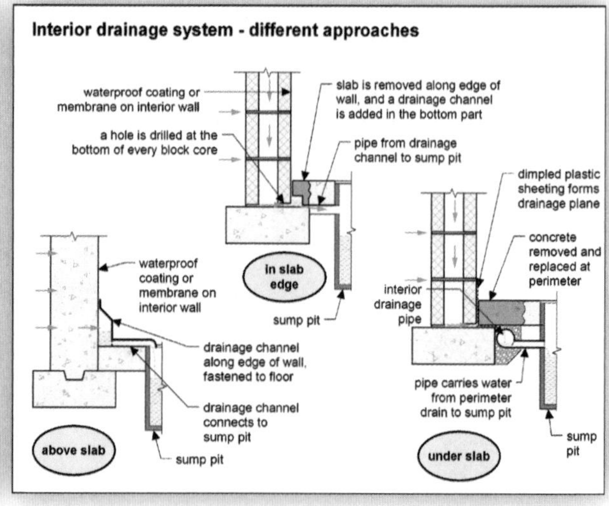

This approach is somewhat less desirable than the exterior approach, since water leaks through the exterior walls before it is carried away by this interior drainage system. The water, of course, must pass through the foundation or footing system, or go under the footing to reach this pipe. In some cases, holes are drilled through the foundation wall just above the footing to allow water to drain into this perimeter footing drain.

The cost of this approach is typically one-third to one-quarter of the cost of exterior work, depending on the difficulties encountered on the outside. There are many cases where this proves satisfactory, although on a case-by-case basis, it is very difficult to know whether it will work.

10.8 Ground Water Problems

DESCRIPTION In the very few cases where the problem is ground water rather than surface water, more extensive solutions are required. Normally, houses are not built below the water table. However, the water table may rise intermittently in areas with heavy seasonal rainfall. Changes in neighborhoods as development increases may raise the natural water table. Underground streams are also an issue in some areas.

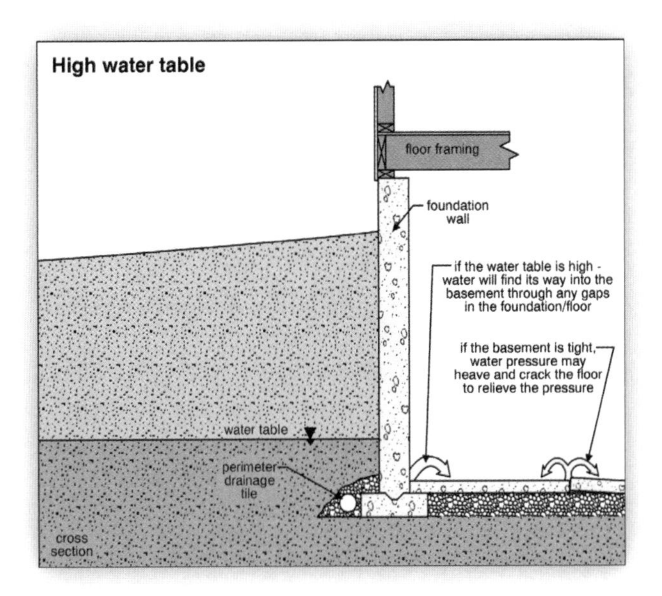

DRAINAGE SYSTEM AND PUMP Where the basement floor is below the water table, there may be chronic basement moisture problems. A drainage system and a sophisticated pumping system, sometimes with dual pumps, is often used. Since the water is constantly present, and pumps are susceptible to either mechanical or electrical failure, a house with this arrangement is always vulnerable to wet basement problems. High water alarms and battery backup systems are sometimes used.

Where the water table is higher than a normal basement floor, buildings without basements are common. Slab-on-grade construction is more suitable.

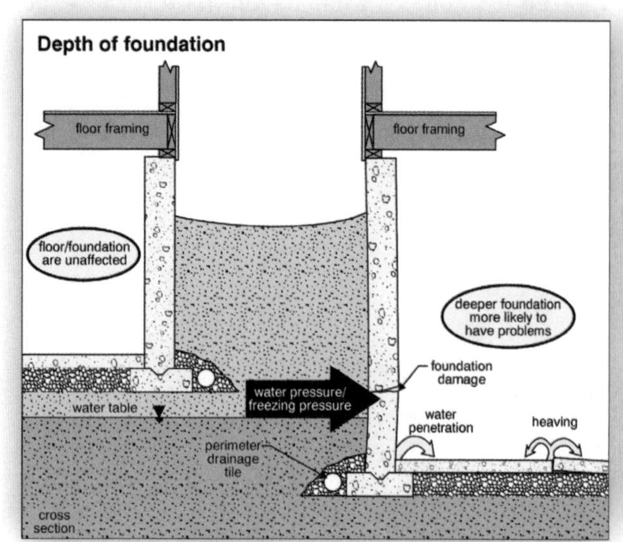

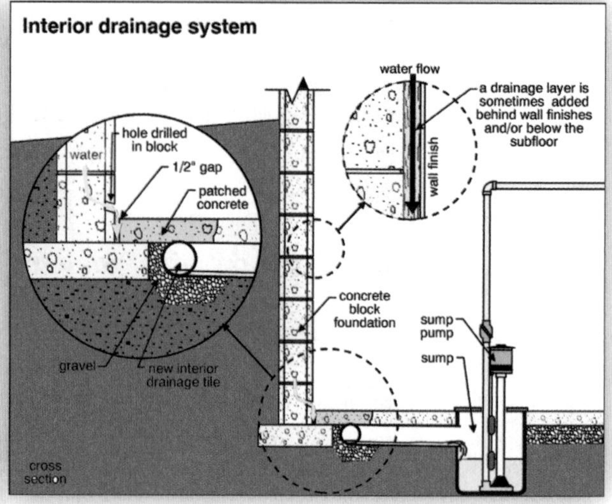

10.9 Basement Floor Leakage

DESCRIPTION Water leakage up through a basement floor slab is usually a result of saturated soil in and around the foundation. This is often accompanied by leakage through the foundation walls. In severe cases, the hydrostatic pressure can cause the floor slab to heave.

DRAINAGE SYSTEM, SUMP AND PUMP, AND NEW FLOOR SLAB The corrective actions for basement wall leakage are also appropriate for water penetration through a floor slab. Ideally, the source of the water is eliminated. If this is not possible, the water has to be collected in a sump. The existing basement floor is often removed. Gravel fill, four to six inches thick, is added before the new slab is poured, and a waterproof membrane (often plastic) may be laid under the new floor. The gravel allows water to move freely under the slab to the sump.

10.10 Summary

STEP-BY-STEP Once the problem is identified as exterior water penetration, the process is as follows.

1. Provide or improve gutters and downspouts as necessary.
2. Re-slope exterior grading so surface water drains away from the building.
3. If problems persist, patch any obvious cracks or gaps from the interior, if the foundation is poured concrete.
4. If problems continue, excavate and patch the foundations where leakage is localized. Drainage tile may have to be provided, repaired or replaced.

INTERIOR OR EXTERIOR DRAINAGE SYSTEM

5. Engage a professional to consult on whether an interior drainage system below the basement floor may be appropriate, or whether excavation, dampproofing and an outside foundation drainage system is better. The system may require a sump and pump, depending on local drainage characteristics.

LOCAL RESEARCH – WHEN ALL ELSE FAILS If chronic flooding is a problem, contact the city and neighbors to determine whether the problem is area wide. Where the problem is a neighborhood situation, the city will often make efforts to improve surface drainage or to control storm water.

City officials and neighbors can often advise whether the problem is related to surface water or ground water. Areas of high water tables are often well known to the city authorities. (High water table areas, of course, make it difficult for utility people to lay water supply and sewer lines below grade level.)

11.0 Smoke and Carbon Monoxide Detectors

DESCRIPTION Smoke detectors should be provided in all sleeping areas of a home and on each floor of a home.

Carbon monoxide detectors should be in every room with a wood burning appliance and are ideally located on every level of the home.

Detectors should be tested monthly and batteries should be replaced annually. Detectors should be replaced every 10 years.

Appliances

INTRODUCTION

MOST MAJOR HOUSEHOLD APPLIANCES HAVE LIFE SPANS OF 10 TO 20 YEARS. TYPICAL APPLIANCES CAN COST SEVERAL HUNDRED DOLLARS TO REPLACE, BUT DO NOT GENERALLY PLAY A MAJOR PART IN THE DECISION TO BUY A HOUSE. IN MORE EXPENSIVE HOMES, APPLIANCES CAN COST THOUSANDS OF DOLLARS EACH. APPLIANCES CAN BE REPLACED MUCH MORE EASILY THAN THE STRUCTURE, ROOF, PLUMBING, HEATING OR ELECTRICAL SYSTEMS.

THIS CHAPTER PROVIDES AN OVERVIEW OF SOME COMMON HOUSEHOLD APPLIANCES. THERE ARE A TREMENDOUS VARIETY OF APPLIANCES, AND ALL ARE NOT CONSIDERED IN THE FOLLOWING PAGES. WE RECOMMEND THAT OWNER'S MANUALS BE CONSULTED FOR REGULAR MAINTENANCE ON ALL HOUSEHOLD APPLIANCES. IF THE MANUALS ARE NOT ON HAND, THEY ARE USUALLY AVAILABLE FROM THE MANUFACTURER, OFTEN ONLINE.

HOUSEHOLD APPLIANCES MAY BE BUILT-IN OR PORTABLE (OFTEN REFERRED TO AS FREESTANDING). GENERALLY SPEAKING, INSTALLED APPLIANCES REMAIN WITH THE HOUSE WHEN IT IS SOLD, BUT FREESTANDING APPLIANCES ARE OFTEN REMOVED. THE PURCHASE AGREEMENT NORMALLY STIPULATES WHICH APPLIANCES STAY WITH THE HOUSE. APPLIANCES ARE NOT INCLUDED IN A STANDARD HOME INSPECTION UNDER THE STANDARDS SET BY CAHPI (CANADIAN ASSOCIATION OF HOME INSPECTORS) AND AIBQ (ASSOCIATION DES INSPECTEURS EN BATIMENTS DU QUEBEC). APPLIANCES ARE INCLUDED IN THE STANDARDS SET BY ASHI (AMERICAN SOCIETY OF HOME INSPECTORS).

1.0 Ranges

DESCRIPTION A range is a cooking appliance that includes a cooktop and an oven. These are also referred to as stoves. The ovens bake and broil, and some have a convection cooking component.

Separate cooktops and wall ovens combine to provide the same functionality as a range. Standalone cooktops and wall ovens provide more flexibility in terms of location and functionality. Wall ovens are often smaller than range ovens, and double wall ovens are common. A range is typically less expensive than a separate cooktop and oven(s). Ovens are discussed in more detail in Section 2.0 of this chapter.

FUELS Ranges can operate on electricity, natural gas, or propane. The determining factors include personal preference and fuel availability. There is often an increased cost in replacing the range if changing from one fuel source to another.

GAS VERSUS ELECTRIC Some people prefer gas burners to electric, since they provide a visual reference to the amount of heat they provide. Controlling the intensity of the flame is quite straightforward – the bigger the flame, the more heat. Gas burners heat up and cool more quickly than electric elements, providing better cooking control according to many. This control is useful when simmering delicate sauces or when providing the quick bursts of heat needed for cooking with a wok, for example.

Electric elements take longer to heat up and cool down than gas burners. They maintain low temperatures by cycling on and off at full current, not by using a steady small amount of electricity. On low settings, they alternate between providing too much heat and none at all. This makes control more difficult.

Some people are not comfortable cooking with gas. They worry about the open flame and the possibility of a gas leak and explosion.

LIFE EXPECTANCY The life expectancies of ranges are typically 10 to 20 years.

ANTI-TIP BRACKETS (RANGE STABILITY DEVICE) There is the potential for serious injury if a freestanding range tips over, which may occur if weight is placed on an open door. Modern units come with a bracket, which is secured to the wall or floor. This bracket holds one of the rear legs of the oven, preventing it from tipping over. These have been required in many jurisdictions since 1991.

1.1 Electric Ranges

Ranges come in a variety of sizes and configurations. The cabinetry and the floor plan of a kitchen usually determine the range's width, with 30 inches being very common. Ranges (cooktops) can be built into the counter top and cabinets or stand by themselves. Freestanding ranges which fit between sections of base cabinets are the most popular. These units typically have four elements or burners on top and an oven below.

CONTROLS The majority of electric ranges have their control knobs located on the back guard where they are easy to see and are out of the reach of children. Others are located at the front, so that one does not have to reach across hot surfaces to adjust controls. Some knobs have to be pushed in before they turn, to help prevent children from turning them on accidentally. All dials are marked to indicate which element they operate. On most, a light indicates which element is on, since a hot element can look much like a cold one.

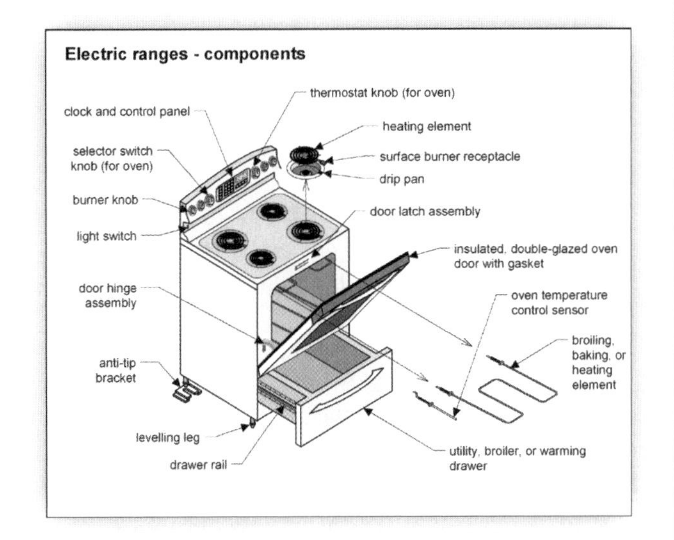

ELECTRIC COILS Traditional heating elements are electric coils. They consist of a metallic-sheathed resistance-coil material wound in a flat spiral. High quality models may have two elements placed side-by-side in a continuous spiral or one element wound in the center portion of the burner and the second around the outside. This allows one half, or the center portion, to be used for small pots while both halves may be turned on for large pots.

MAINTENANCE Drip bowls under each element catch spills and require periodic cleaning. These bowls should never be covered with aluminum foil, since this can result in a shock hazard, improper cooking or damage to the elements. All electric elements are "self cleaning" since spills burn off quickly. Soaking an electric element in water can damage it.

POWER RATINGS Coils come in various sizes and wattages ranging from six-inch diameter, 1,250 watt units, to eight-inch diameter, 2,400 watt elements.

DISKS Solid disks, originally used in Europe, appeared in North America in the early 1980s. They are flat, heavy iron plates with heating elements embedded in them. These units have twice the surface area of conventional coil elements and provide more even heat. Because of their greater contact with the cooking utensil, they are more efficient than coils. Disks do not require reflector pans or drip catchers, making them easy to clean.

PROTECTIVE LIMITER Solid disks are equipped with built-in limiters to prevent overheating. The limiter is activated when a pot is unable to properly conduct heat away from the element. This may occur when an element is left on with no pot or when a pot boils dry. The limiter reduces the wattage, preventing overheating or pot meltdown. This safety feature is not often found with coil elements.

POWER RATINGS Disks range from six-inch diameter, 1,500 watt units, to ten-inch diameter, 2,600 watt units. Although disks are rated at a higher equivalent wattage than coils, coils heat up and cool down faster, since they have a smaller mass.

SAFETY CONCERNS Disks remain grey even when very hot, and they cool down slowly. An element can burn someone when it looks cool. Food will continue to cook longer after the element is turned off. This can make control more difficult. Disks are not recommended for areas supplied with 208-volt electrical services or less (typical of some high-rise buildings).

MAGNETIC INDUCTION Magnetic induction elements generate a high frequency, fluctuating magnetic field. This field causes the metallic molecules in the pot to move in the direction of the field, which changes rapidly. This heats the pot, which then cooks the food. Good control is provided through quick heating and cooling. Power levels are also variable.

COOKWARE Only iron or steel (ferrous metal) cookware is used with induction elements.

These ranges usually have a one-piece cooktop that contains several cooking areas marked so pots can be centered on the coil. Since the range does not get hot, (other than the heat conducted from the pan), it is extremely safe. It is also easy to clean, since spills do not burn onto the surface.

GLASS-CERAMIC These range tops have a large glass-like cooking surface, about 1/4 – inch thick. The elements below the glass conduct heat up through the surface to the pot. The surface allows heat to move up to the pot, but resists heat transfer laterally across its surface. The smooth surface may look the same whether cold or hot, so a light indicates when the surface is hot. This light may be near the control knob or on the cooking surface. The light stays on after the power is turned off, as long as the element is hot. The surface is relatively easy to clean.

HALOGEN Halogen elements use infrared halogen lamps below a flat glass cooktop surface. When turned on, halogen elements glow brightly and provide instant heat. These units provide even heat distribution. They are also as easy to clean as glass ceramic cooktops. Usually, no more than one or two of the four elements on a cooktop are halogen type.

FIRE HAZARDS Curtains and other combustibles should be kept well away from the top of ranges, as they can easily ignite. Generally speaking, combustibles should be at least 30 inches above the range. Range hoods may be 24 inches above the cooking surface. Manufacturers' installation requirements should be observed.

Clearances from ranges to combustibles on either side are also typically determined by the manufacturer.

BUILT-IN EXHAUST Some cooktops have a built-in exhaust to carry steam and odors outdoors. These units, which are often down-draft, include a filter, a fan, metal ductwork and an external vent. Some have the fan on the exterior wall to reduce noise. The ductwork should be kept as short and straight as possible. The filters should be cleaned regularly, as needed. Many filters can be put in a dishwasher.

GRILLS, GRIDDLES, ETC. Some cooktops have interchangeable accessories for various types of cooking. These include grills, griddles, and woks.

Common Problems with Electric Ranges

INOPERATIVE ELEMENT(S) When one or more elements will not work, this may be caused by an interrupted power supply, a burned out element, a reset button that can be pushed, or a defective control.

DAMAGED/ DEFECTIVE/ MISSING – KNOBS /OUTLETS/TIMERS /LIGHTS Other problems include uneven heating conditions, defective outlets and timers, etc. For the most part, these are nuisance issues that can be readily corrected.

1.2 Gas Ranges

CONTROLS Gas ranges burn either natural gas or propane. Switching fuels is possible, but some equipment modifications are necessary. Gas ranges have their controls located on the front to avoid having to reach across an open flame. Most of these controls are also "push and turn", but there may be no indicator light, since it is obvious which burner is on. Gas ranges need 120-volt electrical supplies for their controls and lights.

GAS BURNERS Gas burners rely on convection, conduction and radiation to transfer heat from the burner to the pot. In order to take advantage of the radiant heat transfer, the bowls under the burners should be kept polished and clean. The intensity of the flame is controlled by the throttling valve (the control on the front of the range). For simmering, some units have a small burner in the center of the main burner.

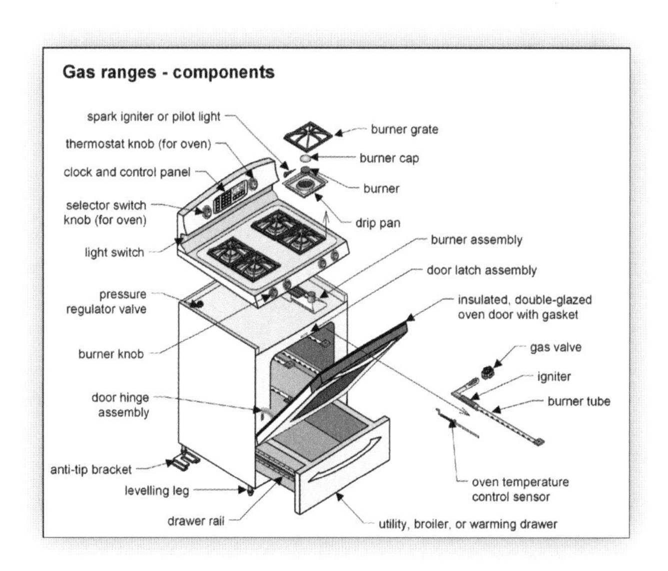

PILOT Traditionally, gas burners have been ignited with a pilot. In this system, a small flame (pilot) is always burning in the center of the range below the range top. When a burner is turned on, gas flows through a small tube towards the pilot. The pilot flame ignites the gas and the flame travels back up the open-ended tube to the burner, igniting the burner.

ELECTRONIC IGNITION Modern systems have electronic ignition, consisting of a transformer and "spark plug" which activates when the burner is turned on. The "spark plug" generates a spark at the burner, igniting the gas.

PIEZO-ELECTRIC IGNITION An alternate system uses a piezo-electric crystal to provide ignition. The crystal is attached to the control knob by a small pin which bends the crystal when the knob is turned. Bending the crystal generates a small amount of electricity which produces a spark.

GAS PIPING Please see the Heating chapter for information on gas piping and gas leaks.

EXHAUST GASES Natural gas produces primarily water and carbon dioxide when burned completely. Incomplete combustion can produce toxic carbon monoxide gas. Although not required, a range exhaust hood vented outside will reduce the risk of carbon monoxide poisoning. Some recommend the use of carbon monoxide sensors in kitchens with gas appliances.

Common Problems with Gas Ranges

GAS LEAK This is a serious condition. If gas is smelled, the occupant should leave the house and contact the utility. No devices should be used in the home that may cause a spark, including cell phones and computers.

BURNER WON'T LIGHT If a burner will not light, this may be caused by no gas supply to the range, no electrical supply to the range, the pilot being out, blocked gas ports, faulty gas valve, faulty igniter or defective controls.

UNEVEN FLAME Blocked or dirty gas ports can result in a burner that does not light evenly.

FLAME COLOR A yellow flame (rather than blue) indicates a poor fuel/air mix, requiring an adjustment.

DRIP PAN MISSING /RUST/DAMAGED Drip pans below burners catch spills and should be kept in place and in good order.

DAMAGED/ DEFECTIVE/ MISSING – KNOBS /OUTLETS/TIMERS /LIGHTS Other conditions include uneven heating conditions, defective outlets and timers, etc. For the most part, these are nuisance issues that can be readily corrected.

2.0 Ovens

FUELS Ovens operate on electricity, natural gas, or propane. Replacing an oven with one which uses a different fuel will involve extra expense if a gas/electric line is not already in place. The life expectancies of ovens are typically 10 to 20 years.

Ovens come in a variety of sizes and configurations; either freestanding or built-in. The cabinetry and floor plan of the kitchen will determine the type used.

FREESTANDING Freestanding ovens (ranges or stoves) are portable appliances that sit on the floor. Ranges are discussed in more detail in Section 1.0 of this chapter. These typically fit between sections of the base kitchen cabinets with the top approximately flush with the counter top. The cooktop normally has four surface elements, and there is typically a storage drawer below the oven. Ranges may be described as freestanding, slide-in or drop-in ranges.

BUILT-IN Wall ovens are built into the cabinetry, often at a height that allows access without stooping. Wall ovens are often doubled, with one installed directly above another. Wall ovens are typically smaller capacity than freestanding ovens.

CONTROLS The oven temperature is thermostatically controlled. Some also have a sensor probe that measures the temperature of the meat at the tip of the probe. Once the meat reaches a pre-determined level, the oven reverts to a keep-warm mode or shuts off.

TIMER Most ovens also have a timer that can be set to start and stop the oven at pre-set times.

2.1 Electric Ovens

Electric oven elements are made of a metallic-sheathed resistance-coil material. Most ovens have two elements that are plugged in so they can be replaced easily. The lower element is used for baking and roasting, and the upper is for broiling.

CONVECTION OVENS Convection ovens have the same elements as conventional ovens, but use a fan to circulate the hot air. The fan works continuously, increasing the convective currents in the oven. This cooks food more quickly, evenly, and with less energy than a conventional oven. Some convection ovens have a third element on the back wall of the oven.

SELF-CLEANING OVENS The most common type of self-cleaning oven uses very high heat (roughly 900°F) to burn food off the inside of the oven. Major spills should be cleaned up before starting a cleaning cycle. Many oven doors are locked closed during the cleaning cycle so people don't burn themselves on the oven. These ovens typically have better insulation than a conventional oven and are typically slightly more expensive. They are more efficient for everyday cooking, since heat escapes from the oven more slowly due to the better insulation levels.

Common Problems with All Ovens

WIRING/ THERMOSTAT/ TIMERS/KNOBS/ LIGHTS Electrical problems with wiring and controls, including thermostats and timers are common.

DOORS/VENTS Defective doors can open violently, or fail to close properly, and obstructed oven vents can cause the oven to overheat. Gasket problems may prevent doors from closing tightly, causing inefficient operation and overheating of the kitchen.

TIPPING Where an anti-tip bracket has not been provided, the oven can tip over and cause injury. This can happen if children stand on an open oven door to reach for something, for example.

Common Problems with Electric Ovens

INOPERATIVE ELEMENTS Electric ovens are fairly simple. Apart from the issues described above, failed baking or broiling elements are the most common problems.

2.2 Gas Ovens

Gas ovens burn either natural gas or propane. Switching fuels is possible but some equipment modifications are required. The burners are most often located at the top and bottom of the oven. The bottom burner is used for baking and roasting; the top for broiling. The lower burner is normally covered with a metal baffle.

Gas ovens require 120-volt electrical power for the controls and lights.

Ventilation slits in the baffle allow the natural circulation of air in the oven while protecting the user from open flames. Because of the burners, gas ovens have a slightly smaller volume than an electric oven of the same external size.

GAS PIPING Please see the Heating chapter for information on gas piping and gas leaks.

SELF-CLEANING OVENS The most common type of self-cleaning oven uses very high heat (roughly 900°F) to burn food off the inside of the oven. Major spills should be cleaned up before starting a cleaning cycle. Many oven doors are locked closed during the cleaning cycle so people don't burn themselves on the oven. These ovens typically have better insulation than a conventional oven and are typically slightly more expensive. They are more efficient, since heat escapes from the oven more slowly due to the better insulation levels.

Common Problems with Gas Ovens

BURNER/PILOT PROBLEMS In addition to the issues with any type of oven described above, gas ovens can have problems with burners that are out of adjustment or clogged. Burners can also suffer corrosion. Pilot, spark and electronic ignition systems may be inoperative or may operate inconsistently.

2.3 Microwave Ovens

These may be portable or built-in, and operate on 120-volt electrical power. Microwave ovens should be plugged into grounded receptacles and are ideally on a dedicated circuit.

MAGNETRON Microwave ovens generate high frequency electro-magnetic radiation. The radiation is generated by increasing the household power from 120 volts AC to 4,000 volts DC. The electricity is then supplied to a device called a magnetron. This electronic tube generates high frequency microwaves with the help of a magnetic field.

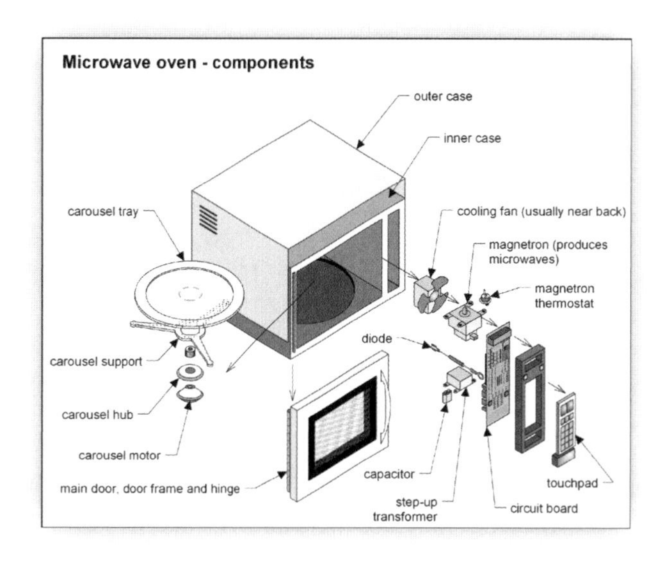

WAVE GUIDE The microwaves are emitted from an antenna, and travel along a metal conduit called a wave guide into the oven. A fan-like device (stirrer) at the top of the oven disperses the microwaves into the oven as they leave the wave guide. In some units, a rotating tray on the oven bottom turns the food to ensure even cooking. A fan removes the heat generated by the food, and helps cool the magnetron.

COOKWARE Microwaves penetrate most materials except metal. Metal reflects microwave energy, causing it to bounce from surface to surface. This can damage the magnetron. Cookware should be designed for use in microwave ovens, and as a general rule, should contain no metal. Aluminum foil should not be used in a microwave oven.

BROWNING Microwaves cause the water molecules in food to vibrate, producing heat from friction, which cooks the food quickly. Because foods are not cooked from the outside in (as in a conventional oven), the browning, typical of a conventional oven, does not occur. Browning can be accomplished using special browning dishes. Some units also have a special browning element.

SAFETY All microwave ovens have a double interlock system to prevent operation when the door latch is released. In addition, a computerized monitoring system stops the oven if one or both of the interlocking systems fail.

The door seal is designed to prevent leakage of microwave energy, and the glass window on the oven door is shielded with a metal screen. Because of the strict safety standards, owner service and disassembly are discouraged. Most manufacturers will void their warranties if the oven has been tampered with. Service technicians can check microwave ovens for leakage.

Microwave ovens should never be turned on when empty, since this may damage the magnetron.

LIFE EXPECTANCY Life expectancies in the range of 10 years are typical.

MICROWAVE/ CONVECTION OVEN This oven combines the speed and efficiency of a microwave with the browning of a conventional oven. Like an ordinary microwave, it makes short work of heating leftovers and thawing foods. Like a traditional oven, it can brown foods. These units operate on microwaves only, convection only, or a combination of the two.

When in the combination mode, the unit cycles back and forth between microwave and convection cooking.

Common Problems with Microwave Ovens

INOPERATIVE An inoperative microwave may be the result of no electrical power, a faulty control system, or a faulty magnetron.

A service technician should be contacted if any problems with the door are suspected. The door gasket should seal tightly, and the microwave should shut off when the door latch is opened.

POOR LOCATION Microwave ovens should not be installed above cooktops unless they are rated for this location. The manufacturer's installation guide will usually indicate this.

3.0 Kitchen Exhaust Fans

Exhaust fans may be located above the cooktop or built into the range. The vents remove moisture, odors and grease as they come off the cooktop. Some exhaust the air outside, while others clean and re-circulate the air. Life expectancies are five to 15 years, depending on original quality, amount of use and maintenance.

BLOWERS All vents contain blowers and electric motors to move the air. The blower can be located in the hood above the range, in the range below the cooktop, or outside, where the vent discharges. The outdoor location is the quietest for people in the home. Some microwave ovens have an exhaust vent for a cooktop built into the bottom. Some vents have variable speed blowers.

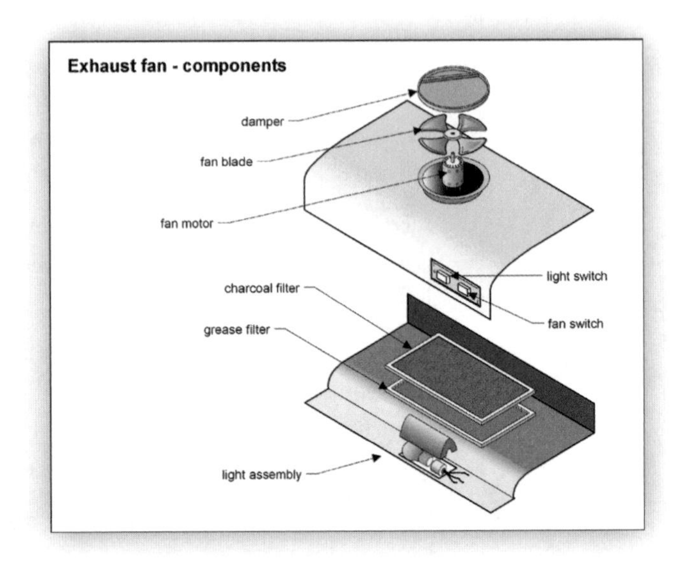

FILTERS Some units have mechanical filters only, while the re-circulating type typically use charcoal filters to help remove odors. In either case, filters are a regular maintenance item. Most mechanical filters are washable, and many can be cleaned in a dishwasher.

DISCHARGE OUTSIDE Vent systems discharging outside should go directly to the exterior through ductwork that is as short and straight as possible. Vents should not discharge into attics, crawl spaces, or chimneys, for example. Ductwork passing through unheated space should be insulated to prevent condensation.

LIGHTS Most vents that are above a cooktop have one or more lights to brighten the work area.

Common Problems with Exhaust Fans

INOPERATIVE Exhaust fans that don't work may have an electrical supply or motor problem, or the fan itself may be seized.

FILTER/DUCT ISSUES Filters may be dirty or missing. Ductwork to the outdoors may be incomplete, disconnected, un-insulated in the attic or have a poor discharge arrangement. The discharge should have a flap that prevents cool air and pests from coming in when the fan is idle.

SWITCHES/LIGHTS /NOISY Common problems include defective switches or lights and noisy blowers. Blowers may be noisy due to balance or bearing problems.

4.0 Refrigerators

Refrigerators can be freestanding or built-in. They may or may not include a freezer. Some high-quality refrigerators look like cabinet drawers.

DEDICATED CIRCUIT Most refrigerators require a grounded 120-volt electrical outlet. The refrigerator circuit is ideally not shared with any other outlets, since a blown fuse or tripped breaker may not be noticed immediately, resulting in spoiled food.

COMPRESSOR The compressor is the heart of the refrigerator. It pumps the refrigerant gas through the system, increasing the gas pressure and temperature. The pumped refrigerant changes pressure and temperature, and changes between a gas and a liquid as it flows through the system. This is what allows heat to be removed from the relatively cool refrigerator and freezer, and dumped into the relatively warm kitchen air.

The compressor is the most expensive single component of the refrigerator. Although compressors can be replaced, it is often more practical to replace than repair a refrigerator with a failed compressor.

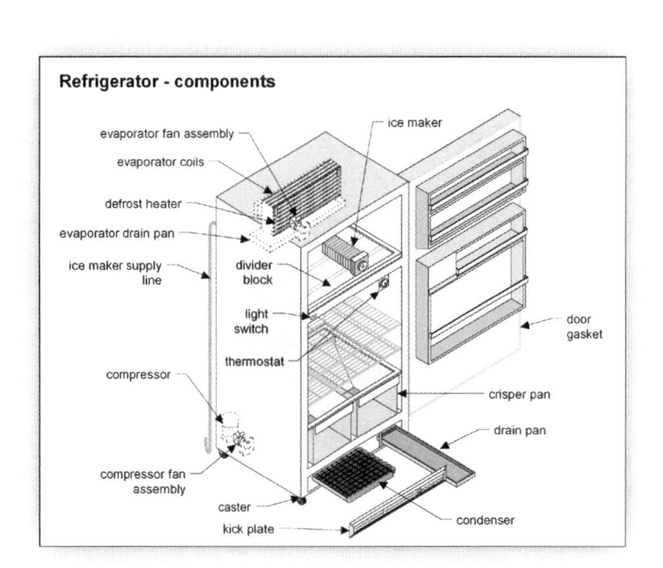

CONDENSER The condenser coils allow the warm refrigerant to transfer heat to the kitchen air as the refrigerant changes from a gas to a liquid. Most refrigerators have natural draft condensers, with the condensing coils on the back of the refrigerator. Air circulation should be maintained around the back and top of these refrigerators. Forced-draft condensers (on the bottom of the refrigerator) use a fan to move air over the coils. All coils should be kept clean (vacuumed) to transfer heat efficiently.

EVAPORATOR The cold refrigerant in the evaporator coils removes heat from the inside of the refrigerator as the refrigerant changes from a liquid to a gas. Condensation on the coils drips into a pan below the refrigerator. This tray should be checked occasionally and emptied as required. The evaporator coils are usually not visible without disassembling the refrigerator.

DEFROSTING METHODS Older refrigerators require manual defrosting. Most new models are frost-free.

FROST FREE Frost-free refrigerators keep the cooling surfaces in a small separate compartment. A fan blows cool air from this space into the storage compartments. This cooling unit is typically defrosted with a small electric heater. This system provides a more even temperature throughout and can be used for both the refrigerator and freezer compartments. The moving air will, however, dry out uncovered foods and increase energy costs.

DOOR GASKET Frost may build up around the door gasket in humid weather. A small heating element is often built into the door edge to prevent this from happening. Energy saving models may have a switch to turn this electric heater off when it is not needed. In some refrigerators, warm refrigerant circulates around the door edge to prevent frost build up.

Poorly sealed door gaskets increase energy consumption. Door gaskets are simple to replace. Cracks in the interior plastic liner should be sealed to prevent moisture soaking the insulation inside.

OTHER FEATURES Many modern refrigerators have ice cube makers, and crushed ice and/or chilled water dispensers. These require water supply piping. Any refrigerator with these accessories should be moved with care to avoid damaging the water supply line.

ENERGY EFFICIENCY Modern refrigerators are considerably more energy efficient than older units. Replacing an older refrigerator can reduce electrical consumption noticeably. Refrigerators use more electricity over the course of the year than most appliances, other than furnaces and water heaters.

LIFE EXPECTANCY The life expectancy of most refrigerators is 12 to 20 years.

Common Problems with Refrigerators

INOPERATIVE If the refrigerator is not running, the power cord may be damaged, the fuse or breaker at the main panel may have tripped, the compressor may be inoperative, or the refrigerator may be turned off or unplugged. There may also be a problem with the thermostat.

NOT COLD If the refrigerator is running, but is not very cold, the temperature setting may be too high, the refrigerant level may be low, the airflow over the cooling surface may be blocked or restricted, the condenser coils may be dirty, the defrost mechanism may be inoperative, or the compressor may be failing.

NOISY A noisy refrigerator may have worn motor bearings for the evaporator or condenser, or the refrigerator may not be level.

CONDENSATION Too much condensation inside may indicate the unit is on "economy" setting or that the heater is inoperative. A leaky door gasket may cause condensation around the door.

LEAK Leaks are often the result of a clogged or disconnected defrost drain line. Leaks may also be from the icemaker or water dispenser.

5.0 Dishwashers

Dishwashers may be built-in or portable. Some portable dishwashers may be converted to built-in units. Typical life expectancies are eight to 15 years.

Most dishwashers require a 120-volt electrical supply and a supply of hot (140°F) water. Built-in units are connected to the waste plumbing system, typically upstream of the trap below the kitchen sink.

SOLENOID Hot water enters the dishwasher through a solenoid (electrically operated) valve. Some dishwashers use a booster heater to raise the temperature to 140°F. This allows the house hot water to be kept at roughly 120°F. An overflow switch shuts the solenoid valve when enough water has entered the machine.

PUMP Water is distributed through the dishwasher by rotating spray arms. A strainer helps prevent food particles from clogging the pump, located at the base of the washer.

Dishwasher soap and rinse agent are dispensed from cups, usually located on the door. The discharge is controlled by the same timer that controls the sequence and duration of the cycles.

WASTE CONNECTION When a wash or rinse cycle is finished, the pump discharges the dirty water into the waste piping below the kitchen sink or through a food waste disposer.

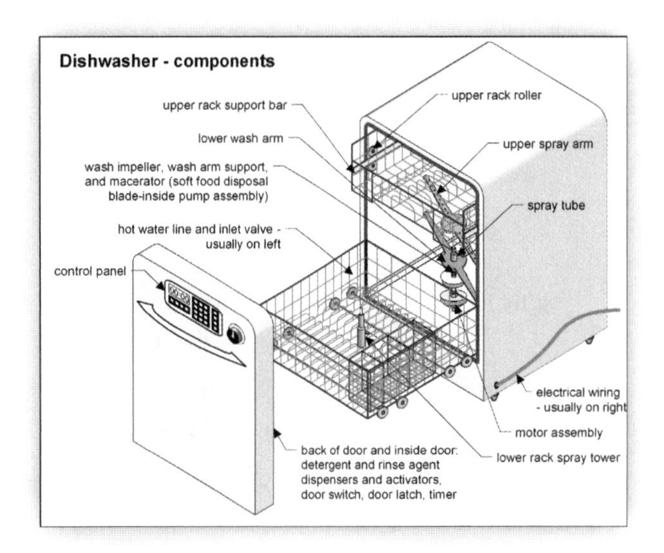

AIR GAP Some areas require an air gap in the waste line to avoid a cross-connection or siphoning. This is typically a chrome device projecting above the counter at the rear of the kitchen sink. Other jurisdictions consider the solenoid valve to be adequate protection.

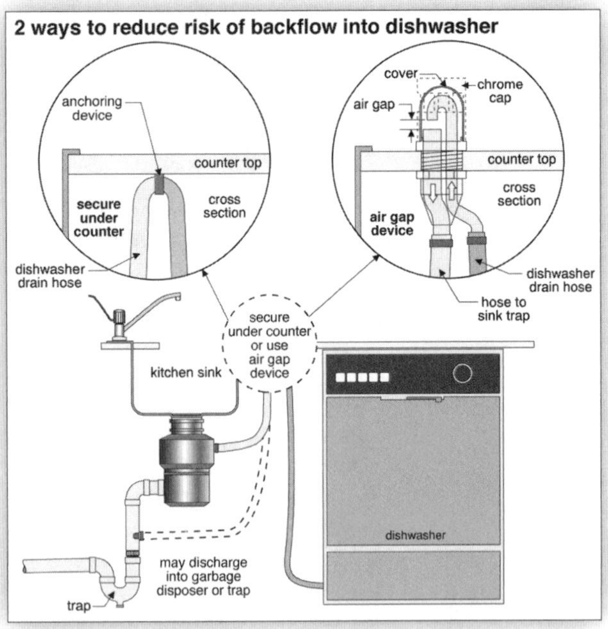

DRYING CYCLE Once the rinse cycle is complete, the dishes are dried by either the heating element in the bottom of the tub or a combination heater and fan. On some units, the dryer element can be turned off to save energy.

DOOR GASKET Door gaskets must seal tightly to avoid leaks. Damaged gaskets can be replaced readily. Door latches that do not close properly may not allow the dishwasher to start.

TIMER The timer controls the sequence of the wash, rinse and dry cycles. Commonly, there are several settings for different cycles.

Common Problems with Dishwashers

INOPERATIVE If the dishwasher does not operate, the fuse or breaker at the main panel may have tripped, the timer may be faulty, there may be a loose electrical connection, one of the switches may be faulty, a high water level switch may have tripped, or the door interlock switch may be defective. A specialist should be engaged to diagnose and correct the problem.

WON'T FILL If the dishwasher will not fill with water, the solenoid valve may be faulty, the timer or overflow switch may be defective, or the supply plumbing may be shut off.

WATER WON'T SHUT OFF If the water does not shut off, the timer or overflow switch may be defective, or the solenoid valve may be inoperative.

WATER WON'T DRAIN If the water does not drain out, the pump motor may be defective or clogged, the drain hose may be blocked, the strainer may be clogged, or the timer may be faulty.

INOPERATIVE HEATER If the heater does not work, the timer may be defective, or the heating element may be loose or burned out.

LEAKS If the dishwasher leaks, there may be a damaged gasket, a broken door hinge, a faulty overflow switch, loose hose clamps, a plugged air gap, or a drain blockage.

NOISY If the dishwasher is noisy, the sprayer arms may need adjusting, or the solenoid valve may be defective.

OTHER ISSUES If the soap dispenser does not open. The door may be obstructed by cutlery, the spring or switch may be broken, the dispenser may be clogged, or the timer may be faulty. Racks and their rollers can be damaged or warped.

The interior compartment or door may be rusted. The dishwasher door may drop open violently if the spring or springs are defective.

6.0 Food Waste Disposers

Food waste disposers are installed below the kitchen sink and connect to the waste plumbing upstream of the trap. They pulverize food waste into particles that move with the water through the drain lines. Some claim that disposals should not be connected to septic systems. Other experts say this is not a problem. The authors are not aware of septic problems caused by disposers, although tanks may need to be emptied more often if a disposer is used.

Some municipalities do not allow waste disposers, based on the premise that these increase the load on the municipal sewage treatment system.

LIFE EXPECTANCY Life expectancies are 6 to 12 years.

GRINDER These units have two basic parts; the grinding unit and the electric motor. The grinding unit, driven by the motor, consists of a rotating plate or flywheel and a stationary shredder ring. The ring is a metal band with a series of sharp-edged holes that cut the waste into pieces. Waste particles entering the hopper are thrown against the shredder ring by the rotating plate (grind wheel) at the bottom of the grinding unit. Once reduced sufficiently in size, the particles pass through the holes in the shredder ring into the waste pipe.

GENERAL WASTE The disposer is designed to grind such things as bones, vegetables, coffee grounds, etc. Fibrous waste such as corn husks, pea pods, or celery should be avoided or mixed with other food waste for disposal.

WATER FLOW A good flow of cold water should run through the disposer and only a small amount of waste should be ground at a time, to minimize the possibility of a blockage. The water not only flushes waste down the pipe, it also lubricates the seal around the motor. Cold water solidifies grease and fat, allowing them to be shredded.

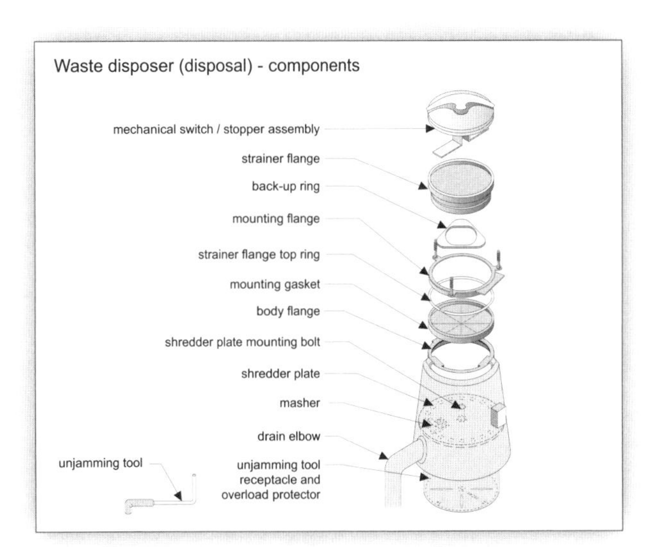

ABUSE The disposer should never be used to grind glass, plastic, metal, styrofoam, seafood shells, cardboard, etc. However, even under normal operating conditions, the unit may jam. If this happens, the motor may stop and hum. The thermal overload protector cuts the power off after roughly 30 seconds. A jammed electric motor will eventually blow the fuse or trip the circuit breaker if the thermal overload does not trip.

If the disposer jams, the flywheel must be freed. On some units, this can be done by switching the disposer to "reverse". With others, the flywheel must be freed using a stick or service wrench. If the problem persists, the material must be removed from the flywheel with pliers or a similar tool. When placing something into the disposer, the unit must be turned off, and under no circumstances should anyone insert their hand into the hopper. After freeing the unit, grinding ice cubes may help to clear and freshen the unit.

OVERLOAD PROTECTOR If the thermal overload protector has tripped, it takes roughly 15 minutes for the motor to cool down. Once cool, the protector can be reset. Some disposers have a reset button on the motor, while others reset themselves. If the fuse has blown or the circuit breaker tripped, it must be replaced or reset.

WIRING Waste disposers may be permanently wired in, or may be plugged into an accessible outlet. If plugged in, the cord should be between 18 and 36 inches in length and should not pass through a cabinet. If flexible conduit is used, the conduit should have a drip loop. Non-metallic sheathed (Romex) cable is not allowed in some jurisdictions. There should be a strain relief clamp on the waste disposer.

CONTINUOUS FEED There are two basic types of disposers; continuous and batch feed. Continuous feed units are activated by a switch located near the unit. The disposer operates continuously while waste is fed down its throat. This allows the unit to handle a large volume of waste quickly.

BATCH FEED Batch feed models are activated with the drain stopper. To load the disposer, the stopper is removed from the drain. Waste is loaded into the disposer chamber, and the stopper is then placed in the drain, closing a switch to turn the disposer on. The unit will operate as long as the stopper is in this position. In either system, cold water should be flushed through the disposer while it operates. (The stopper is in place, but in the open position to allow water to flow.)

Common Problems with Food Waste Disposers

INOPERATIVE If the disposer is inoperative, the fuse or breaker at the main panel may have tripped, the overload protector may have tripped, the stopper or wall switch may be faulty, or the motor may be faulty.

DOES NOT GRIND If the disposer does not grind, the motor may be faulty or the flywheel may be jammed.

GRINDS SLOWLY If the disposer grinds slowly, there may be insufficient water flow, the shredder ring may be dull, a flyweight may be broken, or the drain line may be clogged.

LEAKS If the disposer leaks, there may be a loose plumbing connection or defective gasket.

NOISY If the disposer is noisy, the motor may be faulty, a flyweight may be broken, a metal object may be in the unit, or the unit may be loose.

SPLASH GUARD If the splash guard is worn, damaged or missing, it should be replaced.

LOOSE If the unit is loose, it should be re-secured.

7.0 Trash Compactors

DESCRIPTION AND LIFE EXPECTANCY Trash compactors come in a variety of sizes and configurations. They may be located under the counter top or may stand alone. Compactors operate on a standard 120-volt household circuit, and normally last ten to 15 years.

OPERATION A compactor reduces the volume of waste loaded into it. A ram compresses the waste in a metal bin. The ram, operated by an electric motor, generates forces of up to 5,000 pounds.

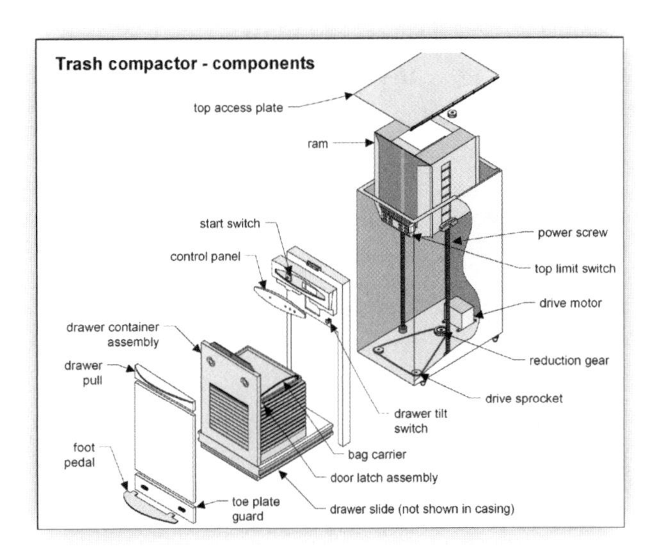

SAFETY Compactors have numerous fail-safe devices. The compactor will not operate if the door is open, the unit is not level, the bin latch mechanism has not been closed, or if the safety interlock switch is not activated.

The switch is a key lock that must be in the "ON" position for the unit to work. The removable key allows the unit to be deactivated. If bottles and glass must be compacted, they should be at the bottom and additional waste placed on top. Aerosol cans or other explosive objects should never be placed in the unit.

ODORS Preferably, only dry trash should be used in the compactor, since this will reduce odors. Most units are equipped with an automatic aerosol deodorant dispenser. This is activated once the ram has completed its cycle.

Common Problems with Trash Compactors

INOPERATIVE If the compactor does not operate at all, the fuse or breaker at the main panel may have tripped, the safety interlock switch may be "off " or faulty, the motor may be faulty, the overload protection switch may have tripped, or there may be a loose electrical connection or damaged cord.

If the ram does not compact trash, the drive chain or belt may be loose or broken, the gears or pulleys may be loose, or the ram may be seized.

NOISY If the compactor is too noisy or vibrates excessively, the drive chain or belt may be loose, the compactor may need lubricating, or there may be loose mechanical connections. If the unit is loose, it should be re-secured.

WON'T OPEN If the drawer will not open, the ram may be jammed, or the unit stopped working part way through a cycle.

If the compactor continues to run, one of the switches may be faulty.

8.0 Washing Machines

Modern washing machines combine water, detergent and mechanical action to clean clothing. There are two common configurations of washing machines – top-loading and front-loading.

TOP LOADERS Top-loading washing machines use a motor-driven agitator to provide the mechanical cleaning action in the water-filled tub. The rotating agitator pulls clothing down to the bottom of the tub and pushes the clothing to the outside of the basket, where it rises to the top to repeat the cycle again. The agitator is used both during the wash cycle and the rinse cycle.

BASKET The basket surrounding the agitator is also driven by the motor during the spin cycle to remove water from the clothing.

PUMP A pump is used to remove water from the tub.

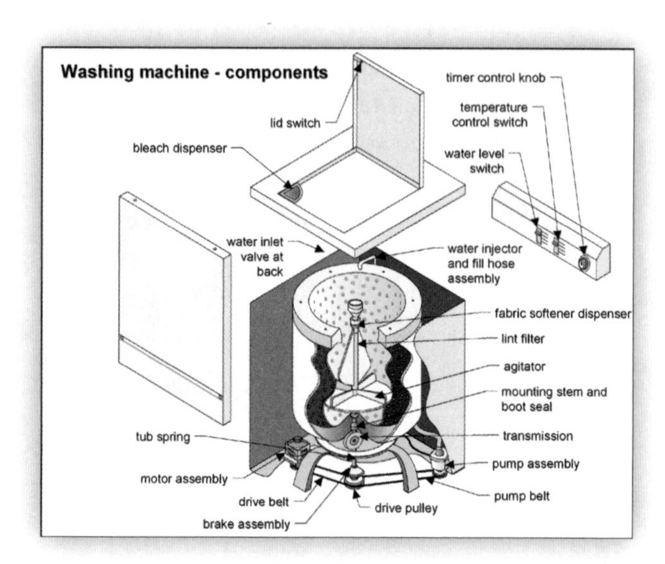

FRONT LOADERS Front-loading washing machines do not use a separate agitator. The rotating action of the horizontally-mounted basket tumbles the clothes to provide agitation. Since the tub does not need to be filled, front loaders use less water and soap. Front loaders are somewhat simpler than top loaders.

ELECTRICITY AND WATER NEEDED Washing machines require a 120-volt electric outlet and supply and waste plumbing. Both hot and cold water hook-up are needed. Isolating valves are typically provided for connecting the hoses. Chambers are provided on the supply plumbing pipes in some cases to prevent "water hammer", which may be caused by quick-closing solenoid valves.

HOSES Braided steel hoses are preferable to rubber hoses for connecting washing machines to supply piping in the home. A ruptured hose can result in serious water damage in a short time, especially if the laundry area is in or above a finished area of the home. For even more protection, there are automatic shut-off valves available that turn off the water in the event of a burst hose.

DRAIN PAN When a leaking washing machine (or hoses) may cause damage to finishes, a washing machine drain pan may be installed to collect water in the event of a failure. Fittings on these pans should be connected to a drain so that the water can be safely discharged.

DISCHARGE HOSE The waste hose can discharge into a laundry sink or into a waste standpipe connected to the waste plumbing through a trap. The waste standpipe (standing waste pipe) should extend 18 to 30 inches above the trap. The drain hose should fit loosely into the standpipe so that there is an air space to prevent back-siphoning.

LIFE EXPECTANCY Washing machines have a typical life expectancy of 10 to 15 years.

Common Problems with Washing Machines

INOPERATIVE If the washing machine does not work, the power cord may be damaged or disconnected, the fuse or breaker at the main panel may have tripped, the motor may be inoperative, a control switch may be defective, or the water may be shut off or disconnected.

WON'T DRAIN If the washing machine won't drain, the pump or one of the control switches may be inoperative. A drip pan and drain should be provided for machines above finished spaces.

WON'T FILL If the washing machine won't fill, one of the solenoid valves or control switches may be inoperative, or the water valves may be closed.

LEAKS Leakage may come from the water supply hoses, pump, tub seals, or the drain hose. There may also be a problem with the water level switch, or the tub itself may be damaged. On front loading machines, there may be a problem with the door or door seal.

NOISY Unbalanced loads or a machine that is not level often cause excessive vibration. There may also be problems with the motor bearings, the transmission or drive belt.

ODOR Front-loading washers can be prone to odor problems. These musty odors are often the result of water that does not completely drain out of the washer. The stagnant water may collect beneath the door gasket, in the fabric softener dispenser, or another location. In many cases, cleaning these areas will correct the problem, and leaving the door open will allow the water to evaporate without becoming stagnant.

9.0 Clothes Dryers

Clothes dryers tumble wet clothing in a rotating drum through which heated air is circulated. The hot air removes moisture from the clothing and is vented to the exterior.

FUEL Heat may be generated by electric elements or by gas burners.

ELECTRIC Electric dryers require a 240-volt electric outlet on a dedicated circuit. This circuit is typically capable of carrying at least 30 amps.

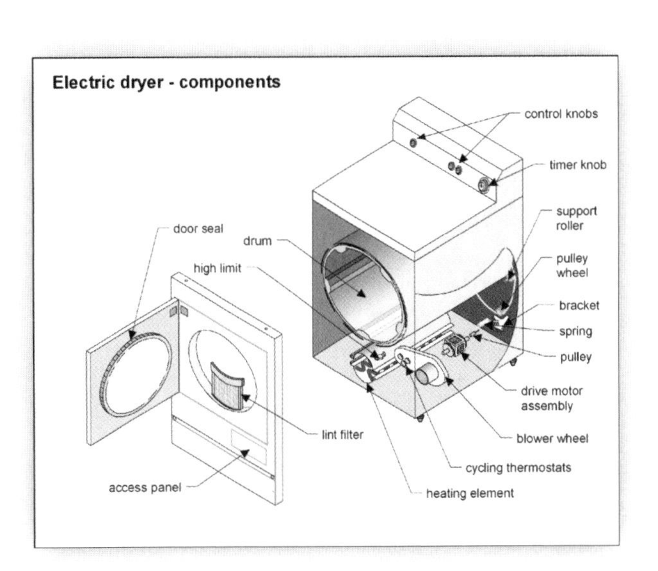

GAS Gas dryers require gas piping with an accessible shut off valve. Please see the Heating chapter for information on gas piping and gas leaks. Gas dryers also require a grounded 120-volt electrical outlet to power the motor and for the controls and timer.

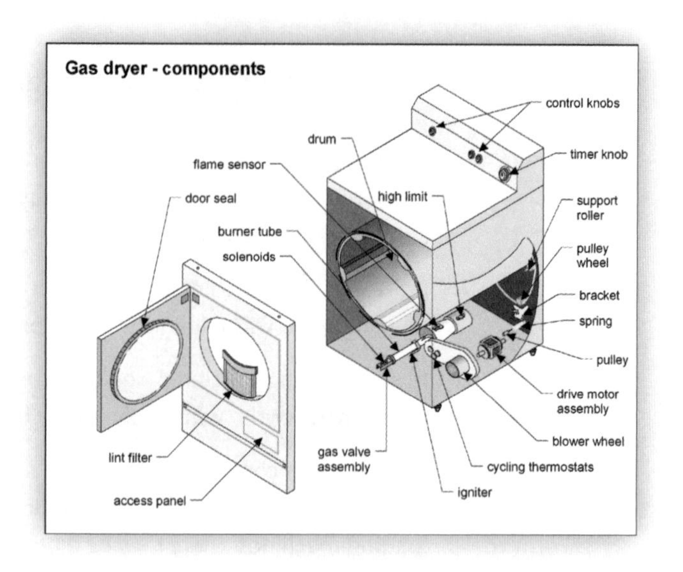

LINT TRAP As the hot air leaves the dryer, it goes through a screen that collects lint. Lint can interfere with the proper venting of exhaust. Lint traps are typically cleaned after each load.

VENT PIPE The exhaust vent pipe connects the dryer to the exterior of the home. The vent pipe should be as short, straight, and smooth as possible to reduce the risk of lint collecting inside the duct. There should be no screws that extend into the duct. Many recommend avoiding flexible plastic ducting, although in some cases, it may be used for short distances as a transition duct as long as it is exposed. Rigid metal ducting is preferred.

ADEQUATE AIR NEEDED Clothes dryers need to move lots of air through them to dry efficiently. They should not be in confined cabinets.

ENERGY EFFICIENCY Dryers that turn off automatically when the clothes are dry use less energy than those that are controlled by a timer.

LIFE EXPECTANCY Common life expectancies for clothes dryers are 12 to 18 years.

Common Problems with Dryers

INOPERATIVE If the dryer is inoperative, the dryer may be unplugged, the breaker or fuse may be tripped or blown, a switch or control may be defective, or the motor may be defective.

DRIES SLOWLY If a dryer takes a long time to dry clothing, the lint trap may be clogged, or the vent may be kinked, clogged, or too long. There may also be lint clogging internal areas. The heating elements or burner may also be inoperative.

NO HEAT If an electric dryer does not generate heat, a breaker or fuse may be tripped or blown, or a heating element or burner may be defective.

If a gas dryer does not heat, the gas valve may be turned off, the pilot light may be out, or the ignition system may be defective.

DISCHARGE INSIDE Although there are heat re-claimers that can be used in the vent ducting to direct dryer air back into the house, these are not recommended. They also direct excess moisture and lint back into the home. These should never be used with gas dryers, since this would send potentially dangerous products of combustion into the house air. Dryers should be vented to the exterior.

POOR EXHAUST VENT Exhaust vents may be damaged, kinked, clogged, leaky, too long, or an inappropriate material.

VENT CAP ON DISCHARGE Dryer vent caps on the exterior wall may be damaged or clogged with lint. Flappers on these caps may be missing or damaged. The discharge point should not be near an air conditioner coil. If covers are missing, pests may get into the system, and heat loss from the house may be increased in cold weather.

NOISY If the dryer is noisy, the motor bearings, pulleys, or rollers may be worn, or the drum belt may be defective.

10.0 Central Vacuum System

A central or whole house vacuum system consists of a canister located in the garage or the basement. A series of lightweight plastic pipes run from the canister to outlets located around the house. The outlet flap is lifted and the vacuum hose is inserted into the outlet. A metal band or similar device on the end of the hose completes a circuit between two contacts in the outlet. This switches the system on. A number of accessories may be attached to the hose.

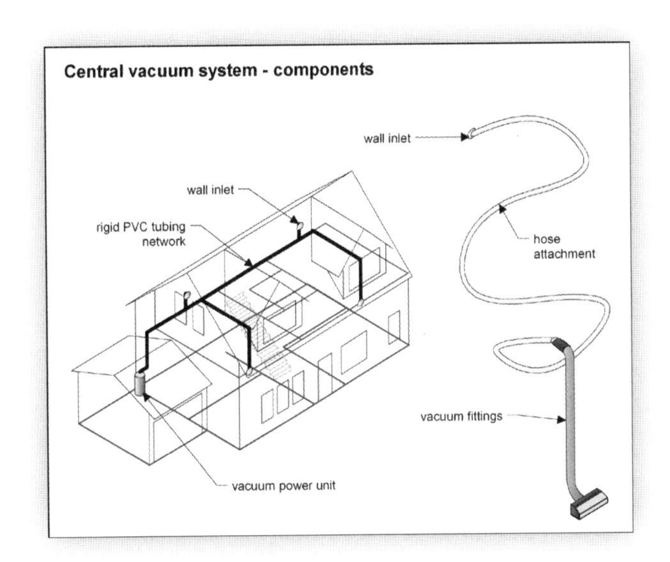

CANISTER The main canister usually has an on/off switch and may have a suction outlet as well. The exhaust may discharge directly from the canister or it may be piped through an exterior wall. Generally, units that do not have a filter must discharge to the exterior. Units equipped with a filter may discharge to the exterior or interior. The canister can be opened or removed to empty the unit. Some filters are self-cleaning while others require cleaning by the homeowner.

MOTOR Units without filters may allow dust to build up on the motor causing it to overheat and burn out sooner than a unit with a filter. Units with an external motor and no filter may allow dust to build up on the fan blades, causing uneven bearing wear. The motor is the most common repair item and may require repair or replacement every five to ten years, depending on how often the unit is used and cleaned.

Common Problems with Central Vacuum Systems

INOPERATIVE If the unit does not operate, the fuse or breaker at the main panel may have blown or tripped, a built-in breaker or thermal overload may have tripped, the wiring or switches may be defective, or the motor may be faulty.

If only one or two outlets do not operate, there may be a problem with the control wiring or switch for the area affected.

WEAK SUCTION If the suction is weak, the canister may be full, the filter may be dirty, the exhaust may be obstructed, or the pipes may be partially obstructed. Disconnected pipes are a less common problem.

Life Cycles and Costs

THE FOLLOWING COSTS ARE BALL PARK ESTIMATES FOR A TYPICAL THREE BEDROOM HOME.

WHERE APPROPRIATE, TYPICAL LIFE EXPECTANCIES ARE INCLUDED IN PARENTHESIS.

THE LIFE EXPECTANCY OF SOME COMPONENTS WILL VARY WITH THE SEVERITY OF WEATHER IN THE REGION. THE DESIGN, QUALITY OF INSTALLATION AND LEVEL OF MAINTENANCE CAN ALSO DRASTICALLY AFFECT LIFE EXPECTANCY.

There are many factors that affect costs:

- Access...How difficult is it to get to? Crawlspaces are harder to work in than basements. Three-story roofs are harder to work on than bungalow roofs. Steep roofs are more difficult than low slope roofs.
- Height...If you need to build scaffolding to get to the chimney, chimney repairs will cost more.
- Complexity of job...Roofs with lots of dormers and skylights are more expensive.
- Weight...Heavy roofing materials are hard to carry up the ladder.
- Disposal costs...Costs to get rid of the old materials vary and can be significant.
- Amount and difficulty of preparation work...Painting is not as expensive as stripping, scraping and sanding to get ready to paint.
- Cost of materials...Clear cedar siding costs more than paint grade wood, which costs more than vinyl siding.
- Availability of materials...Cedar roofing is significantly less expensive on the west coast, than in the east.
- Installation technique...It costs more to glue and screw subflooring in place than to nail it. It costs more to put deck posts on a footing than on the ground.
- Amount of labor...It takes longer to lay a ceramic tile floor than a sheet vinyl floor.
- Skill level of labor...It costs more to tape drywall than to hang it. It costs more to paint a faux finish than a flat finish. Plumbers cost more than handymen.
- Scarcity of labor...In many areas it is hard to find people who do plaster rather than drywall, or work on steam boilers rather than forced air heat.
- Quality of system...Furnaces can cost $2,000 to $8,000, depending on their quality and features. It's a lot like buying a car.
- Economic conditions...Are trades people generally busy and not looking for work, or very slow and anxious to do any job? Is the market competitive, or are there only one or two companies that can do what you are looking for?
- Time of year...In many areas, there are construction seasons that depend on the weather, and renovations and repairs will be more expensive in the high season.
- Reputation of company...Are you looking for an industry leader or someone just getting started? The folks with good reputations and a long list of satisfied clients referring work to them will be harder to find, and more expensive to engage.
- The presence of hazardous materials...Are you required to remove hazardous materials such as asbestos before doing a remodel? Older homes may contain asbestos in the drywall, ceiling tiles, insulation and floor tiles. If so, the project's budget should include proper abatements costs, which may be significant.

The figures that follow include labor and materials. Many home repairs have a minimum fee based on a visit by a tradesperson.

HOME IMPROVEMENT PROJECTS

According to Remodeling Magazine, here are some national average costs for common remodeling projects in the U.S. in 2015 (figures have been rounded to the nearest $500).

	Project	Cost	Per unit
BATHROOM	1. Bathroom remodel	$16,500	Roughly $450/sq. ft.
	2. Bathroom remodel Premium quality (Larger bathroom)	$54,500	Roughly $500/sq. ft.
KITCHEN	3. Major kitchen remodel	$57,000	Roughly $275/sq. ft.
	4. Major kitchen remodel Premium quality	$113,000	Roughly $550/sq. ft.
BASEMENT AND FAMILY ROOM	5. Basement remodel (includes small bath and wet bar)	$65,500	Roughly $100/sq. ft.
	6. Family room addition	$84,000	Roughly $200/sq. ft.
GARAGE	7. Garage Addition	$52,500	Roughly $80/sq. ft.
	8. Garage – New detached Premium quality	$85,500	Roughly $121/sq. ft.
SIDING	9. Re-siding with vinyl	$12,000	Roughly $8/sq. ft.
WINDOWS	10. Replace windows with vinyl	$11,000	Roughly $1,100/window or $75/sq. ft.
	11. Replace windows with premium quality vinyl windows	$14,000	Roughly $1,700/window or $110/sq. ft.
DECK	12. Install wood deck (includes railing, bench and steps)	$10,000	Roughly $30/sq. ft.
	13. Install composite deck (includes railing, bench and steps)	$16,000	Roughly $50/sq. ft.

 Complete city data from the Remodeling 2015 Cost vs. Value Report can be downloaded for free at www.remodeling.hw.net/cost-vs-value/2015

Revised 2015

ROOFING/FLASHINGS/CHIMNEYS

SLOPED ROOF	1. Strip asphalt shingles	$0.75-$1.50 per sq. ft.
	2. Re-roof with conventional asphalt shingles	$2.00-$4.00 per sq. ft. (twelve to twenty yrs)
	3. Re-roof with premium quality asphalt shingles	$4.00-$8.00 per sq. ft. (twenty to thirty yrs)
	4. Strip and re-roof with cedar shingles or shakes	$9.00-$18.00 per sq. ft. (twenty to thirty-five yrs)
	5. Install concrete tile roofing (assuming no structural reinforcement)	$8.00-$16.00 per sq. ft. (fifty yrs and up)
	6. Install new slate roof	$30-$60 per sq. ft. (forty to two-hundred yrs)
	7. Repair loose slates or tiles	$25-50 per slate/tile (minimum $1000)
	8. Install roll roofing	$1.50-$3.00 per sq. ft. (five to ten yrs)
FLAT ROOF	9. Install built-up tar and gravel roof	$10.00-$20.00 per sq. ft. (fifteen to twenty yrs) (minimum $1000)
	10. Install modified bitumen roof membrane	$8.00-$16.00 per sq. ft. (fifteen to twenty-five yrs) (minimum $1000)
	11. Improve flat roof drainage prior to installation of new membrane	$2.00-$4.00 per sq. ft.
	12. Paint modified bitumen membrane	$0.50-$1.00 per sq. ft. (minimum $200)
	13. Install sheet metal on small roof surfaces	$10.00-$20.00 per sq. ft. (minimum $1000)
FLASHINGS	14. Reflash standard chimney:	
	- asphalt shingle roof	$500-$1000
	- built-up or modified bitumen membrane	$700-$1500
	15. Install metal cricket at wide chimney	$400-$800
	16. Reflash standard skylight:	
	- asphalt shingle roof	$500-$1000
	- built-up or modified bitumen membrane	$700-$1500
	18. Repair valley flashings on existing roof	$25-$50 per lin. ft. (minimum $600)
	19. Replace parapet wall flashing	$20-$50 per lin. ft. (minimum $600)

Revised 2015

ROOFING/FLASHINGS/CHIMNEYS (Continued)

	Item	Cost
CHIMNEY	20. Rebuild typical chimney above roofline: (scaffolding not included)	
	- single flue (minimum $1000)	$150-$300 per lin. ft.
	- double flue (minimum $1000)	$200-$400 per lin. ft.
	21. Repoint typical chimney above roof line: (scaffolding not included)	
	- single flue (minimum $400)	$20-$40 per row
	- double flue (minimum $400)	$25-$50 per row
	22. Install concrete cap on typical chimney:	
	- single flue	$250-$500
	- double flue	$400-$800
	23. Install rain cap on typical chimney	$200-$300 each

EXTERIOR

	Item	Cost
GUTTERS AND DOWNSPOUTS	1. Install galvanized or aluminum gutters and downspouts	$5.00-$10.00 per lin. ft. (twenty to thirty yrs)
	2. Install copper gutters and downspouts	$15-$30 per lin. ft (fifty to one hundred yrs)
	3. Install aluminum soffits and fascia	$8.00-$16.00 per lin. ft.
	4. Install	
	- aluminum siding	$4.00-$8.00 per sq. ft.
	- vinyl siding	$6.00-$12.00 per sq. ft.
	- fiber cement siding	$7.00-$14.00 per sq. ft
	5. Install and finish wood siding using:	
	- cedar	$8.00-$16.00 per sq. ft.
	- paint grade	$6.00-$12.00 per sq. ft
	6. Install stucco	$6.00-$12.00 per sq. ft
	7. Repointing:	
	- Soft mortar (minimum $500)	$3.00-$6.00 per sq. ft.
	- Hard mortar (minimum $500)	$5.00-$10.00 per sq. ft.
	8. Replace deteriorated bricks	$25-$50 per sq. ft
	9. Rebuild parapet wall	$25-$50 per sq. ft

Revised 2015

EXTERIOR (Continued)

	Item	Cost
	10. Painting (exclusive of repairs): - trim only (soffits, fascia, door and window frames) - trim and wall surfaces (wood, brick, stucco)	 $2000 and up (four to six yrs) $5000 and up (four to six yrs)
BASEMENT	11. Dampproof foundation Dampproof walls and install drainage tiles	$150-$300 per lin. ft. (minimum $3000)
DRIVEWAY	12. Resurface existing asphalt driveway	$2.00-$4.00 per sq. ft. (ten to twenty yrs)
	13. Seal asphalt driveway	$0.30 per sq. ft. and up (one to three yrs)
	14. Install interlocking brick driveway	$8.00-$16.00 per sq. ft. (fifteen yrs and up)
	15. Install concrete driveway (no pattern)	$8.00-$16.00 per sq. ft. (thirty to forty yrs)
	16. Install drain at bottom of sloped driveway	$2000 and up
PATIO	17. Install concrete slab patio	$5.00-$10.00 per sq. ft. (thirty to forty yrs)
	18. Install concrete patio stones	$2.50-$5.00 per sq. ft. (thirty to forty yrs)
	19. Rebuild exterior basement stairwell	$5000 and up
	20. Install drain at existing basement stairwell	$750-$1500
GARAGE	21. Build detached garage	$70-140 per sq. ft.
	22. Break wood/soil contact at detached garage	$25-$50 per lin. ft. (minimum $1000)
	23. Demolish and remove detached garage	$1500 and up
	24. Install garage door: - single metal one-piece - single wood sectional - double wood sectional	 $500-$1000 $700-$1400 $1200-$2500
	25. Install garage door opener	$300-$600 (eight to twelve yrs)
	26. Build retaining wall: - wood	 $20-$40 per sq. ft. (minimum $500)
	- concrete	$30-$60 per sq. ft. (minimum $500)

Revised 2015

EXTERIOR (Continued)

27. Replace porch steps : - wood - concrete	 $750 and up $1500 and up
28. Replace porch flooring	$4.00-$8.00 per sq. ft.
29. Replace porch skirting	$10-$20 per lin. ft.
30. Replace step railing	$400-$800
31. Install fencing: - wood - chain link	 $20-$50 per lin. ft. $10-$20 per lin. ft.
32. Install lawn sprinkler system	$2000 and up

STRUCTURE

1. Underpin one corner of house	$5000 and up
2. Underpin or add foundations	$300 and up per lin. ft. (minimum $3000)
3. Lower basement floor by underpinning and/or bench footings	$150-$300 and up per lin. ft. (minimum $5000)
4. Replace deteriorating sill beam with concrete	$60 and up per lin. ft. (minimum $2000)
5. Replace main beam in basement (unfinished)	$4000 and up
6. Re-support joist by sistering another alongside	$250 and up
7. Install basement support post with footing	$800-$1600
8. Chemical treatment for termites	$2000 and up (ten to twenty yrs)
9. Termite inspection performed by a specialist	$200-$400
10. Remove or open bearing wall (exclusive of decorating)	$2000 and up
11. Remove partition wall (exclusive of decorating)	$2000 and up
12. Install door opening in interior wall (exclusive of decorating)	$750-$1500

Revised 2015

STRUCTURE (Continued)

13. Rebuild arch above window or door opening	$1000 and up
14. Install lintel above opening in masonry wall	$1000 and up
15. Install exterior basement stairwell	$10000 and up
16. Build an addition: - foundation to roof - additional story	 $200-$400 per sq. ft. $150-$300 per sq. ft.
17. Install collar ties	$30-$60 each (minimum $400)
18. Install lateral bracing on collar ties	$100-$200
19. Replace roof sheathing	$4.00-$8.00 per sq. ft.

ELECTRICAL

1. Upgrade electrical service to 100-amps (including new panel and breakers)	$1500-$3000
2. Upgrade electrical service to 100-amps (if suitably sized panel already exists)	$800-$1600
3. Upgrade electrical service to 200-amps	$1700-$3500
4. Replace main ground: - home on public water system - home on private well (Install ground rods)	 $200-$400 $300-$600
5. Install new breaker panel	$700-$1400 (add $200 for 200A panel)
6. Install auxiliary breaker panel	$350-$700
7. Replace circuit breaker (20 amp or less)	$100-$200
8. Add 120-volt circuit (microwave, freezer, etc.)	$250-$300
9. Install exterior outlet with waterproof cover	$150-$300
10. Add 240-volt circuit (dryer, stove etc.)	$300-$600

Revised 2015

ELECTRICAL (Continued)

11. Add conventional receptacle	$200-$400
12. Add kitchen split receptacle	$200-$400
13. Replace conventional receptacle with ground fault circuit interrupter receptacle	$70-$140 ($200-$400 for kitchen)
14. Replace conventional receptacle with aluminum compatible type (CO/ALR)	$60-$120 each (assuming several are required)
15. Upgrade entire house with aluminum compatible connectors , receptacles etc.	$1000-$2000
16. Rewire electrical outlet with reversed polarity	$5-$10 each ($100 minimum)
17. Rewire entire house from aluminum to copper wiring	$750-$1500 per room
18. Replace switches (dimmer, standard, lighted etc.)	$10-$20 each ($100 minimum)
19. Install standard light fixture	$100-$200
20. Install exterior light	$250-$500
21. Install fluorescent light fixture	$150-$300
22. Rewire entire house during gut or renovations	$750-$1500 per room
23. Replace knob & tube wiring with modern wiring	$1000-$2000 per room

HEATING

1. Install mid efficiency	$2000-$5000 (eighteen to twenty-five yrs) forced-air furnace
2. Install high efficiency forced-air furnace	$3500-$8000 (fifteen to twenty yrs)
3. Annual service	$200 minimum
4. Replace blower and/or motor	$350-$700 (ten to twenty yrs)
5. Replace induced draft fan	$600-$1200
6. Install humidifier	$300-$600 (five to ten yrs)
7. Install electronic air filter	$800-$1600 (ten to twenty yrs)
8. Install pleated air filter	$300-$1600

Revised 2015

HEATING (Continued)

9. Install mid efficiency boiler	$3500-$7000 (fifteen to twenty-five yrs)
10. Install high efficiency boiler	$3500-$12000 (fifteen to twenty-five yrs)
11. Replace refractory pot	$300-$500
12. Install circulating pump	$400-$600 (ten to twenty-five yrs)
13. Install expansion tank	$300-$600
14. Install backflow preventer	$250-$500
15. Install chimney liner (for gas)	$500-$1000
16. Install programmable thermostat	$200-$400
17. Replace indoor oil tank	$1200-$2400
18. Remove oil tank: - interior - underground	 $600 and up $10000 and up
19. Replace radiator valve	$300-$600
20. Replace radiator	$750-$1500
21. Add electric baseboard heater	$250-$500
22. Convert from hot water heating to forced air: - bungalow - two story	 $10000-$20000 $15000-$30000
23. Clean ductwork	$300-$600
24. Install heat recovery ventilator	$2500-$5000

COOLING/HEAT PUMPS

1. Add central air conditioning on existing forced-air system	$3000 and up (ten to fifteen yrs)
2. Add heat pump on existing forced-air system (dependent on source of heat)	$4000-$8000 (ten to fifteen yrs)
3. Install independent air conditioning system	$10000-$20000 (ten to fifteen yrs)
4. Install ductless air conditioning system	$3000-$7000 (ten to fifteen yrs)
5. Annual service	$200 minimum

Revised 2015

INSULATION

Item	Cost
1. Insulate open attic area to modern standards	$.80-$1.60 per sq. ft.
2. Blow insulation into flat roof, cathedral ceiling or wall cavity	$2.00-$4.00 per sq. ft.
3. Improve attic ventilation (supplied while re-roofing)	$30-$60 per vent
4. Install spray foam insulation (typical 2 story, 3 bedroom)	$5000-$10000
5. Insulate basement from interior	$1.00 and up per sq. ft.

PLUMBING

Item	Cost	
1. Replace galvanized piping with copper: - per kitchen - per bathrooom	 $750-$1500 $1500-$3000	 NOTE: Figures do not include repairs to finishes after disruption
2. Replace public water supply pipe to house (min $2000)	$150-$300 per lin. ft.	
3. Replace main shut off valve	$150-$300	
4. Install conventional water heater	$500-$1000 (eight to twelve yrs)	
5. Install induced draft water heater	$800-$1600 (eight to twelve yrs)	
6. Install tankless water heater	$2500-$3500	
7. Typical monthly rental of conventional water heater	$10-$20	
8. Replace toilet	$500 and up (thirty to forty yrs)	
9. Replace toilet flush mechanism	$100-$200	
10. Unclog or remove obstruction from toilet	$100-$200	
11. Replace seal on toilet	$150-$300	
12. Install bidet	$700 and up (thirty to forty yrs)	
13. Replace basin: - vanity - pedestal	 $500 and up (twelve to twenty yrs) $700 and up (twelve to twenty yrs)	

Revised 2015

PLUMBING (Continued)

14. Replace faucet set	$250 and up (ten to fifteen yrs)
15. Replace bathtub, including ceramic tile	$2000 and up (twenty to thirty yrs)
16. Install refinished claw foot bathtub	$2500 and up (fifteen to twenty yrs)
17. Replace bathtub/shower faucet set	$400 and up (ten to fifteen yrs)
18. Install whirlpool bath	$3500 and up (fifteen to twenty-five yrs)
19. Re-tile bathtub enclosure	$1000-$2000
20. Replace leaking shower stall pan	$1000-$2000
21. Rebuild tile shower stall	$2500-$5000
22. Install plastic bathtub enclosure	$500-$1000 (ten to fifteen yrs)
23. Install plastic shower stall	$1000-$2000 (ten to fifteen yrs)
24. Install bathroom exhaust fan	$300-$600 (five to ten yrs)
25. Install modest basement bathroom	$5000 and up
26. Replace laundry tubs	$400-$800 (fifteen to twenty-five yrs)
27. Install laundry facilities	$1000 and up
28. Install kitchen sink: - single - double	 $500 and up (fifteen to twenty-five yrs) $800 and up (fifteen to twenty-five yrs)
29. Install solid waste pump	$1500-$3000 (five to ten yrs)
30. Connect waste plumbing system to municipal sewers	$5000 and up
31. Snake out obstruction in main sewer line below yard	$250-$500
32. Repair collapsed or damaged section of sewer line below yard	$2000 and up
33. Install submersible pump in well	$1000 and up (ten to fifteen yrs)
34. Install suction or jet pump for well	$700 and up (ten to fifteen yrs)
35. Replace water tank for pump	$300-$700

Revised 2015

PLUMBING (Continued)

36. Install water softener	$1000 and up (five to fifteen yrs)
37. Install outdoor faucet	$300-$600
38. Replace sump pump	$350-$700 (two to seven yrs)
39. Install sauna	$3000 and up

INTERIOR

1. Add drywall over plaster	$4.00-$8.00 per sq. ft.
2. Remove old plaster and install drywall	$5.00-$10.00 per sq. ft. (plus disposal costs)
3. Add wire lath and new plaster over existing plaster	$5.00-$10.00 per sq. ft.
4. Spray stipple on existing ceiling	$2.00-$4.00 per sq. ft
5. Install suspended tile ceiling	$5.00-$10.00 per sq. ft.
6. Install drywall on unfinished basement ceiling	$5.00-$10.00 per sq. ft.
7. Sand and refinish hardwood floors	$2.00-$4.00 per sq. ft.
8. Install hardwood floors : - 3/8 inch thick - 3/4 inch thick	 $8 per sq. ft. $12 per sq. ft.
9. Install parquet flooring	$5-$10 per sq. ft.
10. Install ceramic floor tiles	$15 and up per sq. ft.
11. Install vinyl floor tiles	$3 and up per sq. ft.
12. Install sheet vinyl	$6-$12 per sq. ft.
13. Install synthetic wall-to-wall carpet	$25-$50 per sq. yard
14. Install wool wall-to-wall carpet	$60 and up per sq. yard
15. Install laminate flooring	$3.00-$6.00 per sq. yard
16. Clean carpets	$30 per room (minimum $120)

Revised 2015

INTERIOR (Continued)

17. Replacement windows : - Sliding - Casement - Awning - Double hung - Fixed - Bay	 $40-$100 per sq. ft. $60-$120 per sq. ft. $40-$100 per sq. ft. $60-$120 per sq. ft. $35-$80 per sq. ft. $40-$100 per sq. ft.
18. Storm windows	$200-$400 each
19. Convert coal-burning fireplace to wood-burning unit (if possible)	$4000 and up
20. Install masonry fireplace: - with single flue chimney - from rough-in	 $7000 and up $3000 and up
21. Install zero clearance fireplace	$3500 and up
22. Install gas fireplace (excluding interior finishes)	$4000 and up
23. Install glass doors on fireplace	$300 and up
24. Clean fireplace chimney flue	$75-$150 each
25. Install fireplace damper	$700 and up
26. Install interior hollow-core door	$300-$600
27. Install interior custom wood door	$450 and up
28. Install exterior door	$750-$3000
29. Install closer on garage man door	$200-$400
30. Install storm door	$500-$1000 (ten to twenty yrs)
31. Install sliding glass doors : - brick wall - wood frame wall	 $3500-$7000 $2500-$5000
32. Replace sliding glass door	$2000-$5000 (ten to twenty yrs)
33. Install skylight	$3000 and up

Revised 2015

INTERIOR (Continued)

34. Install roof window or ventilating skylight	$1500 and up
35. Install kitchen cabinets	$300 and up per lin. ft.
36. Install kitchen counter	$25 and up per lin. ft.
37. Install ceiling fan	$500 and up
38. Install conventional alarm system	$1000 and up
39. Install central vacuum system	$1000-$2000
40. Install central vacuum canister only	$500-$1000
41. Paint interior (walls, ceilings, doors, trim) of entire house	$3000 and up (five to ten yrs)
42. Hang wallpaper	$3.00 and up per sq. ft.
43. Urethane injection of poured concrete foundation cracks	$400-$800 each
44. Excavate and repair foundation cracks	$1000-$2000 each
45. Injection repair of tie rod hole	$250-$500 each
46. Install interior dampproofing system on inside of foundation walls	$100-$150 per lin. ft.
47. Damp-proof foundation walls and install perimeter drainage tiles	$150-$300 per lin. ft. (minimum $3000)

Revised 2015

Supplementary

THIS SECTION DEALS WITH SOME ISSUES THAT ARE BEYOND THE SCOPE OF A PROFESSIONAL HOME INSPECTION. THIS INFORMATION IS PROVIDED AS A COURTESY OVERVIEW ONLY, AND IS GENERAL IN NATURE. MORE INFORMATION IS AVAILABLE FROM SPECIALISTS IN THESE AREAS.

1.0 Asbestos

DESCRIPTION Asbestos is a fibrous material that was used in many building materials as an acoustic insulator, a fire resistant material, a binder, and a thermal insulator. It is present in hundreds of building products including pipe and duct insulation on heating systems, in sealers on heating boilers, in roofing products, siding, stucco, plaster, drywall compound (spackle), paneling, ceiling tiles, floor tiles and sheet goods, wall and attic insulation, and in asbestos-cement (Transite) pipe. This list is by no means complete.

THE CONCERN The very small asbestos fibers can cause cancer and other types of lung disease if inhaled. The fibers are so small and light that if released into the air, they may float for several days. They are not collected by furnace filters or conventional vacuum cleaners.

Asbestos is considered dangerous only when "friable". This means that the material containing asbestos is broken, has ragged edges, or is otherwise in a state where the fibers may be released into the air. In most building products, asbestos isn't normally friable. However, demolition or renovation work can disturb asbestos-containing materials, causing the asbestos fibers to be released into the air.

IDENTIFICATION Asbestos can only be identified by laboratory analysis. Therefore its identification is beyond the scope of a home inspection. The vast majority of homes contain some asbestos. As discussed, this is not a problem unless it is friable. There are firms in most centers that specialize in identification of asbestos, and in taking corrective action where necessary.

WHAT CAN BE DONE In the majority of cases, doing nothing is the best approach. Where there is a risk of fibers being released into the air, the asbestos-containing material can be isolated from the rest of the house through enclosure or encapsulation. Alternatively, the material can be removed. The latter is the most expensive, since care must be taken not to release fibers into the home, and because disposal of asbestos-containing materials is controlled in many areas.

HOME IMPROVEMENT COSTS Since most home improvements involve some demolition, additional costs may be incurred where asbestos containing materials are suspected. This would apply to such things as boiler replacement, re-roofing, re-siding, flooring replacement, and gutting of interiors, for example.

NOT FOR THE DO-IT-YOURSELFER Corrective actions related to asbestos should not be undertaken by the homeowner, as a general rule. Guidance is available from the Environmental Protection Agency in the U.S. and from Provincial Ministries of Labour, Occupational Health and Safety Divisions in Canada.

2.0 Radon

DESCRIPTION Radon is an invisible, odorless, tasteless gas that occurs naturally in the earth's crust. Radon is a product of the decay of uranium. The decay of uranium to lead is a 14-step process. Radon is formed at the sixth step. It is unique because it is the first decay product that is a gas, not a solid.

THE CONCERN The radon gas itself is not a problem but its decay products are. The radioactive decay products are particles that can attach themselves to lung tissue when radon gas is inhaled. It is primarily the alpha radiation that causes lung cancer. In the United States, it is estimated that over 20,000 deaths are caused every year by radon gas. As with cigarette smoking, the risk is higher with greater exposure. The effects are long term rather than immediate.

WHERE IT IS FOUND Uranium is present in many parts of the earth's crust. Areas subject to high radon gas levels have appreciable concentrations of uranium in the earth and cracks or porous soils through which the gas can migrate up to the surface.

HOW IT GETS INTO HOUSES Radon escaping into the air is not a problem, since it is diluted quickly. In buildings, however, radon gas can be trapped, particularly during winter months when doors and windows are kept closed and ventilation is at a minimum. It is difficult to predict which buildings will have a problem.

Radon enters the building through cracks in basement floors and walls, openings around pipes and electrical services into the basement, through water supplies, and through basement floor drains, for example. Even in areas with high concentrations in the earth, one building may have very high radon levels and a similar building across the street may have very low levels.

TESTING There are several types of detectors available for testing radon levels in buildings. A charcoal canister can be used to absorb radon from the air. There are etch detectors that use a sensitive plastic surface. The radon will leave tracks or etchings on the plastic, which can be measured. There are filtering systems where air is pumped through a filter. There are also grab-sample testers that allow for short term testing by simply taking an air sample. Some of the test procedures require laboratory analysis.

The identification of radon gas in a home is not part of a standard home inspection.

In the U.S., any radon levels above 4 picoCuries/liter bring a recommendation for remedial action. In Canada, the action level is 200 Bequerels per cubic meter (5.4 picoCuries per liter). Since radon levels in a building can vary at different times of the day and seasons of the year, longer testing times are better. Winter testing is generally considered more reliable than summer testing.

There are several techniques used to lower radon levels in houses. They include sealing holes to prevent radon gas getting into houses, pressurizing basements or crawl spaces to keep the gas out, and adding pipes below basement floors to carry radon away from the home. Guidance is available from the Environmental Protection Agency in the U.S. and from Health and Welfare Canada, Environmental Radiation Hazards Division, Canada.

3.0 Urea Formaldehyde Foam Insulation (UFFI)

DESCRIPTION Urea formaldehyde foam insulation (UFFI) became popular as a residential retrofit insulation in the mid-1970s. UFFI was banned in Canada in December 1980 because of the suspected health hazards. In the United States it was banned in 1982, then the ban was lifted.

Different colors and textures of UFFI are variable; however, it can be distinguished from other insulating foams by its frail, crumbly structure and powdery residue. Positive identification can only be made through laboratory testing. Because UFFI is a highly expandable foam, it was used to insulate hard to reach areas. Holes were typically drilled in exterior walls or ceilings and the material injected from the outside. Although it is sometimes possible to see plugged application holes on the exterior, a new siding material, ivy, or even paint can hide evidence of application. Occasionally, UFFI was injected from inside the building, in which case its application is typically disguised by interior finishes.

INSPECTION Some specialists look for UFFI by drilling holes in wall cavities and performing air quality testing. This is not always conclusive. Some maintain that only with the removal of all interior finishes can one say that there is no foam in the building. For this reason, the identification of UFFI is beyond the scope of a professional home inspection.

The U.S. Consumer Product Safety Commission (1-800-638-CPSC or www.cpsc.gov) can provide additional information. A UFFI information booklet can be obtained by contacting Canada Mortgage and Housing Corporation at 1-613-748-2000 or on the web at www.cmhc.ca.

4.0 Lead

DESCRIPTION Lead is a naturally occurring element in the soil. Soil also collects lead from the air and other sources.

IN WATER Lead is also a natural constituent of drinking water. Lead pipe was used in many houses up to the 1950s as the water service line from the street. Lead was also a component of solder for copper pipes until the 1980s. To a lesser extent, lead can also be found in some plumbing fixtures.

Although initially there may be relatively high concentrations of lead in supply piping containing lead solder or in lead service lines, over the years, a build-up of lead oxide on the inside pipe surface reduces contamination. In December 1992, the U.S. EPA (Environmental Protection Agency) action level for lead in drinking water was changed to 15 parts per billion from a first draw off a fixture. As a precautionary measure, residents can run the plumbing fixtures for two to three minutes before drinking the water in order to clear out water that was in contact with the pipes for a long period of time.

In Canada, the action level is 10 parts per billion, but from a fully flushed fixture. In older houses that may have lead in the pipes, flushing the pipes may be desirable, if the water has been at rest for more than 5 to 8 hours. Hot tap water should not be used for drinking or cooking because hot water leaches lead from the pipes or solder joints.

IN PAINT For the typical homeowner, the highest risk of exposure to lead is from paint. Lead was used extensively for pigmentation and as a drying agent in oil-based paints until the early 1950s. Except for a small number of cases, lead was not added to latex paints. Most manufacturers used other substances for pigmentation after the early 1950s; however, lead was still used as a drying agent. Exterior paints contained the highest levels: up to 60 or 70 percent lead by weight.

Currently, the majority of paints on the market conform to U.S. standards, which do not allow lead to be added. The U.S. government banned indoor leaded paint in the 1970s. It wasn't until the mid-1970s that the Canadian government set a limit of 5,000 parts per million of lead for interior paints. No limit was set on exterior paints.

Some estimates suggest that lead is present in roughly 75% of American homes.

THE CONCERN Young children, especially those under the age of four, often play on the floor, touching things that may contain lead particles. Children tend to put their hands in their mouths, which may mean they are ingesting lead. Children absorb lead more easily than adults because their metabolism is faster. Children are particularly vulnerable up to the age of six. Lead affects the child's nervous system by slowing development. These effects may be irreversible and include hearing impairment, behavioral problems and reduced intelligence.

The signs of lead poisoning are difficult to distinguish from normal child-like complaints and children may show no symptoms at all. When they do, the symptoms can be flu-like: stomach cramps, irritability, loss of appetite and general fatigue. Since these symptoms are so general, it's best not to rely solely on them as indicators of lead.

Pregnant women should not be exposed to lead, as it can interfere with development of the fetus.

For other adults, short term exposure to lead may cause temporary illness (upset stomach, headaches, etc), but the effects are not permanent. However, long term or acute exposure can cause serious health problems for adults, such as permanent kidney, nerve, hearing and vision damage.

LEAD DETECTION The guideline is if the house was built before 1980, there could be some lead paint on the interior or exterior of the house. If the house was built before 1950, it almost certainly will.

In order to verify whether or not lead-based paint is present in the house, relatively inexpensive testing kits are available. Studies have shown that these kits are not always accurate.

More reliable detection of lead paint can be undertaken by properly trained professionals.

Testing for lead paint in the house prior to remodeling need only be done if the work is to include the removal of paint, or if there are considerable amounts of peeling and flaking paint.

STRATEGIES FOR REMOVAL OF LEAD PAINT All methods of removing lead paint can be dangerous. This includes heat stripping, sanding, scraping and the use of chemical strippers. Any time you remove lead paint, there is a risk of creating lead dust. The finer the lead dust, the more easily it is absorbed into your system. Removal of lead paint is not a job for the homeowner. Hiring a contractor to do the work is strongly recommended. The contractor should ensure:

1. Family members are protected from lead dust during the removal process.
2. Family members' belongings are protected so they are not contaminated with lead dust.
3. The contractor should conduct a thorough clean-up following the work. This clean-up should include vacuuming with a high efficiency particle accumulator (HEPA) vacuum.

ENCAPSULATION If the condition of the interior plaster or drywall is poor, covering or enclosing the lead paint can be considered. This involves covering the original surfaces with drywall, heavy wallpaper (such as vinyl) or paneling. Liquid epoxy encapsulants that can be painted over lead paint are available. Some of these contain a bitter tasting additive to discourage children putting their mouths on the surfaces.

If the existing surface is in good shape, then repainting with a lead-free paint can be considered. However, some modern paints may not adhere well to old lead-based paints without wall preparation. If the surface is one that may be chewed by children (lead tastes sweet), repainting may not be sufficient.

5.0 Carbon Monoxide

DESCRIPTION Carbon monoxide is a colorless, odorless gas. It is a by-product of combustion of gas, propane and oil burning appliances. (It is actually a by-product of incomplete combustion, but combustion is rarely complete.)

THE CONCERN When you inhale carbon monoxide, it is absorbed into your body the same way as oxygen. It replaces the oxygen on the hemoglobin in your blood, depriving your body of oxygen. The result is an increased heart rate as your heart tries to get more oxygen to your brain and other vital organs.

The symptoms of long term exposure to low concentrations are slight headaches, fatigue and shortness of breath with only moderate exertion. Continued exposure or high concentrations can result in severe headaches, breathing difficulties, dizziness, confusion, cardiac trauma, brain damage and ultimately, death.

ACTION If you sense any of the above symptoms, move immediately to fresh air. Unconscious victims should be moved outdoors. Call for medical assistance and until it arrives, keep those exposed lying down and keep them warm by wrapping them in blankets. Rest is absolutely necessary. Those exposed should not be allowed to walk for several hours after regaining consciousness. If breathing has ceased, artificial respiration should be undertaken immediately.

RISK REDUCTION To help reduce the risk of exposure to carbon monoxide, fuel burning appliances should be inspected annually by a qualified technician. Gas burning equipment that is not properly adjusted often has a flickering yellow flame as opposed to a steady blue flame. If you see this, call a qualified service person.

One of the major causes of carbon monoxide build up in the home is poor draft from fuel burning appliances. This means that the products of combustion are not being safely carried outside through a chimney or vent, and are backing up into the house.

A simple test such as holding a match to the edge of the draft hood on a water heater or a furnace will give an indication of draft. It is common for some products of combustion to leak into the basement when a piece of equipment starts. Good draft should be established after a minute or so and a lit match will be drawn into the exhaust flue rather than being blown downwards or out into the room.

When products of combustion cannot escape from the house, moisture builds up in the exhaust flue and ultimately in the house itself. Look for rusting on flue pipes, furnaces and water heaters, and for water leaking from the base of the chimney. Look for moisture condensing on windows and in extreme cases, on walls near the furnace.

DETECTION In addition to having your fuel burning appliances inspected once a year, carbon monoxide (CO) detectors can be installed in each room where there is a fuel burning appliance. In addition, CO detectors can be installed near sleeping areas. Much like smoke detectors, carbon monoxide detectors can be wired directly into the home's electrical system or they can be battery operated. Also, like smoke detectors, carbon monoxide detectors should be tested monthly.

If a CO detector does go off, immediately open doors and windows to ventilate the house. If anyone is experiencing flu-like symptoms, seek medical attention immediately. Turn off the appliance if you know the source. Reset the alarm. Don't go back into the home until the alarm indicates there is no longer a problem. Never ignore an alarm even if you feel no symptoms.

6.0 Mold

DESCRIPTION Mold is a common term for a large family of fungi that have a cottony or woolly appearance. There are nearly a million species of mold. Mold is a naturally occurring organism that has been around far longer than humans. Mold grows in buildings where there is moisture, air, a food source, and when the temperature is between 40 and 140 degrees F. When conditions for growth are not met, mold becomes dormant; it does not die. Mold spreads by dispersing spores through the air as well as by growth on or within building materials.

MOLD SPORES ARE EVERYWHERE People sometimes tell us that they don't have mold in their home. We ask what happens if they leave bread in a drawer for a month or don't take out the garbage for two weeks. This helps them understand that no matter how clean they keep their home, mold spores are always there ready to grow on any favorable host. There are always mold spores in the air and there is always some mold in buildings, so having an objective of a "mold-free home" is not realistic.

CONCERN Mold spores are present in the air in every building, but this is not necessarily a reason for alarm. If indoor air mold levels are higher than in outdoor air, or if a significant mold colony is growing on building surfaces or in building walls or ceilings, there may be a cause for concern.

Mold risk falls into three broad categories:

1. Some mold is harmless, a cosmetic nuisance.
2. Some mold is allergenic to some people, in much the same way some people are allergic to peanut butter or shellfish.
3. Toxic mold is dangerous for everyone, although young people, old people, and people with respiratory problems or compromised immune systems are most vulnerable.

Media articles about "black mold," especially Stachybotrys, have terrified some people. Actually it is common to find black Stachybotrys chartarum in small amounts in houses where there has been leakage or water entry. It is a toxic mold and it should be removed. But don't assume that anything black on the wall or ceiling is highly toxic mold. Other common black species may be of low or no toxicity.

People may react to mold spores alone. There does not always have to be a visible growth to cause problems for sensitive people.

YOU CAN'T TELL BY LOOKING You cannot tell what kind of mold you are dealing with by looking at it. Competent identification is important. An expert, trained in microscopic identification of a cultured sample of mold, can usually determine its identity. It is not reliable to judge with the naked eye, or on mold color.

Home test kits are not reliable. The swab, culture, settlement dish, or air sample methods from these kits are fundamentally inaccurate: for example, the spores collected and "grown" in culture using these methods could be dead, fail to grow on the culture medium, and still be toxic if inhaled.

KEEPING MOLD IN ITS PLACE Although mold is needed and always with us, we want to keep mold in its place, preferably outdoors. While we will always have some spores in our homes, the goal is to keep the spores from growing to problem levels.

PREVENTION IS THE KEY Four things have to be present to have a mold growth:

1. Mold spores
2. A food source. This is wood or gypsum board, or that old bread in your bread box.
3. Temperatures between 40° and 140°F
4. A moisture source.

So, how do we control mold growth?

1. We have said that mold spores are everywhere.
2. Food sources are present in every home.
3. People are not comfortable in their homes at temperatures below 40° or above 140° F, so this is no help.
4. The only thing left is moisture. The best way to prevent mold from growing is to control moisture. We want to control moisture levels in homes for other reasons anyway.

MOISTURE SOURCES Sources of moisture in homes include:

1. Leaks into or through roofs, walls, door, windows, basements, etc. The leaks that come through usually get corrected quickly. Slow or intermittent leaks that are concealed in walls, for example, often don't get corrected because they are not noticed.
2. Leaks from plumbing or heating systems.
3. High humidity from cooking, bathing, etc., resulting in condensation.
4. Air conditioning systems, humidifiers, dehumidifiers, sump pits and other places where moisture is commonly present.

GETTING RID OF A MOLD PROBLEM The first step in dealing with a mold problem is identification. If the mold is determined to be harmless, it's time to get out the soap and water. If you or any other member of the household is sensitive to mold, or if the mold is determined to be harmful, a specialist should be engaged to clean up the mold.

Once we get rid of the mold, the next step is to remove the moisture source that allowed the mold to grow. Curing leaks, improving drainage and drying things up are important steps in controlling mold.

MAINTENANCE IS IMPORTANT Don't forget to clean your refrigerator, including gaskets, coils, and evaporator tray. Regular furnace and air conditioning service will help ensure that standing water or chronic moisture is not an issue. Gutters and downspouts should be kept clear and leaks should be corrected.

FINDING MOLD Mold comes in many colors and may be visible and distinct. It can also be very subtle. Mold on a surface may be the tip of an iceberg, with considerable mold concealed behind the wall, for example. In other cases, the mold is only on the surface. The toughest situation is when the mold is entirely out of sight. The best clues to look for are areas susceptible to mold, such as high moisture areas.

BEYOND SCOPE OF A HOME INSPECTION As with other environmental issues, finding and identifying mold is outside the scope of a home inspection.

7.0 Household Pests

DESCRIPTION Household pests can range from insects to mice, bats and raccoons. Pests are often not identified during a professional home inspection.

INSECTS Some insect infestations are chronic and long-term. Other insects may infest an area for a single season and never be seen again.

RODENTS Rodents can be very destructive and can pose a threat to human health. Rodents will chew or gnaw on almost anything, particularly at night. Many fires have been caused by rodents chewing on electrical wiring. Food and food supplies can become contaminated when rodents come into contact with them. Flea infested rodents can introduce fleas to a pet or a dwelling. Once a population is established, it may be hard to control.

IDENTIFICATION Rodents can be detected by visual sightings, droppings, and noise or by chewing damage to wooden structures, pipes, clothes and food. Insects are generally detected by visual sightings, or damaged wood, for example.

8.0 Termites and Carpenter Ants

8.1 Subterranean Termites

DESCRIPTION Termites are by far the most serious insect that can attack the home, since they are the only insects that actually consume the wood. Subterranean termites are found throughout the U.S. and in the southern parts of some Canadian provinces.

COLONIES Subterranean termites live in a sophisticated social colony in the soil, not in the wood. In colder climates, their colonies are usually located below the level of frost penetration, and are typically close to some moisture source. When termites travel, they do so by moving through wood, soil or shelter tubes that they construct. Termites will not expose themselves to the open air, as their bodies can dry out very quickly.

SHELTER TUBES Shelter tubes are very small tunnels that the termites build across any open surface they want to travel. The shelter tubes are made of earth, debris, and a material they excrete that acts as a binder to hold the tubes together. These tubes are typically sandy in color and can readily be broken open by hand. An initial tube may be less than one 1/4 inch in width, although several tubes can be built together over time, and the entire grouping may be one or two inches wide.

COLONY MEMBERS A colony is usually made up of the larvae nymphs, reproductives, soldiers, and workers. As their names suggest, the soldiers' function is to protect the colony. The workers build the shelter tubes, tunnel through the earth, and collect the food. The workers are the ones that damage houses.

WORKERS The workers are whitish and usually about 1/8 to 1/4 inch long. They resemble small ants, although this is somewhat academic, since one will never see a termite roaming about a house. The workers enter the wood and consume it, in very small quantities of course. The wood is partially digested, taken back to the colony and regurgitated to feed the other members.

Since termites do not like to be exposed to the air, they will typically eat through the inside of a piece of wood, often following the grain. They tend to eat in parallel galleries, and leave a smooth honey-combed appearance on the inside of the wood. Termites will eat any kind of wood, although damp or rotted wood is slightly easier for them to break down. Termites need a regular supply of moisture, and workers return to the colony every 24 to 48 hours.

FRASS A small amount of frass is usually found inside the damaged wood. These are small gray flecks, and are different than the powdery wood (sawdust) generated by carpenter ants. Carpenter ants will tend to push the wood debris out of the tunnels, while termites consume this material.

NEW COLONIES New colonies can be started by less than 50 insects, and termites are typically moved by the relocation of infested wood or soil. Moving firewood or relocating a shrub or tree can carry a termite infestation to a new area. The natural movement of a colony is very slow, although splinter colonies can break off from the main colony and establish themselves anew.

Barrier type chemical treatments are deterrents, and very few insects are killed during a chemical treatment. The colony simply finds a new source of food and may remain where it is or relocate slightly.

SIGNS The mud-like shelter tubes are usually the first indication. The second indication is usually damaged wood, although damage may remain concealed for some time.

RISK REDUCTION Minimizing the risk of termites includes breaking wood/soil contact and avoiding accumulation of wood scraps around the outside of the house. The dryer the soil is, the less likely a termite colony will become established. Wet areas should be dried out to prevent this from happening. Good control of rainwater running off roofs and good drainage of surface water are important. Crawl spaces and areas under porches can be kept dry with good ventilation.

TERMITE TREATMENT Termite treatment should be performed by a licensed pest control professional. There are two main approaches, baiting and barriers. In a barrier system, a chemical pesticide is injected around the foundation. Termites are either killed or repelled by the barrier. In a bait system, the pesticide is placed in bait stations. Termites bring the slow-acting pesticide back to the colony, where it can kill many more of the insects.

BREAK WOOD/ SOIL CONTACT It is important to remove any wood/soil contact in termite prone areas, even if chemical treatment is undertaken. There should be at least six inches between any wood and soil, both inside the building and out.

Areas of typical wood/soil contact include crawlspaces, porches, stoops, decks, steps, basement windows, window wells, posts, walls, and basement staircases.

CONCEALED WOOD DAMAGE Wherever termite activity or termite treatment is found, there is the possibility of damage to the home. If none is visible, it may be difficult to know whether damage is concealed or has been repaired. Without disassembling the house, this is impossible to verify. The building should be monitored for sagging structural components, floor springiness or other signs of structural weakness. It is not unusual for termites to attack a house, moving through the floor and wall systems up into the attic. Wood damage may occur a considerable distance from the point of attack in the basement. It is not usually possible to see the extent of termite damage, since termites move through the center of wood members, trying not to go through the outer edges.

8.2 Drywood Termites

Drywood termites inhabit the southern United States and the coastal areas of California. Drywood termites are occasionally introduced into other areas through wooden furniture or other wooden objects brought from the southern U.S., Caribbean and even Asia, Africa and Australia. These termites infest utility poles, fence posts, trees, and structures (primarily around perimeter areas and where wood joins other wood).

CHARACTERISTICS Unlike subterranean termites, drywood termites;

a) Do not require soil to build their nests, and do not bring soil into the chambers.
b) Do not construct shelter tubes out of soil (although some species will cement fecal pellets together to bridge a gap in the wood).
c) Cut across the grain of un-decayed, dry wood to excavate large chambers.

DETECTION Fecal matter and other debris (called frass) is stored in unused chambers or pushed out of small kick holes. These holes are often protected by the soldier caste or blocked off by hardened debris. The fecal pellets are hard, six-sided and concave. Piles of these pellets may be found on window sills or beneath other infested surfaces. Other detection methods include
a) Sounding the wood for cavities.
b) Looking for evidence of shed wings.
c) Looking for blistered wood on surfaces where galleries are close to the top.
d) Probing wood to discover live termites.
e) Using a stethoscope to hear activity within the galleries.

Damage is often not as extensive as subterranean termites due to smaller colony sizes.

CONTROL Control is achieved by removal of the damaged wood, and the addition of heat, electrical current, or insecticide injected into the nest and galleries. Tenting and fumigation is used where the infestation is large or the nest is difficult to isolate.

8.3 Dampwood Termites

Most dampwood termites are found tropically worldwide, however, some inhabit deserts. In the United States, they are primarily west of the Rocky Mountains, extending down into California. One species is found in British Columbia.

CHARACTERISTICS Dampwood termites prefer nesting in decayed wood or wood with a high moisture content and will sometimes infest tree roots. They do not require soil to live. The galleries are not kept clean, containing numerous six-sided, concave fecal pellets. A few pellets are discarded from openings in the wood. Some species infest structures, primarily in areas that are poorly maintained as a result of water exposure or wood/soil contact. Moisture control is the primary key to preventing and eliminating dampwood termite infestations.

8.4 Carpenter Ants

Carpenter ants are typically 1/4 to 1/2 inch long, often black or dark brown. Carpenter ants and the other insects mentioned do not actually consume the wood, but make their nests in it.

The amount of structural damage these pests do is very limited, although elimination can be tricky.

Conventional pesticides are used and, with carpenter ants, the nest has to be treated. In cases where the nest cannot be located, the entire building is treated. Carpenter ants like kitchen areas, because of the food. They also are frequently found in damp areas. Rotting wood or wood below leaky windows, roofs, or plumbing fixtures are favored nesting spots. The nest may be in floors, cupboards, doors or frames, window sills, porches, etc., out of sight.

Carpenter ants are not always active, and may not be noted on a one-time inspection. Seeing one or two ants does not necessarily mean an infestation, but this should be watched.

Home Set-up and Maintenance

When moving into a resale home, there are some things that you will want to take care of. This list focuses on things related to the house, rather than all of the administrative issues like change of address notices, setting up utilities, telephone, television, etc. The Home Set-up section deals with things that are done just once. The Home Maintenance Program deals with regular activities.

Home Set-up

1. **Smoke detectors** – Install or replace as needed. (Usually one on every floor level near a sleeping area.) Smoke detectors should be replaced every 10 years, and it is difficult to know how old the existing smoke detectors are. We recommend replacing them all.
2. **Carbon monoxide detectors** – Provide according to manufacturer's recommendations, typically in every sleeping area.
3. **Locks** – Change the locks on all the doors. Deadbolts improve security and may reduce insurance costs.
4. **Heating and air-conditioning systems** – Have these inspected and serviced. We recommend setting up a service contract to ensure the equipment is properly maintained. It makes sense to protect your investment in these expensive systems.
5. **Main shutoffs** – Find and mark the main shutoff for the heating, electrical and plumbing systems. You need to be able to shut things off fast in the event of an emergency.
6. **Electrical circuits** – Label the circuits in the electrical panel, so you can shut off the right fuse or breaker quickly.
7. **Wood burning appliances** – Have the chimney inspected and swept as needed.
8. **Outdoor air-conditioning unit** – Make sure there is at least 3 feet clear around the air conditioner. Cut back trees and shrubs as needed.
9. **Clothes washing machines** – Use braided steel hoses rather than rubber hoses for connecting the washing machine to the supply piping. This reduces the risk of serious water damage due to a ruptured hose.
10. **Clothes dryers** – Use smooth walled (not corrugated) metal exhaust ducts to vent clothes dryers outdoors. Keep the runs as short and straight as possible.
11. **Fire extinguishers** – Provide at least one on every floor. The fire extinguisher near the kitchen should be suitable for grease fires.
12. **Fire escape routes** – Plan fire escape routes from the upper stories. Obtain rope ladders if necessary.
13. **Safety improvements** – If your home inspector has recommended any safety improvements, these should be taken care of immediately. This often includes electrical issues and trip or fall hazards, for example.

Home Maintenance Program

Good maintenance protects your investment, enhances comfort, extends life expectancies and reduces your costs. It makes great sense. Some homeowners do the maintenance themselves, and others get help with it.

Monthly

Smoke detectors – test to make sure they work in the event of a fire

Carbon monoxide detectors – test to make sure they work in the event of an appliance malfunction

Ground fault circuit interrupters and arc fault circuit interrupters – test to make sure they work if there is an electrical problem

Filters/air cleaners on heating and air-conditioning system – clean to reduce heating costs, improve comfort and protect the equipment

Automatic reverse mechanism on garage door openers – test to make sure no one will be injured by the door as it closes

Range hood filters – clean to maintain efficiency, reduce energy costs and minimize the risk of grease fires

Central vacuum system – empty canister and clean filter (if applicable) so system will work effectively (in some homes, this has to be done more frequently than monthly)

Quarterly

Sliding doors and windows – clean tracks and make sure drain holes are open to reduce the risk of water damage in the home

Floor drains – Check that there is water in traps to prevent sewer odors getting into the home

Heat recovery ventilator – clean or replace the filter (every two months is ideal) to ensure proper and cost effective operation

Bathroom exhaust fan – clean grill to ensure good air flow

Spring

Gutters – clean to extend the life of the gutters and keep the basement/crawlspace dry

Air-conditioning system – have it serviced before turning it on – to protect the equipment

Humidifier attached to furnace – turn off and shut off the water so we don't get more humidity than we want in the summer

Humidifiers and central air conditioners – close the damper on the humidifier bypass to avoid short-circuiting the air-conditioning system

Well water – have tested by laboratory to ensure the water is safe to drink (More frequent testing may be appropriate.)

Sump pump – test to make sure it will operate when needed, to avoid flooding

Chimneys for fireplaces and other wood-burning appliances – have inspected and swept as necessary – to reduce the risk of a chimney fire

Fall

Gutters – clean to extend the life of the gutters and keep the basement/crawlspace dry

Heating system – service before turning on to protect the equipment

Gas fireplace – service with other gas appliances; include fireplace in service plan

Outdoor hose bibs – shut off unless they are frost free to prevent freezing damage to pipes

Hot water heating systems – bleed radiators to remove air so the radiators will keep the house warm

Hot water heating systems – lubricate the circulating pump as needed to extend its life

Humidifier connected to furnace – turn on and open the water supply so that the humidifier will work in the heating season

Humidifiers and central air conditioners – open the damper on the humidifier bypass to allow the humidifier to work in the heating season

Electric baseboard heaters – vacuum to remove dust to increase the efficiency and reduce the risk of fire

Well water – have tested by laboratory to ensure the water is safe to drink (More frequent testing may be appropriate.)

Sump pump – test to make sure it will operate when needed, to avoid flooding

Catch basins – test and clean out debris if needed – to make sure they will carry water away

Exterior vents – ensure vent flaps close properly to reduce heat loss and prevent pest entry

Annually

Trees and shrubs – trim back at least 3 feet from air-conditioning to allow the air-conditioning to work properly

Trees and shrubs – trim back from walls and roofs to prevent damage caused by branches rubbing against the building and to reduce the risk of pests getting into the home

Vines – trim away from wood building components

Roofing – perform annual inspection and tune-up. This helps maximize the life of roofs. (Often performed by roofer on an annual service agreement)

Bathtub and shower enclosures – check caulking and grout to prevent concealed water damage

Attic – check for evidence of pests and roof leaks to prevent infestations and water damage

Building exterior – inspect for weather tightness at siding, trim, doors, windows, wall penetrations, etc. to prevent concealed water damage

Exterior paint and stain – check and improve as needed to prevent rot in exterior wood. Pay particular attention to wood close to the ground. Wood in contact with soil is prone to rot.

Exterior grade – check that it slopes down away from the building to drain water away from, rather than toward, the foundation. This helps prevent wet basement and crawlspace problems.

Refrigerators and freezers – vacuum coils to improve efficiency and reduce cost

Fire extinguisher – check gauges to make sure they will operate if needed

Garage door hardware – lubricate to ensure the door moves freely

Garage door operator – lubricate to ensure the operator works freely and minimize the load on the electric motor

Semi-Annually

Exterior air intakes – clean to ensure that it is clear from debris that can block air from entering any mechanical equipment.

Ongoing

Septic systems – set up a program for regular maintenance and inspection with a local service provider. Tanks are typically pumped out every three years.

Appendix A – More About Home Inspections

Standards of Practice

Home inspections are typically performed according to applicable Standards of Practice. These are several organizations of home inspectors in North America. The current wording of the Standards can be referenced on the appropriate association websites. Listed below are the four well-recognized associations and their websites. The Standards of Practice specific to each association can be found on their website.

American Society of Home Inspectors (ASHI) **www.ashi.org**

Canadian Association of Home and Property Inspectors (CAHPI) **www.cahpi.ca**

National Association of Home Inspectors (NAHI) **www.nahi.org**

International Association of Certified Home Inspectors (InterNACHI) **www.nachi.org**

The current wording of the Standards can be referenced at the website for each association. There are other organizations with their own Standards. Inspectors will identify the Standards that they follow. If your state or province has licensing, there may be a specific set of Standards. Some states and provinces also have regional associations with their own Standards.

About Home Inspections

Home inspections provide tremendous value, but this can be a challenge for home inspectors. Because we have very broad knowledge of homes, clients' expectations of home inspectors are often very high. While that is flattering, it is also little dangerous for the client and for the inspector. It is important for the inspector to clearly define the scope of work (Standards of Practice, et al) and for the client to set realistic expectations based on that. Home inspections typically last a few hours and cost a few hundred dollars. The written technical report provides a professional opinion based on less-than-complete information, prepared within a very short time frame.

Home inspectors can't see through walls, ceilings or floors, predict the future, re-create the past, dismantle components or know everything there is to know about everything. We perform field inspections of homes to evaluate their performance, identifying existing recognizable problems. This dramatically improves a client's knowledge of the home, and reduces – but does not remove – the risk in making a decision. Clients need to understand that we will not identify or predict all the issues in any home, but by identifying several conditions, we provide a very valuable service.

When Things Go Wrong: (Next page) This short document maybe useful. Please read it as part of the report.

When Things Go Wrong

There may come a time that you discover something wrong with the house, and you may wonder if your home inspector let you down. There are a few things to consider:

INTERMITTENT OR CONCEALED PROBLEMS Some problems can only be discovered by living in a house. They cannot be discovered during the few hours of a home inspection. For example, some shower stalls leak when water bounces off people in the shower, but do not leak when you simply turn on the tap. Some roofs and basements only leak when rain is very heavy or is accompanied by wind from a certain direction. Some problems will only be discovered when carpets are lifted, furniture and storage are moved or finishes are removed.

NO CLUES These problems may have existed at the time of the inspection but there were no clues as to their existence. Lawyers call these latent defects. Our inspections are based on the past performance of the house. If there are no clues of a past problem, it is unfair to assume we should foresee a future problem. Home inspectors do not identify latent defects.

WE ALWAYS MISS SOME MINOR THINGS Some say we are inconsistent because our reports identify some minor problems but not others. Any minor problems noted were discovered while looking for significant problems that would affect the typical person's decision to purchase. We note them simply as a courtesy.

SAMPLING EXERCISE A home inspection is a sampling exercise with respect to components that are numerous, such as bricks, windows, and electrical receptacles. As a result, some conditions that are visible may go unreported. This is not a failing of the inspector but a result of sampling. A report by a second inspector will always be somewhat different than the first as a result of this sampling approach.

CONTRACTORS' ADVICE A common source of concern with home inspectors comes from comments made by contractors. Contractors' opinions often differ from ours. Don't be surprised that three roofers all say the roof needs replacement when we said that, with some minor repairs, the roof will last a few more years.

LAST MAN IN THEORY While our advice represents the most prudent action in our professional opinion, many contractors are reluctant to undertake these repairs. This is because of the "Last Man In Theory". The contractor fears that if he is the last person to work on the roof, he will get blamed if the roof leaks, whether or not the leak is his fault. Consequently, he won't want to do a minor repair with high liability when he could re-roof the entire house for more money and reduce the likelihood of a callback. This is understandable.

MOST RECENT ADVICE IS BEST There is more to the "Last Man In Theory". It is human nature for homeowners to believe the last "expert" advice they receive, even if it is contrary to previous advice. As home inspectors, we unfortunately find ourselves in the position of "First Man In" and consequently it is our advice that is often disbelieved.

WHY DIDN'T WE SEE IT Contractors and others may say "I can't believe you had this house inspected, and they didn't find this problem". There are several reasons for these apparent oversights:

CONDITIONS DURING INSPECTION

1. It is difficult for homeowners to remember the circumstances in the house, at the time of the inspection. It's easy to forget that it was snowing, there was storage everywhere in the basement or that the furnace could not be turned on because the air conditioning was operating, etc. It's impossible for contractors to know what the circumstances were when the inspection was performed.

THE WISDOM OF HINDSIGHT

2. When the problem manifests itself, it is very easy to have 20/20 hindsight. Anybody can say that the basement leaks when there are 2 inches of water on the floor. Predicting the problem is a different story.

A LONG LOOK

3. If we spent 1/2 an hour under the kitchen sink or two hours removing every electrical switch plate and cover plate, we'd find more problems too. Unfortunately, the inspection would take several days and would cost considerably more.

WE'RE GENERALISTS

4. We are generalists; we are not specialists. The heating contractor may indeed have more heating expertise than we do. This is because we are expected to have heating expertise and plumbing expertise, roofing expertise, electrical expertise, etc. A home inspection is a generalist the same way a family doctor is a generalist. They have wonderfully broad knowledge, but are not cardiologists or respirologists.

AN INVASIVE LOOK

5. Problems often become apparent when carpets or plaster are removed, when fixtures or cabinets are pulled out, and so on. Many issues appear once work begins on a home. A home inspection is a visual examination. We don't perform any invasive or destructive tests.

NOT INSURANCE In conclusion, a home inspection is designed to better your odds. It is not designed to eliminate all risk. For that reason, a home inspection should not be considered an insurance policy. We know of no insurance company that offers a policy with no deductible, no exclusions, no limits and an indefinite policy period.

We hope this is food for thought.

Notes

Notes

Notes

Notes

Notes

Notes

Notes

Notes